ALEXANDRA KOLLONTAI

ALEXANDRA KOLLONTAI

The Lonely Struggle
of the Woman
Who Defied Lenin

CATHY PORTER

The Dial Press New York

Published by
The Dial Press
1 Dag Hammarskjold Plaza
New York, New York 10017

This work was first published in Great Britain by Virago Limited.

Manufactured in the United States of America

First U.S.A. printing

Design by Karin Batten

Library of Congress Cataloging in Publication Data

Porter, Cathy.
   Alexandra Kollontai, the lonely struggle of the woman who defied Lenin.

   Bibliography: p.
   Includes index.
   1. Kollontaĭ, Aleksandra Mikhaĭlovna, 1872–1952.
2. Revolutionists—Russia—Biography. 3. Communists—
Russia—Biography. I. Title.
DK268.K56P67   947.084′092′4 [B]   80–13058
ISBN 0–8037–0129–2

CONTENTS

CHRONOLOGY

Brief chronology of events in Europe and Russia and in the life of Alexandra Kollontai. Dates will follow the old Russian calendar (thirteen days before the West), until January 1918, when Russia adopted the Western calendar.

1861 Serfs emancipated.

1862 Beginnings of Land and Liberty Party.

1864 Marx's International Workingmen's Association (First International) founded in London.

1870 Russian section of First International, led by Bakunin in Geneva. Lenin born. First factory strikes in St. Petersburg. Men and women in Land and Liberty propagandize in villages.

1872 Mikhail and Alexandra Domontovich, aristocratic landowners, give birth to their daughter Alexandra on March 19 in St. Petersburg.

1877– Russo-Turkish war in Balkans. March—great public trial of wom-
78   en Land and Liberty members. October–January 1878—second public show trial of revolutionaries.

1878 Domontovich family goes to Sofia. Russia swept by assassination attempts by revolutionaries against prominent Russian officials.

1879 Summer—formation of new (terrorist) People's Will Party. Domontoviches return to St. Petersburg. Trotsky born.

1881 March—assassination of Tsar Alexander II by People's Will. April —public hanging of five leading terrorists, including Sofya Perovskaya, which makes great impression on Alexandra. She starts lessons with governess.

1888 Alexandra gains teaching diploma. Attends private courses in literature and history.

1890 Alexandra meets and falls in love with Vladimir Kollontai.

1892 Taken abroad for first time with family, to Berlin and Paris.

Reads *Communist Manifesto*. Visits German socialist meetings.

1893   Alexandra marries Vladimir Kollontai. Lenin joins his first Marxist study group in St. Petersburg.

1894   Alexandra Kollontai's son, Misha, born. She teaches at workers' evening classes. Nicholas II comes to throne.

1895   Marxist groups in St. Petersburg united by Lenin into Union of Struggle for the Emancipation of the Working Class. Kollontai extends teaching to work for Political Red Cross. December— Lenin arrested.

1896   Kollontai's first horrifying visit to large factory. May–June—huge textile-workers' strike in St. Petersburg. Kollontai distributes leaflets, helps organize strike funds.

1898   Russian Social Democratic Workers' Party (Marxist) founded in Minsk from nucleus of members of Union of Struggle for the Emancipation of the Working Class. Second Socialist International founded. August—Kollontai leaves husband and son to study Marxist economics in Zurich. September—her first article, on education, published in Russia.

1899   Summer—Kollontai to London. Autumn—back to St. Petersburg. Winter—begins underground political activity for Russia's Marxist Social Democratic Party.

1900   Kollontai's articles on Finland published. Lenin released from exile to Europe.

1901   Socialist Revolutionary Party formed, heirs to the People's Will terrorists. Kollontai to Zurich, Geneva, and Paris to continue studies.

1902   Publication of Lenin's *What Is To Be Done?*, a Marxist refutation of the populists. Kollontai writes number of articles on Finland.

1903   January—Kollontai first speaks at public meeting (against Nietzsche). February—her book on Finnish workers appears. July–August—Second Congress of Russian Social Democratic Party in Brussels and London, at which split appears between Bolsheviks and Mensheviks. Kollontai abroad too at this time. On her return continues to teach at workers' night classes. Works as Marxist agitator (committed to neither faction of the Social Democratic

Party), and works to keep Finnish and Russian workers' movements in contact.

1904   January—Lenin seeks Kollontai's collaboration for Bolshevik periodical. February—Russo-Japanese War. Strikes and demonstrations. November—Kollontai joins Bolsheviks and conducts classes on Marxism for workers.

1905   January—"Bloody Sunday," thousands killed by police in peaceful demonstration in which Kollontai participates. Revolution begins. Spring—she writes and distributes illegal leaflets calling for overthrow of Tsar. March—becomes treasurer of Bolshevik-dominated St. Petersburg Social Democratic committee. April—attends first meeting of liberal-feminist Women's Union, denouncing idea that one movement can contain women of diametrically opposing class interests. July—her pamphlet, *On the Question of the Class Struggle,* appears. August—Treaty of Portsmouth ends Russo-Japanese War. September–October—mass strikes. Kollontai addresses factory meetings, writes for various Marxist journals. October—attends first meeting of St. Petersburg Soviet. October—Constitutional Democratic Party formed; Tsar issues manifesto promising reforms. December—mass uprising in Moscow. Suppression of revolution.

1906   Kollontai joins Mensheviks. Struggles against both Social Democratic Party and feminist Women's Union to organize factory women into socialist women's movement. Her collection of articles on Finland appears in autumn. September—attends German Social Democratic Party Congress, and Congress of German Socialist Women, in Mannheim.

1907   Spring—begins work with women textile-workers in St. Petersburg. August—attends Seventh Congress of the International in Stuttgart and, as only Russian representative, First International Women's Congress. Autumn—returns to organize first legal working-women's club in St. Petersburg.

1908   Feminists plan great All-Russian Women's Congress, and Kollontai organizes working women, throughout spring and summer, to raise there their own demands. Writes *Social Basis of the Women's Question,* outlining socialist approach to women's movement. September—warrant for her arrest for belonging to

Social Democratic Party and calling for armed uprising. She goes underground but attends numerous meetings in disguise. December—feminist congress. Kollontai spotted by police. Forced to leave Russia for Berlin.

1909   Lives in Berlin. Joins German Socialist Party (SPD). April—first trip as agitator for SPD to Rheinland villages and towns. End of April to May 2—to London with Klara Zetkin. May—another agitational trip around Germany.

1910   August—attends Eighth Congress of International in Copenhagen, and Second Congress of Socialist Women. September—goes on to address public meetings in Sweden.

1911   February–March—teaches at socialist school organized in Bologna by Gorky and company. Spring—to Paris, to give talks and raise money for Russian exiles there. Writes *Around Workers' Europe* (about experiences in Germany, etc.), and first articles on sexuality. Works with French Socialist Party. Visits Belgium to address miners there.

1912   Trips to Belgium, Sweden, England, Switzerland, back to Germany.

1913   June to November—in London working at the British Museum Library on her book *Society and Motherhood.*

1914   May—organizes women's meetings in Berlin against war. Warrant for her arrest by Berlin police. Leaves for Tyrol to avoid arrest, and plans International Women's Congress. August 1—leaves Tyrol for Berlin on day war is announced. Arrested and imprisoned. Released, leaves Germany in September for Denmark. Leaves in October for Sweden. Socialist parties split by war. Kollontai joins Bolsheviks. November—arrested in Stockholm. From then on in touch constantly with Lenin (who is living in Switzerland).

1915   January—to Copenhagen. February—to Norway, where she works for Bolsheviks' "northern underground." Organizes Norwegian radical delegation for Bolshevik-inspired antiwar meeting in Zimmerwald in Switzerland, to pass resolution to turn imperialist war into revolutionary war. Spring—Russian defeat in war beyond question. Summer—writes *Who Needs War?* for front-line soldiers in Europe. August—invited to do speaking tour in USA. October—leaves Norway for New York.

1916   March—returns from USA to Norway. *Society and Motherhood* published in Petrograd. August—again to America, with son. Speaking publicly and writing.

1917   January 28—returns from USA to Norway. March 1—hears of bourgeois revolution in Russia. March 9—receives Lenin's "Letters From Afar" (containing his call to turn the war into a revolutionary war), which she is to take to Russia to be published by the Bolsheviks' paper *Pravda*. March 18—returns to Petrograd, writes for *Pravda*, is elected delegate to Petrograd Soviet. April 3—meets Lenin returning from Switzerland. Only Bolshevik to support his revolutionary *April Theses*. April to October—speaks at factories, on streets, on battleships, and at women workers' meetings, supporting the Bolsheviks and calling for revolution. Works for Bolshevik women's paper *Rabotnitsa*. June 2–5—Russian delegate to Ninth Congress of the Finnish Social Democratic Party. June 3–24—speaks on nationality question and Finland at First All-Russian Congress of Soviets in Petrograd. June 21—speech on women's needs at First All-Russian Trade Union Conference in Petrograd. Leads city's laundresses in a strike. End of June—with V. V. Vorovsky to Stockholm, as Bolshevik delegate to antiwar meeting. Early July—returns to Petrograd and is arrested by Provisional Government as "German agent." July 26 to August 3— elected while in prison to Bolshevik central committee at Sixth Party Congress. August 21—released on bail. September—proposes women's bureau in Party and plans, with other *Rabotnitsa* workers, First Working Women's Congress in Petrograd. October 10—attends historic meeting of Party in which it is decided to launch armed uprising against government. October 22 ("Day of the Petrograd Soviet")—speaks at countless meetings. October 24 —article in *Pravda* on proposed Women's Congress. Night of October 24–25—in Smolny, headquarters of the armed rising. Attends historic meeting of Petrograd Soviet at which revolution is launched. October 25–26—at Second All-Russian Congress of Soviets power is taken by the Bolsheviks. Alexandra is elected Commissar of Social Welfare. November 5—participates in First Congress of Petrograd Working Women, to whom she delivers paper on maternity protection. December—many of her popular pamphlets published and reprinted.

1918   March 2—central committee sends her to lead delegation to Sweden, England, and France to raise support for Bolsheviks, menaced by the Germans and their former allies in the war and divided among themselves over the proper line to take. March 6–8—speaks at Seventh Party Congress against Brest-Litovsk peace treaty with Germany. Capital moves from Petrograd to Moscow. March 14–16—delegate at the Fourth Congress of Soviets, where peace treaty ratified. Resigns from Commissariat. Spring and summer—civil war begins and Kollontai does speaking tour in the autumn to textile towns near Moscow, where she meets many women workers. Organizes First All-Russian Congress of Working and Peasant Women, to be held in Moscow from November 16 to 21, where she reads her (subsequently published) work *Communism and the Family.*

1919   New Year—heart attack. March 2–6—attends First (founding) Congress of the Third (Communist) International (Comintern), where she speaks on need for women's participation. March 18–23 —as central-committee member, speaks at Eighth Party Congress, on women's work, and the family. April—agitational trip to the Ukraine, and women's work in Kharkov. May—travels as agitator to Donets Basin, Bakhmut, Lugansk. June—to the Crimea, where appointed President of the Political Department of the Crimean Republic. July to August—Crimea falls to Whites. Kollontai to Kiev, where appointed Commissar of Propaganda and Agitation for the Ukraine. She writes many pamphlets, etc. September—Ukraine evacuated as Whites attack. Kollontai back to Moscow, where she works with the Women's Department of the Party (the Zhenotdel), formed that month. Ill with typhus, blood poisoning, nephritis, and heart trouble until the following autumn.

1920   November—appointed director of Zhenotdel, organizing exhibitions, lectures, poster displays, and writing articles for working women (and prostitutes) throughout Russia. End of year, joins Workers' Opposition.

1921   February to July—reads course of lectures at radical Sverdlov University in Moscow, on women in the economy, and on communist morality. February—openly works for Workers' Opposition. March 8–16—presents her Workers' Opposition pamphlet to Tenth Party Congress and is attacked by all Party leaders. June 9–15—speaks on women's work at Second International Conference of Communist Women. Elected vice-president of women's secretariat of Comintern. June 22 to July 12—presents Workers' Opposition's case to Third Comintern Congress. Continues work with Zhenotdel.

1922   February—with other Workers' Oppositionists presents "Declaration of Twenty-Two" (listing grievances against the Bolshevik Party) to special Comintern commission. March 27 to April 2— Eleventh Party Congress. Workers' Opposition, and Kollontai especially, condemned and threatened with expulsion from Party. April 3—Stalin becomes acting party secretary. May 26—Lenin's first stroke, which removes him from politics. Kollontai to Odessa in disgrace. Summer—summoned back to Moscow by Stalin and promised diplomatic appointment. October 4—Kollontai appointed member of Soviet trade delegation in Oslo.

1923   Appointed head of trade delegation in Oslo, the first woman to receive such an appointment. Her articles on sexual morality attacked in Russia.

1924   February—Kollontai concludes trade agreement with Norway and Russia on exchange of wheat and herring. Norway recognizes USSR in law. Kollontai appointed Soviet Ambassador.

1925   Summer and autumn—returns to Moscow to participate in debate on proposed new marriage law. Her ideas attacked.

1926   September—appointed Soviet trade delegate in Mexico.

1927   June—health reasons force her to leave Mexico. October—returns as Ambassador to Norway. November—Trotsky and Zinoviev expelled from the Party.

1928   Left oppositionists exiled and imprisoned.

1929   February—Bukharin, Tomsky, Rykov, and many other prominent old Bolsheviks condemned by Stalin. Trotsky deported from Siberia to Turkey. April—first Five-Year plan. December—Stalin calls for accelerated collectivization of the peasantry.

1930   June–July—Sixteenth Party Congress. Leading trade unionist Tomsky removed from his post. Autumn—Kollontai appointed to work in Soviet Embassy in Stockholm.

1933   March—Kollontai awarded Order of Lenin for work among women. June—secures return of gold reserves, hidden in Sweden after the revolution by Kerensky, to Russia.

1934 December—assassination of Stalin's supporter Kirov is signal for savage new party purges.

1935 January—first trial of Kamenev and Zinoviev. May—Kollontai establishes Russian-Swedish cultural association in Stockholm. September—joins Russian delegation at League of Nations, and is working on legal rights of women.

1936 August 19–24—first show trial begins, of Zinoviev and Kamenev. Tomsky commits suicide.

1937 January 23–30—second show trial, of Radek, Pyatakov. June— secret trial and execution of General Tukhachevsky. Purge of army begins.

1937– Secret purge of Stalin's former allies. March 1938—third show
38 trial, of Bukharin and Rykov.

1939 August 23—Russian-German pact signed. Two weeks later Hitler invades Poland.

1940 January to March—Kollontai negotiates peace between Finland and Russia. August 20—Trotsky assassinated in Mexico.

1942 Kollontai awarded Red Banner of Labor for her diplomatic work, on her seventieth birthday. Heads Soviet diplomatic corps in Sweden. June 22—Hitler invades Russia.

1945 Kollontai returns to Russia. Nominated for Nobel Peace Prize, awarded second Red Banner of Labor.

1946– Works as adviser to the Soviet Ministry of Foreign Affairs.
52

1952 March 9—dies of heart attack.

INTRODUCTION

I wrote this biography of Alexandra Kollontai because I wanted to cast light on some of the unexplored aspects of the Russian revolution, which has been so central to our understanding of our own history. Sometimes when assembling the various parts of this woman's exceptional life, I suddenly experienced a more complete understanding of history which then raised new questions, enlarged the perspectives from which I had been writing, and required me to rethink past judgments. This questioning process did not finish for me with the ending of the book. The struggles which Alexandra Kollontai lived through and wrote about continue, and we can constantly draw new strength from a greater understanding of their historical origins.

Biographies of many of the revolution's major male leaders—Lenin, Trotsky, and Bukharin for instance—give the impression that they gave little thought to their personal lives and that they existed virtually outside any experience of sexual relations. We know that this cannot be true and that however strong these leaders might outwardly have been, they were human beings whose hearts were torn apart by many of the same conflicts that we are confronted with now. We know that however undivided their revolutionary commitment might have been, most Bolsheviks hated violence but believed it might sometimes be the lesser of two evils. We know that although when the First World War broke out, many revolutionaries recognized the leadership of the Bolshevik party as the only party which could lead Russia toward socialism, many still distrusted a party which could demand such total commitment from its members. Few Russian revolutionaries articulated these conflicts as candidly as did Alexandra Kollontai.

The liberation of women from sexual exploitation and ignorance was an essential component of Alexandra Kollontai's hopes as a socialist when she first joined the revolutionary movement at the turn of the century. She saw the ways in which sexual relationships were changing in industrialized Europe as an integral part of a revolution already underway in which workers were beginning to rise up against their employers. Since in autocratic Russia, to strike necessarily involved rising up against the Tsar and the state as well, this struggle had by 1905 gained the momentum of a revolution. Alexandra Kollontai's personal life and thoughts were deeply involved in the political struggle of the next two decades in Russia in which men and women tried to create new, freer social relationships and a new, more just society.

Her attempt to extend the terms of socialist debate in Russia and to relate the specific oppression of women to that of the working class is seen in her extensive writings, many of which are now accessible to us in English translation. As a Marxist, she believed that women's liberation was inseparably connected to the liberation of all women and men from capitalism, and she very explicitly dissociated herself from the feminist movement of her time, which saw educational and political reforms for women as attainable within capitalist society. It is largely because of her disavowal of feminism that her ideas did not become popular in the West until the 1920's, when she was already out of favor with the Bolshevik government.

In the political resurgence of the late 1960's, when women in the West began once again to explore their needs for self-determination and personal emancipation, Alexandra Kollontai was rediscovered (despite her disavowals) as a feminist of enormous historical and inspirational value and extraordinary originality. In England her work was first translated and explained in the early '70's by Alix Holt, and to her I owe a great debt of gratitude; her pioneering work, the clarity and honesty she has brought to bear on discussion of Kollontai over the past few years, have helped me to unravel many knots and prejudices in my thinking, and without her I would never have written this book.

I want also to thank Greg Andrusz, of Birmingham University, for numerous helpful suggestions on the manuscript; Bea Campbell for making me clarify my ideas on the 1905 period; Prudence Chamberlaine for letting me use her notes on Klara Zetkin and the German socialist women's movement; Dick Chappell for sharing some of the results of his research on the Civil War in Russia, and for allowing me to consult his translation of Shlyapnikov's book *On the Eve of 1917;* Lena Wickman for telling me some of her memories of Kollontai in Stockholm in the 1930's; Chris Goodey and Yarko Koshiw, both of whom have helped me to ask myself new questions about the Russian revolution; and Ursula Owen, the book's editor, for her encouragement. I should also like to acknowledge a grant from the Arts Council.

Two biographies of Alexandra Kollontai have already appeared. In her official Soviet biography, written by Anna Itkina, a friend of hers during the revolution and a colleague in the Women's Department during the Civil War, she emerges as a shadowy figure. The book was first published in 1964 and was reissued in a second edition in 1970. It is as sparing in its discussion of her ideas about erotic love as it is about her disagreements with the Party in the 1920's. Isabel Palencia, a friend of Kollontai's in the '30's in Stockholm, wrote the first English biography of her in 1947; her book is marred by a certain sentimental over-reverence for its subject, and since it contains virtually no political analysis it is best treated as a personal memoir rather than as a biography. But she knew Kollontai in the cruelest period of Soviet history, when censorship made it impossible to write the truth and when terror entered the heart of every Russian who wanted to stay alive. It is impossible for those who have not themselves lived through this period to do proper justice to Alexandra Kollontai's life in these terrible years.

I have used as the basis of my book part of Alexandra Kollontai's own voluminous autobiographical writings, many of which are filled with engagingly honest insights into her personal and political thoughts. She wrote the first of these in 1912; *Around Workers' Europe,* published in St. Petersburg, is a personal narrative of her experiences over the past four years when she was living in exile. In the '20's she published fragments of her equally personal diary of the year 1914, as well as an account of her imprisonment by Kerensky's government in July 1917. In 1921 she wrote an *Autobiographical Essay,* a far more formal account of her political activities up to that period, which lacked much of the elegance, humor, and spontaneity of her previous autobiographical writings.

In 1926 she was asked to contribute a piece to a series published in Germany on the lives of European women, and she tried to recapture her earlier style of writing. But there is a certain dismal leadenness about the resulting work, *The Aims and Worth of My Life* (translated into English as *The Autobiography of a Sexually Emancipated Woman*), caused by the many deletions (restored in the English translation) she felt she had, for political reasons, to make.

In 1939 she began to draw on diaries, which she had kept throughout her life, to embark on a more complete account of her life up to that date. It was to be a massive work, only the first part of which, *The First Steps,* was completed. This was published in Swedish in 1945, and a version of it appeared in that year, translated into Russian and slightly expurgated, in the Soviet journal *October.* The rest of her projected autobiographical work, of which she had already written a great deal when she died in 1952, forms part of the vast archive of her writings which now lies, accessible only to a very small number of Soviet scholars, in Moscow's Marx-Lenin Institute.

One of these scholars, I. M. Dazhina, has recently edited a selection of Kollontai's less controversial writings entitled *From My Life and Work;* she has also edited out all references to the two issues most central to Kollontai's thinking: people's capacity in revolution to develop a new erotic sensitivity and a capacity for a more generous form of sexual love, and her passionate espousal of the Workers' Opposition in 1921. Anna Itkina, in writing her biography, had access to certain letters and diary excerpts from this archive, as has another scholar named Grigory Petrov, who wrote several articles on Kollontai's activities before and during the First World War. I have quoted from both these writers' findings in my book.

I was not sure how to refer to Alexandra Kollontai in writing her life. The proper form, indicating both comradeship and a certain respectful distance, would have been the first name and patronymic, "Alexandra Mikhailovna," but this was unwieldy, as was "Alexandra Kollontai." Simply "Kollontai" seemed rather too impersonal—more appropriate, I felt, to a purely political biography than to a more personal account of her life. And so I have referred to her as "Alexandra," uneasily aware that this sounds both presumptuous and sentimental. I hope that her distinguished life retains enough of its dignity in my account of it and that it is not trivialized by this and many other flaws.

Cathy Porter
London 1979

ALEXANDRA KOLLONTAI

1

Too Much Family Happiness

On March 18, 1872, a bedraggled knot of revolutionaries met in a dingy London pub to drink to the first sad anniversary of the Paris Commune. Although they did not know it, they were also drinking to the death of the great First International, of which they were all members. Formed in London in 1864 by Marx, the First International (The International Workingmen's Association) had lived its finest hour—and died—in the Paris Commune. News of the Commune and its aftermath had ruffled the pages of the Russian press like a light breeze, and most liberal Russians, after it was all over and Paris had lost 170,000 of its working citizens, breathed a deep sigh of relief and turned to matters nearer home. For Mikhail Domontovich and Alexandra Masalina, the anniversary of the Commune was a different, more personal triumph—the triumph of six years' passion over the conventions of class, not to speak of the scandal of Alexandra's divorce—and on March 19, the birth of their daughter.

It was only eleven years earlier that the serfs, eighty percent of Russia's population, had been officially emancipated. But despite this and Tsar Alexander II's many other reforms (of the judiciary, local government, and the universities), Russia was still chained to the dark feudal ignorance in which she had lain for the past seven centuries. Few landowners and aristocrats were as progressive and as in touch with Western ideas as Mikhail and Alexandra Domontovich, but even they were mere servants of the Tsar, without political power. As a liberal army officer Mikhail was as powerless as those officers in the Crimean War who had led thousands of Russian soldiers to their death.

It was the Sevastopol catastrophe of 1854 which had prompted serfs all over Russia to awaken from their slumbers and to loot and burn the

1

property of their masters. The question of the serfs' emancipation began to overshadow all other issues of human emancipation, and the Russian family, whose hierarchical structure rested on roles unchallenged since the twelfth century, also woke from its deep sleep; the aristocratic pater-familias gradually lost all authority not only over his serfs but over his wife and children too.

In 1861 the landlords were bought out by the tsarist state and the serfs were turned overnight into "free" peasants; landless, overtaxed, and stranded, they shuffled seasonally from the village to the town, where their labor was used to work Russia's small, overcrowded, and squalid factories. For countless women too—of the peasantry, the merchantry, and the impoverished aristocracy—the emancipation came as the signal for them to leave behind the dull prison of family life, the constraints of religion, and the urge to self-sacrifice. Throughout the 1860's thousands of them left the provinces for Russia's major cities, where they too struggled for some economic security and the chance for solidarity. It was these women who brought the "woman question" to the forefront of the discussion groups in which young radicals tried to relate their study of socialism to the social revolution which by now seemed a reality in Russia. By the late 1860's women in most Russian cities were forming similar discussion groups, for women only, in order to support each other in their new lives of independence. And having realized that their own needs could only be satisfied through social revolution, many of them joined the men in a program of study in preparation for this revolution.

Unmarried, women could not get the passports they needed if they were to leave home legally for travel around Russia and abroad. Without passports, many women's lives in the cities were fraught with fears of arrest. By the 1860's, however, the romantic love match was increasingly replaced by a more utilitarian marriage of convenience. In these "fictitious marriages" an enlightened man would often undertake to marry a woman merely in order to deliver her from her parents and give her her passport to freedom, although sometimes the intention was also to give her the coaching she needed to qualify as a governess, continue her education, or find a job. Many couples agreed to part immediately after the ceremony; some of them got hopelessly entangled in all the conflicts between sexual passion and independence which they had hitherto so blithely dismissed; some "fictitious marriages" turned into deep and lasting sexual relation-ships. But a more profound attempt to transform sexual relationships in a rational manner and to create a new kind of family life within the socialist movement was made by the men and women who created the communes which sprang up in every Russian city. Not only did these communes provide shelter for women without work or accommodations and allow them to live cheaply and simply, they allowed men and women to bring some of their socialist ideas into their everyday lives and to establish relationships with each other in which convention and insincerity were replaced by honesty and mutual respect. As a proof that they had renounced the old decadent ways of their devalued past, women cropped their hair, hid their eyes behind blue-tinted spectacles, smoked on the streets, and clumped around in heavy peasant boots and short skirts. Many of these women, dubbed "nihilists" (people who believed in nothing) by the conservative press, were still in their teens.

In the semi-feudal Russia of the 1860's capitalism was regarded by almost all these young populist radicals as a temporary phenomenon. They believed that the peasants were to be the agents of the revolution. With a wonderful optimism they also assumed that the problems of women's liberation were amenable to rapid and rational solution: women would then dissolve their independent discussion groups, join the "common task," and embark with their male comrades on their great journey "to the people."

By the late 1860's many women were traveling alone or with men to the villages of Russia as teachers, doctors, and "apostles" of the peasant revolution. Yet it was with deep reservations that Sofya Perovskaya and a group of her young radical women friends in the capital decided in 1870 to merge their discussion circle with a similar circle of male students. It was the group born of this merger, the Chaikovskyists, which began to unite various groups of populists throughout the country into Russia's first revolutionary party, Land and Liberty.

Hundreds of women, however, still shared Sofya Perovskaya's reservations and felt unprepared to join the "common task." Many who longed for the university education still denied to them were becoming disillusioned with the campaign for women's higher education so tirelessly pursued by prominent public-spirited women like Nadezhda Stasova, Anna Filosofova, and Maria Trubnikova. Such campaigns would be useless, they concluded, so long as these women relied on personal friendships with highly placed government officials to promote them.

By the early 1870's hundreds of women were beginning to leave their aristocratic and peasant families in oppressive Russia for Zurich University, where they enrolled in the medical faculty in order to serve the populist movement as qualified doctors when they returned home. A few of them did manage to qualify before being summoned back to Russia by a threatening ukase (a Russian government edict with the force of law). But for many others, innocent of the politics of Zurich's Russian student community, and mostly also very young, their meeting in Zurich with the great Russian anarchist revolutionary Bakunin was decisive, and they threw away their books. For Bakunin's instinct had told him that the revolutionary flame must burn most fiercely in those who had no stake in the existing order; he was especially attuned to all the vagaries and contradictions which women faced as revolutionaries, and he assigned a major role in the revolutionary movement to the primitive peasantry, the *lumpenproletariat*, and the various déclassé elements of the bourgeoisie. By 1874 a group of young women was returning to Russia from their meeting with Bakunin in Zurich to carry their revolutionary convictions to the women who sweated out their lives in Moscow's fetid factories. What these women members of the "Moscow Group" learned of the factory women's lives was written on their haggard faces when they emerged, shortly afterward, under arrest.

The experiment was not repeated. In the years that followed, increasing numbers of Land and Liberty members carried their socialist propaganda to the countryside and were arrested, imprisoned, and exiled in the process. Mikhail and Alexandra Domontovich, like the good liberals they were, may have had a secret respect for their idealism. This first heroic period of the Russian revolution certainly inspired the respect of many liberal aristocratic women engaged in charity work and campaigns for women's higher education; the connection between political liberation and the liberation of women was made by both men and women in Land and Liberty with an instinctive and inspiring confidence. This clearsighted commitment had again and again to be hoisted out of the realms of theory by the more militant women workers and intellectuals who followed them.

If they had entertained any such sympathies, however, the Domontoviches would have been careful not to let this be known, since it would have been considered scandalous, and tantamount to courting prison. Even in the cosmopolitan St. Petersburg of the 1870's, the union of an aristocratic Ukrainian grenadier officer in the prestigious Poltava regiment and a former Finnish peasant's daughter and divorcee was considered scandalous enough. And this despite the fact that by the reign of Alexander II most inhabitants of the capital were well aware that Peter the Great's "window on Europe" had been wrenched open in the eighteenth century only by seizing Finland, turning her into a Russian Grand Duchy, and so increasing access to the Baltic. In the process Russia had secured an endless source of cheap and acquiescent laborers to work its woodland estates. On one such estate, richly covered with conifers and dense with deciduous alder, ash, and oak, Alexandra Masalina's father had been born into a serf's family. By the age of eighteen, however, he had already accumulated and stolen enough wood to leave serfdom behind him for good, and set out to walk barefoot to St. Petersburg, there to sell his wood and find himself a wife. That, at any rate, was the story Alexandra never tired of telling her daughter later on.

Masalin accomplished both these tasks in the capital with character-istic briskness and was soon on his way back to Finland with his new wife, a young Russian girl named Krylovaya. He returned not to his old serf estate, however, but went farther north to the Karelian Isthmus, where the forests begin to thin, trees yield to lichen, and not far off are the sphagnum bogs of the northern tundra. Kuusa, on the White Sea five hundred miles north of Lake Ladoga, is now in the Soviet Union. Here, nature seemed to accomplish the task of building roads without human help, which is to say that timber was floated down the rivers in the ice-free months and all other transport waited until winter, when snow cover allowed the passage by sledge. By the 1850's, when Masalin began to build his house at Kuusa, there were only 3300 miles of railways in the whole of Russia, most of these leading to the slow death of Siberian exile. Only where "defects of nature" made transport along rivers and ice impossible were railway lines belatedly laid. The first of these, built in 1837, was the 27 km line from St. Petersburg to Tsarskoe Selo, the Tsar's country palace —"From capital to cabaret," said the wits.

Kuusa was well connected by rivers to Helsingfors (now Helsinki) and St. Petersburg, and Masalin's timber business flourished. Krylovaya bore three children (two daughters and a son), kept the family cows and chickens, tended the vegetable plot, and evidently did not find her exile from Russia too burdensome. The loneliness of Kuusa was relieved by frequent visitors, most of them Russian and Scandinavian architects who came to admire the simple timbered elegance of the house. Many progres-sive spirits and Finnish nationalists, repelled by St. Petersburg's massive granite and all the imperialistic vanity and human sacrifice it stood for, saw Kuusa as a model of simple, stylish good taste. However, although Masalin's nationalistic pride was flattered by such visitors, he was too much of a businessman to look for Finnish husbands for his daughters, Alexandra and Nadezhda. And so, when it was time to bring Alexandra out, the Kuusa house was closed and the family went south to St. Petersburg, there to cultivate a taste for the opera and look around for a couple of husbands.

It was at the first night of the Italian opera season that Mikhail Domontovich first set eyes on the "three northern beauties," as his soldier friends had named the two Masalina girls and their mother. Recently graduated from the grenadier guards, young Domontovich was awaiting a military post and so was more interested in the social pleasures of the capital than in looking for a wife. After one meeting with Alexandra his priorities were reversed, and after a swift and secretive courtship he went to Masalin to ask for his daughter's hand. He was rejected curtly, and shortly afterward led a regiment off to find death or glory in the Austro-Hungarian war. Proud Masalin, who had no interest in frivolous young officers for his sons-in-law, feared that Alexandra would pine until Mikhail returned and operated quickly to ensure she would be safely married before the war ended. And so the unhappy Alexandra was married, much against her will and still in some disfavor with her father, to an older and more conventional man, Konstantin Mravinsky. She had three children, Adele, Evgenia (known as Jenny), and Alexander, and lived comfortably in St. Petersburg for the next five years, regularly visiting Kuusa every summer.

It was at a society ball that she met Mikhail again. This time she was determined that nothing should interfere with a love which five years' separation had done nothing to diminish. Leaving Alexander with his father, she set off at once with Adele and Jenny for Kuusa, where she embarked on lengthy and stressful divorce proceedings—made more stressful by the fact that she was already pregnant by Mikhail.

Alexandra's move was a sign of great courage. At that time, divorce was almost unheard of in Russia; marriage, as indestructible as the Church itself, transformed men into its divinely appointed domestic bishops. Alexandra and Mikhail were to find great happiness with each other for the rest of their lives together, but the divorce was not granted before both had confessed their adultery before a special session of the Holy Synod and Mikhail had entered into negotiations with officials of the Church with whom he had family connections—for his family was one of the noblest in Russia and quite as well endowed with legend as was Alexandra's.

By the time of his marriage Mikhail Domontovich had been promoted to inspector of the Tsar's cavalry. But he could hardly have avoided promotion. His attachment to the Tsar's army had a glorious tradition behind it, and his family proudly traced its line to the folk hero Prince Dovmont, who ruled Pskov in the thirteenth century.

Dovmont was one of many semi-mythical saintly warriors to emerge in turbulent periods of Russian history. (Alexander Nevsky, the most famous of these warrior princes, was in fact his father-in-law.) A pagan Lithuanian convert to Christianity who devoted his life to fighting for Christ, he died of the plague in 1299, "having given his life for the people and the Orthodox faith." Thus did the fourteenth-century Pskov Chronicle record his death, and from that time on the church bells of that town were rung to welcome any member of the Domontovich family (who moved to the Ukraine in the eighteenth century).

The fifteenth century had seen the first great division of Russians into the *muzhy* and the *muzhiki* (the "men" and the "little men," or serfs), and the emergence of the central Muscovite state. The Muscovite Tsars put an end to people's right to travel, fixed landowners to the estates granted them by the Tsar in exchange for military service, reduced to serfdom virtually the rest of the population, and set up a greatly expanded aristocratic service class to ensure that the social estates fulfilled their divinely ordained duties. This rapidly turned into a bureaucracy demanding maximum social rigidity, since any social change confused the books. So there were laws to forbid peasants to leave the farms they were born on, laws to forbid tradesmen to change residence, laws severely limiting the movement of women, and laws ordaining that priests' sons should follow their fathers into the clergy. In the eighteenth century Peter the Great's Table of Ranks introduced into this unmanageably complex service structure the notion of *chin* (bureaucratic rank), which has proved tenacious enough to survive even the Bolshevik revolution.

Mikhail Domontovich belonged to this aristocratic service class—which, by the nineteenth century, functioned as a reservoir of state skills and filled all the leading positions in the army, the administration, and the judiciary and the diplomatic corps. As he rose to his inevitable inherited destination of general, liberal ideas became incompatible with his status and were gradually confined to the reading of progressive periodicals, and hushed discussions behind closed doors. It was Alexandra, with her energetic espousal of self-reliance, self-discipline, and self-education, who best expressed the classically liberal values of the Domontovich home. Although she allied herself with none of the campaigns which Russian women were launching in the 1870's for educational and professional equality, and although feminism was not yet a political force in Russia, she was in her own moderate way a kind of "domestic" feminist.

By the time they married, Mikhail was able to move his pregnant wife and her two daughters, age seven and eight (her son, Alexander, stayed with his father), as well as a large company of aunts, distant relatives, old retainers, and persistent houseguests, into the bleakly opulent living-quarters of the tsarist cavalry barracks on Sredne Podyacheskaya Street. Alexandra, who did not like the city, hated this house and insisted they spend every summer at Kuusa. When the time for her confinement arrived, she moved to the comfortable family house of the General's cousin and it was here, on March 19, that their daughter was born.

The weather was gusty, but the midwife's speculations about the baby's stormy future were of no concern at all to her adoring parents. The Paris Commune had been ceremonially buried the day before in London, Marx's *Capital* had appeared that year in Russian translation (the censors regarding it as too dull to be of interest to any but the most academic economists), and the Domontoviches had the highest hopes of raising their child as a person of liberal culture and independent mind. The priest who came the next day to christen her had such a good time and got so drunk that he mistook her for a boy, and so she was officially named Alexander for the next twenty years without anyone being any the wiser.

English and French nannies were hired for the affectionately named "Shura,"[1] to whom they spoke in Finnish and Russian. Perhaps they tried too hard, for Shura remembered giving them a lot of trouble. She was a stubborn, lively, attractive little girl, regarded by her two half-sisters, perhaps with some jealousy, as precocious and spoilt. She certainly emerges from her own autobiographical description of her childhood as almost impossibly advanced for her years, since, according to her, two of the first words to enter her consciousness were "war" and "prison"; "from my earliest childhood I was used to hearing heated political arguments from my father's study, and grew familiar with all the words relating to international politics: international agreements, peace congresses, wars of liberation, diplomatic victory, diplomatic retreat—I didn't understand then what it all meant, but the words were firmly implanted in my memory as a child."[2]

Shura's early familiarity with prisons was not surprising, as the barrack building did remarkably resemble one. The view from her nursery, which she shared with her English nanny, Miss Gudgeon, was of a gloomy rectangular courtyard painted that dull yellow which flattens and eventually deadens the imagination. Much of her time as a very young child was spent watching the young cavalrymen in their bright, tight uniforms parading and drilling outside her window.

Her mother ran the household with the kind of spiritual certainty that moves mountains, regimenting her numerous servants and mediating between them and her querulous old dependents with all the tact of an excellent general. For these ancient women had an inexhaustible need for servants to perform their little tasks and attend to all their needs, and had no qualms about using their walking sticks when giving orders. In general the Domontovich house servants were better off than most. They were not expected to leap to attention when in the presence of the gentry, and even if they slept on nothing better than the floor, they were not expected to stay up until all hours. When Shura was very young, however, she realized that little more than buckwheat and potatoes were eaten in the servants' quarters, and she evidently took to heart her mother's entreaties to eat everything on her plate. She soon understood the significance of the evening ritual in which her mother would distribute the servants' meager sugar allowance for the following day. Their pay was average—about five rubles a month[3]—and this made shoes an indulgence and overcoats a rare luxury to be shared and treasured for the intensest cold.

Miss Gudgeon, a modest and capable woman, daughter of an English sea captain, helped Alexandra to run the house. She held definite opinions and found it hard to restrain herself from expressing criticisms of the Russian government. Since Shura was evidently closer to her than to her parents in her early years, she naturally adopted Miss Gudgeon's questioning attitude toward Russian society.

The atmosphere in the Domontovich home was very different from that in the moldering pleasure palaces of most wealthy landowners bankrupted by the emancipation of the serfs. A devotee of the "new hygiene" and rational dress, Alexandra would run around the house uncorseted, flinging open the windows even in the harshest northern winters. Her husband occasionally grumbled that they would all catch their death of pneumonia, but obligingly did not interfere in the running of the house, tending to appear only at the dinner table, which seldom sat less than fifteen people. He was tall and handsome, remotely affectionate to his daughter, who regarded him as a god. "I remember how one time I crept surreptitiously into my father's study," she wrote later. "He did not notice me. I stood on tiptoe to kiss him on the forehead, and Father looked surprised, as if he had never seen me before. Then he smiled."[4] He was scarcely more talkative with other members of the household. A scholarly man, he spent most of his time reading military history in his study—

although Shura recalled the cut-glass toilet bottles on his dressing table and the vanity which she and her mother used to make fun of. Alexandra had long abandoned the crinoline, wore the same straight gray dress every day in the house, and had only one dress for special occasions, so had no need for personal maids or dressmakers. "Your grandfather was a peasant, never forget that," as she always told her daughters when entreating them to tidy up after themselves, sew on their own buttons, and generally be self-sufficient.

Although Shura was brought up as one of three sisters (only learning much later that they had different fathers), Jenny and Adele were so much older that she enjoyed many of the privileges of an only child while precociously sharing—and often rejecting—her sisters' interests in fashion, admirers, and music. She soon made it clear that she was not going to be musical (she preferred to listen to Jenny, who had an enchantingly pretty voice and played the piano exquisitely) but had an excellent ear for languages. Unless Jenny was playing the piano, she tended to avoid the sitting room, which was always filled with the old women and their needy nomadic friends, who after a lifetime spent cowed by their husbands or employers shuffled pathetically from one relative's household to another, waiting only to follow their spouses into the grave. Alexandra tried unsuccessfully to divert her daughters' attention from their dull-witted gossip about the court and the theater, and to interest them instead in knitting and preserving mushrooms and berries for the winter.

Religion was not explicitly rejected in the Domontovich home, for it was still part of the spiritual heritage of any well-bred Russian aristocrat. But, as reason obviously led nowhere with the scriptures, their study was replaced by a strictly rational and practical type of philanthropy. Charity had to be deserved, proved by courage in adversity: this was why the Domontoviches never fired any of their old servants or turned away any of their relatives. However, a little religious belief probably lingered on— from habit, regard for propriety, and a general desire to be on the safe side and set an example to the servants.

The house on Sredne Podyacheskaya Street was filled with books and journals, and Jenny and Adele had many student friends and admirers who turned it into a popular meeting place for discussions and musical evenings. Alexandra eagerly read every book suggested by her daughters and, as a self-educated woman, was naturally drawn to the works of J. S. Mill and Herbert Spencer, as well as George Sand, Victor Hugo, Turgenev, and Ibsen.

It was writers like Spencer and Pasteur, with their Protestant-based individualism, who guided Alexandra in her attitude toward her youngest child. Spencer's essays, *Education: Intellectual, Moral and Physical,* are now all but forgotten, but they were highly influential in the 1870's. In them Spencer stressed the importance of rationality rather than repression in the teaching of the very young; society could only achieve equilibrium, he believed, if a tolerant laissez-faire philosophy was established within the family. In Pasteur, Alexandra found not only innovative ideas about health, self-help medicine, and the temperance movement, but also the enlightened new teaching methods by which Pasteur spread his ideas among the workers at factory night schools. Alexandra's favorite book, a popular account of the temperance, rational dress, and hygiene movements, was called *Be Healthy!,* a title which utterly mystified Shura.

It was in the summer months at Kuusa that the family breathed more freely. Everyone would go off to the woods to pick mushrooms and berries, organize picnics, play skittles, admire the scenery, or leaf through the liberal papers on the veranda. Shura was encouraged to help with the pickling and preserving. But she rarely saw her mother at Kuusa; for Masalin had died, leaving the estate to Alexandra, and she had decided to convert his flourishing timber business into a dairy. She would leave the house early in the morning and return home late at night, exhausted. Her energy and resourcefulness, inspired by the passionate desire to be financially independent of her husband, were soon bringing her in a comfortable income over which she had complete control. Until she was five, Shura wandered freely over the Kuusa estate, often losing her nanny for hours at a time and seeing her parents for little more than a few moments every few days.

There were times when Mikhail took his daughter for a walk—during which he would talk, more to himself than to her, of war and politics. But most of his days in Kuusa, as in St. Petersburg, he spent immured in his study assessing Russia's military failures in the Balkans, upon which melancholy subject he was writing an immense book. (Shura was to inherit the incomplete manuscript of his life's work when he died some twenty-five years later.) As a child, Shura learned to resign herself to the mysterious importance of this work which removed her father from her, but what she later remembered most clearly about Kuusa were those rare occasions when her father did leave his study and relax with her. He would take her for a long walk in the forest, ask her to carry his axe, and then he would take off his jacket and cut down a tree. It was during one of these walks, in 1877, that Domontovich began to talk to her with a bewildering intensity of Bulgaria, which suffered under the tyranny of the

Turks and was fighting for a constitution. What he did not tell her was that Bulgaria was also oppressed by the tyranny of Russia: the Russo-Turkish War had started that April, and he was being called to the front. Garish pictures of heroic Russian generals and barbaric Turks slicing babies were hung on Shura's nursery wall; with the help of her nanny, who discreetly condemned Russia, she learned to read by studying the chauvinistic texts accompanying them.

She learned, too, something of the territorial greed and religious hypocrisy behind the Tsar's "holy war" on Turkey, but this first political lesson was a bewildering one. The Balkan crisis of 1877 was bewildering for millions of Russians, for most of whom Bulgaria had hitherto been little more than a very vague geographical term, synonymous only with the poorest Balkan peasantry; cut off from the migrations of neighboring Slavic peoples by the impenetrable Balkan and Rila mountain ranges, the Bulgarians were a kind of "lost race" as far as most Russians were concerned.

In 1876, the year in which the Turks savagely crushed an uprising in Bulgaria, the men and women working as propagandists in the Russian countryside first connected the cause of Bulgaria with that of peasant Russia. In that year, when these young radicals merged their discussion and propaganda groups into the Land and Liberty Party, many of them were romantically prone to revere the "lost race" of the Bulgarians as the repository of everything inspiring and valuable in Slavic history and culture. In 1817 this tiny strip of Balkan land had won an autonomous church, the Greeks had rebelled on a large scale against the Turks, and Russia had intervened as self-proclaimed protector of Orthodox Christians against Islam—and been bidder for this handy Balkan foothold. When Russia declared war on Turkey in 1877, many Land and Liberty members—men and women—set off to fight with the Bulgarian partisans against their Russian and Turkish overlords. Bakunin's faith that the revolutionary instinct must be strongest among those who were most oppressed was their inspiration, and they were confident that the Bulgarians' heroism would seize the imagination of the Russian peasants and soldiers. Marx limited himself to the more cautious observation that the war would be followed by similarly disastrous Russian military ventures, which would further the Russian revolutionary movement.

During that terrible war, which continued for the next eighteen months, the revolutionaries' talk of land and liberty was greeted with increasing enthusiasm by the peasants. As, one by one, revolutionaries were arrested, finally to be sentenced to prison and exile in the great show-trial of 1878, those at liberty gradually formed themselves into a more centralized, clandestine party, the People's Will. By 1879 that party had committed itself to killing the Tsar; until that time there could be no political liberty they said, no hope for peaceful propaganda.

As Mikhail Domontovich set off for Bulgaria, as a colonel on the Russian General Staff, he hoped with all his liberal heart to see this futile war ended with a Bulgarian constitution. He knew as well as any of his superiors the chaotic state of the Russian forces, decimated by the Crimean War twenty-five years earlier, and he knew what belated and ineffective military reforms that tragedy had prompted. He was aware too of the efficiency of the Turks, who relied on quick scourges and massacres and a ready supply of bashi-bazouk irregulars to carry them out. Alexandra wept and worried about his safety, but Shura realized that there were also political worries surrounding his departure; to Alexander II the word "constitution" was synonymous with revolution, the very mention of which ensured imprisonment and exile. After Mikhail left, Alexandra lived in a state of permanent anxiety, tormented by the old women's nagging criticisms both of Mikhail's "dangerous" ideas and of Jenny's friends, many of whom passionately supported the Bulgarian partisans.

The cavalry departed, the yard outside Shura's nursery was empty of soldiers, and there was little for the women in the house to do but knit stockings for the troops and endlessly imagine new catastrophes at the front. Shura had her new talent for reading to console her and her father's military manuals to practice on. Portraits of Generals Gurko, Radetzky, and Dragomirov, all resplendently uniformed on their brilliant white chargers, were hung on her wall. But the first news from the front was that it was not the generals but the engineers who had brilliantly carried out the initial crossing of the Danube, and so made possible the eventual capture of the Turkish stronghold of Pleven.

In the winter of 1877, during the long Pleven siege, a young officer came visiting with greetings from Domontovich. He was soon followed by a ghastly procession of invalids, maimed, frozen and angry, full of stories not of white chargers but of rotten food, dead comrades-in-arms, cholera, dysentery, and bureaucratic corruption. Shura lost all fondness for the generals on her wall and sought out the company of the little servant boys who came to polish the parquet floors. With these children she enjoyed some rare childish games, sliding about on the floors and running about, and she also asked them a great many questions, trying to understand something of the poverty of their wretched lives. She understood soon enough when the little boy she was fondest of failed to appear one

day, and his replacement woodenly announced that he had just died for
want of an overcoat:

> I did not know the meaning of privation. Yet I saw how other children
> were forced to give up things, and I was particularly and painfully
> shocked by the little peasant children who were my playmates . . . Already
> as a small child I criticized the injustice of adults and I experienced as
> a blatant contradiction the fact that everything was offered to me
> whereas so much was denied to the other children . . .[5]

Alexandra did all she could to discourage these friendships and to prevent
her daughter from becoming so painfully aware of the realities of life and
war. But it was too late. The coddled baby of the Domontovich family
now began to place this coddling at the root of her protest against everything around her.

> Too much was done for me to make me happy. I had no freedom of
> maneuver either in the children's games I played or in the desires I
> wanted to express. At the same time I wanted to be free, to express
> desires on my own, to shape my own little life . . . My criticisms shar-
> pened as time passed and the feeling of revolt against the many proofs
> of love around me grew apace; already early in life I had eyes for the social
> injustices prevailing in Russia . . .[6]

When her father returned early in 1878, he was a hero and a general,
decorated in gold medals. But Shura's aversion for gold and the heroism
of leaders had gone very deep and, taking one look at him, she ran sobbing
from the room and was sent to bed with castor oil. A little while after this
she annoyed her parents again by refusing to pass cigarettes to a friend
of theirs who had dropped some offensive remark about the peasants.
Deprived of friends and confined almost permanently to the house, Shura
began to develop the unshakable conviction that her mother's little dog
was a child in magical disguise; she read to it for hours in the hope that
it would return to its human form. It must have been a relief for all of
them to leave St. Petersburg that spring. The general, who had left earlier,
had been appointed first governor of Trnovo and then vice-consul of
Bulgaria, and was now ready to receive his family in Sofia.

When Shura set off with her mother, her sisters, and Miss Gudgeon
over the Balkan ranges, their carriage was escorted on this intrepid journey
by no less a person than General Totleben. As governor-general of Odessa
he had earned himself a reputation for such savage cruelty that the
People's Will members there, who usually opposed random killings, had

laid plans to assassinate him. Shura evidently had no liking for him either: at dangerous points along their mountain path they had to go on foot, and when he took her on his shoulders she shuddered to realize the meaning of his German name; in the company of General "Death-in-life" she felt closer to death.

Between the ages of six and seven Shura lived in Sofia. "It was there," she wrote later, "that my character began to be formed. It was there that I began to observe and think."[7] Here she was less strictly supervised and was even allowed to walk alone on the streets. She made friends with a boy and his donkey, and first met the little girl who was to be her lifelong companion, Zoya Shadurskaya. A particularly vivid memory of that year was the dismal spectacle of some Bulgarian partisans being led off to be shot on the street along which she, Zoya, and her parents were passing. She burst out crying and shouting, and swore that when she and Zoya were adults they would not allow such cruelty. She returned home sobbing inconsolably, convinced that she should have persuaded her father to stop the firing squad. Miss Gudgeon put her gently to bed, and to her Shura "confessed that I felt guilty for the fact that the partisans and other prisoners had been shot, and all because I was a foolish person. Miss Gudgeon, with her usual patience, asked me about everything and gave me syrup to drink. I fell asleep holding her hand."[8]

From the windows of the bare white two-story house into which the Domontoviches moved in Sofia there was a wonderful view of the minarets of the town; hills scattered with sheep stretched away and up to the purple line of the Vitosh Mountains. Family life was more relaxed there. Jenny and Adele enjoyed themselves with large numbers of worshipful young men with whom they embarked on picnics and dances and long horseback rides into the mountains. Shura would watch fascinated as they stood "like tall blue Amazons" in their riding habits, waiting for their horses to be brought round and conversing with their young escorts.

But she had enough friends of her own not to feel excluded as her sisters cantered off into the hills. Zoya Shadurskaya was to become "the dearest person in the whole world to me, besides my son."[9]—indeed, despite years of exile and separation, the friendship survived until Zoya's death just before the Second World War. Zoya and Shura were the same age, but Zoya was the eldest child and her parents, who were younger than Shura's, gave her more attention. Her mother was great friends with Adele and Jenny, and her father liked to accompany them on the piano. Zoya could tell her new friend about the black slaves in America, about Lincoln and the American Constitution, about the Bulgarian constitution which Shura's own father was drawing up, about Garibaldi in the red shirt who summoned the partisans and liberated Italy from the Austrian oppressors —and together they spent hours in the Domontoviches' overgrown garden talking about the moon and the planets and their futures.

All this talk excited Shura's desire to go to school, and it now seemed that this might be possible, for Alexandra's dream was to establish in Sofia the first Bulgarian girls' school. Shura was to be the first pupil, as she needed to "learn more languages," to add to her already fluent English, French, and German. She entered into this plan with great enthusiasm, sitting beside her mother at the dining-room table at meetings attended by kerchiefed Bulgarian women, and keeping the papers in order: " 'Everyone must help in this scheme, even in trifles,' said mama gravely." For the Bulgarians, more used to the Russian prostitutes who followed the soldiers and construction-workers to those parts, Alexandra's scheme was apparently not so easy to accept, and the school was not started during their stay there.

Their year in Sofia did, however, fortify Jenny's determination to train as an opera singer; the house was always filled with the sweet smell of violets and the sounds of her voice. Adele was an enthusiastic actress, and Shura too developed a taste for the stage, standing once on her chair to deliver some advice to Adele (who was playing the distressed heroine) and stopping the show.

On April 22, 1879, a little less than a year after their arrival in Bulgaria, the constitution which Domontovich and his Bulgarian friends had drawn up was finally passed by the national assembly, after some heavy amendments from St. Petersburg which did not augur too well for the general's political future. That sultry summer of 1879 as Shura and her family stopped with some Domontovich relatives on the way back to St. Petersburg she instinctively sensed from her parents' whispered conversations that the revolutionaries were intensifying their attack. Political discussions had to be conducted in whispers because there was hardly a house, factory, government office, or university classroom which was not now infested with police spies.

In the spring of 1878 a woman Land and Liberty member called Vera Zasulich had shot Trepov, governor-general of St. Petersburg, and wounded him seriously. So deeply was liberal public opinion outraged by Trepov's past cruelties and impressed by Vera Zasulich's evident idealism that she was acquitted. "Russian absolutism has been killed!" wrote the revolutionary Kravchinsky from the Balkans, where he was fighting with the Bulgarian partisans: "The 31st March was the last day of its life." It was in that year, the "year of the attempted assassinations"—when revolutionaries launched a series of individual attacks on local governors and high officials—that Land and Liberty steeled itself to concentrate its efforts on killing the Tsar. The new terrorist party, the People's Will, was formed in the summer of 1879—dedicated to killing Tsar Alexander II. A third of its executive committee members were women, most of them from the aristocracy, most of them former populists and members of the discussion groups of the 1860's and 1870's. Many of these women were initially regarded by their male comrades as naïve populists incapable of terrorism. But it was these women, women like Sofya Perovskaya and Vera Figner, who brought to the members of the People's Will the awareness that their survival as a group united against internal antagonisms and the mounting external repression of the tsarist state depended on their ability to carry their political principles into their relationships with each other.

However progressive and benevolent they might be, Alexandra and Mikhail Domontovich could only regard with panic Jenny's determination to leave home to become an opera singer and seven-year-old Shura's precociously rebellious ways. They became guarded in all their conversations with the girls and were profoundly grateful that Adele wished for nothing more than a comfortable marriage. But among Jenny's student friends who visited the house when they returned to St. Petersburg there were many who now openly supported the People's Will. It was impossible not to realize that this party was seriously intending to kill the Tsar, and the general's position was too sensitive to allow this sort of thing to be discussed in his house. Besides, Shura seemed to be picking up bad habits. She had told Miss Gudgeon that the Tsar, who had made her father's life so difficult, was a wicked man. Miss Gudgeon retorted that such words could cause her father's arrest, but Shura, undeterred, began to call the Tsar all the ugly names she could think of. She was once seen by her parents standing on a chair, cursing Tsar Alexander. Jenny must be sent back to her father.

This came as a great blow to Shura, who had not yet realized that she and her sisters had different fathers, but Jenny was untroubled, declaring that all she wanted to do was to train her voice to sing opera. Alexandra mediated by insisting that "we all finish medium schooling and furnish ourselves with references in preparation for every eventuality in life." So it was agreed that Jenny should stay on condition that she studied. A tutor, Maria Strakhova, was hired for her—to her great delight: she had always preferred reading and playing the piano to accompanying Adele and her mother on their trips to the shops or to balls.

If Alexandra thought to dissuade Jenny from the dangerous and disreputable life of the stage by insisting that she work for it, she was wrong. Jenny was a tough character; she stuck to her books and passed her exams. She absorbed herself in mythological history to recreate the characters of the great operas, and this study taught her the sincerity and control that later made her so popular as a singer. During long evenings at the piano or while practicing exercises in front of the mirror, she would ask Shura's help, and Shura would delightedly sing Mephistopheles to Jenny's Faust or Rigoletto to her Gilda, as Jenny rehearsed her repertoire of Gounod and Verdi operas. She passed her exams brilliantly and automatically won that prize most sought after by every Russian girl who longed to leave home in those years—a teaching certificate. This offered her the opportunity of becoming a governess like Maria Strakhova should her operatic ambitions collapse. To her parents it offered the consoling assurance that she should be able to get a job relatively easily if she left home, and would not, like hundreds of women of her age and temperament, have to resort to the painful expedient of a "fictitious marriage." The Domontoviches must have seen how many girls like Jenny idealistically embarked on platonic "marriages" with men friends who pledged to help them study and find work while providing them with passports. And they must have seen how many of these girls, despite their determination to be independent, became ensnared in all the torments of love, often losing the chance to become self-supporting and opting for a conventional marriage with their partners, or, worse, being abandoned the moment the ceremony was over. The incentives for such women to join the revolutionary movement were, as the Domontoviches must have realized, very great.

It was Maria Strakhova, with her modesty, self-reliance, and clear-sightedness, who persuaded Jenny that she would have to work hard for her freedom, and it was to Maria Strakhova that seven-year-old Shura turned with most of her questions about the universe. Maria made an immediate impression on her.

> She dressed extremely simply, wore thick boots, and combed her hair flat. In her appearance Strakhova distinguished herself from everyone I had ever met before. She always paid great attention to me, and there was

something in her manner which made one respect and even fear her a little . . . Mother said that Strakhova was a good hard-working girl. "She's had a difficult life, and we mustn't attach any significance to her awkward manners and ugly hairstyle," she said.[10]

More urgently than anything, however, Shura wanted to go to school and find her own freedom outside the house—which still reminded her of a prison for the good reason that she was seldom allowed to leave it. Alexandra's weak protest that school exposed one to too many germs convinced nobody. Shura knew quite well that her fear was of "dangerous ideas": "mother of course considered I was already sufficiently critically (that is rebelliously) inclined as it was."[11] And so, rebelliously and very grudgingly, Shura began to take lessons in drawing and music and dancing, and prepared herself to start her serious education with Maria Strakhova. She was told not to spoil her eyes by reading and in every way discouraged from following Jenny's path—too many girls of good family had taken their freedom, "gone to the people" as peasant teachers, and now wished to kill the Tsar and foment revolution. If Shura went to school, she would inevitably be trailed by the police agents and freelance hooligans who attended all ladies' schools in search of women who conformed to the Tsar's image of the "nihilist woman" student—all cropped hair and dark glasses.

Maria Strakhova was radical, of course, but a populist of the old school and not a terrorist. She was poor and therefore could be paid little, she had good manners, the general liked to argue with her (which was a definite advantage, for there were fewer and fewer people he enjoyed talking to these days), and Jenny and Shura loved her. If they had had more political imagination, the Domontoviches might have been disturbed by the social criticism Maria managed to insert into a visit to the Hermitage art gallery, where, in telling her pupil of the Dutch School, she also told her of the heroic struggles of the Dutch against the Catholic Church and Philip II of Spain. Shura's clumsy sketches of geometrical shapes and classical profiles were abandoned. She listened fascinated as Maria talked of Darwin and Mill; she read Hugo and Sand to her in French; she was touched by Ibsen, whose plays Maria read to her in translation. Rather precociously, she also embarked with her teacher upon Buckle's massive *History of Civilization*, her mother's great standby. With the return to St. Petersburg, the family had reestablished the old routine of spending their summers at Kuusa, and there the eight-year-old Shura and her governess wandered about with greater freedom, seizing books and journals from the large library and telling one another stories. Imperceptibly Maria was teaching Shura to understand Russian society and its contradictions.

Her carefree apprenticeship was abruptly cut short. All the buried fears and suspicions of the past three years exploded in people's faces on March 1, 1881. Throughout that evening, mounted police clattered up and down the empty streets. Candles were lit in the Domontovich household as the family waited to hear whether the Tsar had died or not. At first, news of the Tsar's assassination arrived at the Domontovich home as a rumor. But this was enough to set off shockwaves of speculation, interpretation, and bewilderment. One aunt worried quietly about her student son, a grandmother saw it as a crime of royal adulterous passion, many servants wept, while others remarked that the Tsar who had emancipated them twenty years before had not improved the peasants' lives one bit. A young officer, a relative of the general's, arrived to deliver the news officially and stayed to vent his views on students and nihilists.

Shura was deeply impressed by the heroism of the terrorists, with their promises of glory and revolution; like many young people, she was inspired by the revolutionary self-sacrifice of the People's Will. The idea proposed by Marx and his foremost Russian exponent, Plekhanov—that people were imprisoned by their economic circumstances—she would have found almost offensive in its anonymity. The new and better world which Shura had begun to glimpse could only be achieved by the heroism of individual men and women. Few could fail to realize, though, that not five, nor fifty, nor five hundred people would topple the imperial colossus.

The young men and women who killed the Tsar—almost none of whom had read Marx—believed that social revolution was an abiding inspiration to those who suffered. The Marxists who followed them believed that suffering lives could only be justified and fortified, that revolution itself would only be realized, by struggling first for political liberty. The terrorists logically extended previous populist assumptions that the industrial workers were but dislodged migratory peasants—the people whom Bakunin had embraced so warmly in his travels as an agitator. Plekhanov and the Marxists argued that the peasants could never be the agents of revolution, and that to avoid the catastrophe of open class warfare led by a small and unprepared proletariat of only 2,500,000, revolutionaries should direct their attention to the economic struggle in the factories.

The assassination opened up not a new peaceful era of propaganda in the countryside but the most drastic police measures Russia had witnessed, and a ferocious hunt for anybody remotely connected to the People's Will. On March 16, it was announced that six people (four men and two women) would be hanged. Gesya Hanfman, who was pregnant, was temporarily reprieved, but Sofya Perovskaya's hanging haunted Shura. Maria Strakhova fainted on hearing the news; Jenny sat for hours in sad silence at the piano; but Alexandra and Adele were incensed that a girl from a good family, General Perovsky's daughter, should have been so thoughtless of her mother. Shura laid plans for her escape.

At six in the morning of April 3, a scaffold was erected on Semë-novsky Square, and twelve thousand troops waited for the three tumbrils to deliver their prisoners. That day cast a shadow over Shura's ninth year, which only Maria Strakhova and the books they read together were able to lighten. School was now completely out of the question, and when Alexandra talked of the dangers of "germs," she was clearly talking about police spies. Twenty-year-old Adele was propelled relentlessly toward marriage with a distant cousin forty years her senior, the owner of the Sredne Podyacheskaya Street house. Although a liberal in the days of the emancipation of the serfs, he was now withdrawing more and more into the certainties of the French Enlightenment, burying himself in the works of Diderot and Montesquieu and advocating free trade as the national panacea. Memories of her parents' broken marriage had made Adele timid of seeking a love match. Moreover, the girls were shocked to learn that their father, who was only a very moderate liberal, had been arrested for having been in contact with terrorists. Engineer Mravinsky had been inspecting water-pipes in the basements of St. Petersburg on the night of the assassination. He was accompanied on this inspection not by sewer workers but by police, by whom he had been hired to help search for terrorist bombers and their underground tunnels. The search yielded neither terrorists nor tunnels, and Mravinsky was arrested for misleading the police. Domontovich managed to intercede with the government and save Mravinsky from Siberia; he was sent instead to exile in European Russia. All this could not but add to the climate of fear which ruled Shura's family house. Tensions began to appear in the Domontoviches' marriage, and they were ostracized by several of their former St. Petersburg friends for their connection with Mravinsky. Many had not forgiven Alexandra for her adulterous marriage to Domontovich.

The family's isolation encouraged Shura to daydream. She imagined herself rushing up to the Tsar's widow and begging for Mravinsky's freedom: she would be a heroine. When Zoya came to stay, "we both sat on my bed in our very long white nightshirts (in the English style). We had no light in the nursery apart from the candle fluttering in the little red glass of oil hanging in front of an icon in the corner."[12] Zoya had just read a book about the storming of the Bastille and suggested that they should enlist the help of some revolutionaries to lead an assault on the prison in which Mravinsky was held. It then occurred to them that they knew no revolutionaries. From 1881 onward political action became the center of Shura's fantasies.

With her eldest daughter settled into a quiet, loveless marriage, Alexandra sighed with relief. Her mother died and was followed shortly afterward by several other old ladies who had been living with them. It was time for the family to move to a smaller house, the elegant residential wing of the large St. Petersburg mansion belonging to the general's cousin —the house where Shura was born, spent her youth, got married, had her son—"and it was from this house that I left my family behind me forever for the revolution."[13]

The part of the house that faced the street had the kind of formal, spacious elegance suitable for bringing two girls out into the world. The large, carpeted drawing room, its formal chill increased by Alexandra's fondness for open windows, was heated by just one small wrought-iron stove, lit by heavy bronze candelabras and filled with heavy furniture upholstered in dark-blue velvet. But the other two wings leading out onto the courtyard at the back had been allowed to deteriorate and were let to the families of factory workers, who lived in horrible poverty right under the Domontoviches' eyes. The yard was an eyesore far too close for comfort as far as Alexandra was concerned, and she resolutely determined to keep Shura under close guard lest she pick up the germs and revolting language of these depressing neighbors of theirs. The thin smoke that rose from their chimneys seemed to her to be laden with foul disease, and for once her fears may have been well-founded, for many of the pale, rickety children whom Shura did manage to meet as they sat listlessly about in the yard were swept off by cholera and diphtheria. All through Shura's tenth and eleventh years hardly a day passed when she would not disobey her mother's strict instructions and slip down to the yard, watching the men leave at dawn for work and gazing at the women and children who slipped in and out scavenging for food and firewood. Even the young Domontovich house servants, who usually supported Shura against her mother, refused to give her bread for people they considered disgusting; they regarded Shura's surreptitious visits outside with a mixture of bafflement and contempt.

For Shura it was a depressing time. By the age of eleven her mother's blue drawing room seemed increasingly blurred and unreal to her. Adele was a frequent visitor and evidently preferred the company of her mother and her greatly reduced "senate" of relatives and friends to that of her ageing husband. Shura heard them hold court on Sarah Bernhardt and her black gloves, on the royal family and its scandals—as if the assassination of the Tsar, the poverty beneath their windows, and the hanging of the revolutionaries were mere fading newspaper photographs. Meanwhile from the general's study came the usual sound of voices raised in argument; for there was a constant procession of Bulgarian nationalists arriving at the house after the Russians had written their oppressive conditions into the Bulgarian constitution of 1879. They had fled the country, Shura's father told her, "in nothing but the trousers they stood up in." But she noticed that despite the kindness and patience with which he welcomed these men into his study and arranged loans, jobs, university places, and accommodations for them, he would curtail any argument containing the slightest implied criticism of the Tsar.

Alexander III, who had delayed his coronation until all the People's Will members had been arrested, had by 1883 enormously extended the powers of his secret police. He was a convinced and extreme autocrat, hostile to all his father's limited reforms, terrified of revolution, and keen to return to the well-trodden path of rigid autocracy. He was also of the opinion that however violent and bloody, revolution was preferable to a constitution. The general, whose constitutional sympathies were well known, therefore lived in fear of arrest. He also feared that the imperial axe would fall again on Bulgaria in another war with Turkey; but as the Tsar deigned only to discuss his foreign policy with God and His earthly representative, the Procurator of the Holy Synod, Pobedonostsev, he was as much in the dark about his own future as about that of the Balkans.

Shura watched her parents walking up and down the hall, arm in arm, in the late afternoons after dinner. During these hushed private conversations Mikhail would pat Alexandra's hand reassuringly: "There, there. We've done our best for our country dear," he would say. Burdened with so much muted anxiety and herself the focus of so much of it, Shura would run eagerly to her lessons with Maria Strakhova. Into their reading of literature and history Maria had introduced the "laws of creation," botany and geography, which Shura studied avidly for a year. But by the time she was eleven she was already becoming impatient with facts that left her no wiser about the causes of war and poverty. With great daring and after considerable thought, she steeled herself one day to ask Maria Strakhova for lessons in political geography. Maria Strakhova's favored position in the Domontovich household made it particularly difficult for her to discuss politics openly with her pupil, and she merely offered Shura a useless little book on social reforms in New Zealand.

There was a newcomer to the house, however, with whom Shura began to spend much of her time, and in him she found neither her father's fears about the new regime, nor her mother's strictness, nor Maria Strakhova's increasing timidity. This was Alexander Mravinsky, her half-brother, a successful young lawyer full of confidence in Western capitalism and technology, from which, he insisted, Russia had a great deal to learn. His friends were mostly liberal civil servants and managers of the new concessional businesses, and Shura, who began to loathe the gossip of the blue drawing room, often sought out Alexander's company, listening excitedly to his friends talk about their visits to Europe, the wonders of electricity (still confined in Russia to the houses of the wealthy and the offices of government), and the novelties of scientific technique.

When Jenny was just nineteen, wide-eyed and optimistic, she was accepted to sing at the Marinsky Opera House (now the Kirov), but she was determined to go abroad first to widen her musical experience. Alexandra, eventually persuaded of Jenny's sincerity, decided that she and twelve-year-old Shura would accompany her to Milan, where both girls could learn Italian, visit the art galleries, and learn something of the sources and history of opera. They took a modest little flat, from which the fascinating glass-roofed galleries of the Victor Emmanuel Museum were visible, and lived for the first time in Shura's life without servants. They woke early, coffee was heated on an oil stove while Shura went to buy bread, and then Jenny would leave for her singing lesson, while her sister did her exercises in French, German, or English. After a simple lunch the two girls were set free to wander about the amphitheater, the cathedral with its lacy marble and fading frescoes, and the cafés. Shura adored Jenny's company: "beautiful as a Raphael madonna, modest, serious . . . she sang without any affectation, like the birds."[14] After a few months in Milan, Alexandra felt confident that Jenny could be left to make her own arrangements, and in September Shura and her mother returned to Kuusa, where they heard soon afterward that Jenny had signed a contract to sing in the little town of Vittoria, near Venice (she was to sing the part of Gilda, for which Shura had cued her).

The following year Jenny returned to St. Petersburg to sing at the magnificent Marinsky Opera House. She told Shura of the many indecent propositions she used to receive through the post and at her dressing-room, always assuring her at the same time that she was well able to protect her dignity. Evgenia Mravina, as she now called herself, became well known in Russia for her lovely coloratura voice, for the naïve passion of her acting, and for her lack of "temperament"; her interpretation of Glinka, Dargomirzhsky, and Tchaikovsky was without parallel, and she brought a refreshing simplicity to Wagner and Verdi too. She was especially popular, however, among radical students, and she was in constant demand for benefit performances which Shura, as "Marvina's little sister," was allowed to attend. After a year of immense popularity Jenny's proud and healthy independence gave out. She could cope no longer with the propositions and "admirers"—not to mention the genuine admirers of her voice—and decided that marriage was her only protection. Shura was well aware that this marriage of convenience had none of the radical honesty of a fictitious marriage, as Jenny tried eagerly to explain in private to her sister why she felt forced to marry a man whom she could never fully love. The young guards officer who had worshipped her for so long eventually won the Domontoviches' resigned approval. But marriage to an actress was considered a great scandal, and it cost him his career after military protocol forced him to resign his post.

Jenny moved out, leaving the blue drawing room to its tireless speculations about her marriage. Shura sought out the company of her amiable half-brother, for she was interested by his friends' talk of state finances and Russia's expanding industrial program in the 1880's. These young men represented a new class of industrialists, some of them descended from the old merchant class, some of them connected to the foreign capital that was beginning to flow into Russia from England and Germany, and all of them in close contact with government officials. Twenty years after the emancipation of the serfs, with agriculture stagnating and heavy industry lurching ahead erratically, it was only the government that had the capital to invest in agricultural improvements. But while drawing the bulk of its revenue from the countryside, the government preferred to place its capital in privately financed railways, and to this end was encouraging all heavy industry, and particularly metallurgy, to expand. Import tariffs, which had been low throughout the 1850's and 1860's in accordance with the prevailing European free-trade policies, had shot up in the 1880's in an attempt to support Russian industry, increase state revenue, and create a good trade balance.

Alexander and his friends reasoned that however useful the mighty monarchies of Germany and Austria might be as allies, it was to France that Russia must look for capital investment, since French silks, wines, and luxuries were flooding the markets of Europe, and holding out tantalizing offers of investment. Shura was fourteen when Alexander took her to the docks to welcome the first French trading ships, telling her how the Tsar had been forced to grovel for his French capital by taking off his hat while the "Marseillaise" was played. This was the prelude to a festival of international solidarity of exceptional liveliness. As the flag-festooned French trade ships approached they all sang the "Marseillaise" at the tops of their voices, and as the French trooped off their ships the Russian sailors and dock-workers rushed forward to embrace them, shouting "Long live Republican France!" Young women workers ran out of the local sweets factory to give the sailors violets, and ran off again to avoid their embraces. Then everyone escorted them triumphantly into town.

But these outings were rare, for in two years Shura was to sit for her school-leaving certificate. As she sat in her sunny classroom with Maria Strakhova, she dreamed of the heroines not only of Turgenev and Tolstoy but of the People's Will and the populists; the precious certificate would qualify her as a teacher and open up to her a new world of work and independence, still wonderfully vague in her mind. However, one precise ambition was gradually emerging out of this pleasant chaos of possibilities, and that was the ambition to write.

Like many other fifteen-year-old Russian girls of her class, with relatively free access to the books and journals in her parents' library, Shura read Dobrolyubov, Pisarev, and Chernyshevsky, whose writings had so inspired populists over the past twenty years. When Nikolai Dobrolyubov, son of a moderately wealthy provincial priest, wrote his first literary articles in the late 1850's, he inspired a whole generation of socialist writers and activists to grasp the social criticisms contained in the works of Pushkin, Gogol, and Turgenev. The new classless intelligentsia of the 1860's to which both Chernyshevsky and Pisarev also belonged, were rationalists and materialists, more interested in literature for its social content than for its traditionally romantic values. Until his death in 1861 Dobrolyubov had urged that women should have the same educational opportunities as men; but it was his article "The Realm of Darkness" that particularly seized the imagination of hundreds of women in Russia. In reviewing the eighteenth-century playwright Ostrovsky, he exposed the whole sordid, loveless monotony of Russian family life among the merchant classes, a life in which tyrannical patriarchs beat their children and drove their wives to prostitution by keeping them in a state of perpetual economic dependence.

Dmitry Pisarev, who pursued many of Dobrolyubov's ideas in the mid-1860's, explicitly rejected all art that had no precise political purpose or framework. Shura read his articles, in many of which he eloquently urged that the benefits of universal education should be accessible to women and that the purpose of this education must be to "develop a person's physical, intellectual, and moral potential, and to allow for completely free and natural inclinations; any limitation in education, any directing toward a preconceived and narrow goal (such as that of housewife) leads to harmful consequences, especially if only one goal is allotted to half the human race." But it was Pisarev's contemporary, Nikolay Chernyshevsky, who most eloquently connected the early populists' struggle for socialist liberation with the liberation of women. It was when Shura was fifteen that she first read *What Is To Be Done?*, the novel Chernyshevsky wrote in 1864, during the twenty years he spent in prison and exile for his revolutionary activities. This novel had an immense influence on the men and women in Land and Liberty, and was to be an abiding inspiration to the young people like Shura who later followed them in the socialist movement. She would return to the work again a few years later with an even deeper understanding of the dilemmas of Chernyshevsky's central character, Vera Pavlovna, and her struggle to live an honest, happy, and independent life. When she first read it, however, what struck her most deeply was the realization that fiction could change people and lift them out of their despair. She had kept a diary ever since she learned to write. Gradually she started to try her hand at fiction.

The Domontoviches did not encourage this, and they did all they could to foster her new friendship with Sonya Dragomirova, whose father, a wounded hero of the Pleven siege and an old friend of the general's, had once adorned Shura's nursery wall. The famous contemporary painter Repin had painted a portrait of Sonya (in her Ukranian national dress) which now hangs in the Tretyakov Gallery in Moscow: her handsome face shows just the sort of happy self-confidence which the Domontoviches hoped would encourage their daughter out into society. It was while the two girls were taking a walk in the Dragomirovs' garden that Shura first met Sonya's brother, Vanya. Like Shura, Vanya was fifteen. His perpetual brooding resentment against his parents and society, his moody unstable temperament, his sudden inexplicable fits of depression and guilt—all this Shura found fascinating. They began to meet secretly while Shura was out with Sonya, and they communicated (in invisible ink) in very long and passionate love letters. Vanya was haunted by the feeling that he was not worthy of her and became increasingly depressed and ill. Shura could think of little but him and began to neglect her lessons.

On one of their secret assignations they kissed with especial passion, and the next day Vanya shot himself. "When you get this letter I shall no longer be alive," he wrote to her. "What happened today showed what a vile wretch I am and how little self-control I have. Be happy my angel, and never forget me. Farewell forever." Shura entered a state of shocked depression and was taken to Kuusa to recover. She was given a horse, Jenny gave her a magnificent riding habit, and "by the time the first shock of Vanya's suicide passed I found myself in Kuusa surrounded by the beauty of early spring; I felt strangely free and full of life. It was the first time that death's shadow had passed so close to me, but it only made me appreciate more deeply the beauty of life."[15]

But in some ways she was still quite a childish fifteen-year-old. When Alexandra took her and a new friend called Lyolya Vitkovskaya to Stockholm that summer for a two-week holiday to ease her grief at Vanya's death, she was more interested in ice-cream and waffles than in the architecture, or the revolution which had toppled the Vasa dynasty. The fact was that the closer she came to taking her exams, the more alarming she found the prospect of independence, and the more timid she felt and incapable of any kind of "useful work." When she did pass the following year (sitting for the exams in the boys' *gimnazium*), no magic door opened and she was no wiser about her future. Her first great battle with Alexandra was not over her future studies but over her demand for a tight, boned corset. Alexandra's views on matters of dress were considered advanced and even indecent by her daughters, and her warnings on the dangers of tight lacing fell on deaf ears. Despite Alexandra's sensible words on correct room temperature and skin condition, and her healthy respect for sweat and hard work and physical education, there was actually no physical outlet in St. Petersburg for a lively sixteen-year-old girl who had no interest in balls. In the Domontovich house there was none of the lying down in darkened rooms that formed such a part of the menstruation ritual of most women at that time; but as sports and gymnastics were evidently out of the question for Shura, it was a real problem to find some physical activity that would fill her day, distract her mind, and develop her body.

Judging from a photograph of her as a somewhat sulky sixteen-year-old, Shura evidently won her battle over the corset. But she was unable to resist Alexandra's well-meant scheme (probably inspired by Chernyshevsky) for her daughter to learn the "useful" craft of bookbinding. Shura was excruciatingly embarrassed when a shabby bookbinder called Pavel Ivanovich appeared to give her lessons, but although quite mystified by his pupil's motives, he was happy to earn three rubles an hour and asked no questions. Shura soon appreciated his tact and sensitivity, and after a brief visit to his workshop, where he lived in squalid poverty with his two hungry children, she doubled her lessons. Maupassant's story, *The Necklace*, seemed appropriate for her first attempt at binding.

Delighted by this enthusiasm, Alexandra deferred her plans to bring Shura out, and Shura made use of this brief reprieve to take up her old campaign for a proper course of lessons outside the home. It was ten years earlier that the tireless pioneering women campaigners in Russian cities had won their fight to establish courses to prepare women for the university. From 1876 onward girls of the St. Petersburg middle classes had trooped along to the government-sponsored Bestuzhev courses, which opened in that year to prepare them for university studies. There they had sought liberation through study and a political program in the groups they formed outside the classroom. Throughout the 1880's, however, education was gradually equated with revolution in the official mind, and these courses, which had once represented the summit of all Shura's ambitions, turned into a seedy, police-infested trap for "nihilists." Any Russian woman leaving to study in Zurich was now liable to be called home by the government on pain of imprisonment. The Domontoviches were confident that Shura could be persuaded to look elsewhere for her further education.

Sonya Dragomirova persuaded Shura that a small private school would be far more congenial than the Bestuzhev courses, more conducive to the sort of informal self-education group that they both wanted to join. And so they enrolled in classes run by a Mademoiselle Trub for "girls of wealthy family"—which were not as frivolous as they might sound. Shura particularly enjoyed her history classes with Professor Menzhinsky (liberal university professors sympathetic to the cause of women's education often preferred to teach at private schools rather than at the Bestuzhev courses), and she used to stay behind after classes were over, discussing the struggle against the Spanish Inquisition and comparing it to the persecution of the Protestants which continued in France and Spain. Returning home, she would often continue these discussions in her lessons with Maria Strakhova. But more often she would disappear into her room and write. It was Maria who eventually managed to persuade Alexandra that her eighteen-year-old daughter had literary talents that should be encouraged; Alexandra—who suffered from no false modesty where her daughter's talents were concerned, only fears about their application—approached Professor Ostrogorsky, the distinguished literary scholar at St. Petersburg University, for private literature lessons for Shura.

Shura later wrote that Ostrogorsky took one look at his elegantly dressed and remarkably pretty young tutee, decided she was frivolous, and felt inclined to leave. But once convinced of her real eagerness to learn, he set out to correct her tendency to verbosity and her love of epithets. They read Tolstoy and Turgenev together, and she learned the simple clarity of style which informed all her own later writing, and which she considered her only real literary talent. "I don't consider myself a talented writer," she wrote when she was seventy-eight, "just very average. A good clear style—that's something I do have. But my images are pale. I'm best when I'm doing silhouettes of people . . ."[16]

Now that she was being initiated into the rituals of "visiting," Shura was able to compare the characters of fiction with those she was meeting in life. The hero of one of her favorite novels—Turgenev's *On the Eve*, written in 1869—had come to life for her in the fleeing Bulgarian nationalists who came knocking on the general's door begging him to find them work, but between Turgenev's heroic Bulgarian revolutionary, Insarov (heir to Chernyshevsky and the People's Will), and these ragged students who were more interested in professional advancement than in national revolution, she found puzzling discrepancies. Despite great efforts to overcome her shyness, she still preferred reading and writing to her new social life. Her curious education had left its harmful and long-lasting effects, and she felt "utterly inept in the practical matters of life," relaxing only with old friends like Sonya and Zoya Shadurskaya (in whom she confided everything), and incapable of looking young men in the face.

There was apparently another young man with whom Shura fell in love after Vanya died, but the romance did not last. There was one young man, however, whom everyone loved for his cheerful good looks, and that was Vladimir Kollontai—a second cousin of Polish origin whom Shura had first met when accompanying her father on a business trip to Tiflis. He had had a difficult childhood: his father had been exiled to Siberia shortly after his son's birth, and his mother had trained as a teacher to support her children. Vladimir was a student officer and keen to forget his painful past. Despite the obvious fascination his impoverished and romantic history held for his young cousin, he tended to stop all her questions and talk by sweeping her off her feet to dance. By the time she was nineteen, Vladimir was a constant visitor, a regular escort, and a serious admirer.

It was obvious that Vanya Dragomirov's suicide had little to do with Shura's behavior toward him, but already Alexandra was worrying that her daughter might prove inconstant in love. She and the general realized that what Vladimir wanted was a pretty wife and that he shared none of their daughter's intellectual interests—and they were right, for although dancing the mazurka was an excellent way of crashing through the barriers of passive femininity, Shura had very little to talk about with Vladimir afterward. She was distressed when he returned a volume of Dobrolyubov to her unread, and he showed a positive hostility to her "impractical" questions about politics and philosophy. And yet the more opposed the Domontoviches were to the marriage, the more determinedly Shura insisted on her right to go through with it and the more she desired to comfort poor Vladimir, whose childhood had been so hard. She was ready for marriage, and when her mother retorted that she was incapable of supporting herself or caring for a child, she simply produced her teaching certificate, protesting that she could work to support a family.

" 'You, work!' mother sniffed. 'You, who can't even make up your own bed to look neat and tidy! You, who never even picked up a needle! You, who go marching through the house like a princess and never help the servants with their work! You, who are just like your father going around dreaming and leaving your books on every chair and table in the house!' "[17] There were many of these angry scenes, although Alexandra generally chided her daughter in French, for in this language reproaches sounded gentler. The love affair flourished. Her parents began to take seriously Shura's threat to elope; Vladimir was evidently quite capable of qualifying as an engineer and supporting a wife, and gradually Shura realized that her mother was collecting a trousseau for her.

There was only one remaining tactic, and that was the European tour, on which flighty daughters traditionally found new admirers, reviewed their past, and grew up. Shortly after her twentieth birthday, Shura and her parents left for Berlin, where she headed straight off to the bookshops. The first thing that caught her eye was the *Communist Manifesto*, which spoke to her with such resounding good sense that she escaped her parents for long periods and sought out meetings of the German Socialist Party. From Berlin they moved to Paris, where she read Engels's *Origin of the Family* for the first time, as well as the literature of the early French Utopian Socialists—Fourier, Cabet, Saint Simon. She returned to St. Petersburg having missed and moped for Vladimir very little, but delighted to see him and confirm the wedding for the following April.

At last Vladimir was grudgingly received as Shura's official fiancé—and considering the dangerously rebellious turn their daughter's ideas had taken abroad, the Domontoviches realized they could have done a great deal worse. As one of the newly created corps of factory inspectors, Vladimir was full of liberal optimism about the possibilities of improving working people's lives and was also earning good money—not quite as good as he would have had them believe, however, for in his anxiety to give Shura a memorable honeymoon in the Finnish resort of Imatra, he had borrowed from all sides. Shura herself had pawned all her bracelets and necklaces and a valuable diamond ring, a gift from Adele, which raised only sixty-three rubles.

The day of the wedding, in April 1893, began badly and ended worse. Alexandra continued to carp and critize her daughter's choice of husband. She refused to wear her best dress for the wedding, insisting that paupers could not be choosers. "This is *not* a big day," she insisted, "it's merely the stupidity and obstinacy of a stubborn girl."[18] The cat killed Shura's beloved canary, Shura took a violent dislike to her white satin wedding dress, and she developed such a heavy cold that it was only thanks to Jenny, who powdered her red nose and put up her hair, that she felt able to go through with it. Alexandra warned her son-in-law that if he slept with Shura that night he would have to answer for her death, and Vladimir, deferentially kissing the ladies' hands, took his leave. The honeymoon was postponed, and twenty-two-year-old Shura sat up all night chattering in her old bedroom with her friend Lydia. After longing for marriage as an escape from her family, the compliant life of a wife suddenly seemed to her even less enticing than the smothering affection surrounding her in her parents' home. Now the "grand passion" loomed up on her childish horizon as yet one more trap to stifle her anger, curb her initiative, and numb her sense of social injustice. That night neither the "grand passion" nor the reading of Marx and Engels, nor her fleeting acquaintance with German socialism tempted her sufficiently to leave her childhood behind.[19]

2

Small Deeds

Marriage did not prove capable of uniting Alexandra's two daydreams, the social and the romantic, and they continued to collide and subvert all her well-laid plans for an orderly, useful life. She had learned in recent years to calculate her every movement so as not to waste a second of the day, had devised a method of dressing and putting up her hair so as not to spend more than ten minutes on what took most of her friends two hours. Now she began to admit bitterly to herself that she had no activity to fill all those precious saved minutes, and was even creating more hated household tasks to fill the oceans of wasted time. Although the socialist in her knew quite well that in the end she could no more thwart her capacity for work than obstruct the laws of motion, there was still an impractical romantic in her who longed for the realms of leisured passion.

Shortly after their dismal wedding Vladimir and Alexandra Kollontai left for Georgia, where he had his first report to make as a factory inspector. In Tiflis, Alexandra (who knew that there was more to money than the small amounts that went into ladies' purses) managed the household accounts, augmenting Vladimir's salary with pin-money which she received every month from the general. She was happy to be living, and eating more simply than she had at her parents', and happier still to discover she was pregnant. They moved back to St. Petersburg, where they rented a small flat. She gave birth to their son, Mikhail (affectionately called Misha), in the house where she had been born and had grown up, and when she returned to her own flat her mother insisted that an old family servant, Anna Petrovna, move in to help her with Misha and the housework.

All the time she was breast-feeding Misha and later when he began to crawl around the flat, she was quite unable to surrender him to Anna Petrovna's care, and she grew increasingly angry with herself as she felt all energy and enthusiasm for reading and writing draining away. No sooner had she sat down to read some Plekhanov or a socialist journal than her eyes would glide off the page to Misha and every other thought would leave her head; the very idea of shutting her door on him to write, as her friend Zoya urged her to, was out of the question. When Vladimir returned from work with friends, she would entertain them all with tea and cakes and seethe in silence with a rage that none of her young married women friends seemed to share, and which seemed to have no words to describe it.

Later she was able to write: "Although I personally raised my child with great care, motherhood was never the kernel of my existence. A child was not able to draw the bonds of my marriage tighter. I still loved my husband, but the contented life of a housewife and spouse became for me a 'cage' ".[1] In the early years of her marriage, before she had discovered the kernel of a more satisfying existence, she could not have put words to this feeling of unease and bitterly reflected on the naïve dreams she had entertained of her married life. "I had often longed for the time when I got married and had two lovely little daughters, whose hair I would plait and curl into ringlets, like you see in English paintings—and I would be very, very happy. But then at once I would think 'Happy? And what am I going to do all day? I can't just plait my little girls' hair, I'll have to think of something else to do . . .' "[2]

Chernyshevsky was the first writer who had found the words to express Russian women's yearning for work, and he provided his Vera Pavlovna (in *What Is To Be Done?*) with the first radical solution to their problem. Alexandra had read the novel when she was fourteen and had been persuaded to dabble in bookbinding while under its influence. Now she turned to Vera Pavlovna with a more practical desire to learn how hard physical work might bring her emotional and economic independence, as well as enriching the physical pleasures of love. For despite her mother's example and the constant reminders of the benefits of labor, she felt quite incapable of organizing her life around any kind of socially useful work. Taught from her earliest childhood to plan out each day so as to ensure a rational balance between study and recreation, pleasure and physical work, she still belonged, like Vera, to a generation of women who were taught to love before they were taught to work.

Since contraception would not be available to educated women in Russia for another fifteen years or more (and even then it was often unreliable), Russian women lagged far behind women elsewhere in Europe in the struggle to raise the issues of their health and happiness to the status of economic considerations. Alexandra would probably, like her mother, have had access to contraception from Europe and would have regarded birth control much as she regarded preventive self-help medicine and a healthy diet. But she must have seen how equally privileged women who preached restraint for working-class women were shamed out of their hypocrisy by women revolutionaries for whom chastity really was the only alternative to unwanted pregnancies. Alexandra might have described herself in those days as a populist, but she had been too deeply affected by the collapse of the People's Will to accept renunciation. Her imagination had been kindled too early in adolescence by Sand, Chernyshevsky, and Fourier, and the promise of greater sexual pleasure, to contemplate sublimating eros into desperate acts of terrorism.

For her mother, self-reliant and fulfilled through her daughters, her dependents and her dairy, there *was* no "women's problem"; nor was there a separate "women's problem" (or, at least, there were no articles in the socialist press Alexandra read to suggest there was) in the illegal St. Petersburg discussion groups of the 1890's in which socialists were beginning to find, in the works of Marx a more satisfactory analysis of class struggle than the doomed philosophy of the terrorist People's Will. And so it was that for the first two years of her marriage Alexandra believed the problem must be in her, or in her marriage.

And then in 1895 there appeared an abridged Russian translation from the German of Bebel's book *Woman and Socialism,* and for the first time it dawned on Alexandra that women struggling for their political rights and sexual freedom might find their natural allies in the workers' movement. August Bebel, a woodturner by trade, had joined the German workers' movement in his youth. A personal friend of Marx and Engels, he had worked to ensure that when the German Socialist Party (the SPD) was founded in 1875, it adopted the Marxist principles of proletarian revolution. He was to be one of the most authoritative spokesmen of this party until his death in 1913. He was also one of the very few members of the SPD who had enlightened views on the status of women, and for many decades his book was the most eloquent commitment to their liberation to come out of the Marxist movement. Women's liberation must be the work of women themselves, he said; since men had systematically oppressed and subordinated women, they "must not wait for men to help them out of this condition, just as workers do not wait for help from the bourgeoisie."

The book opened with a history of the subjection of women through the ages which anticipated much in Engels's *Origin of the Family,* which appeared five years later. Then followed an analysis of women's present condition and the hypocrisy and sufferings imposed by bourgeois marriage: "Our bourgeois society is like a great carnival costume party where each seeks to deceive the other and to make a fool of him or her; where each wears his official mask with dignity, only to give in to his unofficial likes and passions with less restraint. And all the time in appearance everything drips with virtue, religion and morality."[3] Only when private property had been abolished, the means of production were under public control, and the bonds of the oppressive monogamous family had been dissolved, he contended, could women find their true liberation. Only when men and women shared equally in the productive work of society could individuals' leisure be increased and their capacity for fuller love relationships be realized.

Bebel's depiction of women's double oppression—economic and sexual, in the factory and in the home—was filled with sympathy, for he wrote with passionate admiration of the pride, dignity, and beauty of women who in the past had struggled for their freedom; his confident prediction of women's future equality filled Alexandra with hope. For Bebel did not merely repeat Marx's and Engels's observations on the interdependence between productive relations under capitalism and women's oppressed situation, but was able to link this positively with the future and show that woman without rights was not a permanent or inevitable historical category. In her introduction to the first unabridged Russian edition in 1918, Alexandra described the work as the "woman's bible";[4] it forced the European socialist movement to pay serious attention to the women's question, laid the basis for a socialist women's movement, and led many women like Alexandra to Marxism and political activity.

As for Vladimir, married and with a position to keep up, he was like some character out of Chekhov: with the first gray hair his liberalism was slipping away. More and more often in discussions with the friends he brought back after work Alexandra would contradict and argue with him, and social evenings at the flat would often collapse into angry shouting matches between "materialists" and "idealists": those who believed that the injustices of the present could only be removed by radical social changes, and those who looked back to the religious philosophies of the past, and held that it was only people's thoughts and feelings, never their social institutions, which were amenable to change. Vladimir generally acted as peacemaker, urging them all to stop "philosophizing" or they would wake the baby, and getting them to whistle and sing and dance instead. For a while Alexandra was quite happy to dance instead of arguing, but her desire to read was inflamed by mention of Nietzsche, Plekhanov, and Marx (whose *Civil War in France* was very popular in Russia at that time).[5]

Instinctively Alexandra agreed with the "materialists"; she was convinced that social progress was born in class consciousness and struggle. Vladimir's placid faith in education as the chief moving force of history infuriated her; it was obviously impossible to implant knowledge and education in autocratic Russia, where every living thought was stifled and where, that very year, the Minister of the Interior had complained that he had failed to curb subversion in the universities with his policy of appointing reactionary professors, dismissing all suspected radicals, raising fees, and raiding libraries for the works of Mill and Spencer and Marx. Yet however much she felt that Vladimir was blinding himself to the devastating technological and social changes which capitalism was bringing to Russia, she was too uncomfortably aware of her own political ignorance and inactivity to take her arguments much further. Emotionally she was still very much a populist.

She was also tiring of political arguments that led nowhere but to more books. Her old governess, Maria Strakhova, then suggested she join her as a volunteer worker at the Mobile Museum of Teaching Aids, which operated under the respectable roof of the writer N. A. Rubakin and was in contact with the men and women of the People's Will who had been sentenced to life imprisonment in the terrible Schlüsselburg fortress. Imprisonment and hanging had extinguished none of the old populist hopes of spreading political education among the urban workers through Sunday Schools and evening classes. The main problem was to make it interesting enough for workers who were half dead on their feet after a sixteen-hour day at the factory. Nadezhda Krupskaya, Elena Stasova, and many other women inspired by their persecuted women predecessors in the People's Will devoted much time to devising new teaching methods, then putting them into practice in classes in poor workers' districts of St. Petersburg.

Alexandra began to attend the Museum with Zoya, who moved into her flat when her father, the Domontoviches' old friend from Sofia, died. Twice a week they would prepare magic-lantern slides and stick labels onto botanical specimens. Alexandra donated her own mineral collection, prepared catalogues, helped to organize fund-raising musical evenings, and began to give geography lessons to young workers. But showing slides of giraffes and elephants was not at all how she had imagined the great populist task of enlightenment would be. However much Maria Strakhova complained of the Museum's contacts with the revolutionary underground, and although Alexandra knew that Elena Stasova (known affectionately as Lyolya) was herself in touch with the revolutionary movement, her political activities remained at this level of legal "small deeds" for the next year. The Museum and its growing number of volunteers was coming under intensified police surveillance. Marx's *Capital* began to be smuggled into the Schlüsselburg fortress along with botanical specimens, and Alexandra, Lyolya, and the two Menzhinskaya sisters, Vera and Lyudmilla, expanded their slide shows to discuss the latest socialist periodicals, the populist *Russian Wealth* and the Marxist *Northern Herald.* It was in the workers' discussions of these journals that she began to learn something of their lives and to abandon her humanitarian faith in "small deeds." She asked Lyolya Stasova to introduce her to the revolutionary underground.

All St. Petersburg intellectuals were familiar with the Stasov family. Lyolya's father, the noted progressive music critic Vladimir Stasov, had made a radical name for himself by daring to offer a true interpretation of the revolutionary message of Mussorgsky's *Boris Godunov;* he won Alexandra over by his warmly favorable reviews of Jenny's performances at the Marinsky Opera. His sister Nadezhda, who had pioneered women's education in the 1860's, continued to give her support to populist educational schemes, and the family house on Furshtadskaya Street became a popular venue for charity concerts, lectures, and cultural soirées. When the family was out, Lyolya invited her own radical friends over, and many revolutionary discussion groups were launched under the respectable cover of Furshtadskaya Street. Alexandra's admiration for Lyolya was evidently not reciprocated; she is barely mentioned in Elena Stasova's memoirs of her long political life.[6] For her part, wrapped up as she was in her baby, her husband, and her writing, Alexandra felt reproached by Lyolya's political seriousness and her apparently sexless life; her severe black dress, scraped-back hair, and pince-nez. It took a long time to wheedle an invitation to one of her meetings.

At home Alexandra was being encouraged to write by Zoya and by a friend of Vladimir's whom she nicknamed "the Martian" for his rational temperament and his enthusiasm for technology and science—he was short, pale, and ugly but had an intelligent and expressive face. She confessed her disappointments and frustrations to Zoya and even considered the idea of leaving, so difficult did she find it to write at home. Later she would refer to being torn in the early years of her marriage between two men. It is possible that she embarked on a brief love affair with the Martian, but it is more probable that she only felt able to break free of one man when she had formed a lasting relationship with another. So many women of her own and her mother's generation had become entangled with two men; she wrote later, "Did we really love both of them? Or was it just the fear of losing a love which had changed to friendship, and the suspicion that the new love wouldn't endure?" What a fetish women of her generation had made of erotic love, she lamented.

> How much energy and time we wasted in all our endless love tragedies and their complications! But it was also we, the women of the 1890's, who taught ourselves and those younger than we that love is not the most important thing in a woman's life. And that if she must choose between love and work, she should never hesitate: it is work, a woman's own creative work, that gives her the only real satisfaction and makes her life worth living.[7]

However emotionally confused she may have felt in these early years of her marriage, she could never seriously have considered leaving Vladimir. He had far too much respect for her to imagine that the care of Misha could fill her life: he bought her books and listened, slightly patronizingly, as she rambled on about all the plots for stories which filled her head. Gradually she learned to shut herself in her bedroom and write—for hours at a time, and for publication.

Since the 1860's women had been writing stories and novels inspired by George Sand and Russian populist writers like Dobrolyubov, Pisarev, and Chernyshevsky. They wrote to keep their own natural passions alive and to save other women from slow domestic suffocation. Alexandra wanted her first finished short story to do more than that. She wanted to expose the double morality and through the power of her writing to inspire women to act on it. "My story demanded complete equality," she said.[8] It concerned a woman of forty who had rejected love in order to be self-supporting and then discovered passion with a much younger man: she proposed that they go abroad, live together as comrades and lovers not bound by any formal marriage, and then return and go their own ways without guilt or recrimination. Alexandra's friends considered the story extremely bold, especially Maria Strakhova; it was also sexually outspoken enough to be considered politically suspect by the censors. Nevertheless Alexandra sent Zoya off to deliver the manuscript to the offices of the journal *Russian Wealth,* whose editor, Korolenko, they considered to be one of the finest writers of the time. Weeks passed before her precious handwritten manuscript was returned with a short note from Korolenko who described the plot as "crude and oversimplified" and "unsuccessful as literature," despite the "evident literary talents of its young author."

"If you'd written propaganda leaflets, you'd have been more successful." This, the Martian tactfully pointed out, was the key to Korolenko's *political* distaste for her story, as well as his fears of what the censors might do with it. Alexandra tried to ignore Vladimir's unhelpful observation that Korolenko should not have been expected to identify with an old maid and that she should have made her heroine more glamorous—as "young men love pretty girls." She tried instead to face the fact that she did not have the ability to make literature express the ideas she wanted it to and that it was this that so often overloaded her fluent and observant style with verbose and inappropriate judgments. Zoya was inclined to agree with Korolenko (her style was flat, she said) and told her that if she could not face the truth about her literary shortcomings that was because she had been too susceptible to flattery in the past.

Alexandra decided that her next writing project would be carefully researched and based on her personal experiences of Misha's first two years. The Martian took her to the physiology lectures of Professor Leshaft, who was interested in child development and had for the past twenty years been helping women to qualify as doctors and enter the universities. From him she learned to apply the deductive methods of laboratory science to her reading. She read Pirogov, the great liberal educational theorist of the 1860's, as well as Pestalozzi and Ushinsky, whose ideas on child development were equally popular in Russia. And through them she came to read the socialist educational theories of Dobrolyubov and Chernyshevsky, both of them former teachers who had attacked the tsarist educational system and encouraged people to educate themselves and their children independently.

Her first long article matured in her head as she sat up nursing Misha through his first agonizing sickness. "Is it really possible," she wrote, "to instil in children the ideals of altruism and real love for other people, when in practice it is never possible for them to achieve their own desires?" The article, published in three parts in 1898 in the journal *Education* (republished later that year as a booklet and recently reprinted in the 1972 edition of the Soviet journal *National Education*), was called "The Educational Principles of Dobrolyubov."[9] But although she used the concepts of "desire," "feelings," "mind" and "will" (roughly equivalent to the

Freudian concepts of subconscious, id, ego, and superego) in the same scientific manner as Dobrolyubov, the article was filled with her own personal observations, accumulated during the two years in which she painstakingly researched the work.

Dobrolyubov is remembered now as a social critic, littérateur, and champion of women's rights; his radical education theories are often forgotten. Yet as early as the 1840's—long before anyone was reading Marx in Russia—he was insisting, as had Locke and Hume, that children were shaped entirely by their environment and was refusing to concede any inheritable spiritual qualities. He stressed that until people understood the experiences of childhood, it would be impossible to form any stable adult view of the world. His liberating and radical conclusion was to reject the myth of the all-powerful word, forget Rousseau's insistence on children's innate goodness, and be free of Spencer's view that children's innate malice and egotism had to be "educated" out of them and that cuddling and playing were "unhygienic."

In a long section in her article on physical cruelty and negligence toward children, Alexandra insisted that children should be welcomed into the world from their first months not only with talk and laughter but with a great deal of physical contact and play. Since mind and body operated on the same principles, they must be trained on the same principles (although she talked not of training but of formative influences). Children brought up on an over-rich intellectual diet would lack any physical knowledge of the world and would grow up "feverish and spasmodic, with more powers of feeling and imagination than of sound common sense." Although she did concede that different brain structures might be susceptible to different experiences of life, she explicitly rejected the views made fashionable by many pedagogues that it was people's nervous systems that fundamentally affected their development. Guiding the whole article, however, was the idea (central also to Dobrolyubov) that the form of the family, where the child's temperament itself was formed, was in all societies dictated by the social structure and institutions which contained it. There was nothing very original, of course, in that analysis of family relations, and she was later criticized for her excessive use of quotations. But she said enough to give a glimpse of the new form of the family, "purified" by revolution, which had been so briefly sketched by Bebel, Marx, and Engels and to which she would return in her later investigations. She was beginning to glimpse a time when in socialist society men and women would be brought together by natural sexual attraction, emotional compatibility, and a desire for friendship, in which women were no longer encumbered by their economic and sexual dependence on men. This vision, which was to inspire her life's work in the socialist movement, was gradually to acquire a more precise political significance for her as she developed her ideas on the importance of women's personal struggles to the whole of that movement.

In common with many revolutionaries converted from populism to Marxism in the 1890's, Alexandra found that political "small deeds" combined well with the logical elegance of historical research. But by 1894 the class war of the factories was becoming more real—as every month brought yet another strike for shorter working hours and better conditions, and every month brought a fresh wave of arrests which decimated the most militant workers and drove more and more radicals to adopt underground tactics. As well as doing general work for the Mobile Museum, Alexandra conducted classes under its auspices for young workers, whom she helped to qualify for better jobs. As a side benefit to the skills of negotiation and argument they developed, they discovered in the weekly discussion meetings she and Lyolya held in their homes that there were other discussion groups in St. Petersburg, groups of young radical intellectuals attempting to find some way in which they might help the workers in their struggles in the factories. The Museum also brought Alexandra into contact with the Political Red Cross, formed to give support and books to political prisoners; for this organization Alexandra began to carry out all sorts of tasks, legal, and illegal, such as the storing of literature and the delivering of messages.

If she had no women as pupils, this was because illiteracy was twice as widespread among women as among men in the factories. Alexandra realised that the demoralization and fear that made women the traditionally "docile" elements in the factories also made them completely unreachable by these traditional propaganda methods. Since the women of the "Moscow group" had tried to introduce their urban populism to the women of the factories in 1874 and had promptly been arrested for it few revolutionaries had cared to repeat the experiment; they preferred to meet workers in study groups or taverns, both of which were traditionally male meeting places. Nadezhda Krupskaya and a very few other women revolutionaries would occasionally cover themselves in shawls and mingle with women workers at the factory gates, but the risk of arrest was too great for this to be a practical method of propaganda. Alexandra began to find out from the men who came to her classes about the utter desperation which drove the factory women into the strike movement.

Just one week in a Moscow factory had turned Berta Kaminskaya of the Moscow group from a fresh rosy girl into a pale, exhausted shadow whose appearance spoke volumes for the women inside. Since the early eighteenth century, when Peter the Great had taken women out of the prisons to work the new industrial enterprises, the woman factory worker had been treated as little better than a criminal. Her wages were anything between half to two-thirds of those of a man's, so that she was always inadequately nourished for the unremittingly hard labor of her working day. As it was out of the question that she should be paid during pregnancy, she tended to work twelve, sixteen, even eighteen hours a day right up to the time she started labor, often giving birth beside the work bench. (Factory inspectors' reports confirmed how common this was.) Once the baby was born, the temptation to kill or abandon it was great, as a mother could never be sure of keeping her job, and babies were allowed into the factories only in exceptional cases. For most mothers, however, malnutrition performed the same function as infanticide, only more slowly. Babies sent back to the villages stood a better chance of surviving than those left at home with older children or handed out to the often unscrupulous "baby-farmers"; many mothers would themselves then return to the villages to bring in the harvest and visit their children.[10]

It was these seasonal workers whom the populists always cited when trying to prove that capitalism was only a passing phenomenon in Russia, and it was these women who led Alexandra to exactly the opposite conclusion, and to the Marxism of the St. Petersburg radical circles (the embryonic social-democratic movement in Russia) and of Lenin's *What Are the Friends of the People?* It was true that many of Russia's 3,000,000 factory workers were economic amphibians: without security or resilience, shuffling seasonally from village to town, continuing a real relationship with the land they still owned and left in the care of wives and daughters, and remaining legally peasants. But by the 1890's a second-generation proletariat had grown up; those who still had ties with the villages were relinquishing them, and though many still clung to peasant customs in the cities, there was an angry young strike movement to prove that the docile, disorientated migrant worker was a person of the past. The populists insisted that the extreme "indiscipline" of the strikers only proved their point that factory workers were but peasants who had temporarily abandoned the plow, serfs in urban dress, and that capitalism was an "artificial creation" which destroyed the very productive forces which brought it into being. The first signs of this "indiscipline" were being greeted with joy by the Marxists, however. It was beginning to be especially marked among women workers and would continue to be over the next twenty years. By the 1890's women were already bursting out into angry industrial militancy in their thousands; ten years later they were coming out on strike with their own demands; ten years after that it was the revolutionary Marxists who would be noting with alarm the "indiscipline" of tradition-ally docile and "backward" women—and that was long after everyone had ceased to question capitalism's grip on the economy.

Lenin's name meant little to Alexandra when at the end of 1895 she first read his *What Are the Friends of the People?* (published illegally the previous year in St. Petersburg). Here she discovered the same logical clarity she had admired in Plekhanov—who, since his break with the People's Will in 1879, had settled in Geneva, where he had become the foremost Russian exponent of Marxism and the political mentor of count-less revolutionaries in the following two decades. But in Lenin, Alexandra also found an understanding of the power and anger of the urban workers which Plekhanov's more scholarly prose lacked. The populists had unques-tionably retreated from the revolutionary position they had held in the 1870's, Lenin said. It was now nothing but utopian, not to say reactionary, to envisage saving the peasantry by means of popular banks, cheap credit, and rural cooperatives, which could easily be converted to capitalist enter-prises. Capitalism was neither an "artificial creation" nor an unmitigated tragedy and source of all evil, as the populists would have it—but an enormous social advance. He sharply condemned the idea that the peas-antry (or any other social class) was inherently socialist, stressing instead that the working class—capitalism's enemies and grave-diggers—could only lead the revolution against capitalism when they had strengthened and perfected their resistance movement. He likened these early days of the strike movement to the first uprisings of the peasants, "so crushed and stultified by centuries of slavery that they were incapable of anything, at the time of their emancipation, except sporadic and isolated rebellions, or rather riots, unenlightened by any political consciousness." And he pointed out that just as the peasants' anger had traditionally been interpre-ted by a small group of intellectuals—populists determined to kill the Tsar —so now the workers relied on organized Marxist intellectuals to "trans-form their present sporadic economic war into a conscious class struggle. Then will the Russian workers rise at the head of all democratic elements, overthrow absolutism and lead the Russian proletariat, side by side with the proletariat of all countries, along the straight road of open political struggle towards the victorious communist revolution."[11]

It was not until late 1895 that this organization of Marxist intellectu-als became a reality, when the Union of Struggle (formed by Lenin and various other revolutionary Marxists to unite all the Marxist discussion groups in the capital) began at last to make some real contact with the factory workers.[12] For the past twenty years economics and politics (revolutionary intellectuals and workers) had run along on their own parallel lines. These converged only with the massive strike movement of the late 1890's.

In the years 1870–79 there had been 176 strikes, most of them in the textile mills where anything from a quarter to a half of the workforce was made up of women. One of these in 1878 involved women from two St. Petersburg tobacco factories, who marched out to negotiate with the management over a sudden reduction of their piecework rates; when they were greeted with obscenities and threats, they went straight back to the factories and threw everything out of the windows. By the end of that decade similar confrontations had involved so much destruction of equipment that the first feeble factory law was finally passed in 1882; a team of factory inspectors was appointed by Tsar Alexander III to ensure that no children under twelve were employed and that children under fifteen were employed for no longer than eight hours a day. Vladimir Kollontai had been inspired by this first generation of factory inspectors, idealistically setting about their task of collecting information for new factory laws. But their first reports gave such a devastatingly honest picture of factory conditions that they soon stopped being published, and the inspectors' recommendations were routinely ignored.

The factory law of 1885 prohibited women and children from working night shifts (this too was ignored or manipulated). The following year there was legislation against payment in kind and various other paltry reforms in the relations between employers and workers—but the penalties for encouraging or taking part in strikes were simultaneously increased, and workers soon discovered the punitive realities behind these "protective" factory laws. During a strike at the Morozov textile factory in Tver in 1885, the management called in the police to force the workers to "negotiate," and when the "delegates" had left, workers demolished buildings and machines. The "delegates" were all fired by management and the demands ignored. As strikes continued in this explosive and more or less spontaneous manner into the 1890's, workers struggled to create organizations to assist and sustain their economic battles and to look outwards toward the revolutionary groups, particularly the Union of Struggle which promised them practical support and advice.

By then factory inspectors no longer represented to them the high-minded hard-working optimists of ten years before. Most inspectors were addicted to the greased palm and the bottle. Vladimir and like-minded doctors and sanitary officials, who were acquainted with the literature on the incomparably better factory conditions in England and Germany, were exceptions—fighting a losing battle against the employers, the government, and their fellow inspectors alike. But they did continue their struggle to improve conditions for workers, and they were especially sensitive to the position of women workers and the extreme hardships of their double shift. As the liberal inspector Yanzhul observed, "All conditions of factory life reflect more harshly on women workers than on men."[13] Officials like him reasoned that since women were capable of extremely hard labor in the fields and had been conscripted to dig ore and mine coal since the mid-nineteenth century, their aim should be to improve, not abolish, women's labor. But as the numbers of women employed in the factories steadily increased, it became evident that they were not taking the more mechanized jobs at all but the most arduous and worst-paid jobs. It was this tendency which effaced all the modest attempts of Vladimir and his friends to introduce some maternity care into the factories and ensure generally that the weakest and most defenseless workers had some kind of protection against factory hazards. Even the most rudimentary rulings of the factory acts continued to be violated by employers, and it was not until 1903 that they were made to provide any kind of compensation for injuries at work. Industrial amputations, stillbirths, and disease— for the victims of these everyday dangers of factory life Vladimir could only suggest more fans, first-aid kits, or heaters.

As Vladimir saw one well-intentioned plan for factory improvements after another collapse, Alexandra began to feel that his optimism was nothing less than blind. There was only one thing for it, he decided: he would himself show her one of his more imaginative schemes for a new ventilator. He had been working on this for several months with the engineers, and by the New Year of 1896 it would be ready to be installed. The trip with Vladimir to see the new ventilation system in action at the Krengholm textile factory was to have a devastating effect on Alexandra. She lost forever her former confidence that the lives of people in Russia could be improved by means of reforms, however progressive they might be.

With the death of Alexander III in 1894 and the accession to the throne of Nicholas II any hopes Alexandra may have had of reform must have seemed increasingly unrealistic. The old political doctrine of "orthodoxy, autocracy, and nationalism," first adopted in 1825 by Nicholas I, had lapsed during the reign of Alexander II. It was faithfully restored by Alexander's two successors, and official policies between his assassination in 1881 and the revolution of 1905 became markedly more obscurantist and repressive. At the end of 1895, when students were asked to take the oath of allegiance to the new Tsar, most of them in Moscow, St. Petersburg, and Kiev refused to do so. At the coronation shortly afterward mounted police stampeded the placid crowd of onlookers and left thousands wounded and several dead in a quite gratuitous massacre, which bothered the frivolous young Tsar not at all. He received his crown from the Metropolitan of All Russia as "symbolic of the invisible crown set upon the Head of all the Russian people by our Lord Jesus Christ"—and proceeded to try and run the country. Like his predecessor, he planned to curtail all Alexander II's reforms in the universities and in local government, discriminate against Jews and national minorities, impose states of emergency whenever he wished to bypass the official judiciary (partially reformed in the 1860's), and increase drastically the numbers of agents provocateurs and the membership of his imperial secret police. He it was who led the most important of the official militantly right-wing nationalist organizations that sprang up under his reign—the Union of Russian People. He it was who sanctioned the gangs of union thugs, known as the Black Hundreds, who organized savage pogroms against Jews, university students, and in the early years of the next century the whole populations of several cities in Russia.

One of Tsar Nicholas's fondest hopes was to have the word "intellectual" removed from the language; he was anxious that eighty per cent of the Russian population should remain in the same state of illiterate poverty as their serf ancestors. As far as any positive policies were concerned, he had no plans. "I haven't the least idea how to address my ministers," was his first breezy declaration as the new Tsar, "and I understand absolutely nothing of matters of state." His mad, mystical wife, Alexandra, who offered the advice that "Russians love to be caressed with the horsewhip—such is the nature of the people," helped to turn the court into a lunatic asylum, controlled by superstition and fear.

When in the winter of 1895 Alexandra set out with Zoya, Vladimir, and his engineer colleagues for Narva, 150 miles south of St. Petersburg on the Gulf of Finland, she was determined not to argue. Vladimir's plans for a sophisticated new ventilation system for the huge Krengholm textile factory had been accepted, and he was jubilant. He would be supervising the engineers in setting up the new apparatus and, as he was staying there for a week, had suggested that Alexandra and Zoya join him, to enjoy some skating and dancing and look over one of Russia's most modern factories while they were about it. They took their skates and toboggans with them, as the snow was still thick on the ground.

From their first-class hotel there was a beautiful view of the ancient snow-covered town, and as they ate an excellent dinner that first evening a small orchestra played Tchaikovsky and Strauss waltzes. None of these unfamiliar luxuries managed to dampen their spirits, however, as they discussed whether—as the young engineers were insisting—technology really could save the human race from the miseries that plagued it. Zoya argued against them, saying that all that technological progress did was to destroy natural beauty; Alexandra wanted to discuss the possibilities the new technology opened up for social change and political liberty. "What do you mean by this liberty you're always so concerned about?" Vladimir interrupted her. "Complete liberty is a sure recipe for chaos. People need laws, just laws of course, but firm." Far from the small St. Petersburg flat she felt quite irrepressible and did not bother to argue. Although preoccupied with herself and with the human condition, she was nevertheless feeling expansive and hopeful.

Early the next morning she and Zoya set off in the same buoyant mood for the Krengholm factory, which lay outside the town, across the river Narva. One glance at the monstrous old building was enough to curb their high spirits, and as they went to the administrator's office to get their visitors' permits they were struck by the lifeless silence of the place. An elderly retired worker in the adjacent "first-aid room" told them he had seen enough accidents to perform any operations that might be needed. From there they were taken to the library, the pride of the factory—with its tattered copies of Pushkin, Gogol, and Turgenev, but a complete absence of any technical literature. In this room, half-hearted literacy classes were held at the end of the working day for the workers, ninety percent of whom were illiterate.

Alexandra and Zoya, their former high spirits mocked by this rotten, dusty old dump, were furious with themselves for having expected anything else. Their heads ached with the dust and fibers that filled the air, and Zoya began to feel too ill to carry on. Their guide at last realized that they were speechless with horror rather than wonder and left them to their own devices.

Alexandra wandered on her own through the workshops trying to talk to the workers. The older men would not acknowledge her questions, and the women only answered reluctantly, but the younger people were eager to tell her about themselves. They told her how they worked anything from twelve to eighteen hours a day. Imprisoned within the factory walls, they were allowed out only once a week, on Sundays; few workers had their own living quarters, and most lived in vast dormitory barracks—families, babies, single people and children all stacked one above the other on narrow bunk beds or on the floor. Some women ventured to tell Alexandra that it suited them better to live in the factory, since it meant that their husbands could not drink away all their wages; but the young people complained bitterly that the long working day sapped all their vital energy. Most of them earnestly wished to study, to better themselves, even to become engineers, and they were angrily aware that they had not the freedom to learn anything or read. But the great anxiety which preyed on them all was the air pollution. Most of them were stricken with tuberculosis after three or four years working in air thick with textile fibers, and they quickly tended to become listless and nauseous. Few of them expected to live to be thirty.

Leaving the factory floor, Alexandra wandered over to the dormitory. She found it empty except for some subdued children playing on the floor and a baby boy of Misha's age watched over by a careworn little girl. As she stooped over the baby to hold him, it was horribly obvious that he was dead. "It does sometimes happen to them that they die during the day," explained the little nanny with a terrible premature seriousness. "Auntie will come at six and take him away."[14]

Heavy with the woes of this desolate place, Alexandra could bear no more and fled to the hotel. She and Zoya talked for many hours then, trying to rid themselves of the haunting guilt and futility they felt, the foolishness of all hopes for reform, the inanity of their laughter on the skating rink only the day before. They were still deep in discussion when Vladimir and his friends burst in, waving tickets for a new operetta and laughingly urging the two women to hurry and get dressed.

He stopped short, seeing the grim expression on her face. "Why, whatever's the matter with you, Shura? Has someone been rude to you at the factory, or have you hurt yourself?" She stared back at him. Sometimes this gentle tyrant's concern for her seemed to detach him altogether from the world around him. In great agitation she tried to tell him something of what she had experienced earlier on. "We can't go on living like this, while other people live like animals," she said. But she wasted her words. The engineers tried to persuade her that this was precisely why they had come—to fit new ventilators. She retorted that she was talking about economic relations not ventilators. Vladimir urged them all to hurry along to the opera—"And Shura's workers shall have their rights and freedom! Why don't you make us all one of your speeches about it in the restaurant afterwards?"[15]

At this Alexandra lost her temper completely, shouting that she had no desire ever again to sit in restaurants listening to sweet music. "I don't want to live like that any longer! Go on, all of you, from now on we'll go our separate ways!" Flinging herself on the bed, she buried her head in the pillow and left them to their night on the town.

The subdued tourists returned to St. Petersburg, and Alexandra began at once to beg her friends at the Museum for all the revolutionary books and leaflets they could give her. The first she read was Lenin's recent leaflet to workers at the English-managed Thornton factory in St. Petersburg. In the Union of Struggle paper *Workers' Thought,* and in discussion with her friends she learned of the 1500 women involved in the violent strike at the Laferme cigarette factory in the capital, the previous November. Their rage over their employers' lewd behavior and the introduction of piece-rates had reached boiling point, and they had rushed through the factory, breaking windows, and smashing equipment, and out onto the streets of the city's Vasilev Island, where they had told the people gathered outside of their complaints. Their demands were partly met, but not before they had all been advised to balance their family budgets by taking to the streets as prostitutes, and not before the thirty ringleaders had been banished from the city.

Once workers realized through painful experience that the demands for which they went on strike were unattainable under the present autocratic government, said *Workers' Thought,* their strikes would automatically become political and the workers would become class conscious. But the St. Petersburg social democrats in the Union of Struggle were above all eager to reflect workers' feelings and aspirations, and they saw their first job as raising strike funds and giving practical support to the strikers' demands for a ten-hour day and better working conditions. It was this practical organization that Lenin meant when he said that "organizing the socialist workers' party is the first task of the Russian revolutionary movement." Alexandra turned now to *What Are the Friends of the People?* with greater understanding.

But she still felt more drawn to the ideas of Plekhanov, who had introduced Lenin and most other young Russian socialists to the works of Marx. Although plenty of academic economists in Russia in the past decade had greeted Marxism as a theoretical model and social law, Plekhanov was the first Russian socialist to apply this law to the suffering of the people. He had broken with the terrorists in 1879 in order to pursue some more realizable theory of revolution, and had shortly afterwards come into headlong collision with Marx himself who considered that Russian revolutionaries would be courting disaster if they worked for open class warfare led by such a tiny and unprepared proletariat.

Lyolya Stasova later accused Alexandra of taking a very long time in making up her mind about political matters and committing herself to revolutionary work. But this was because Alexandra's approach to revolutionary politics was a thoughtful (Lyolya might have said bookish) one; she did not seize on the latest idea as just a way of liberating herself from whatever happened to be bothering her. After reading Plekhanov's *Development of a Monist View of History,* she embarked on Volumes One and Two of *Capital,* which the Martian brought for her. She puzzled for a long time over its more theoretical chapters, but Marx's revolutionary philosophy of history—which held that every historical development was the outcome of the political struggle between the class of the exploiters (who owned the wealth and the labor which created it) and that of the exploited—had a logic that appealed to her immediately. Marx made history accessible and therefore capable of revolutionary modification; it seemed a short step from educating people about the society which so oppressed them to mobilizing their anger through education, propaganda, and agitation.

More important to her, however, as she delved with increasing fascination into the earlier works of Marx, was his humanism, his denunciation of the conditions which, by debasing women, debased all human relationships. "The infinite degradation in which a human being exists for him or herself is expressed in the relationship between man and woman," he had written in his *Economic and Philosophical Manuscripts of 1844:*

> . . . The immediate, natural, and necessary relationship of one human being to another is the relationship between *man* and *woman.* In this *natural* special relationship, the human being's relation to nature is immediately his/her relationship to the human being, just as the relationship to human beings is his/her relationship to nature, his/her *natural* determination. Thus the measure in which the human essence has become nature for the human being *manifests* itself *sensually* (i.e. reduced to an observable fact) in this relationship. Hence on the basis of this relationship one can judge the entire stage of development of the human being. From the character of this relationship one can conclude how far the human being, as a *species* and as an *individual* being, has become

him/herself and grasped him/herself . . . This relationship also reveals the extent to which a human being's need has turned into *human* need, to which therefore . . . he/she in his/her most individual essence is at the same time a social being.[16]

It was around this time, after two years of Nicholas II's reign, that many Russian intellectuals, sympathetically drawn, like Alexandra, to socialism, were drawn to Marx. Those in St. Petersburg became increasingly aware of the small group of radical intellectuals who had been driven to adopt underground tactics and risk prison and exile as they struggled to support the striking workers in the capital. Overshadowing all Alexandra's needs in 1896 was the need to contact the members of Russia's first revolutionary Marxist party, the Union of Struggle for the Emancipation of the Working Class. This, she realized, she would accomplish only if she earned Lyolya's approval, for Lyolya was deeply respected by Union members. Lyolya was not herself a full member, however. Her family had some claim to fame in cultured Russian circles, and her comrades urged her not to join the underground, since she could conveniently hold meetings in the elegant Stasov flat with relatively little risk of police spies in the building making arrests. Lenin and many other Union members had already been arrested and were making good use of their exile by studying and writing. Those in St. Petersburg struggled to continue distributing Lenin's proclamations to factory workers and to produce their own agitational works.

Alexandra probably knew, from an influential article by Plekhanov, of the distinction between propaganda and agitation—propaganda being the way one should present a series of ideas to a group of people or an individual, agitation being the methods used to present an idea to an entire class of people. She probably also read a mimeographed pamphlet, *On Agitation,* which was smuggled into St. Petersburg from the south by the fighting Jewish workers' organization, the Bund. This continued to speak to young revolutionaries there long after their small groups had dissolved themselves into the Union of Struggle, and was the inspiration for many to commit themselves to agitation among the working class; propaganda and theory could wait until workers had won themselves a shorter working day and were no longer too dead on their feet to learn about socialist politics.

The Mobile Museum was attracting more and more intellectuals eager to teach and make contact with the St. Petersburg factory workers. Under Lyolya's guidance it was, like the Red Cross and many other such ostensibly charitable ventures, covertly changing its focus from education to more practical support of strike organizations. Alexandra was probably not the only person working at the Museum whom Lyolya asked to deliver parcels around the city and to store in her flat illegal pamphlets with titles like *The Workers' Day, Who Lives on What?,* and *You Can't Do Anything About Us.* But since she came from a family as prestigious in its way as the Stasovs, she realized that she was expected also to beg her relatives for donations to the Museum.

As a young girl in Kuusa she had so often dreamed of underground work in terms of iron-willed youths in candlelit cellars that, however foolish she knew these fantasies to be, she could not quite banish them from the more ordinary realities of this political work of hers. She had no idea that she, Vladimir, Misha, and Zoya might easily have been arrested for the revolutionary postal work she undertook so blithely; instead as she visited strangers' flats, exchanging passwords and delivering her bundles of pamphlets, she could not help feeling that all this was rather a compromise of the grand resolutions she had made a month ago at Narva. Her resolve to contact the Union of Struggle had come to nothing. Lyolya obviously still doubted her political seriousness and was unwilling to entrust her with more responsible work; she did, however, try to explain the dedication expected of members of the Union and warned Alexandra against expecting any major assignments or playing any starring roles. It was all very well to study the labor theory of value and the works of Lenin, she told her, but not if they stood in the way of devotion to the Union. Once she had convinced the others that she understood discipline, was prepared to renounce all bourgeois mannerisms and would not get waylaid by theory, she would be asked to perform more responsible jobs for the group.

When Lyolya took her aside shortly after this galling little lecture to whisper an invitation to a secret meeting, Alexandra flushed with excitement and could only mumble grateful acceptance; for the next few days she wandered around in a fog of flustered nerves. Arriving at the Furshtadskaya Street house precisely on time, she gave two conspiratorial rings at the front door; it was opened by Lyolya, who explained that her parents had gone off to the opera and had given the servants the evening off. As they sat down at the dining-room table to drink tea with preserves in the company of six men from the Union of Struggle, Alexandra was reminded of all the other social gatherings she had attended at the Stasovs' mansion. She was crestfallen when she discovered shortly afterward why they had invited her. Apparently the police had raided their printing press: they wanted to print a pamphlet of Lenin's without delay, and were asking her to raise the cash from her wealthy relatives.[17]

As Alexandra walked home dejectedly along the drizzling St. Petersburg streets Lyolya's words about bourgeois roles and mannerisms returned to her and made her ashamed of her disappointment. But she had fears which Lyolya could not possibly understand; fears for Misha, and fears of further estranging herself from Vladimir, from her family, and from her old friends—Maria Strakhova for one. Maria had on several occasions expressed to Alexandra her alarm at the contacts the Museum was cultivating with the revolutionary underground. Nevertheless, if only to avoid arrest in her next, undoubtedly illegal assignment, Alexandra resolved that she would be less of an individualist in the future. Soon after that meeting in the Stasovs' flat she was helping to smuggle leaflets into the factories themselves and to collect money for strike funds. Both of these highly illegal activities were vital to the Union of Struggle. Confining its leafleting activities to one factory at a time, the Union used the demands being raised by each group of workers as a rallying point for further, political action; it was through the strike funds that it mobilized and supported the most capable leaders of the workers' movement.

By the spring of 1896 the Union's first year of activity was beginning to show results; in May an amazing wave of strikes swept through the textile mills along St. Petersburg's Obvodny Canal and Neva River—the first "mass strike" in the history of Russia. Alexandra tended to ascribe a very modest role in all this to the Union of Struggle, however. "The development of a conscious proletariat in conditions of such complete oppression and inequality" was a revelation to many other intellectuals besides her, whose political existence had until a few months ago been lived out through books and pamphlets. And as strike followed strike into June, it became obvious that women were often outdoing the men in anger and militancy:

> It was indeed wonderful to see the politically naive factory girl, hopelessly bowed down by unbearably harsh working conditions, despised by one and all (even by the female half of the urban petty-bourgeoisie, from whom she differed in her firm allegiance to old peasant customs), now in the vanguard, fighting for the rights of the working class and the emancipation of women . . . In fighting for the rights of her class, the working woman was unconsciously paving the way for the liberation of her sex from those special chains which created, even within the working class, inequality of status and inequality of working conditions.[18]

Lyolya Stasova, Nadezhda Krupskaya, and a very few other intellectuals had managed to make contact with promising women workers and had encouraged them to lead the others on the factory floor; it was out of these experiences that Nadezhda Krupskaya wrote the first booklet on the subject, *The Woman Worker*. But the women's militancy surprised even them. Even though, as Marxists, everyone in the Union recognized working women's double oppression, their commitment to include women in the revolutionary struggle (not only for their own emancipation but also for the success of the entire proletarian struggle) was still at the level of theory rather than of any organizational reality.

In 1896 an international women's socialist movement became a possibility (if not yet a reality) when Klara Zetkin and Lily Braun from the German Social Democratic Party stood up at the International Congress of Socialist Workers and Trade Unionists in London and demanded that the trade unions repeat their commitment to accept working women as members, to fight for equal pay for equal work by men and women, and to press their governments to take responsibility for supporting women after childbirth until they could return to work. Shortly after this, at an SPD congress in Gotha, Klara Zetkin introduced the guidelines on party work among women which she had first proposed seven years before in a pamphlet. Continuing many of the ideas of Bebel's *Woman and Socialism* and taking up his criticisms of the sexual prejudices of many male party members, she went in some detail into the effects of women entering the workforce (from 1895 to 1907 the number of working women in Germany increased by 44.3%),[19] dwelling on the ways in which this affected the wages of men. To abolish female labor, as many SPD members were trying to do, would do nothing more than return women to the care of their husbands. Rather than trying to reverse the facts of economic life under capitalism, the party should recognize the consequences of its correct insistence that women's complete liberation would only come with the liberation of labor from capital; the party must recognize that if women workers were to be brought into solidarity with the men of their own class, they would need special political education and support.

In Russia the middle-class women's movement of the 1870's which had campaigned for equal educational opportunities had all but died out. But by the mid-1890's large numbers of educated women in Germany were organizing together to fight prostitution and alcoholism, and for the right to dispose of their property. This was why, in 1896, Klara Zetkin found it necessary to amplify her original proposals to insist that for women of the bourgeoisie and for those of the working class, the "woman question" occupied wholly different political spheres. Bourgeois women, she said, waged their struggle *against the men of their own class, for the rights of that class,* while working women fought *with the men of their own class, against capital.* She recognized, however, that this could only be true when men and women joined in the same struggle—and even an organized women workers' movement could not hope automatically to remove the antagonisms between men and women in the labor market.

It was after this congress that Klara Zetkin began to agitate for a separate women's organization within the German party, a scheme which found an immediate and enthusiastic response from women workers there. For Alexandra, one of the very few women attached to the Union of Struggle, these developments within the German party were of deep significance. They showed her how she might be able to find a way out of her isolation in the Russian revolutionary movement, and they confirmed the economic and political power that women workers in Russia were now beginning to demonstrate.

However, the opportunity to discuss such matters in the Russian police state would have to wait. Of more immediate concern to the Union members, as they saw prized militants picked up, fired, and arrested, was that spontaneous strikes would endanger the very existence of the group and that concrete economic demands would suppress the larger revolutionary aspirations of the workers. Alexandra was less prone than many in the Union to fear for the life of this movement which had flung a quarter of a million workers and countless intellectuals into the political struggle. People who lived out their lives in the factory naturally wanted to focus all their struggle on the shop floor, their district groups, and the strike-aid organizations, and had neither time nor experience to make proper security arrangements. This, she felt, would come in time. But it was against just this simple thesis—that workers would learn revolution in their own time—that Lenin first proposed his bold and brilliant model of an illegal professional revolutionary party, formed of people outside the sphere of relations between employers and producers.

By June 17 the summer strike storm had passed, hundreds of militant workers had been arrested and the Union of Struggle members had been rounded up en masse and packed off to Siberia. The workers gained no concessions, and many of them and their families suffered from permanent unemployment and police harassment. For these families Alexandra worked in poverty relief organizations, many of which were theoretically legal but came under constant police vigilance and pressure. It was thanks to these organizations that workers managed to form the effective negotiating committees (which included several women) with which they met the second eruption of strikes in 1897. These committees, the precedent for that uniquely Russian historical phenomenon, the soviet, proved to Alexandra that in this first crucial convergence of workers and intellectuals the strikers were quite capable of deciding how best to use non-workers in support of their strikes. When Lenin returned to the capital in 1897, in a brief interlude between exiles, he was horrified by the strikers' excessively "economist" orientation. But Alexandra was barely aware of the Homeric struggles between the "politicians" and the "economists"; she could not imagine how the strikers' fighting morale could be sustained without a concrete economic goal in sight.

A year of exhausting militancy was already taking its toll of the women textile workers, many of whom trooped off to sewing bees and lectures organized by a small but steadily growing group of middle-class women charity workers. Although Nadezhda Stasova, Lyolya's aunt, continued her work helping women students until her death in 1897, most of the women who had campaigned for women's education in the 1860's and 1870's had died or withdrawn from the struggle. It was in the mid-1890's that the charity work pursued by these public-spirited women began to be reestablished in a small way in a few towns in Russia. In 1895 the most important women's charity organization before 1905 was launched in St. Petersburg—a women-only club, based on the American model, for the "intellectual and moral improvement of women." Since the idea of a women's club was strictly banned by Nicholas II's Minister of the Interior, it adopted the innocuous title of the Russian Women's Mutual Philanthropic Society. For ten years this society battled against official censure and numerous obscene articles and cartoons attacking it in the conservative press, and drew up commissions to fight alcoholism and inequality in education and the professions. In its charity work it aimed to extend the range of the squalid, officially sponsored orphans' homes and shelters in St. Petersburg, and to establish day nurseries and cheap eating places for impoverished professional women with children. Despite the internal antagonisms provoked by its somewhat autocratic leadership, this practical charity work earned the society considerable prestige in the capital and attracted many of the more conservative aristocratic patronesses of the tsarist Union of Charity Organizations.

Another enterprise catering to educated women was the "House of Diligence," founded in 1896 on the principle that "the only rational form of charity is to provide the needy with paid employment"; its aim was to help high-school girls and qualified governesses to make a living.

It was in the middle of the great strike movement of 1896 that the first charitable organization aiming to "protect young girls, primarily of the working class, from the morally damaging conditions of their lives" was established in St. Petersburg. Unlike many women charity workers, the organizers of the Society to Assist Young Girls evidently did not see women's work in the factories as an unmitigated evil, but one could fairly speculate that their desire was to show working women that it was the damaging influence of men in the factories that had led them to strike and rebel against their old demoralized docility. Yet the society did have some success, and ten years later around 2000 working women were regularly attending its meetings.[20]

Alexandra had glimpsed, from the recent discussions within the SPD, the possibility of an international socialist organization of women workers. What she did not apparently realize was that in 1896 the basis for a feminist movement in Russia was being laid: a movement concerned with self-help, with the improvement of middle-class women's professional, educational, and legal status, and with the abolition of alcoholism and sexual intemperance. By 1896 two embryonic women's movements, the socialist and the bourgeois, existed side by side in Russia without either of them knowing it. Socialist women like Alexandra believed that women's liberation could only be a part of the larger human liberation for which the social democrats were fighting; the women in the charity organizations of the mid-1890's sought only the equality of bourgeois women with the men of their own class. It was only in 1905 that these women developed a more coherent feminist philosophy and allied themselves with the political parties which began to spring up in the defense of middle-class interests in Russia; it was only during Russia's first failed revolution and the years following it that these two antagonistic visions of women's liberation came into bitter conflict.

Alexandra's first article, "The Educational Principles of Dobrolyubov," was now in the writing stage and she felt more and more that all her fund-raising activities were subordinate to her main ambition, which was to write on social and economic subjects. But she still felt very ignorant. She began to feel increasingly confident—and a summer holiday she took in the Urals in 1897 with Maria Strakhova confirmed this feeling —that only by making a new and independent life for herself could she work for social improvement in Russia and find her own political path. Writing was the first step on this path. Zoya, whose ambition had always been to write art criticism for the progressive journals, was also learning to shut herself away to read and write. Since returning from Narva both of them had been attending lectures at the university on political economy and various social questions. They were particularly impressed by the lectures of the liberal factory inspector Ivan Yanzhul, who ten years ago had exposed the terrible conditions under which women and children labored in the factories. But what Alexandra was discovering as she continued eagerly to plumb the depths of *Capital* was that most of the professors—and increasing numbers of politicians too—were arguing that the state must take some action to intervene between employers and producers. None of them now seemed to be talking of the "natural" laws of capitalist economics or calling for charity to soften its harshness, and many of these liberals seemed quite taken with Marxism, regarding it not as a theory of revolution, but as an explanation of the measures by which the state might guarantee the workers some sort of minimal existence. But however devoutly these well-meaning Russians might pray for the sort of progressive factory laws being passed in bourgeois democracies like England, it was simply not a realistic dream in autocratic Russia. The Russian bourgeoisie, made up largely of state officials without economic or political independence from the Tsar, lacked the status of the enterprising English middle classes, and it was not until 1905 that they formed a party to represent both their own interests and those of the newly emerging feminist movement. Vladimir and his liberal friends in their tsarist uniforms were fighting a battle that was already lost.

For Russian academics whose hearts were warmed by Marx's scientific method and Western orientation but were not so keen on his revolutionary politics, Eduard Bernstein's tinkerings with *Capital* were seen as an enormous improvement on the original. At the end of 1896 this distinguished SPD member and personal friend of Engels had set out to disprove every one of Marx's basic propositions. Claiming that some friendly reevaluation and "revision" of Marxism was needed in the light of the past ten years' events in Germany, he effectively rejected the entire revolutionary basis upon which the SPD had first been established. His personal starting point was a deep distaste for the prospect of revolution and an infinite faith in the value of the economic reforms which were to be won by the trade unions. In the three years following the publication of his book *Evolutionary Socialism* (inspired largely by the Fabians he had met in London) the leaders of the SPD threw themselves into a free-for-all of debates and polemics on the role of the unions, the possibilities of a mass strike, and the perspectives of the revolution. In those three years the party crystalized into two opposing groups, the "revisionists" and the orthodox Marxist revolutionaries, with most members floating uneasily somewhere between the two positions.[21]

Under capitalism, said Bernstein, profits did not fall (as Marx had predicted they would), poverty did not increase, limitless reforms were possible, and revolution was both painful and unprofitable. Not surprisingly, these mellow views were welcomed eagerly by many liberal professors at Russia's universities who wanted for Russia precisely the sort of constitutional reforms which Bernstein seemed to be proposing. More surprisingly, some former Marxists who now rejected the necessity for revolution and even some members of the Union of Struggle began to agree with Bernstein that "the movement is all, the goal nothing," that the economic struggle was primary, and that the revolution could be indefinitely postponed. Bernstein's "revisionism" fitted the "economist" tendencies of the demoralized strike movement like a kid glove and formed a combination dangerous to all revolutionary hopes.

For socialists living today in the bourgeois democracies of Western Europe the distinction between Bernstein and Marx is not so clearcut, although it is still central to all our debates. By the end of 1897 in Russia and the second strike wave there, it was obvious to Alexandra that all these hankerings for piecemeal reforms and peace and quiet were quite futile in the land of the tsars. The strikes had squeezed out of the government some paltry legislation for a maximum eleven-hour day for adults, a nine-and-a-half-hour day for adolescents, and a universal rest day on Sunday. This law, like its predecessors, was so flagrantly flouted that the Minister of Finance personally issued a document the following year authorizing the extension of the working day.

In March 1898, with the strike movement in eclipse and most Union of Struggle members in exile, the Union's official transformation into the All-Russian Social Democratic Party was a small affair. A few days after the nine delegates (mostly members of the Jewish Bund) had gathered in Minsk for this First Party Congress, they were all arrested—not, however, before issuing their manifesto, which pledged the party explicitly to the two stages of the revolution envisaged by Marx—the bourgeois and the proletarian—and placed the liberation of women from "domestic slavery" in the more distant perspective of that second revolution.

With the tightening of the party ranks in the capital, Alexandra's usefulness as a fund-raiser and distributer of leaflets came to an end. And with most of her new friends (except Lyolya) in exile or abroad, her thoughts turned longingly to the idea of at last realizing her old dream of studying abroad. The excitement over Bernstein in Russia meant little to her—she realized that she could only familiarize herself with the debates (on women's organization and on the whole nature of the revolution) outside Russia. She thought of the hundreds of women and girls in the 1870's who had left everything behind and traveled to Zurich from all parts of Russia to study medicine, law, and philosophy and prepare themselves as doctors and teachers in the Russian villages. She thought of the founder of Russian Marxism—Plekhanov—who had done most of his writing abroad, and of his colleague Axelrod, who had gone so far as to insist that in tsarist Russia it was so hard for workers and intellectuals to work together that intellectuals should elaborate their revolutionary plans outside Russia, otherwise they would inevitably be crushed.

She had already discussed with Vladimir her dreams of going to Zurich to study, and he had not seemed too apprehensive at the idea. For the past fifty years, after all, Russian men and women had preferred the comparatively liberal universities of Europe to the oppressive atmosphere of the universities at home. And since the 1870's, when women had started their campaign for higher education, they too, unlike their sisters everywhere else in Europe, had been leaving in large numbers to study in Germany, France, and Switzerland. However, Alexandra could not ignore the fact that in doing so many of them were leaving their parents, husbands, and children behind them for good; they often returned to Russia not as docile wives and daughters but as committed revolutionaries. Despite the fact that her relationship with Vladimir and with her parents was becoming increasingly distant, neither study nor revolution offered sufficient temptation for her in the summer of 1898 to abandon her family and risk losing her beloved son.

Misha was staying at Kuusa with her parents that August as she waited for her article to appear in *Education;* Vladimir was away, drawing up a report in Lublin. Now was the time for the great brave leap: she would enroll at Zurich University as a research student with a Marxist economist called Professor Herkner, whose book *The Workers' Question* had greatly impressed her and her friends when they read it in its second edition.

She went to see the general, who was staying in the family home on a brief visit from Kuusa, and she tried to tell him how important this was to her; despite haunting anxieties about Misha she knew he would be happy at Kuusa without her. The general was not overly keen on the plan and foresaw even greater objections from her mother. He insisted on increasing her "pin money" to a regular monthly allowance and doubtless consoled himself for her departure by insisting the truth be hidden from her mother, who would be told that the doctor had ordered Shura to take the waters in Switzerland.

When in August 1898 she boarded the fast train from St. Petersburg to Zurich carrying her small suitcase, she imagined that the responsibilities and worries would melt away with the passing miles. But the burden of them increased to the point that she was soon sobbing with grief and guilt. All she could think of was how happy she had been with her gentle, loving husband and how much she missed Misha's soft little hands: how criminal it was of her to leave him, how foolish to leave Vladimir, who would not wait forever—and all for some unknown Professor Herkner. By the time she reached the Lithuanian border station of Verzhbolovo she had worked herself into such a turmoil of longing for Misha and jealous anxiety about Zoya's young actress sister that she was ready to jump out of the train and get the first one back to St. Petersburg.

Instead she wrote Vladimir a long letter. She assured him how much she loved him, how her heart would break if he left her, and how she longed to see him again. To Zoya she wrote more calmly then that her heart was set on more important things than marriage and that she was going to make use of this first freedom to study. She posted her two contradictory and yet congruent letters at Verzhbolovo, and when she woke up next morning in Germany her spirits were high in anticipation of her new life of study.[22]

3

Populists and Marxists

The railway line that carried Alexandra, joyful and restless, from Berlin to her destination, had been laid thirty years earlier. It had made Zurich the meeting-point for German craftsmen, who generally spent their "wander years" as migrant workers in Switzerland. With their fierce resistance to mass production and their hostility to rich merchants and meek trade unions, they quickly turned Zurich into a center for syndicalist activists (those, that is, who believed that the general strike was the workers' chief weapon against capitalism) and this faith spread all over Europe to Italy, Belgium, France, and Spain. The route to Russia was more circuitous.

Russian populists saw so many similarities between these German workers and the "migrant" workers of early Russian capitalism at the end of the nineteenth century that Zurich soon became quite a place of pilgrimage; eventually it was the nerve center of Russian socialism in exile. For the thousands of young people who left Russia throughout the 1860's and 1870's to enroll in Zurich's liberal university, Bakunin stood for an ideal, a Russian form of socialism, far more attuned than Marx to the vagaries of the *déclassé* intellectual, the ambiguous position of women in society, and the elemental rage of the poorest workers and most backward peasants. In the program of Bakunin's loosely formed Democratic Alliance the second point was a forcefully worded commitment to the liberation of women; on the women's question Russian populists certainly regarded him as more humane than Marx. And it was the young Russian women students who carried Bakunin's brand of populist agitation back to the factories and the villages. Long after these women had been arrested and Bakunin himself had become a worn-out old agitator, his image continued to inspire the populists of the 1880's and 1890's.

Through reading *Capital,* Alexandra was learning to distinguish between the real benefits open to women who joined the labor force and the actual misery of their lives. But for all the wealth of information she had gathered on mortality rates among factory women, child sickness, and atrocious poverty, it often required a superhuman effort to look beyond the heart-rending realities of working women's lives and to see their entry into the workforce as a progressive step, essential to a united workers' movement. The women who had stormed the textile mills the previous year had given her new perspectives, new courage. But in the end it was with her own superhuman effort of moving away from Vladimir and Misha that she began to clear her mind of the old populist dreams and start to remake her life.

As she entered her new life she felt that all her emotional needs were changing:

> Love, marriage, family, all were secondary matters now, transient. They were there, and they intertwined with my life again and again. But as great as was my love for my husband, [the moment] it transgressed a certain limit in relation to my female willingness to make sacrifices, rebellion flared in me anew. I had to go away, I had to break with the man of my choice, otherwise (this was an unconscious feeling in me) I would have exposed myself to the danger of losing my selfhood . . . It was life that taught me my political course, as well as uninterrupted study from books.[1]

Work was to be the great comforter. She would soon have to work in order to eat; now she needed it just as much as a link to the past, a guide to the future, a protection against loneliness, and a release from falsehood onto her own difficult but chosen path.

Arriving in Zurich, she moved into one of the cheap students' lodging-houses grouped around the hill overlooking the university buildings. She had traveled light. Despite her later legendary elegance, she rarely traveled with more than one change of dress, cut with expensive simplicity. (She had abandoned the whalebone prison and the "forward" severe line of the bustle for softer lines, and generally wore gray or brown.) She never abandoned the habit of putting cream on her face, powdering her nose, putting her hair in curl papers, and possessing one good dress that could be worn anywhere and forgotten about. After putting up her hair in the morning, she would generally cover it with a large elaborate hat, for hats were her great love.

In every other way her tastes were simple. The allowance she received from her father would have to be spent carefully if it was to stretch to all the new economics books she needed. She planned to eat her main meal in the students' canteen and make tea on a spirit stove in her room. She did not smoke or drink, but she had a great craving for sweets and cakes which she budgeted for, along with stamps for her voluminous letters to her parents, Misha, and Vladimir. It is likely that a stable childhood had made it easy for her to adapt to this boarding-house life. She did not fear being uprooted and was not perpetually trying, during her travels, to set up centers from which she could not be moved. But she did need to order her emotional affairs before she could contemplate her new life, and she was already facing the fact that a final break with Vladimir might be inevitable.

Her long, troubled letters to him were filled with guilt and jealousy, for she knew he would not hesitate to look for another wife if he thought she would not return to him. He begged her to return: "You remain the only person whom I love infinitely, and for whom I would agree to anything."[2] But by the time she got his letter her independence was already beginning to be less burdensome.

Perhaps it was just as well for her that Professor Herkner turned out to be such a convert to the fashionably liberal views of Bernstein, for she was soon so irritated by his classes that her wit and high spirits began to return. The latest edition of his book bore no relation to the one she had read, and like so many people who have abandoned their principles he was excessively concerned with "objectivity." Having for the last eight years had to cope with Rosa Luxemburg's repartee, "academic socialists" like Herkner were doubtless quick to deflect rebellious pupils towards more moderate socialist works. But Rosa—who had departed for Berlin three months before Alexandra arrived, after almost nine years in Zurich writing her doctoral thesis on "Industrial Development in Poland"—had left behind a small mountain of articles, many of them in the SPD paper, *Neue Zeit*, which Alexandra devoured along with the women's paper, *Die Gleichheit*. The result was that "the deeper I delved into the laws of economics and the more I became an orthodox Marxist, the more my tutor moved to the right and the further he departed from Marx's theories, so that by the fifth edition of his book he had become a real renegade."[3] As "revisionism" crept into the vocabulary of Marxist intellectuals, she became immersed in the past and current debates inside the German party (the SPD) where all these debates originated. She knew quite well that Bernstein's impact on questions of the mass strike and the revolution, of social relations and the family, went far beyond mere slanging matches and polemics in the theoretical journals of the SPD.

For Alexandra, as for so many Russian revolutionaries in exile or emigration, the SPD was simply "the party," and even while she was in Zurich it was a kind of political home for her; for socialist movements throughout the world, however, the German labor movement was an inspiration and a model. Its birth coincided with the birth of the German Reich, its power corresponded with the growing military and economic power of Germany, and it continued to challenge the autocracy even while Germany's imperial rulers were preparing to challenge Britain in war.

The SPD had been founded in 1875 at Gotha, uniting various socialist groups among which the most prominent were the supporters of the syndicalist Lassalle and those of the Marxist Eisenach. Its establishment eloquently expressed the increasing discrepancies between Germany's economic development and the backwardness of her political system. Economically, Germany, with her huge industrial and financial combines, modern equipment and industrial efficiency, was beginning to overtake Britain, then at the height of her power; politically, Germany was the most reactionary of all the great powers, incapable of dealing with the labor problem which inevitably accompanied her meteoric economic growth. Three years after it was established, the new party and the German trade-union movement (which had existed for some ten years) were both driven underground by Bismarck's harsh Anti-Socialist Law, and there they remained until these laws were repealed.

For the next twelve years of its existence, therefore, the SPD struggled illegally against a political system in which most workers were denied the elementary right to combine, and even such trade unions as did exist were handicapped by the harsh criminal code which threatened and degraded every worker in the Reich. In Prussia, the heart of the Reich, the very mention of equal suffrage would have been considered criminally subversive. So it was that the chief goal of the suppressed labor movement became the attainment of political democracy, for it was only organized labor that had any stake in this goal. The middle classes could prosper under absolutism, and the armaments lords were capable of gaining great power; industrialists, merchants, and bankers all stood to benefit from the imperial policies of Bismarck and the Kaiser, as did the Prussian landed gentry, the Junkers, who were the country's political masters. Unlike the middle classes elsewhere in Europe, where the development of capitalism was thwarted by feudal privileges, the middle class had no compelling interest in struggling for democracy. For the German workers, on the other hand, the struggle against absolutism meant the struggle not only for political power but for their daily bread.

In Germany, in complete contrast to England, the unions gained economic influence only in proportion to the political power of the SPD, which for twelve years, in conditions of extreme hardship, led the struggle against the Kaiser, the landed aristocrats (most powerfully represented by the Prussian army), and the privileged middle class. It was in this early struggle for democracy against the feudal lords and capitalists of Germany, united by an aggressive militarism which served the interests of both, that the German working class displayed such courage and defiance; withstanding the first twelve years of Bismarck's oppression, the SPD emerged even stronger and more conscious of this strength than before. In these years the fight for democracy had taken on all the significance of a revolutionary class struggle.

Under the Anti-Socialist Law almost every workers' organization and newspaper had been closed, and countless socialists had been living as outlaws, in exile or in prison. However, one month after Bismarck's attempt to enact a permanent anti-socialist law was defeated in 1890 (the government was by then confident that it could manipulate the socialists to support whatever policies it might be advancing), the SPD enjoyed a spectacular success in the elections to parliament; the number of socialist voters increased from 500,000 to 1,500,000, and the number of socialist members of parliament leaped from twelve to thirty-five. By 1903 of a total of 9,000,000 voters 3,000,000 were voting for the SPD.

Yet although the German parliament, the Reichstag, gave the SPD a useful platform from which to air its propaganda, it was, as one socialist member, Wilhelm Liebknecht, put it, no more than a "fig-leaf for absolutism," incapable of helping the workers to share political power. This power they inherited after the expiration of the Anti-Socialist Law, when the trade unions established an organization along the lines of the English Trade Union Congress, whose membership of 278,000 exceeded that of the SPD. By the mid-1890's a large and lively press was serving both the party and the unions. (There were ninety party and union newspapers in 1914, as well as numerous journals.) Despite the price increases caused by Bismarck's protectionist policies, and despite the increase in indirect taxation which allowed the arms magnates Krupp and Mannesmann to build their battleships and submarines, workers' wages were rising.

In his attempt to destroy the influence of the SPD Bismarck passed various social reforms, but most union members felt that they owed these benefits not to their rulers' "bribes to workers" but to the intervention of the SPD. Gradually, as the prestige of the labor movement increased its political outlook changed, and even those most thoroughly trained in revolutionary Marxism could not help suspecting that once Germany had lost the vestiges of its old feudal power, there would be no limits to the economic benefits it would be able to grant its workers.

It was in the mid-1890's, then, that Bernstein emerged as the most eloquent spokesman for the view that workers had a great deal more to lose than their chains—that to work for revolution was "utopian" and "obsolete," and could only handicap the workers' day-to-day struggles. The majority of the party's leaders immediately sprang to the defense of its original revolutionary goals, with Rosa Luxemburg, Franz Mehring, Karl Liebknecht, Leo Jögiches, Julian Karski, and Klara Zetkin taking a particularly intransigent line against Bernstein; Karl Kautsky too, and the orthodox Marxists of the party "center," rejected the new revisionist heresy. But the number of radicals who, like Rosa Luxemburg, explicitly called for a revolutionary overthrow of the Kaiser's regime represented only a small wing within the SPD. And although an ostensibly united front of the leftists and the center aligned themselves against Bernstein, Rosa Luxemburg was later to remark perceptively that the center opposed this new trend only because its members were incurably conservative; Marxism happened to be the accepted orthodoxy with which the party had grown up, and it thus had to be defended against all innovations, revisionist or otherwise.

Revisionism quickly seized the imagination of many trade-union representatives, as well as a number of Reichstag deputies from south Germany, where the political rulers were the conservative landowners and the more liberally inclined middle classes. But in general the division of the SPD into revisionists and Marxists meant little. As Alexandra was to discover in her later wanderings in Germany, many issues concerning workers' daily lives which were ignored by the party—particularly those concerning women—were rejected by the center as "revisionist" and tending to lead the masses away from the goal of social revolution. It must have been clear to her even from her first eager perusal of the German socialist press, however, that women were emerging as the most consistent voices of the party's left wing.[4]

Women who had formed self-education groups as a way of organizing politically had suffered from their dispersal during the underground years of the SPD; for twelve years they were subjected to particularly harsh repression and barred from attending any meetings or joining groups. But as one SPD member, Emma Ihrer, put it, assessing the impact of this period on women: "Every meeting that was banned or broken up, each new closure or condemnation or closure of an association, has led not only individuals but innumerable women to think again about law and justice, and that is the best way to bring women to class consciousness . . ."[5]

In 1890 Luise Zietz and Klara Zetkin told a trade-union congress that as long as private property, inheritance laws, and possessive marriage existed, no amount of special labor-protection laws could be of real benefit to women and that the proper demands should therefore be for labor-protection laws for all workers. This extreme proposal was rejected, but it set the tone for the militancy which Alexandra discovered in *Die Gleichheit*, which was now firmly rejecting all the revisionists' attempts to depoliticize and "popularize" its articles. This consistent radicalism impressed Alexandra very deeply and seemed to her to be based on the unique way women's work was carried out against all legal obstacles, and yet was still reconciled with the need for a strong and unified party.

It was not so easy to see how the details of this work might be applied to Russia, where the Tsar's special secret police, the Third Department, made all political work infinitely more difficult than in Germany, even with its harsh Combination Laws. In Germany some degree of cooperation between the SPD and the philanthropic women's groups was possible.

At the first congress of the SPD at Gotha in 1875 August Bebel had insisted that the SPD commit itself to universal suffrage for all citizens. While avoiding the explicit question of whether or not women actually were citizens, the vote became a central issue for reformists, who looked to women's votes to help them in their parliamentary ambitions, and for revolutionaries, who looked to the suffrage campaign as a major method of educating women and involving them in politics. After the Anti-Socialist Law expired in 1890, large numbers of women who had fought for better schooling and nurseries and an end to prostitution began to cooperate with the SPD and to shift the issue from the abolition of prostitution to the vote. Two years later, as a way of getting round the Combination Laws, women *Vertrauenspersonen* ("trustpeople") began to stand as party representatives for women in the factories and educational circles; they educated these women in trade union and political matters, and then reported their responses back to the party. In 1896 Klara Zetkin submitted her eight-point program on women to a party congress: active voting rights for industrial courts, extension of protection for women

workers, equal political rights, equality of education and freedom of occupation for both sexes, equal status in civil law, equal pay for equal work,
an end to private servants—all these demands became part of the SPD
program.

Ever since the days of the First International when Bebel and Liebknecht had taken issue with Proudhon and Lassalle (who essentially
wanted to protect women from the evils of wage work and strengthen
their ties to the home and the family), these issues had been of central
importance to German socialists. Soon after Engels's *Origin of the Family*
appeared in 1884, even leading SPD theoreticians like Kautsky and
Cunow were rejecting as too redolent of bourgeois psychology the high
value Engels reluctantly placed on monogamy, and were going beyond his
hypothesis that the driving force behind the transition from polygamy was
women's longing for "chastity," "temporary or lasting marriage with a
single man," or "deliverance." The articles that had been appearing in
Kautsky's *Neue Zeit* on women in the labor force and on marriage helped
Alexandra to start looking more closely at the ways in which both Engels
and Bebel had shown that the sexual division of labor under capitalism
oppressed women.

In his introduction to the *Origin of the Family* Engels had stressed
that the family's role in "producing new human beings" could not be
isolated from industry's "production of the means of existence." But in
the following chapters he had not returned to this understanding of the
family in every society as an integral part of the mode of production. It
was of great concern to many German socialists who followed him, therefore, to specify the place of women in the economy as housewives and
mothers. What Alexandra did find was that Engels removed the economic
relationships underlying all sexual relationships from the realm of academic abstraction to a historical reality she could grasp.

Women's personal oppression within the family, said Engels, re-
sulted from the family's place within a capitalist mode of production
based on class division and private property. At the same time that private
property had arisen among primitive peoples out of a surplus above what
was necessary to sustain life, production outside the home had begun to
expand more rapidly than production within the household. After the
domestic economy had dwindled in importance men had overthrown the
old matrilineal kinship system, turning women into the "first domestic
servant, pushed out of her part in social production." Chained to the
household, her labor as mother and housewife debased, woman's degradation had been fixed by the creation of a new authority, the state, "whose

aim is to safeguard private individuals' property against the communistic traditions of the gentile order."[6]

Since woman's domestic oppression (an oppression recently intensified with her employment outside the home) was based wholly upon private property, Engels stressed that the former would be ended only with the abolition of the latter: for "man's predominance in marriage is simply a consequence of his economic predominance, and will vanish with it automatically." "Private housekeeping" and the raising of children would be "transformed into a social industry," and as industry thus entered the sphere of the family, so women would increasingly enter the sphere of industry: "women's liberation becomes possible only when women are enabled to take part in production on a large, social scale."[7]

With developments in contraception and the replacement of manual labor by technology, today we may not so easily accept Engels's stress on the virtues of the old sexual division of labor, once freed from the oppressive conditions of capitalist production. Alexandra evidently warmed to his and Bebel's insistence on the increasingly non-functional nature of the family; what she may not so easily have accepted was that male supremacy and the conflicts women experienced between the private and public spheres of ther lives would "automatically" vanish under socialism, or that people's personal relationships could be transformed and that a refined form of sexual love could "automatically" spring up without a lengthy and self-conscious political struggle.[8]

By the 1890's the SPD seemed strong enough to lead not only the German working class but the entire European labor movement, and by then its debates had taken on added importance; in 1889 the Second International was officially launched to rally the socialists of every country in the world against the militaristic policies of their governments. As each social democratic party had the right to shape policies in the light of its own national conditions, the real political power of this huge, clumsy federal body inevitably lay with the SPD; behind all its urgent investigations into life under capitalism, therefore, lurked the two specters of capitalist war and class war.

After the initial euphoria of realizing her old dreams of study, Alexandra was far more concerned about using her reading to open up new avenues of political activity and research than to embark on any lengthy project. During her year in Zurich she did, however, develop the discipline and method that would later stand her in good stead. In leaving Vladimir and opting instead for work, she evidently condemned herself to a severely solitary life, for she made few friends, spent all her days in the library, rarely haunted the university taverns or cafés, and spent her free time walking in the hills with a book under her arm.

The works that most impressed her in Zurich were Rosa Luxemburg's articles for the *Leipziger Volkszeitung,* published together the following year as *Social Reform or Revolution.* [9] She had left Russia filled with a sentimental and optimistic kind of internationalism; now her eyes were opened to the insatiable global appetite of world capitalism, the developing rivalries between the imperialist countries for new markets and the inexhaustible supplies of labor to work those markets. After tearing to shreds Bernstein's book *Evolutionary Socialism,* [10] Rosa Luxemburg went on to a defense and an elaboration of Marxist theory which put her to the far left of the SPD and struck an appreciative chord with all Russian revolutionaries. Developing the Marxist premise that workers were becoming steadily more wretched, she insisted that as small enterprises were periodically mowed down and replaced by larger combinations, the trade-union struggle was reduced to a Sisyphean labor, with the unions pathetically crying out to bourgeois authority, which was essentially extralegal. As capitalism reached the limits of its powers, the capitalist countries of Europe struggled through slumps and crises to survive, dragging their proletarian victims through ever greater misery, sacrifice, and unemployment. Thus did Rosa Luxemburg rescue the goal of revolution from the increasingly far-off position envisaged for it by Kautsky and the more moderate majority. For Alexandra and most Russian revolutionaries, the prospect of the huge German labor movement learning to organize its own mass strikes and leading the small Russian movement in confidence, class-consciousness, and organization was, despite Rosa Luxemburg's warnings, deeply exciting. If Alexandra had started out with the intention of writing a thesis, she became too impatient to return to political work in Russia to give it much further thought.

In February 1899 this impatience increased when she learned that the Tsar had passed the death sentence on the Finnish constitution. Ever since Finland became a Grand Duchy in 1809 and acquired its constitution, the Russian high officials living in Finland had treated the people with overwhelming arrogance and cruelty. She herself well remembered how the wealthy Russians who had *dachas* on the Finnish border often flogged and bullied the Finns; such incidents were periodically reported in the conservative Russian press as Finnish "independence riots." Now an archetypal Russian bully named General Bobrikov was to be installed as governor-general; the Finnish language would be replaced by Russian, the Finnish army would be disbanded, freedom of speech and assembly would be revoked, and the Seim, the Finnish parliament, would be reduced to a powerless consultative assembly.

Finland was "reduced to the status of a Russian serf, without voice or rights."[11] Alexandra could think of little else but of returning. She missed Misha badly. Moreover she had heard that her mother had taken to her bed, stricken with heart disease, and as she was not wont to cope with her anxieties in this way, it seemed as if, for the first time in her life, she might really be ill. The only thing that kept her abroad was a letter she got that spring from Vladimir, who had decided to bury his first love and wanted a divorce. Although she readily gave her consent, the decision caused her a great deal of unhappiness, for added to the process of divorce itself—as punishing and complicated as it had been in her mother's day —there was the painful fact that Vladimir now wanted to remarry. Although she missed Misha badly, Alexandra decided to postpone her return for a couple of months and take up Professor Herkner's suggestion that she go to London and collect herself in the company of his Fabian friends. England, reasoned Herkner, would be just the remedy for his restless student. He gave her a letter of introduction to Beatrice and Sidney Webb, with whom she was to stay, and that summer she left Zurich for London.

"If London can mellow Marx, it can mellow me," Bernstein had said when he first left Germany after the passing of the Anti-Socialist Law. And it was in the congenial company of the Webbs, Hubert Bland, and Lord Olivier that he developed his high opinion of liberalism—the only philosophy which kept alive the concept of the individual as economically, morally, and socially responsible to himself, and the historical precursor of socialism.

Alexandra was apparently welcomed by the Webbs without a great deal of warmth when she arrived in London in the spring of 1899. Her first response to them was utter amazement, for although her English was perfectly good, she could scarcely understand what they were talking about. It was nothing out of the ordinary to hear their guests comfortably anticipate over the dinner table the day when the land would pass to the workers, the trusts would be seized, and all stubborn barriers to the advance of socialism would be painlessly dismantled. Whereas in Zurich even the bitterest anti-Marxists went no further than describing themselves as "critical Marxists," the Fabians did not speak any language she recognized because they just did not come from the Marxist family. Their socialism derived from Ricardo and Mill, and they were now only too happy that Bernstein's vision of gradual economic reform had enabled them all to return to the old pre-Marxist view of things.

After she had got over her amazement she grew impatient. ("A bunch of bourgeois humbugs whose aim it is to demoralize the workers," Lenin called them—and Alexandra may well have agreed with him— "people whose advanced view of capitalist society does not stop them helplessly fussing around with questions like 'what is capital,' 'what is the role of savings' and so on.")[12] Eventually Alexandra managed to escape the Webbs' chilly sitting room to walk about London on her own. She visited the Toynbee Hall settlement, spent several evenings in socialist meetings at churches and workers' clubs, and to her great relief discovered that she understood rather better the language spoken by the working-class people she met there than that spoken at the Webbs' dinner table. She could not wait to get back to St. Petersburg.

She returned to her family house in September 1899 to find her father, Jenny, Adele, and Alexander distraught and in mourning. Her mother had not been much more than fifty when she finally outlived her strength and gaiety, and she died before Alexandra could see her. Perhaps letters had crossed, or perhaps the general had simply thought it better not to call her back. At any rate Alexandra never felt forgiven for deceiving her mother in the frantic dash to Zurich, and for a long time she felt the loss very deeply. It was possibly feelings of guilt that prompted Alexandra Domontovich to leave Kuusa to Jenny, Alexander, and Adele, the children of her first marriage. There can be little doubt that Alexandra's exclusion from her mother's will compounded her bitter regrets that they had not been properly reconciled. "I caused my mother a great deal of trouble through my determination 'not to live like other people' "—this feeling remained painfully on her conscience for many years.

Misha was now five, and she gradually won back his confidence and established a life with him and her father in the Domontovich mansion. After the ordeal of solemnizing the divorce before the Holy Synod, Vladimir married his new wife, Maria Ipateva, who was very fond of Misha, and Alexandra set about picking up the pieces of her life. Misha's old nurse Anna Petrovna ("Annushka") had married while Alexandra was abroad, but was persuaded to remain in the Domontovich house and help her to care for him while she was out at meetings. She occasionally took him along with her when she visited the houses of her old friends. The first person she contacted on her return was her old friend Lyolya, and shortly after her return she joined the small, illegal, Russian Social Democratic Party, just a year after the founding congress in Minsk. She joined as writer, propagandist, and organizer, thus resuming the sort of work she had been doing the previous year. With the party underground and most of its leading theorists and militants abroad or in exile, she now learned the importance of attention to detail and punctuality, and of memorizing names and messages and codes. Lyolya was a superb organizer, and soon had Alexandra storing piles of pamphlets, helping her and other comrades to write proclamations, and in the evenings teaching the militant and articulate workers who lived and worked near St. Petersburg's Nevsky Gate. These classes were legal as long as the ideas of Marxism and revolution were presented under the harmless guise of geography or arithmetic lessons, and through them a great many workers passed into the party. Alexandra learned to escape the attention of the inevitable police spies who attended these classes by avoiding the use of certain subversive key words. She depicted Marx's theory of labor and surplus value (the labor which workers expend to keep themselves alive, and the surplus created by labor—the profit—which capitalist exploiters extract from them) more directly to her audience in terms of her own impressions of their harrowing lives. And with her immaculate appearance and gentle voice she was so unlike the stereotyped woman revolutionary "nihilist" whom the spies had been looking out for in the 1870's that most of them tended not to listen to a word she said.

Avoiding arrest by assuming the appearance of legality was, however, a very different matter from "legalizing" Marxism. Having learned in Zurich that Marxism could be made to mean all things to all socialists, Alexandra soon discovered that now that populism had been thoroughly discredited virtually all St. Petersburg intellectuals were describing themselves as Marxists (a phenomenon with which socialists nowadays are equally familiar), but she also discovered that the very concept of revolution was being questioned by large numbers of people who called themselves "legal Marxists."

Ever since the mid-1890's, leading Marxist intellectuals like Peter Struve, Bulgakov, and Tugan-Baranovsky had been skillfully presenting their ideas in such a way as to get them past the censorship. It was Struve who had written the program of the first congress of the Russian Social Democratic Party committing the party to the generally accepted "two stages" of revolution (that bourgeois capitalism must be fully developed before socialism could be achieved). But in the year Alexandra was away she had discovered that the aspiration of the "legal Marxists" for a progressive bourgeois democracy had pushed aside all of the sort of inspiring hopes for social equality that had emboldened those in the Union of Struggle to bypass the first, bourgeois stage in their strategy and fight directly for the second, revolutionary stage envisaged in the *Communist Manifesto*. It was time, said Struve, for Marxists to curb their flighty daydreams of "storming heaven" and to learn instead in "the school of capitalism, recognizing our lack of education"; Russian radicals should work for a constitution before they considered the task of making a Marxist revolution. All this was immediately reminiscent to Alexandra of Bernstein, with his talk of working in the "furrows of the field" and his obvious hostility to revolutionary change.

That summer Lenin and some fellow exiles had sharply denounced the "legal" line from Siberia, reminding party members that the Russian worker was perfectly capable of carrying "the work of conquering political liberty on his strong shoulders." But, as Nietzsche had said, it is pointless to lecture an earthquake. In the troubled times that followed the defeat of the first mass-strike movement, many Marxists turned to the idealism of those Russian philosophers who preached self-perfection rather than social revolution and to Nietzsche, who preached the "aristocracy of the spirit." Alexandra found herself with few friends on her return. "I came back to St. Petersburg with optimistic hopes of finding myself among like-minded people, but the Russia of the autumn of 1899 was not the Russia of the previous years. The honeymoon unity between legal and underground Marxists had come to an end, and legal Marxism was openly turning to the defence of large industrial capital."[13] The "up-and-coming elements, like Ilin [Lenin], Maslov, and others," who were elaborating a theoretical basis for the party's underground tactics, had all been driven into remote exile after the strike movement of 1896, and the party had not yet launched its own newspaper. Zoya was living outside St. Petersburg and working as a journalist for art periodicals, and Alexandra's closest friends of that time apart from Lyolya were Alexander Bogdanov, Vladimir Bazarov, Ignat Stepanov, Vladimir Avilov, and a man named Rumyantsev—all of them young radical intellectuals upon whom Plekhanov had been a formative political influence.

As most of the debates between "legal" and revolutionary Marxists had to be conducted under the legal cover of lectures for which an admission fee was charged, the revolutionaries' interventions often provoked rude and acrimonious arguments. On one occasion Lyolya's father arranged a soirée to raise money for the Political Red Cross. Ticketholders were carefully vetted, for Struve was to speak on Bernstein, and Stasov wanted there to be no heckling. But even though Alexandra and her friends managed to slip in, Struve's words were met with almost unanimous applause, and only Avilov spoke up against him. As all the leading intellectual lights and "names" stood up, one after the other, to praise Bernstein, Alexandra "took the floor, although this was granted reluctantly to one so little known":

> My defense of the "orthodox" [leftists] was too heated. It met with general disapproval and even an indignant shrugging of the shoulders. One person declared it was unprecedented impudence to speak against such generally accepted authorities as Struve and Tugan. Another thought that such a speech played into the hands of the reactionaries. A third believed that we had already outgrown "phrases" and must become sober politicians . . .[14]

After returning to Russia, Alexandra had sent off a number of articles attacking Bernstein to the progressive journal, *Educational Review;* by the time the censors' red and blue pencils had finished with them, they were unfit to publish. But one long article she began at this time, "The Question of the Class Struggle," did see the light of day in the summer of 1905, when it circulated briefly in manuscript before being confiscated. Here she set out to link the hopes for economic reform which had been stirred up by Bernstein to the individualist ethic of religious Russian philosophers like Bulgakov and Berdyaev, who, citing the ideas of the eighteenth-century German philosopher Kant, called on the Russian state to recognize the limits of its power and people's right to self-determination. These sentiments, many of which were evident in Marx's early writings, had a particular attraction for the "legal Marxists."

But it was action, not philosophy, that claimed most of her time and thoughts, which were devoted to the problem of Finland, where she was a frequent visitor in that year. She was inspired by the spirit of resistance in the tiny social democratic party which had just been formed there, and she helped to collect money for the first strike fund in Abo. This was the start of a lifelong collaboration with the Finnish socialist movement, and she always tried to make several visits every year to her mother's homeland whose history, language, and people were so familiar to her. She wandered through the forests on the large timber estates, observing how the lumberjacks and raftsmen lived, and visited the towns of Helsingfors and Abo, where she saw that "the growing power of the industrial proletariat, recognized by few people, marked sharpening class contradictions and a developing new Finnish workers' party, in opposition to the bourgeois nationalist parties of the Swedophiles, the Finnophiles, and the Young Finns" (those, that is, who supported Sweden's capitalist interests there, and those who favored Finnish capitalists' own management of the developing economy, independently of either Russia or Sweden). As she jotted down her impressions and gathered economic statistics for a book she was thinking of writing on the workers in Finland, she began a series of articles, the first of which appeared the following year in German in the SPD economic journal, *Soziale Praxis*. [15] Speculating about the future of the Finnish workers' party and its need for a strong strike movement, she emphasized that the Finnish middle classes were far more powerful than in Russia, far more venal, and prepared for unprincipled alliances.

She found Finland a relief from St. Petersburg, not only because people there talked a more positive and earthy socialism than the virtuously remote tones of the legal Marxists, but because militant nationalism had produced a militant feminism far more attuned to the needs of working women than were the small number of public-spirited Russian women engaged in charity work, who could think only about vodka prohibition, disdained politics, and did not display any real appreciation of the problems of women in the factories. For Alexandra and the very small number of women intellectuals like her in the Party, there seemed nothing for it but to accept most Party members' oversimplified Marxist view of the economic basis of women's oppression; there seemed to be no alternative to this virtual rejection of their sex but isolation and ridicule. Accusations of "reformism" ensured that the very few revolutionaries who had attempted to reach factory women in the strikes of the previous years still tended to regard separate women's work as a compromise with the splendid ideal of the united Party. Of course the problem had not been articulated in these—or any—terms, partly because liberal feminism had not yet begun to make its threateningly successful appeals to working women, but mostly because Social Democrats believed that sexual divisions in the working class and in the Party would be most likely to go away if they were ignored. If Alexandra looked to Bebel for some guidance on women's chances of emancipation within the workers' movement, his passing references to "the measures and special institutions" required must have seemed woefully sketchy after the initial excitement at his liberating message.

It is a fair guess that when Alexandra was silenced at the Stasovs' soirée by "indignant shrugging of shoulders," her comrade Avilov was received more politely. Without the support of a women workers' movement it was hard to know how to behave at such a meeting, and there seemed little chance that the Party would give priority to women in their propaganda until the women themselves forced the Party to respond to their needs. The strike movement died away at the end of 1898 with a final eruption of female anger, when striking women at two St. Petersburg tobacco factories threw tobacco in the eyes of the advancing police and brought women from several other towns out in support of their audacity. In general, however, women were still regarded by employers as more reliable and coercible, and they were used regularly to replace men, who could be fired without cause or warning. During the years 1900–1901 alone the number of women in the workforce in Russia increased by 12,000 and the number of men decreased by 13,000; large numbers of these men had been fired for strike activities. Women's greatly increased presence in the factories intensified the simmering antagonisms between men and women factory workers over the next ten years, as Vera Karelina, one of the very few women factory workers who joined the underground in the 1890's, revealed in 1905: "The masses of the workers held the opinion that politics was not a woman's business. Her business at the factory was at the machine; at home, the children, the nappies, the pots and pans . . ."[16]

The first attempt to take up the issue of women's inhumane and exhausting working conditions and to give political direction to women's readiness to strike appeared at the end of 1900 with the first issue of the Party's first paper.

Lenin had left his Siberian exile earlier that year for Geneva, where he joined forces with Plekhanov. Plekhanov had parted company with the Land and Liberty Party in 1879, when it transformed itself into the terrorist People's Will. He had left shortly after its formation for Geneva, where he had been joined by another former Land and Liberty member, Vera Zasulich. It was her attempted assassination of the governor-general of St Petersburg, Trepov, in 1878 which had ushered in a series of individual terrorist attacks on prominent officials of equally notorious cruelty and had forced the populists officially to adopt the tactics of terror. Miraculously acquitted by the force of liberal public opinion in St. Petersburg, Vera Zasulich had swiftly left for Geneva, where she adamantly denounced her action and the adoption of terrorist tactics. She and Plekhanov were joined in Geneva over the next few years by a number of Russian Marxists such as Pavel Axelrod, Yuri Martov, and Alexander Potresov, and together in 1883 they had formed a small organization of Russian émigré revolutionaries, the Marxist Liberation of Labor group. This group had a major influence on revolutionaries in Russia and subsequently on the members of the Union of Struggle.

The results of Lenin's collaboration with the Liberation of Labor in 1900 were two major new publications, *Iskra (Spark)*, a popular weekly, and *Zarya (Dawn),* a theoretical monthly. These papers managed to give political and theoretical direction to the scattered revolutionary movement, to draw Party members together in smuggling issues into the country, and to form a great network of people throughout Russia who could connect the exiled leadership with the factory centers. Throughout 1900, as this great *Iskra* chain of command was being forged, Alexandra gradually lost contact with her old stalwart companion of the underground, Lyolya, who was now coming into her own as the very personification of all the virtues required of an *Iskrovka,* or woman *Iskra* agent. Her great powers of concentration, observation, attention to detail and memory were rewarded by new responsibilities, and she was often called on at short notice to drop everything, travel to distant parts of Russia, and make new contacts for the party. "Comrade Absolute" was what her friends called this genius of cryptography and organization.

The editors of *Iskra,* however, were beset by political differences, differences which were afterward to divide the Russian Social Democratic Party into two conflicting trends. The intellectual prestige of this journal was considerably enhanced by the occasional contributions of Peter Struve, then in Geneva. His program for the founding congress of the Party two years before had persuaded many Party members that he and other "legal Marxists," such as the philosophers Bulgakov and Berdayev, were the true intellectual heirs of the populists. The intellectuals—by Marx's definition bourgeois—must lead the first stage of the Russian revolution, said Struve: It was not until capitalism had been fully developed that the proletariat would be strong enough to carry through the second, socialist stage of the revolution which had been depicted by Marx.

These differences were only later to assume the proportions of an urgent political debate within the Party. For Alexandra, the publication of *Iskra* in 1900 meant that she would inevitably have to store and distribute great new piles of literature. She began to feel uneasy about living under her father's respectable roof and exposing him and Misha to the constant threat of arrest. She had not reverted to her family name, attributing this to the warm feelings she had for Vladimir. But her choice must also have been prompted by a desire not to associate her father and his highly placed relatives with her activities.

Since her return from Zurich and her mother's death she had evidently had little chance to talk to him, and he was depressed and in poor health. Surrounded by servants and the memories of happier times, he did not survive his wife for more than a few months; even the presence of Alexandra and Misha failed to cheer his lonely last days in the gloomy

Domontovich mansion. In the middle of 1900 he fell while walking in the city and died soon afterward. The family house was once more in mourning, and Alexandra mourned his death more openly than she had grieved for her mother.

> With the death of my father I knew the pain of despair from irrevocable loss. The most frightful moment was when we returned from the funeral to the house, which struck us as terribly calm and deserted. Tea was laid out for us in the dining room and the lamp burned as usual, lighting the snow-white tablecloth. I went into father's study: four candles under a green shade burned as they had always done on his desk. Father's beloved roomy armchair was drawn up at the round table on which stood a lighted lamp. A book lay open on it, about Macedonia and Eastern Rumelia. Everything in that room awaited the return of its master. There, and only at that moment, did I realise with the full force of my imagination that my father would never come back to that table.[17]

When Alexandra wrote later of the "new woman" of the working class, taught by the cruelty of her life to despise bourgeois morality and struggle for independence, she contrasted (almost as a footnote) the more solitary experience of the middle-class woman who, in shaking free of marriage, struggled alone against her class. She may not have been driven by hunger into the class struggle, but she could speak from experience of the forcible break with the old emotional dependency experienced by all women; of the need to harmonize inner freedom and self-reliance with the "all-consuming passion of love"; of the need for work, not emotion, as the basis for the emerging social personality of the new woman.[18] Her evocation of the isolation of the middle-class woman Marxist in early twentieth-century Russia has great resonance for the equivalent stratum of women today in the West.

After her father's death she moved out of his house and found a small flat where she and Misha could live on her restricted means. The process of extricating herself from this last tender trap of her old "legal" life was doubtless as painful as it was beset with financial difficulties. General Domontovich had bequeathed to her a small sum of money which she put aside for Misha's education, which was to start the following year at a school in St. Petersburg noted for its progressive pedagogical methods. The uncle to whom the family house belonged agreed to continue paying her the modest allowance she had received from her father. She also inherited from her father the uncompleted manuscript of his work on the history of the Balkans, that massive work in which he had been so totally absorbed throughout the whole of his life, and it was a great consolation to her that she was able to find a publisher. She found consolation in her own writing also; she finished off an article in German on the Finnish workers' movement and started on two articles for Russian educational journals on Finnish industry and housing.[19]

Her original departure for Zurich had been hurried and fraught with anxieties about her parents, and Vladimir and Misha. Lingering in her mind now there was still a sense of unfinished business about all that she had read there and not had time to assimilate properly. She still felt quite unprepared to argue points of theory with the "legal Marxists." Nor did she feel able, now that there seemed finally to be a strong revolutionary organization coalescing around Lenin and his supporters on *Iskra,* to commit herself fully to the illegal life of a revolutionary; she was too bound by her old life and her commitments to Misha to join the underground.

She continued to live on her father's allowance, teaching geography and Marxism during the evenings to the militant workers employed at the factories by St. Petersburg's Nevsky Gate, and when seven-year-old Misha started school, she was able to devote her days entirely to writing. From her first observations of Finnish political resistance to Russia she had developed an interest in Russian-Finnish trading relationships, in the economics of Finland's metal-working and timber industries, and in the lives of the raftsmen of Finland's forests. A book was taking shape. By the early months of 1901 she was eager to leave Russia again to use the libraries of Zurich and Paris. This time, just as before her first departure from Russia, her fighting spirit was stirred by another great wave of women's militancy in factories throughout the country.

That spring masses of workers poured onto the streets of St. Petersburg in a series of angry strikes and demonstrations which were met head-on by the police and left many dead and wounded. "We lacked the training and numbers to march at their head and convert this spontaneous action into one of political consciousness," lamented Lenin in *Iskra.* It was not only training and numbers that were lacking: few in the Party appreciated how important it was that women were joining in the street fighting for the first time. It was during the workers' defense of the Nevsky district that an eighteen-year-old woman ran out of one of the factories and began handing cobblestones to the men. "We stand behind our brothers!" she was heard to shout. (It is quite possible that some of Alexandra's words to the young working men she taught had been repeated by them to their women friends and relatives.) In the much larger demonstrations that followed the workers' defense of the Obukhov quarter of St. Petersburg, the cities of the South saw hundreds of women fighting in the streets beside the men, and along with the men they were shot down by the police, flogged, and thrown into jail.

The Party that produced *Iskra*—a party of consummate intellectuals —again and again praised the virtues of revolutionary "consciousness" as against this kind of "spontaneity," which was met with police bullets. While Lenin was elaborating his theory of "the underground party," the underground itself became increasingly prone to distrust workers' attempts to protest against their intolerable lives, and gave the impression of arrogance, which deterred many like Alexandra from committing herself fully to Party work. There seemed to be no way to combine caring for Misha with the absolute dedication required by the underground revolutionary movement. In 1901, emotionally unprepared and politically confused, she steeled herself once more to leave seven-year-old Misha in St. Petersburg (probably in the affectionate care of Annushka, and visited frequently by Vladimir and his second wife) and to go abroad again to continue her studies of the international socialist movement. She finished her article on Finnish trade and industry, sent it off to *Educational Review*, and set off once more, in the late spring of that year, for Zurich.

Her political views had been shaped by the lucidity of Plekhanov and the militancy of Rosa Luxemburg. Unfortunately these two had had a major feud eleven years earlier when they embarked on a joint publishing venture together and were now bitter enemies, so that when Alexandra met Rosa Luxemburg in Zurich, she was not greeted with very much warmth. In fact, Plekhanov had behaved with Rosa Luxemburg and her lover, Jögiches, with extreme personal touchiness and more than a hint of anti-Semitism, but Alexandra knew little about the personal politics of the emigration, could never have credited her first teacher with pettiness or arrogance, and so was naturally inclined to take Plekhanov's side. It was after a few such unpleasant incidents that she learned that, along with all the generous internationalist impulses which flourished in emigration, there were constraints, loneliness, poverty, and an irritable, nationalistic narrowmindedness, which haunted every émigré café in Europe. She and Rosa Luxemburg parted with the understanding that they would meet again and possibly correspond. Friendship or no friendship, Alexandra recognized an ally in Rosa Luxemburg, with her passionate denunciations of capitalist morality; she was not yet ready to challenge Luxemburg's equally passionate denunciation of the "women's question" as peripheral to the larger revolutionary struggle.

She finished her business in Zurich and went on to Paris, where she visited the Bibliothèque Nationale, wandered around émigré haunts like the Turgenev Library, and went out to the pretty Paris suburb of Draveil, where she spent an evening with Paul and Laura Lafargue, Marx's daughter and son-in-law. Finally she moved on to Geneva, which Plekhanov had turned into the very center of the Russian emigration with his Liberation of Labor group, and where Lenin was now effectively replacing him as editor of *Iskra* and *Zarya*. One of the first people she met in Geneva was Karl Kautsky, who was paying a brief visit there. Kautsky was then at the height of his popularity as editor of *Neue Zeit*, and it was after talking to him that Alexandra started on an article for that paper on Finland. She resumed her earlier student life, arriving early every morning at the library, putting most of the day into researching for her book, and reading all the latest socialist literature she could get hold of.

Lily Braun's book, *The Woman's Question* (1901), had just come out and was being received with great excitement by German women for the passionate tones in which she charted the history of women's oppression and miseducation, attacked the many variants of the double standard, and stressed the psychic revolution that must accompany any socialist revolution. With this book Lily Braun lost many of her old friends in the SPD; Klara Zetkin, for one, felt that she conceded far too much to "idealistic" individualistic solutions to political problems and disliked her proposal for working with middle-class women in establishing household cooperatives. Yet although Lily Braun did part company with the SPD in stressing that women should attack the oppression of their daily lives through campaigns for maternity insurance and for the freedom to hold meetings, Alexandra kept her high opinion of her even when Lily Braun and Klara Zetkin were no longer on speaking terms, and her detailed depiction of the family and housing unit of the future had a great impact on Alexandra's future writings.

But any reading Alexandra did on the women's question was still strictly subordinated to the study of economics: Rosa Luxemburg's philosophy—that her sex was irrelevant to her competence—would have to sustain her for the time being. She did, however, meet Plekhanov one day over the catalogues of the Geneva library, and after conquering her tongue-tied awe of the father of Russian Marxism, she agreed to contribute an article to *Zarya* on Finland. Plekhanov begged her to ask him for any help she might need, and this marked the beginning of a friendship sustained as much by certain temperamental similarities as by her gratifyingly eager response to Plekhanov's work. When her article appeared the following year, Plekhanov wrote off to Axelrod, his colleague in the Liberation of Labor group in Geneva, to draw his attention to its promising young author.[20]

It was all too dismayingly clear to Alexandra that the ageing Plekhanov was gradually losing his preeminence in the Russian Party, and as Lenin and the younger Party members tried to push the long-established Liberation of Labor group off the *Iskra* editorial board, Plekhanov remarked to Axelrod that "of such stuff Robespierres are made."

4

What Is To
Be Done?

By the time Alexandra returned to St. Petersburg in the middle of 1902,
Lenin had already produced his major work on revolutionary organization,
What Is To Be Done?, and over the next few months *Iskra* carried articles
setting out the program of the revolution. This program, unchanged until
1919, was guided by the assumption that capitalism was reaching its most
acute crisis, and that since the Russian middle classes lacked the political
power to carry through the first Marxist stage of the revolution, this would
have to be accomplished by a small number of its most revolutionary
elements (the Party) in association with the working class. The most
extreme measures thought to be acceptable to the middle-class radicals
whom Lenin aimed to win over to support these early stages of the
proletarian revolution included universal suffrage, the separation of
Church and State, limitations on work for women, an end to the employment of children, an eight-hour day, and the return to the peasants of the
land removed from them at the time of the emancipation of the serfs. The
nature of the Party that would lead this revolution continued to be
debated long after the Russian Social Democratic Party had split into
Bolsheviks and Mensheviks in 1903; and long after the Bolshevik revolution it still raises questions of very great political importance.

The fact remains, however, that a great many social democrats did
not, in 1903, feel impelled to commit themselves to either the Bolsheviks
or the Mensheviks, because the differences between them did not initially
seem that great; not as great, anyway, as the differences dividing revolutionaries from the "legal Marxists" who throughout 1902 were drawn to
Peter Struve's Liberation group (formed in Geneva in that year, and
issuing its own journal of the same name). The "legal Marxists," who

attempted to win support from liberal Russian landowners by taking up the defense of their interests, could have little to do, as far as Alexandra was concerned, with revolutionary Marxism:

> Two antagonistic forces were coming into ever more bitter conflict; underground Russia marching towards the revolution and the autocracy stubbornly clinging to power. Struve's group took a middle position. Many of my close friends joined Liberation, considering that pure socialism was a utopia, given the Russia of that time, and I had to make a clean break with many recent comrades-in-arms and recent associates.[1]

Among those Alexandra was probably referring to was Vladimir. Eight-year-old Misha evidently still saw quite a lot of his father, so the "clean break" cannot have been so simple for her in this case as she suggested. Her later writings indicate some of the conflicts and difficulties she must have suffered in transferring her loyalties from the remnants of her old family life to the collective family life of the Party while still bringing up Misha (who had just started school).

In September 1902 the long-established progressive journal, *Russian Wealth*, published Alexandra's article on the lives of the Finnish raftsmen.[2] Many Russians, who had tended to regard Finland with a somewhat detached eye for its possibilities as a haven for exiles, were struck by her evocative description of the animal poverty of the raftsmen's existence in the depths of the forests, huddling by night around bonfires, awakened at dawn by the shrieks of their foremen, and forced by day to haul timber until they dropped exhausted. From these observant and generous writings, rather reminiscent of Engels's *Conditions of the Working Class in England*, it was quite clear that Alexandra had no interest in the feverish abstract speculations that so often gripped Russian revolutionaries in times of reaction. It was in these years that Nietzsche became such a cult figure among student "nihilists" and radical drifters, who claimed that his brand of lonely despair and cynicism was really the most radical way of exposing the sordid tatter of bourgeois relationships. At an open-air meeting on January 3 (St. Tatiana's Day) 1903, at which young student "idealists" sang hymns of praise to Nietzsche, Alexandra delivered a spirited speech attacking all the posturing falsity of the Nietzscheans. She concluded her defense of socialism to a highly skeptical audience with the rousing words: "Our slogan is not the triumph of individualism but the victory of collective consciousness." If this youthful audience was skeptical, even more skeptical was the publisher to whom she took the manuscript of her book on Finland. "Wouldn't it be better if your papa came in person to discuss the statistical tables, rather than sending an intermediary?" he asked her.[3] He was eventually convinced that she was indeed the author, and in February 1903 the book slipped past the censors with the innocuous title *Life of the Finnish Workers.*[4] It was well received by Social Democrats—who noted that she had added some revolutionary conclusions to the observations in her earlier articles—and Lenin, on the divided *Iskra* board, noted down her name as a future contributor. Nothing came of this, however, for *Iskra* was to pass to the control of Plekhanov when the Russian Social Democratic Party finally split that summer at its Second Party Congress (which met in Brussels and was forced by the police to reconvene in London). Alexandra went abroad that summer; although it is not clear where she went or what her purpose was, it is most likely that she wanted to keep in touch with this crucially important congress. She may have travelled with Lyolya, who went as an *Iskra* delegate.

Waves of peasant uprisings and strikes were sweeping over southern Russia in the summer of 1903, when fifty-seven delegates (most of them exiles) from twenty-five different Russian socialist organizations met up in a disused storeroom of a Brussels cooperative society to discuss three main points: the formation of a generally acceptable political program, the adoption of a constitution, and the election of officials. Plekhanov's intellectual authority was immense, matched only by Lenin's astounding powers of concentration; each was quite confident that his own vision of the Party would be accepted at this meeting.

The three points announced for discussion were dealt with relatively easily. Everyone cheered Lenin's broadsides against the economists, agreed that all constitutional rights must be subordinated to the needs of revolution, supported the death penalty as a possible means of getting rid of the Tsar, and agreed that there was need for a strongly centralized revolutionary Party. And since Lenin's views about the need for a highly disciplined, illegal organization of professional revolutionaries were known to all who had read *What Is To Be Done?*, the arguments for and against these views started off in a very friendly fashion. Martov and Plekhanov wanted a more open party, which anybody could join as long as he or she accepted its program, helped it materially, and supported it according to the orders he or she was given. It was only as Lenin's "hard" line was consistently outvoted that he began to juggle around with the *Iskra* votes in order to gain a thoroughly unrepresentative majority, and then consolidated that victory by calling his supporters "the majority group," the Bolsheviks.

Alexandra had shared Lenin's views on the need for members' total commitment to the Party, rather than the "minority" Mensheviks' faith that every individual member could decide the extent of his or her commitment; but like many other revolutionaries working in Russia, she regarded the split as an émigré affair, and the personal politics of Lenin's vote-rigging can only have enhanced the attraction of the Mensheviks. Added to this was the "charm of Plekhanov's personality," which kept her from breaking with them. On her return to Russia that autumn she wrote: "I did not join either of the Party groups, offering my services to both factions for agitation, writing proclamations and other urgent tasks."[5]

Apart from the evening classes she taught in the Nevsky district, the main part of her agitational work was in Finland. She frequently addressed meetings in all the major towns and then reported back on the situation in the Finnish Social Democratic Party. In January of the following year Lenin was writing to Bogdanov, editor of the new Bolshevik paper, *Forward,* that he should contact her immediately, as "articles on Finland are ultranecessary."[6]

By the beginning of 1904 the mounting tension and anger throughout Russia was leading Alexandra to the Bolsheviks. Despite the attractions which the Mensheviks' vision of a larger, more decentralized, and more spontaneous Party may have had for her, she realized that only the Bolsheviks, with their dedication and intransigence, were capable of developing into the party that might lead the masses to revolution. The strike movement was now intensifying to the point that workers appeared as never before to be threatening the basis of Nicholas II's state. Increasing numbers of women were active participants in this strike movement.

Even as the Second Party Congress was meeting in Brussels the previous summer, the entire southern part of Russia had been in the throes of a great strike; there were repeated peasant uprisings, and the universities were seething with unrest. In the cities the employers were using their time-honored method of hiring more women to crush the strike movement, and a factory inspector's report of 1904 observed that "factory owners everywhere are replacing men by women, not only among adults, but also among the young, believing the female element in the factories to be more docile and steady."[7] In the years 1901–1910 while the number of industrial workers in Russia increased by 141,000, eighty-one percent of these were women. And yet for the first five years of the new century the Bolsheviks paid almost no attention to the needs of women. Unlike the populists' Sunday schools of the 1860's, Alexandra's evening classes had only a very small number of women pupils, and she observed that although she was later to meet many of her former male pupils in the ranks of the Bolshevik Party, "the working women were still avoiding life and struggle, believing that their destiny was the cooking pot, the washtub and the cradle."[8] It was the burden of the tragic Russo-Japanese War that finally broke working and peasant women out of this docility, leading them to riot and strike, and persuaded countless young intellectual women to pursue the terror tactics of the Socialist Revolutionary Party, formed in 1902.

Even before this, ever since the 1890's, the old populist traditions had continued to have a special appeal for young women inspired by their predecessors in the People's Will. In the years that had followed the collapse of that party a new generation of men and women had grown up, disillusioned neither by the humiliations and defeat suffered by the People's Will in 1881, nor by the numerous liberal Russian landowners, inspired by Tolstoy, who described themselves as populists. The new Socialist Revolutionary Party, which aimed to attract all socialists of populist leanings whether terrorists or liberals, was a large and amorphous organization which soon split under the weight of its differences. But among the women who joined this Party there were many former Land and Liberty members, like Ekaterina Breshkovskaya, for example, who had just been released from a long and harrowing sentence of exile. These women, like their predecessors, provided Alexandra and many other women Marxists with the confidence that women could find their own emancipation within the ranks of the revolutionary movement.

Ever since Sofya Perovskaya was hanged, when Alexandra was nine, for directing the assassination plot against Alexander II, this heroism had deeply affected her; she was later to write of Sofya Perovskaya's "daring 'male' mind, and her ability to subordinate her woman's 'ego' and her loving passionate heart to the cause of the revolution."[9] The extreme anti-feminism of this tribute was some indication of Alexandra's view that women could only fight for their sexual equality within the organized revolutionary movement. It was, however, a tribute to a phase of the revolution which had passed, a phase inspired by those who, like Ekaterina Breshkovskaya, believed that history was made by "people of high intellectual and moral aspirations," and "persons of outstanding character."[10] Marxism rejected the notion that history was made by individuals, but its class-based philosophy of history did not seem incompatible with the idea that within the workers' movement women might organize a struggle for their own specific needs. The resilience and self-confidence of the women in the Socialist Revolutionary Party (if not their commitment to terrorism) inspired Alexandra with the hope that such a struggle might soon be a reality. In the fury with which men and women throughout Russia greeted the outbreak of the Russo-Japanese War in 1904, however, many Bolsheviks began intuitively to sympathize with the terror tactics of the Socialist Revolutionaries.

Under the pretext of finishing work on the Trans-Siberian Railway, the Tsar had ordered troops to occupy Manchuria and had taken a ninety-nine-year lease on Port Arthur from the Chinese. When a private company, the Yalu Timber Company, began moving Russian soldiers into Korea in early 1904 in order to acquire a new Russian province, war was inevitable. In February the Japanese destroyed the first of many Russian squadrons in this disastrous war. Eighteen months later most of the Russian fleet was at the bottom of the Tsushima Straits; the Russian defeat was crushing, and the peace terms apallingly humiliating.

In the midst of all the carnage, with the peasants all over Russia rioting and the Socialist Revolutionaries conducting their own vendetta against the more barbarously cruel local governors, Peter Struve's Liberation group chose to launch the "springtime of liberalism." Reports of their "political banquets," at which government liberals like Prince Svyatopolk-Mirsky thrilled their audiences by calling for a tsarist constitution, decided Alexandra once and for all that the Mensheviks' hopes for collaboration with liberals in the government were deluded. Bernstein, as she had predicted, was now required reading for every police spy and government minister.

In the SPD itself, however, the opponents of Bernstein were not necessarily the friends of Lenin. Kautsky refused to publish Lenin's defense of the Bolsheviks in *Neue Zeit,* and in July that paper published a harsh attack by Rosa Luxemburg on Lenin's undemocratic ways and "ultra-centralism." By the time it published Alexandra's article on Finland later that year, she had fully and openly committed herself to the Bolshevik party.

In July 1904, even sober Bolsheviks could not resist a moment of joy when the Socialist Revolutionaries hit their first major target and assassinated Von Plehve, the notoriously cruel prime minister. But when he was replaced by the unctuous Svyatopolk-Mirsky, who promised "cordial relations" between government and people, everyone waited for the inevitable backlash. By the end of the year he had ordered that all unauthorized gatherings should be dispersed "with the hiss of the knout," and all Bolsheviks now lived under the shadow of arrest.

With Lyolya and Vladimir Avilov, her closest friends in the Bolshevik party, Alexandra attended the huge student demonstration in November 1904, at which hundreds of people were arrested. She took the initiative in arranging for supplies to reach them in the prisons, acting so swiftly that the police suspected the backing of a large organization. The Bolsheviks had in fact taken no part in planning either the demonstration or the large meeting of socialist groups that was to follow it that evening in the halls of the Technological Institute. It was at Alexandra's insistence that the Bolsheviks met, under heavy disguise and false names, at a separate meeting in another hall.

She must have derived new spirit at the end of this harrowing year from a series of riots in which peasant women all over Russia began to shake off their old docile image and cry out against the war and the ways it was hurting them. For throughout that year, as men were carted off to war, thousands of women found they could no longer support their families by working alone on their plots of land. Most of those who arrived in the cities in that period, desperate for work, ended up as the lowest-paid servants or in the most squalid factories and sweatshops, whose wages were not generally thought to be compatible with survival. After eighteen hours toiling at her workbench, the newly recruited woman worker would return to her fetid barracks with no thought but of sleep and no explanation for her sufferings other than that she had somehow deserved the wrath of God. Thousands of those who did not have the fortune to find jobs resorted to prostitution. The children of these women too, as Alexandra was to write later, were to get their only education from the streets.

It was these women, however, coming to the cities to learn their rights, who learned to hate the Tsar, his ministers, and all those who referred contemptuously to the *babi bunty,* the peasant women's riots. (*Baba,* a particularly offensive term roughly translatable as "peasant hag," was used indiscriminately by many conservatives—and, to their eternal discredit, by many revolutionaries in later years—to include all women.) "For the first time," wrote Alexandra later, "peasant women left their homes, their passivity, and their ignorance behind them, and hurried to the towns to tread the corridors of government institutions in the hope of news from a husband, a son, or a father, to stick up for their allowances and fight for various other rights . . . They returned to the villages in a sober hardened mood."[11] And so began the women's riots, which continued all through the following year, fighting detachments of Cossacks and braving rape and humiliation.

"The spark which ignited this rotting nest of universal discontentment," as Alexandra put it,[12] was the strike that began on January 3, 1905, at the huge Putilov armaments factory. The moving force behind this, and behind all the meetings that preceded it, was the shadowy figure of the peasant priest, Father Gapon, and his government-sponsored Union of Russian Factory Hands. Despite its opposition to equal pay for women, this organization attracted some 300 women workers, who had to fight against a great deal of prejudice from the men to join. "I remember what I had to put up with when there was the question of women joining the organization," said Vera Karelina, a factory activist for the past fifteen years who led this women's section. "There wasn't a single mention of the woman worker, as if she was non-existent, like some kind of appendage—and despite the fact that there were some organizations in which the workers were exclusively women."[13] A few Bolshevik women infiltrated the organization to persuade women to leave, but Alexandra felt that strike fever was approaching the point where Gapon would be swept away and forgotten about.

During this first week of 1905 Bolshevik meetings and her activities in the factories can have left Alexandra with little time to spend with Misha, and it is possible that he began to spend more time with his father. As she redoubled her commitment to the Bolsheviks it was with the painful awareness of "how little our Party concerned itself with the fate of working-class women, and how inadequate was its interest in their liberation."[14] Any organization which helped factory women to express themselves—even that of Gapon—would seem preferable to the Social Democrats' almost total silence on the subject.

By January 5, 1905, the Putilov strike had spread to the Nevsky shipyards; on the sixth the bakers came out. On that day the decision was taken, heavily guided by the hand of Gapon, to march to the Winter Palace to beg the Tsar for a constitution. Neither the Bolsheviks nor the Mensheviks had any doubt that with such a demonstration the workers would unwittingly be taking Russia a step further toward a revolution for which nobody was prepared, and they helplessly tried to intervene against Gapon, whom they regarded as mad, misguided, and a dangerous provocateur; the prospect of the vulnerable and inexperienced St. Petersburg proletariat launching a botched bourgeois revolution was too terrifying to contemplate. For Alexandra, however, as for the many other Bolsheviks who walked with the procession of workers to the Winter Palace on January 9, their alarm was irrelevant: "However woefully this first show of workers' strength might end, it was an inevitable first lesson for them on the road to revolution."[15]

The sun was hot on the snow that Sunday morning as hundreds of thousands of workers, dressed in their Sunday best and accompanied by elderly relatives and children, moved off in respectful silence toward the Winter Palace. And there they stood, holding their banners, church gonfalons, and portraits of the Tsar, waiting for him for two cold, patient hours in the snow. A shot was fired and they stamped their feet; another, and they laughed that it must be blanks; a third, and suddenly the blood was pouring and women and children slumped dead in the snow. And still the people standing beside Alexandra kept reassuring her that it was a mistake and that the Tsar would not shoot unarmed subjects. But by then the gendarmes were galloping into the crowd and the slaughter was starting. Something like 3000 workers were killed that day, their blood spilled on the Schlüsselburg Highway, the Troitsky Bridge, the corner of Gogol Street and Nevsky Prospect, at the Narva Gates, and the Alexandrov Park. Barricades went up that afternoon on Vasilev Island, and by evening some of the bolder people had raided the Schaff arms factory, but few of the demonstrators were able to defend themselves. Bloody Sunday riveted for ever in Alexandra's memory the images of "the trusting expectant faces; the fateful signal of the troops stationed around the Palace; the pools of blood on the snow; the halloing of the gendarmes; the dead, the wounded, the children shot. . . ." What the Tsar's servants did not realize, though, was that "they had killed something even greater—they had killed superstition, the faith of the mass of the workers that they could ever achieve justice from the Tsar. From that day on Russia was different and new. January 9 saw the start of a great mass movement against old bourgeois landowning Russia . . ."[16]

Strikes again broke out all over Russia, and as she traveled frequently from St. Petersburg to Finland, Alexandra was in touch also with the great wave of sympathy strikes in Finland: on January 10 workers left the power stations; on the eleventh Moscow, Vilno and Kovno were hit by near-general strikes and all Finns were ordered out of Russia; on the twelfth Riga, Revel, and Kiev were immobilized by general strikes; a few days later Svyatopolk-Mirsky resigned; and on January 19 the Tsar summoned a delegation of workers to see about satisfying some of their grievances— or rather to inform them they were to elect representatives to the government's Shidlovsky Commission. Despite the Bolsheviks' insistence that such cooperation was a waste of time, they did so, and among those elected were a number of women. When the government refused to find seats for them, the women organized an angry protest demonstration in the name of all working women of St. Petersburg, and the men also protested at this discrimination; for "the hardships men and women had been through together had brought them closer together, and it seemed particularly unjust to emphasize woman's inferior status at a time when she had shown herself such an able fighter and worthy citizen."[17] The workers soon lost interest in the commission, which collapsed the following month, but the incident was enough to show how if challenged, working men could gradually be educated to abandon their old prejudices and working women could become articulate.

Removed by their family responsibilities from the social life of the strike movement and cut off by their illiteracy from the political and strike literature that flooded the factories in that year, most women remained acutely shy of standing up at meetings and exposing their ignorance. For countless striking women who suffered and struggled in that year there was no suffering to equal that of being jeered at by their male colleagues. "Well, yes, I do want to express myself," one woman told Vera Karelina, who was trying to recruit her into her workers' group." But then I think it over—so many people will be looking at me, and what if someone laughs at me? I grow cold with terror at such a thought. And so you just go on sitting in silence while your heart is enflamed."[18] Throughout the early months of 1905 Alexandra realized more clearly that the Bolsheviks could not seriously consider giving political direction to the strike movement while women, almost forty percent of the work force, felt so discouraged from expressing their feelings.

Shortly after January 9, Alexandra received an official reprimand from the St. Petersburg committee of the Party for joining in the demonstration. She defended herself and went on to make amends by her dedicated work for the committee over the following months. The revolution launched by workers all over Russia in response to the Bloody Sunday massacre gained its momentum over nine months of strikes and expropriations with little help from either of the Party's two factions, which both tried to lead it. The Party had been greatly weakened by the split two years before. The Mensheviks, although larger and richer, denied any intention of seizing power and described themselves as a party of revolutionary opposition to the government; the Bolsheviks boldly declared their desire to lead the working class to armed insurrection against the autocracy, but they were chronically poor and lacking in numbers. Between them the two

96 | ALEXANDRA KOLLONTAI

factions could count on no more than a few hundred supporters, whereas the Socialist Revolutionary Party, now in its heyday, numbered as many as 10,000 members and already had in Victor Chernov a theoretical leader of some stature. The small-scale peasant economy, he insisted, could easily compete in efficiency with large-scale agriculture; the peasants were therefore to be the agents of the revolution, the first stage of which was to be the physical liquidation of the large landowners.

Alexandra threw herself into underground work, and Zoya, who had returned to the capital and moved in with her, also took on various tasks for the Bolsheviks, whose ambitions greatly exceeded their numbers. "We perish not only in bloody battles but in printing our pamphlets, selling books, distributing journals, and holding conferences," said one Russian delegate to the Second International. "The average life of a committee is one to two months, that of a paper one to two issues . . ." Alexandra helped to draw up proclamations calling for an armed insurrection; she wrote a leaflet calling for a truly representative people's constituent assembly, a leaflet which was widely circulated and well received; she helped to write, lay out, and print the first and last issue of the illegal Bolshevik newspaper, *Petersburg Working Week,* which came out on March 20; she traveled regularly to Finland and addressed meetings there; and some time in March these labors were rewarded when she was appointed treasurer of the Social Democratic Party's St. Petersburg committee, a majority of whose members were Bolsheviks. Her appointment was a small but significant indication of the new responsibilities opening up to women in the underground.

Before 1905 the small number of women underground workers had limited themselves to perfecting all the exceedingly sensitive tasks of underground communication. Nobody could match Nadezhda Krupskaya or Lyolya Stasova in the fine arts of preparing invisible ink, putting messages into code and ensuring their delivery, scrambling telegrams, and organizing conspiratorial hideouts and meeting places. Even if they did resent this comparatively menial work, their resentment can only have led them to put even greater hopes for their liberation into the cause to which they sacrificed so much of their own initiative. By 1905, however, educated women began to join the underground on their own terms; they joined the strikes and demonstrations and, under the odd underground names they gave themselves like "Bunny," "Auntie," or "Beast," they worked as nurses, street-fighters, and agitators.

Neither pogroms nor arrests could demoralize this great strike movement, for people had stifled their anger for too long. From the end of

January 1905 the country was virtually paralyzed by a rail strike. February opened with the slaughter of the people of Baku on the Caspian Sea and the students at the major university town of Kazan, 700 miles southeast of St. Petersburg. Then the peasants of the Orlov and Kursk districts began to riot, and the Tsar retaliated by sending Cossacks into Kursk to kill the schoolchildren. At this the peasants in Kursk began to loot and burn in real earnest. Shortly after this, on February 24, there was a week of comparative quiet after the news that Mukden had been bombarded and that the Russians were withdrawing from the war with Japan. Then the strikes started up again. Throughout March there were waves of pogroms in the Crimea and Yalta, peasant uprisings in Samara, major riots in the tsarist satellite of Poland, including a great popular rebellion in Warsaw which left almost 100 dead, and a student mutiny in Tambov. Yet month after month, in town after town, workers continued to come out on strike for a shorter working day and more humane working conditions. Women shook off their old servility, left their machines, and gave the strike movement a quite unprecedented sense of solidarity and confidence. "As the working woman gradually came to understand the world she was living in and the injustice of the capitalist system, she began to feel all the more bitter at the sufferings and difficulties women experienced. The voices of the working class began to ring out even more forcefully . . . for the specific needs of working women to be recognized."[19]

These specific needs were indeed recognized in almost every strike document of that time, and they invariably included demands for paid maternity leave (four weeks before the birth and six weeks after), time off during the day to breast-feed infants, and the provision of nurseries at the factories. A very few even went so far as to demand equal pay for women. Nevertheless the sort of strike leaflet which exhorted "all workers, sons of labor" to behold "your endless toil, and your wife's tears" was unfortunately still all too common.[20]

As for the Bolsheviks, since Nadezhda Krupskaya's booklet, *The Woman Worker*, which had focused their attention on the subject five years earlier, little else had been produced. One popular pamphlet they did produce in 1905 was entitled *A Woman's Lot*. This described how a wretched factory woman named Mitrevna evolved into a politically conscious citizen after her husband returned from war to explain to her the greater political causes of her misery. It concluded with an appeal to women to spread the word among themselves (for "you understand each other better") and take their place "beside husbands and brothers." However courageous the women were who joined the strike movement, they clearly could not be expected to sustain any political commitment if they were not provided with something more substantial than sentimental leaflets of this kind. They were finding their new guidance in a resuscitated, energetic feminist movement.

When Alexandra had drawn swords with Struve's Union of Liberation the previous year, she did not mention the numerous women who were being invited to adorn its banquets. It had not seemed possible that classical liberal feminism could have any appeal outside this small middle-class circle, and existing feminist organizations like the Mutual Philanthropic Society, established ten years before, were providing few outlets for any political activities. But by 1904 that Society had already begun to lose members; many women, inspired by the success of the Finnish women's suffrage campaign (which had just won women there the vote), were now taking heart from energetic journalists and doctors like Ariadna Tyrkova, Anna Milyukova, and Anna Kalmanovich who were urging them to fight for the vote, and for professional and educational equality. The Union of Women's Equality was gradually taking shape.

Like the other professional organizations which were emerging throughout 1905, the Union took its constitutional monarchist philosophy from Svyatopolk-Mirsky's "springtime of liberalism"; added to this were detailed demands for the liberation of women. According to Alexandra, it was "the first women's organization in Russia to adopt a defined political platform,"[21] and its appeal to newly politicized women in the cities was considerable. In the months before its official inauguration in April the Union joined forces with the Mutual Philanthropic Society in making contact with women of the trade unions and the Gapon organization, and also with a few socialists who had hitherto been writing in isolation on women's politics rather than joining revolutionary groups; two Bolshevik sympathizers, Anna Bazarova and Lyubov Gurevich, the prolific Socialist Revolutionary journalist Olga Volkenstein, and a Menshevik named Morgulis all formed a "socialist contingent" of working women who trooped along to the Union's preliminary meetings en masse. And they did not go to heckle.

As Ariadna Tyrkova and Anna Kalmanovich explained to their mainly middle-class audiences why women must unite with the workers if they were to win the vote, the factory women (who had had their first experience of voting with the disastrous elections to the Shidlovsky Commission) listened with bewildered eagerness. Even the maids and cooks whom their mistresses had induced to attend the meetings found the prospect of a united women's movement so irresistible that they often did not question whether their employers were really the best people to lead them. "The working-class women who had begun to sense their inferior political status in terms of their sex were not yet ready to connect this with the general struggle of their class. They had yet to find the path that would lead the proletarian women to their liberation, and so they still clung to the skirts of the bourgeois feminists."[22]

On April 10, 1905 the first political meeting of women ever held in Russia opened in the splendid hall of St. Petersburg's Tenishevsky Educational Institute, the formal inauguration of the Union of Women's Equality. Over a thousand people attended: women professionals and philanthropists from all over Russia, as well as a few workers and Social Democrats. Ariadna Tyrkova and Anna Milyukova urged them all to unite in the fight for the vote and were warmly applauded. But when Alexandra Kollontai, a woman known to few in the Women's Union, stood up to speak, all decorum soon broke down completely and her words were interrupted by volleys of hissing and jeering. She angrily attacked the notion that there could be any class-united women's movement at a time when the strike movement was spreading and open class war fast approaching; it was clear why, at this of all times, the Union should want to lure working women away from their proper place among the Social Democrats, who alone had recognized the economic causes of women's oppression and were committed to abolishing them. The speech made her only one friend, a solitary woman worker, and enraged most of the others in the audience. One woman yelled that she was playing into the hands of the anti-Semitic thugs of Nicholas II's Black Hundreds, another that she was "unleashing base passions in the workers," and another that she was no better than a "hooligan." A writer named Krandievskaya hurled herself at her crying "strangling's too good for you!" and she left the meeting painfully aware that not only had she broken for good with the conservative feminists, but she had also antagonized many socialist women who had despaired of the Social Democrats.

Her speech did have some positive results, however, and her words were evidently not lost on the many women workers who joined the Bolsheviks that April. But although the act of joining the Party indicated a tremendously increased confidence on the part of these women workers, she felt as if she were recruiting them under false pretenses, for "we did not know then how to use them, how to awaken their independence and class consciousness."[23] Large numbers of working women continued to go to the meetings of the Union and the newly politicized Mutual Philanthropic Society. But although they listened attentively they did not respond with much enthusiasm:

> . . . the speakers gave no suggestion as to how the urgent problems of those enslaved by capital might be resolved, nor how they might help working-class women who suffered from harsh working conditions, hunger and insecurity. Their most urgent demands were: a shorter working day, higher wages, more humane treatment from the factory authorities, less police supervision, and more scope for "independent action."[24]

Throughout the next months, as the Union petitioned the St. Petersburg city council (the Duma) and the local administrative authority (the *zemstvo*) for their right to vote, Alexandra and a handful of Bolshevik working women attended their meetings to raise troublesome questions about the implications of this suffrage demand for working women. These activities failed to impress her Bolshevik comrades in the St. Petersburg Party organization. Since universal suffrage was one of the first demands they had formulated for the first stage of the revolution, they saw no need at all for a working women's suffrage campaign and saw Alexandra's interventions at feminist meetings as at best a waste of valuable energy and at worst symptomatic of a hankering after feminism.

If the Bolsheviks were expressing themselves more confidently that spring, it was because they were now moving firmly against the Mensheviks in the direction of a harder line and more centralized Party. Two weeks after the Union of Women's Equality held their inaugural meeting, the Bolsheviks met in London for a congress at which they rejected as dishonest the Socialist Revolutionaries' promises of an immediate seizure of power, resolved to avoid all acts of premature insurrection, and resigned themselves instead to a long process of strengthening and educating the workers' movement to the point where power could be seized. They also gave their full support to workers' military units which would defend strikers against the army and police. It was Nadezhda Krupskaya who described the "committee man" who was born out of the new confidence of this congress, remarkably uninterested in the more personal questions confronting the rapidly changing workers' movement and the Party: "The committee man was usually a self-confident person, who as a rule did not recognize any internal Party democracy, did not want any innovations, did not desire, and did not know how to adapt himself to rapidly changing conditions."[25] Such a man was clearly going to take a dim view of accommodating women's needs within the stringent demands of the new Party organization, and it is probably the attitudes he represented that made Alexandra go against the Party on the question of women's work, however much she supported their line on the armed insurrection.

By summer the Union of Women's Equality had been accepted into the Union of Unions—an organization led by Peter Struve which included a large number of liberals and members of professional groups who, like Struve, desired a constitutional monarchy for Russia. This body transformed itself later that year into the Constitutional Democratic Party; the Union of Women's Equality, moving steadily toward the more conservative position of this party, began to campaign for its members and its feminist platform to be admitted to its ranks. As working women continued to suffer and strike, Alexandra continued to heckle the feminists' Union meetings in the hope of attracting women into the Bolshevik party.

On June 3, 1905, twenty-eight women and children in Ivanovo-Voznesensk near Moscow were bestially killed when some 11,000 women textile workers came out in one of the largest strikes ever seen in Russia. Olga Gankina, a Bolshevik activist, was torn limb from limb when she was discovered with a suitcase full of weapons by a group of Black Hundreds thugs, and her example inspired more and more women to join the Bolshevik street-fighting groups. That summer too the *babi bunty* reached their height as still no word was heard of the promised peace with Japan: the peasant women were now organizing to resist and beat up the Cossacks sent into the villages to smash them, and their resistance was not broken by imprisonment and floggings. As pogroms and random Cossack massacres continued throughout June in the South, the citizens of Odessa prepared to retaliate. July 9 saw the Odessa armed rising which, supported by the mutiny of the sailors on the battleship *Potëmkin,* turned into a general strike and spread to the sailors at Riga. Until the red flag was raised over the *Potëmkin*—the most powerful man-of-war of the entire Black Sea fleet—most Bolsheviks had regarded the peasants who joined the navy as lagging behind the urban workers and craftsmen who tended to join the army. This attitude, however vigorously disproved by events, lingered on for several years and reflected a certain doctrinaire approach to recent events which ensured firstly that their novelty was neglected, and secondly that they became compressed into rigid compartmentalized modes of interpretation. It was partly these factors that had such an inhibiting effect on most men in the Party—the middle-class leadership of the proletarian rank and file—and make them appear to us now to have been so blind to the gamut of demands raised by women.

By August roving gangs of uncontrollable Black Hundreds thugs made the streets of every town dangerous, and they were countered by almost daily Socialist Revolutionary attacks of increasing ferocity on prominent local officials. The Tsar eventually concluded the Treaty of Portsmouth and began to consider the possibility of appeasing his people with some kind of parliament. The previous month Alexandra's pamphlet *The Question of the Class Struggle* had been distributed in the capital in manuscript, but it was soon confiscated by the police. In the series of huge meetings that were held day and night in all the factories and universities, Bolshevik speakers would urge their audience to keep up morale. Alexandra spoke at St. Petersburg University, which had turned into a meeting hall where working men and women sat beside students and schoolchildren. She spoke at a series of great meetings in the factories by the Nevsky Gate, where she already had many friends from her evening classes; she also spoke at factory meetings in the Okhta quarter of the city and on Vasilev Island. With these factory audiences she was one of the most popular speakers. In spite of her extreme nervousness at public speaking, which she only overcame many years later, Alexandra rarely addressed fewer than two or three thousand people. Meetings like these went on all over Russia throughout September in the third great strike wave of that revolutionary year, which now began to assume an openly political character.

The 1905 strike movement had so far developed without the support of trade unions. The illegal Social Democratic Party, to a far larger extent than its membership would indicate, had replaced them, both in the kind of agitational work Alexandra was involved in and in actual participation (particularly in the economic general strike in Ivanovo-Voznesensk that June). Despite the Bolsheviks' studied disregard in all their strike leaflets of the strikers' economic demands, and despite their emphasis on political preparation, their attempts to separate themselves from the Mensheviks were of little concern to the vast majority of workers.

Although the Bolsheviks were in control of the St. Petersburg committee of the Party, the Mensheviks were still more popular throughout the rest of the country. The Mensheviks appreciated the disorganization and chaos to which economic strikes could reduce the government, they welcomed the new forces such strikes would bring into the struggle, and they welcomed the workers' seizing of rights previously denied to them —which the authorities, they realized, would be too nervous to withdraw. They were also, however, advocating a limited collaboration with liberal groups in Russia, and although there were many reasons for Alexandra to feel increasingly drawn in the later months of 1905 to the Mensheviks, this last tactic was utterly unacceptable to her. But in early October her new friends in the Nevsky and Vasilev factories were telling her about the Mensheviks' proposals to hold "revolutionary elections" to a workers' council, or soviet, which would coordinate and direct the strike movement. She unreservedly welcomed this proposal—which seemed to her to transcend all factional allegiances—as the first real attempt to understand and find expression for the intensifying anger of the striking workers.

On October 8 there was a rail strike in Moscow, which later turned into a general strike, with the workers putting up barricades to defend themselves against the soldiers' bullets and the more audacious of them shouting anti-tsarist slogans. In the next few days strikes spread throughout Russia. By October 12 St. Petersburg railway junction was hit, the factory workers were in a mood to fight, the St. Petersburg committee of the Party was calling for a general strike, and at packed excited meetings in the factories workers begged agitators for political guidance on whether to call a mass strike. Only organization was lacking.

Workers' negotiating committees had, of course, sprung up in the strike movement of the 1890's. After January 1905 militant groups of Social Democrats had appeared in every industrial town in Russia with incomparably greater power to direct the strike movement, provide it with funds, and keep it in touch with the underground organization. It was Trotsky who understood that these committees were capable of fulfilling a vastly more ambitious purpose for the workers—that of revolutionary self-government.

In 1902, after some six years as a revolutionary activist, Leon Trotsky had escaped from Siberian exile and arrived in Geneva, where he joined the editorial board of *Iskra*. When, at the Social Democratic Party's congress the following year in Brussels, that Party had split into opposing Bolshevik and Menshevik factions, he had joined the latter, standing out for a larger workers' party than the Bolsheviks were prepared to concede. Trotsky continued to work for *Iskra*, which had now passed into Menshevik hands; he also joined the Menshevik "center" (formed to combat the Bolsheviks) and helped to formulate those measures by which new Menshevik bodies were formed at every level of the Party as a counterweight to the Bolsheviks. In 1904, however, he broke with the Mensheviks over their policy of finding allies in liberal circles in Russia, and it was then, as a member of neither faction, that he elaborated his theory of the "permanent revolution." The revolution, he stated, would begin as bourgeois in its immediate tasks, but would soon reveal powerful class contradictions, and would only achieve victory after relinquishing power to the

one class capable of putting itself at the head of the oppressed masses—
the proletariat.[26]

"A political strike of the proletariat ought to turn into a political
demonstration of the population, this is the first prerequisite of success."
These sentiments, so close to those expressed by Rosa Luxemburg, were
evidently close to Alexandra's heart, and this was why in March 1905 she
welcomed with such enthusiasm Trotsky's vision of a greatly expanded
centralized workers' council, which he propounded after his return to St.
Petersburg from Geneva in March 1905. For it was this council, or soviet,
that would assume the great task of coordinating the revolutionary mass
strike which was now appearing on the horizon.

When on October 11 the Mensheviks in St. Petersburg began openly
to urge that workers' strike committees throughout the country be expanded into soviets and that nationwide elections to them be held, they
did so with the specific purpose of directing a general strike. Thanks to
her contacts in the factories Alexandra was able to attend the first meeting
of the St. Petersburg Soviet, along with ninety elected delegates, at the
Technological Institute on October 14, the day after her Bolshevik comrades on the St. Petersburg Party committee had belatedly called for a
general strike.

Once this first and most important soviet had been established in St.
Petersburg under the leadership of Trotsky, soviets spread rapidly
throughout all the major towns of Russia, uniting the members of various
socialist parties. In February 1917 the soviets in every town in Russia were
known as "soviets of soldiers' and workers' deputies"; the creation of the
new Petrograd Soviet and the assumption of power by the Provisional
Government happened within days of each other and inaugurated a
period of dual power, in which the Soviet constantly undermined the
government authority, especially over the army. When Lenin returned to
Russia from exile in April 1917 to demand "all power to the soviets," he
meant not only the Bolsheviks in the soviets but the soviets themselves,
as a rudimentary but inspiring form of revolutionary self-government.
Because of this slogan and the faith behind it Bolsheviks and soviets were
often confusingly referred to after the October revolution in 1917 as if
they were interchangeable.

In October 1905 the Bolsheviks were prepared to work actively with
the St. Petersburg Soviet, but only, as we shall see, with severe reservations. By its first meeting most Bolsheviks had overcome their distrust of
the soviets as a "Menshevik intrigue" and an example of the sort of broad
non-Party organization through which many Mensheviks wanted to legal-

ize the Social Democratic Party. But Alexandra found quite incomprehensible the withering criticisms of its political amorphousness expressed by Bolshevik comrades like Bogdanov; still less could she understand his desire to present the St. Petersburg Soviet with an "ultimatum" that it accept the program of the Social Democrats (that is, the Bolsheviks), or the Bolsheviks would leave. Their distrust of this crucial organization of workers' power lost them many supporters, and it was at this time that Alexandra began to question her previous whole-hearted support of Bolshevik tactics.

The Bolsheviks' "ultimatum" was obviously without any substance, however, for the strike movement was already too powerful to be directed by any political party. Proof came three days after that first meeting of the striking Russian workers' power to frighten the Tsar.

The famous "four freedoms" of Nicholas II's manifesto of October 17, 1905, were also without substance, as the later widespread arrests of those who tried to make use of them proved; as for his vaunted parliament, or Duma, discriminatory voting rights would later turn it into a sort of members' enclosure, which failed to satisfy even conservatives in the government and was a severe blow to the feminists' suffrage hopes. But what was notable about this manifesto was that it was the first time the Tsar had responded to popular anger not with the pogrom and the knout, but with some attempt, however feeble, to appease it.

5

After Bloody Sunday

In 1905 the Russian people rose up against their oppressors and demonstrated a rage so great, so unexpected, and so unprecedented that its reverberations throughout Russia in the following years earned it the sacred name of a revolution. A thousand questions are raised by that revolution, the "dress rehearsal" for the successful Bolshevik revolution in October 1917, and a thousand answers may be found to explain why it failed. I have tried to answer only a few of these questions.

For Alexandra, 1905 spelled the beginning of a new life of total commitment to the revolution. Of course, no revolution can take place twenty-four hours of every day; what happens after everyone goes home is of equal importance and interest—and is rarely written about with the seriousness it deserves. Alexandra's particular personal commitment to ensuring that eleven-year-old Misha's life was not too disrupted must have been quite equal to her commitment as a revolutionary—yet, as in all revolutions, collective work and struggle did for a while take precedence over many other aspects of her personal life. During this period we have exasperatingly little information about Alexandra's home life in the little flat she shared with her son, or about her relationships with him, with Vladimir, with her two sisters Jenny and Adele, or with her comrades in the Social Democratic Party. This lack of information is particularly exasperating since we are exploring the life of someone who insisted so eloquently that the revolutionary movement must broaden its aspirations to include the more personal desires which the men and women involved became conscious of as they made that revolution.

If Alexandra does not mention in her autobiographical writings the personal conflicts she must have experienced as a revolutionary and as a mother, this was because it was in precisely these conflicts, so little appreciated by the male majority in the Party, that she was so isolated both from her class and from her male comrades in the Party. But between 1905 and 1908, in her political writings and at meetings, she was clearly speaking of her own needs and from her own experience when she emphasized time and again that the Social Democratic Party must integrate working women's needs into its program if it was to succeed. Economically (as workers within a capitalist system) and sexually (in an oppression they shared with all women), working women suffered an exploitation twice as cruel as that suffered by men. Working women's participation in the revolutionary struggle was therefore essential for their own emancipation; it was also an essential precondition for the success of that revolution. These arguments of hers were asking little more than some support from the Party for the Marxist traditions on which that Party was based; according to these traditions, which had inspired Alexandra to join the struggle against capitalism, the liberation of women was an integral part of the Marxist revolution.

After 1905 to the Social Democrats' anxieties about a divided and disorganized workers' movement (anxieties especially pronounced among the Bolsheviks, as evidenced by their initial distrust of the soviet) was added a new fear: the fear that if large numbers of independent and articulate women workers joined the strike movement to express their own needs, they would create a new, sexual division within the proletariat. What they were unable to recognize was that this division had existed for as long as women and men had worked in the factories together. As far as most Social Democrats could see, any attempt to mobilize women workers could only be inspired by "feminism"; Alexandra (herself intransigently opposed to the liberal feminism of the women's groups that sprang up after 1905) was therefore branded by her Marxist comrades as a "feminist," and the term thus became hopelessly confused.

In the political context of 1905 Alexandra herself was in no confusion about the term; no group, feminist or otherwise, could possibly unite the two great classes in Russia—the propertied and the propertyless—who shared nothing but their mutual antagonism. As for many women workers, however, it did indeed become likely that they might be induced to abandon the struggle of their class to support the liberal groups in the Tsar's parliament, among whom the new feminist organization, the Women's Union, had its natural allies. This was why she devoted such enormous energy between 1905 and 1908 to a campaign, in which few Social Democrats supported her, to lead working women against the

Women's Union and into the only party which could possibly support them, the Social Democratic Party.

The Bolsheviks' distrust of the "spontaneous" manner in which the 1905 strike movement had erupted had, of course, a history that went back to the crushed strike movement of 1896 and the early persecuted days of the Union of Struggle; the need for a politically conscious Party to lead the disorganized workers as they rose up spontaneously to protest against their intolerable sufferings had been inspiringly expressed by Lenin in *What Is To Be Done?* Between 1896 and 1905, however, many Bolsheviks, like Lenin, had visited Russia only during very brief intervals between periods of exile and imprisonment for daring to organize an illegal Marxist party in Russia, but they lacked the daring to recognize that since 1896 the workers had created, in the soviet, a strike organization of considerable sophistication. But there were many underground Bolshevik activists inside Russia who also deplored the "anarchy" of the events there between 1904 and 1905. One of these was Alexandra's comrade, Alexander Bogdanov.

In April 1904, at the Bolsheviks' first congress after their formation as a separate faction, it was Bogdanov and another underground activist named Anatoly Lunacharsky who had drawn up the main report on the tactics by which the workers were to be led in an armed uprising against the Tsar. Bogdanov's brief derogatory report on the chaotic strike movement of that year was unquestioningly accepted: "All it took was for one worker to cry 'Right fellows, stop work!' and a strike was on—and anyone who spoke out against it was dubbed a provocateur."[1] Just how far removed Bogdanov's account was from the realities of the increasingly organized strike movement many Bolsheviks were to discover when they returned to Russia in the brief period in 1905 between October 17 and early December known as the "days of freedom."

They discovered not only that there were efficient and legal workers' soviets in many Russian towns, but that the Tsar's manifesto had considerably expanded the scope of legal political activity. Everywhere in Russia social democracy was emerging from the underground; Party organizations concerned themselves less with faction fighting than with Party democracy, and a desire for unity between Bolsheviks and Mensheviks was eagerly expressed by workers at factory meetings, which Alexandra continued to address. She learned how closely intertwined in the workers' minds were the hopes for Party democracy and for healing the rift between the two factions, and she saw no hope of her working within the St. Petersburg Soviet unless there was some sort of formal unity between them. So when Bolsheviks and Mensheviks met immediately after October 17 to plan a joint council in which both might work for a reunited Social Democratic Party, she greeted this breakthrough with delight. Now she could contemplate continuing her innumerable small jobs for the Soviet, without these conflicting with her work for the Bolsheviks as treasurer of the St. Petersburg organization of the Party and as a Bolshevik agitator.

Trade unions sprang up like mushrooms, and day and night in the Technological Institute the Soviet sat and debated, its numbers steadily increasing under Trotsky's leadership to 550 delegates, representing 275,-000 workers. It was at a session of the Soviet shortly after October 14 that Alexandra met Trotsky for the first time. She was deeply impressed by his speech: "He had taken the measure of the soviet, intuitively grasped its significance, and with graphic clarity he went on to trace the tasks of this new organization of 'workers' unity,' which had not yet realized fully its own significance."[2]

Apart from arranging meeting places and finding speakers, delivering messages, and performing various other small jobs, Alexandra was responsible, as treasurer of the St. Petersburg organization of the Party, for ensuring a steady flow of funds to the Soviet. But since her Bolshevik Party comrades were anxious that strike funds should not be contributed directly to the Soviet, each organization was responsible for collecting the money separately, which led to an exasperating reduplication of paperwork. "I reckoned that the money collected through the St. Petersburg committee tied us up in red tape, and also that it cramped the initiative of the masses, who would far rather have made their donations directly to the Soviet. On this matter I had quite a few altercations with the St. Petersburg [Party] committee."[3] The Party strike fund was a deeply emotional business, to judge from an article in the Party workers' paper, *Workers' Thought*, at that time; of fifty-two paragraphs outlining its mode of operation, twenty-three dealt in painstaking detail with the structure and method of its work—and yet the strike-fund offices were constantly being raided by the police, who were thus provided with an endless supply of revolutionaries' names and addresses, and of money. Alexandra's differences, as treasurer, with the line of the Bolshevik-dominated St. Petersburg committee underlined her more serious differences, as an agitator, with the Bolsheviks as a whole.

Until Lenin returned to St. Petersburg on November 8, 1905, and encouraged a more favorable attitude toward the Soviet, most of the younger or more recently recruited Bolshevik agitators were plagued by the anti-soviet campaign of their elders. On the level of abstraction it was all very well to represent the soviet as the "spontaneity" of the labor movement, to be subordinated to the Social Democratic Party, which stood for the revolutionary "consciousness" of the proletariat. For Alexandra, as for various other agitators (including one young intellectual named Voitinsky, who had abandoned university studies for the Bolsheviks), the question was of passionate concern; they intensely resented the Bolsheviks' drastic attempts to turn the Soviet into a mere Party cell. Not only was this unworkable, a waste of agitators' valuable time in the factories and a cause of strained relations between Bolsheviks and the Soviet; it was also, more importantly, a waste of an invaluable opportunity to open up political discussion and work to non-Party workers. Right from the first day of the Soviet, Alexandra stood closer to Trotsky and the Mensheviks than to most of her Bolshevik comrades; as she worked to strengthen and preserve the Soviet it became possible to see the basis for a movement which would ultimately transform all revolutionary groups in Russia into a united Social Democratic Party, a true Party of the laboring masses.

Before 1905 it would have been hard to imagine a political party *less* working-class in its composition than the Bolsheviks. Professional revolutionaries like Alexandra generally came from educated families and many of them, like her, had small private incomes; they had time to study and the social confidence needed to make speeches and propaganda. After 1905, however, the Bolsheviks' social composition was radically altered by numbers of new recruits—the factory workers with whom Alexandra had been associating, young intellectuals like Voitinsky, and even groups of schoolchildren (many of them not much older than eleven-year-old Misha) who were caught up in this mass movement of protest and revolt, rebelled against their teachers, and formed their own schoolchildren's Bolshevik cells. The Bolsheviks now had to reconsider the iron discipline and organization on which they had based all their previous tactics. For many of them the habits of the underground died hard; but for Alexandra, the brief "days of freedom" spelled an exhilarating freedom from the rigors of illegal work.

An increasing number of factory women whom she began to meet were also emboldened during these days to attend strike meetings; few, however, of those who had bravely overcome their fears of arrest and of participating in mass meetings dared yet to speak up at these meetings for their own needs as strikers. It was after the Tsar's manifesto of October 1905 that an increasingly vocal and well-organized group of women in the Union of Women's Equality began to exhort women in Russia's factories to join the Union; it was only the Union, they said, that had leaders organized and articulate enough to campaign within the Tsar's Duma to improve working women's lives. Furthermore—as Union members stressed in a series of women's meetings which they organized throughout Russia after October—this campaign could only succeed if working women supported the Union in its struggle to win for propertied women the right to vote in the Duma.

Alexandra, along with a small but growing number of working women, attended a number of these meetings in St. Petersburg. There she heard Union leaders describe how their enfranchisement would open up a new era for working women in tsarist Russia, with freer divorce and legitimacy laws, the abolition of state-licensed prostitution, equal rights to the land for peasant women, coeducation, an end to militarism, and abolition of the death penalty. Alexandra had no illusions that to propose such reforms without acknowledging the necessity for a revolution against the autocracy—that is, to attempt to "liberalize" tsarism—was a hopeless and dangerous cause; the Union's faith in the reforming power of the Duma made nonsense of their slogans. The Tsar had ensured that the Duma, in which landowners were to have the vast majority of the seats, would be a body without any control whatsoever over the decisions of ministers, themselves directly answerable to the Tsar. It was to deal exclusively with minor budgetary and financial matters, although even this power was to be strictly subordinated to the Tsar's decisions. The Duma could not hope, therefore, to become a counterweight to the autocracy; "liberal tsarism" was a contradiction in terms.

It became alarmingly clear to Alexandra, however, that the feminists' slogans, their promises of sisterhood in a movement which united women of all classes, rang out for many working women with a quite captivating militancy. Unlike the very small number of male workers who were to be admitted to the Duma, working women were, like all women, to be excluded from it. For many of them, therefore, the mere prospect of representation there was one which for a while filled them with hope and overshadowed the more complicated issue of how propertied women, whose interests were so directly opposed to theirs, could be expected to represent them:

> The working women began to sense their inferior political status in terms of their sex, and were not yet able to connect this with the general struggle of their class. They had yet to find the path that would lead proletarian women to their liberation; they still clung to the skirts of the

> bourgeois feminists. And the feminists tried every means of establishing contact with the working women and winning them to their side.[4]

As neither Bolsheviks nor Mensheviks had any specific proposals for how working women might find this path within the Russian Social Democratic Party, it became for Alexandra a matter of intense urgency to convince these women that their struggle for a better life was best served not within the Union but within the workers' movement and its party, for the universal human liberation for which this party worked was linked both by the historical traditions of revolutionary Marxism, and by the inspiring practice of the SPD, with a commitment to women's liberation. To stand up at the feminists' meetings, as she frequently did, and shout "Paper promises!" was no way to organize a serious campaign of political enlightenment. But it was a start.

Tsar Nicholas II's manifesto increased the freedom of the press and the right to hold meetings. It also led those in the Union for Women's Equality to hope that their right to vote in his parliament of landowners —scorned by every Bolshevik—was not too far off. As the Union members exhorted factory women and domestic servants to sponsor their petition for admission, they also set to work to find more serious political allies; they confronted more opposition in the process than they had bargained for.

At the first congress of the Constitutional Democratic (Kadet) Party, founded in October 1905 by Peter Struve, Ariadna Tyrkova and Anna Milyukova were mortified by the flippancy with which their proposal for women's suffrage was greeted. Struve's strange argument against it, according to Alexandra, was that since Muslim law denied the vote to women of the East, it would be unreasonable for Russian women to demand this privilege; Milyukov, in an awkward political confrontation with his wife, emphasized that women's suffrage would offend against peasant values. Few of the working women who attended the Union meetings in those days can have had any idea of how low a priority their interests would have for the feminists as they engaged in this first political campaign within the Constitutional Democratic Party. The fact that this was the only party which appeared likely to provide the Union with the political allies it needed lent their campaign a special passion.[5]

The Constitutional Democratic Party (the largest liberal monarchist party formed after the manifesto) united a multitude of professionals, businessmen, landowners, and members of masonic organizations. If business and communications were not to grind to a halt in Russia, they maintained, a democratic system must be established immediately, with a Duma—based on universal, equal, direct, and secret vote—which would be responsible for directing government decisions. In 1905 only a very small number of Kadets were republicans. Most were convinced that the harshness of the autocracy could be modified and that the Tsar could be induced to relinquish his iron grip on the government and the Duma. It was in the Duma that they planned to express these demands. For Social Democrats, both Bolsheviks and Mensheviks, it was of prime importance to expose the Kadets' pious promises of social reform; for Alexandra, these promises differed little from those made by the Women's Union. Subsequently in the Duma Social Democrats would only have to mention specific and militant demands for an eight-hour day and a truly representative constituent assembly to send the Kadets scuttling, in fear of revolution, back to the Tsar's throne whence they had come. Alexandra's first attempts to employ similar tactics at Women's Union meetings had no such Party support, however; few Social Democrats considered it necessary to argue politics with feminists.

But by the end of 1905 there were at least four working women, Bolshevik and Menshevik, who were following Alexandra's example and angrily intervening at feminist meetings. It was quite a few months before they could summon up the confidence to risk the Party's disapproval and launch a more positive and organized campaign to draw some of Russia's women into the revolutionary movement. They could by then take heart from the many women who were already becoming disillusioned with the feminists—domestic servants, for example. One of the Women's Union's more ambitious schemes was "to organize servants according to its formula of an idyllic union of lady employers and their employees; the servants turned away and, to the chagrin of the feminists, transferred themselves to the Party of their own class, organizing their own special trade unions. This happened in Moscow, Penza, Kharkov, and other towns too."[6]

The feminists were not the only people at whom Alexandra directed her sarcastic repartee, but she certainly considered that their appeal to working women justified the most bitter and polemical attacks. Without understanding just how militant their language must have been for them to have persuaded so many women to abandon revolutionary politics and strike action for Women's Union meetings, it may be hard for us to understand why she assailed them so relentlessly.

That October she was provoked into another sharp exchange with a Kadet politician and philosopher named Pokrovsky. In an article of his

entitled "The Ethical Basis of Politics," which appeared in the conservative journal *Pole Star*, Pokrovsky announced that the socialist party was
a "Party of amoralists," more concerned with their own narrow class
interests than with the general good: why, he wanted to know, was
"proletarian morality" considered any better than capitalist morality?
Alexandra's reply to this and Pokrovsky's subsequent articles ran in three
issues of the progressive journal *Education*, which had published her first
article on Dobrolyubov. The answer was very simple, she said in the first
article, "The Problem of Morality from the Positive Point of View":
Pokrovsky was afraid of the proletariat and alarmed about his own precarious class interests. Of course, these sordid, selfish fears were veiled in talk
of "supra-class morality." But "however high these gentlemen idealists
soar in their attempt to rise above narrow class interests," they still retain
unmistakably all the features of their own class bias. The morality of the
ruling class means shooting workers. Is that done in the interests of the
entire Russian population?" How, therefore, could the metaphysical "idealistic" ethical principles, so fashionable among the ruling class in Russia
at that time, be credited when these were so clearly a mere veil for
brutality and class exploitation?[7]

The Marxists, on the other hand, believed, like the positivists before
them, that "morality arises because of the real mutual relations of people,
that it develops under precise social and economic conditions, since the
social cohabitation of people is morality's source, its cause, and its goal."
People created moral laws, she continued in her second article, in order
to protect social harmony, guarantee the survival of the group, and ensure
that no individual could pursue his own self-interest to the detriment of
that harmony. In a period of revolution people naturally challenged the
old moral imperatives and experienced a painful conflict between self-
interest and the larger good of society. The assertion of individuality, the
passion for Nietzsche and Kant, arose from these preoccupations, but they
could not serve the whole of society, for they were not based on the
empirical observations, fundamental to Marxism, of the moral laws of
social harmony.

This was why all talk of a "supra-class morality" was so absurd in her
opinion.

> The social democrats believe, that under the present social and economic
> relations, in this particular stage of our historical development, the inter-
> ests of the proletariat—and of no other class—correspond more closely
> than anything else to the highest and most general interests of the human

race; that it is the leading principles of this, and no other class, that most closely coincide with moral criteria that are fundamental to everyone.

For within the working class "values serve one single purpose and pursue one single goal: to validate and support community: in other words, the social cohabitation of people." These values she described as "solidarity, unity, self-sacrifice, and the subordination of private individual interests to the interests of the group." It was from these virtues that the working class would eventually derive its power to control the economy and create a new world "still far from us, [in which] there will no longer be any place for compulsion, and in which personal desires will correspond with social imperatives."

She envisaged a society in which individuals discovered both autonomy and collectivity. She did not explore the moral dimensions of this future society but described instead the moral imperatives which were demanded by the present period and which served that noble goal.

> As a goal, self-sacrifice, self-restraint, and self-denial in the interests of society are seen by the positivists as moral only when natural necessity causes them to flow out of living social interests.

She concluded her second article, rather more specifically, with a justification of the moral necessity of an armed uprising:

> When society as a whole is threatened by one social group, then self-defense, whatever form it may take, should be recognized as moral, and the principle of non-resistance to evil must be seen as the greatest moral crime.[8]

When Lenin returned to St. Petersburg on November 8, he was so filled with admiration for the way Bolsheviks and Mensheviks had buried their differences and were working together that he proposed that the two factions should hold separate simultaneous congresses to bring about a merger of all the Party organizations. But unification had already gone so far ahead that most Party workers regarded this as a quite unnecessarily complicated plan. There was no need to delay, said Martov; unification could go ahead immediately and there could be one Party congress to represent the newly reunited Party. The appeal of this plan was so great that Lenin eventually had to accept it; but the differences between the two groups remained, and there could be no thought of planning a joint congress before there had been a great deal of discussion.

Of all the issues separating the factions the peasant question was perhaps the most contentious. It was one on which Alexandra tended to agree with the Mensheviks and with their past year's campaign, in which they had urged liberal landowners and peasants to work together for social reforms in the countryside, using the *zemstvo* (the Tsar's provincial administrative organ) as their common platform. She had observed how throughout the months of looting and expropriations, in which peasant women participated and supported the men, the *zemstvo* not only provided a forum in which the women could stand up for their share of the redistributed pieces of land, but often forced the men to realize the purely economic argument behind demanding land for the "female souls" as well. The Bolsheviks, on the other hand, saw in this collaboration with the *zemstvo* a dangerous political compromise—a clear indication of the Mensheviks' liberal tendencies. The Bolsheviks' own program called for the land to be nationalized, but they did not elaborate satisfactorily how this would be carried out, nor, it seemed to Alexandra, did they have any very great understanding of the peasants' centuries-old desire for land.

Shortly after Lenin's return to St. Petersburg in the middle of November Alexandra made sure that she got an invitation to an illegal meeting at the Technological Institute at which he would be discussing the agrarian question with Martov before a small audience of about twenty people.[9] This was the first time she met Lenin in person. The agrarian question was briskly dealt with. Lenin did not particularly want to go into the Mensheviks' dubious liberal connections in the *zemstvo*; he wanted to get on to the thorny issue of Bolshevik-Menshevik relations.

Immediately after his return he had extended a cautious greeting to the soviet as "neither a parliament, nor a revolutionary organ of proletarian government, but a fighting organ for a specific purpose," and had suggested that all the flourishing new legal workers' clubs and unions could combine very well with the old underground apparatus, as long as they elected a central committee to keep them in touch with the Party. He wanted the Mensheviks to renounce their foolish hankering after a broader legal Party and for the abandonment of the conspiratorial tradition. As he argued with Martov, who sat at the table behind his customary mounds of paperwork, Lenin paced up and down before him, listening intently, knitting his brows, referring contemptuously to Martov's liberal alliances, and arguing that the only proper alliance in the actual making of the revolution was between workers and peasants.

It was only two weeks later that the full weight of Lenin's arguments for underground caution began to be felt. On December 2 the Bolshevik and Menshevik newspapers, *New Life* and *Beginning,* were closed down by the police, and Alexandra and eleven-year-old Misha waited for the inevitable midnight knock on the door. The following day the St. Petersburg Soviet published its categorical warning that the victorious revolution would honor none of the Romanovs' debts; the entire Soviet was promptly arrested. A state of emergency was declared in Moscow, more factory workers were locked out in St. Petersburg, and new barricades went up overnight. As people were killed in the ensuing street fighting, revolutionaries were caught and the committee of the Socialist Revolutionary Party was arrested. Workers resentfully went back to work. But in Moscow the fighting and lock-outs continued, and the losses were infinitely more serious; 400 were arrested, and 620 people killed. Large numbers of Social Democrats carried guns, but Alexandra preferred to avoid police attention with the elegant dress, combed hair, calm demeanor, and untroubled gaze of a "lady."

The "days of freedom" were over. On December 11 the Tsar announced the electoral qualifications and political composition of the new Duma. These were so grossly discriminatory that the Bolsheviks immediately declared themselves for a boycott—against the Mensheviks, who wanted limited collaboration with the Duma. Lenin was in no mood to collaborate with a lot of Kadets and music-hall peasants in the Tsar's graciously granted parliament and ferociously attacked all Menshevik sympathizers as "liquidators," plotting to disband the underground Party. Although it was true that many Mensheviks, defeated by the new onslaught of state repression, did drop out of revolutionary activities to work within the framework of the tsarist system, by no means all of them did so. The dreadful accusation of "liquidator" was nevertheless hard to shake off, as Alexandra discovered to her cost.

During the winter of 1905–1906, shortly after the "days of freedom" had ended, Alexandra joined the Mensheviks. She was prompted to do so chiefly by their tactical support for work within the Duma; even though Lenin himself was very shortly afterward to regret his initial hasty reaction against this pseudo-parliament, Alexandra was consistently to stand out for a far fuller use of it than the Bolsheviks were ever prepared to concede. She continued officially to be a member of the Menshevik faction for the next nine years. Since she spent most of these years in exile abroad, where Russian revolutionary organizations were ostensibly run by a united Social Democratic Party and where factional differences were less pronounced than in Russia, she took little part in debates between the two groups. Between 1905 and 1908, however, before she was forced to flee Russia as an exile, her Menshevik sympathies brought her into repeated conflict with the Bolshevik-dominated St. Petersburg Party committee. She first came to blows with this committee over the issue of working with the Soviet; later it was over her work with the women of St. Petersburg's Menshevik-led textile union, but the conflict she experienced most acutely in the winter of 1905 was that between Mensheviks and Bolsheviks over the issue of whether or not to participate in the Duma.

For the Bolsheviks that winter, just as unification plans were going ahead, a major fear was that the Mensheviks, once they occupied all the Social Democrats' seats in the Tsar's parliament, would then set about forming an alliance with the Kadets in order to hasten the bourgeois revolution. But there was a vast difference between the blinkered views of the more faint-hearted Mensheviks, who wished only for this, and the generous vision of many of them who, like Alexandra, outdid even the Bolsheviks in their antipathy to liberal alliances and saw the Duma not only as a platform for revolutionary propaganda but as a genuine rallying point from which mass strikes could be fomented. A number of Alexandra's fellow Mensheviks at this time even went so far as to accuse her of adopting an "anarcho-syndicalist" position—of seeing the revolution developing into a massive nationwide strike during which the workers would seize power.

Many other revolutionaries, most notably Rosa Luxemburg, were also disparagingly described as "syndicalists" by their more cautious comrades for their limitless faith in the workers' capacity for struggle. But for Alexandra, as for Rosa Luxemburg, the need for spontaneity and organization in the revolutionary struggle were of equal and interconnected importance. The truer syndicalists were to be found in France, Italy, and Spain, where Bakunin had in the 1870's so eloquently expressed to workers and peasants his instinctive faith in their spontaneous riots and strikes. It was there that syndicalism emerged as a coherent philosophy attacking the way in which, so it was felt, Marx's class analysis stifled people's natural revolutionary ardor. In Russia the dangers of state repression were too great for any revolutionary to imagine seriously that workers could topple the Tsar without the leadership of a disciplined party.

As regarded alliances with the liberals Alexandra felt that the Mensheviks seriously overestimated the power of their remorseless revolutionary logic. Her own experience of heckling had possibly led her to this conclusion. They planned to attack the Kadets with a rhetoric so resounding and ambitious that they would be incapable of answering back and would be driven against their will to adopting revolutionary resolutions.

By the end of 1905 this scheme was hardly realistic. Most liberal groups were either disintegrating or, like the Kadets, turning to the right; Alexandra saw this process most clearly at work in the Women's Union, whose 8000 members now varied too widely in their political views for it to be able to support its claim to represent a united women's movement.

In October 1905, when the Tsar announced his plans for the new Duma, he had slammed the door shut on "persons of the female sex"; Duma regulations expressly forbade women taking any jobs there but the most lowly positions as stenographers. After this blow many women from the Union and the Mutual Philanthropic Society were inclined to give up altogether on begging concessions from men in the main political parties, and on December 15 the conservative separatist Women's Progressive Party was launched almost single-handedly by Dr. Maria Pokrovskaya. A member of the Mutual Philanthropic Society since its formation in 1895, Dr. Pokrovskaya had for many years practiced among factory women, for whom she had a serious, if distant, regard. From long experience of treating prostitutes she had developed a powerful contempt for their clients, which she had projected onto the whole world of men and of conventional politics. The Women's Union allowed men to join; the Progressive Party not only excluded them as members but warned that any collaboration with the opposite sex would bring advantages to men alone. Its program included most of the feminist demands of the Women's Union, minus the broader social reforms, and stood out firmly for the gradual improvement of factory women's lives, rather along the lines of the first factory acts of the 1880's and '90's. When the Kadets eventually made support of women's suffrage a condition of membership, the Progressive Party, along with the Women's Union, found a natural home with them.

With a great many of the older and more conservatively inclined members of the Women's Union leaving in the winter of 1905 to 1906 to join Dr. Pokrovskaya's party, a group of articulate and radical feminists emerged within the Union. Determined not to allow their disappointment over the Tsar's decision to stand in the way of their suffrage campaign, they embarked on a search for political allies which split the Union in several directions. In the process the various parties which were to be represented in the Duma revealed their deep reluctance to discuss the needs of women.

For the ultra-conservative monarchist parties—the Russian Assembly, the Russian Non-Class Union, and the Monarchist Constitutionalists —which were deeply hostile to the idea of women's suffrage, the issue was a peripheral one, and they believed that the old autocratic basis of the family should remain. But most of the Kadets, for whom the issue was of more central importance, displayed an almost equal hostility to their women members' demands. When this party was first formed in October 1905 they had proved themselves less than sympathetic to the interests of middle-class women, and it was only after Ariadna Tyrkova confronted them irately at their party congress in January 1906 that a few members began to support the feminists' suffrage demands. For many months, however, the party was to be divided over the issue.

Members of another liberal monarchist party, formed at the same time as the Kadets and vying with them as the single strongest party in the Duma when it opened in April 1906, were inclined to lapse into obscenities or religious mumblings when discussing the issues of women's liberation. This party, the Union of October Seventeenth, was formed of wealthy businessmen and landowners, satisfied with the voting rights in the Duma which were granted to them by the manifesto; these "Octobrists," as they were called, regarded a rather more liberal autocracy as essential to Russia's industrial development. The extent of their liberal views may be judged, however, by their intransigent opposition to women's suffrage and their stress on the profound psychological gulf between the sexes and those "special, innately female" capacities for inordinate love and cruelty. Their program omitted any mention at all of the feminists' demands.

The Socialist Revolutionaries, heirs to the old populist traditions of sexual equality, had included a clause upholding universal suffrage "without distinction of sex" in their party's program in 1904. But throughout the following year at various meetings of the Peasant Union, upon whose support the Socialist Revolutionaries largely relied, a number of peasant delegates had voiced their objections to this principle. Peasant women began to demonstrate in force for their voting rights to the Peasant Union, so that when in the early months of 1906, the Peasant Union officially affiliated with the Socialist Revolutionaries, that party openly came out in support of women's equality. Its more conservative members were to be represented in the Duma by the newly formed Trudovik (or "Laborite") Party, and it was therefore to them that the radical feminists in the Union eventually addressed their petition for the vote when the Duma opened.[10]

The only other party, apart from the Socialist Revolutionaries, to endorse the principles of women's liberation explicitly, historically, and to some extent practically were the Social Democrats, who were certainly sensitive to all the baser forms of sexism that were current in tsarist Russia. It became increasingly clear to Alexandra that her Party would lose the support of large numbers of working women if it did not elaborate for their benefit its somewhat abstract revolutionary demand for universal suffrage and spell out the fact that the participation in the Duma of a few propertied members of the Women's Union would serve not to win the vote for all women, but only to perpetuate Russia's glaring class inequalities. The Social Democrats would therefore have to persuade the cruelly oppressed women of Russia's proletariat and peasantry that it was only by joining the Social Democrats as fighters for a socialist revolution and for the abolition of private property that working women would be able to introduce their own specific demands into the program of that party.

As the Women's Union started up an immense campaign to petition the Duma for an extension of the franchise, the more radical of its members addressed their own petition to the Laborite Party. At the beginning of 1906 they also opened their own club, the Women's Political Club, to promote this campaign, and for a while it attracted an impressive number of women workers, as well as a number of women Socialist Revolutionaries and even Social Democrats. They failed to persuade Alexandra to attend, however. For her this club represented just one more attempt by bourgeois women to introduce confusion among the politically inexperienced women of the factories by persuading them that the feminists could campaign for their interests. And those who formed the club were themselves equally confused in their politics, she felt: "They were unsure whether they should defend the interests of factory women, peasant women, or working women in general, and whether they should pursue exclusively feminist aims or involve themselves in more general political questions; shuffling indecisively between these alternatives, the club was doomed to a short existence."[11]

To judge from Alexandra's subsequent campaigning style among Russian working women over the next two years, she learned a great deal from the feminists' organizational talents, which were certainly impressive. By March the Women's Union had opened four women's political clubs, was sending women out to the villages and into the factories to secure signatures for their petition to the Duma, was holding meetings throughout the country, and was even invading the Duma cloakrooms and refusing to move, in true suffragette spirit. By then Alexandra had made firm friends with four working women, Bolsheviks and Mensheviks: Marusya Burko was a tailoress, Maria Antonova a weaver, Anna Semënova a textile worker, and Comrade Solovëva a typesetter. They were soon joined by several more women who spontaneously distrusted the feminists and wanted to rouse the women they worked with out of their passive ignorance. In the early part of 1906 this group began in a small way to coordinate their hitherto isolated and lonely attempts to explain the ideas of revolutionary Marxism on the women's question to working women and to embark on the infinitely more frustrating task of explaining its necessity to their suspicious male comrades—or rather, since the women's question was very far from most comrades' minds, not explaining anything at all unless they actually broached the subject. For the first few months of that year Alexandra and her new friends confined themselves to attacking complacency about the women's question at factory meetings and workers' clubs. On January 18 Alexandra gave a talk in Vilno on "The role of feminists and proletarian women in the women's liberation movement," which she wrote up as an article for the illegal paper, *Northwestern Voice*. [12]

Literature on the women's question was in woefully short supply; the only serious work was Nadezhda Krupskaya's illegal pamphlet, *The Woman Worker*. But since most of the women whom Alexandra and her Marxist friends were trying to reach were illiterate, literature was mainly needed as a guide to new agitators and as consciousness-raising material for men in the Party, most of whom were more interested in amassing large caches of guns than in attacking sexual prejudice.

Alexandra too, in her general agitation, made the call to arms a central part of her speeches. It was in Vilno, on the same occasion, that she called rather too openly for an armed insurrection against the Tsar; the hall was quickly filled with police, whom she managed to escape thanks only to the meeting's organizers, who smuggled her out through the police cordon and to a safe conspiratorial flat.

It was only when the Party sent her on these speaking trips outside the capital that she behaved in such an unguarded way. In St. Petersburg her concern for Misha, who was now at school, must have made her cautious. There were plenty of other twelve-year-old boys and girls, more neglected and angry, or perhaps less privileged, who were slipping into revolutionary meetings, throwing rocks at policemen, joining schoolchildren's "cells," generally living the life of the streets and looking admiringly up to their "elders"—fifteen-year-olds like Nikolay Bukharin and Ilya Ehrenburg who played such an important part in the underground Bolshevik Party; (indeed, it was discovered shortly after the 1917 revolution that something like a third of the Bolshevik central committee had joined in 1905 at the age of fifteen). Alexandra wanted no such precocious political experiences for her son and tried to spare him details of her Party work. This protective attitude toward Misha, evidently the result of much deliberation, guided her in her approach to the upbringing of her adolescent son. Never in any stage in his later life did he show any interest (beyond a general sympathy with his mother's work) in the complexities of political debate, and so we may conclude that she was successful in her aim.

Thanks to the chaotic state of the police force she was not yet on the wanted list in St. Petersburg despite the warrant for her arrest in Vilno. When she next met Lenin, early in 1906 in the offices of the short-lived legal Bolshevik newspaper *Forward,* it was to give him a message about the hiding of some guns. He broke off the discussion he was having when she came in and questioned her closely about the conspiratorial flat she had in mind, about the landlady, her neighbors, and the people who visited her. He warned her never to use an arms cache as a secret meeting place or hideout, and then asked her what she had written since her pamphlet on the class struggle had been confiscated.[13] She was by this time finishing her second work on Finland (a history of the Finnish socialist movement) and was also embarking on an ambitious collaborative writing project involving Bolsheviks and Mensheviks.

As the St. Petersburg party treasurer, Alexandra was always looking for new ways to raise badly needed strike funds. She hit on the idea of producing a workers' annual, which would contain bright and readable articles on the strike movement throughout the country, personal reminiscences by workers, biographies of socialist leaders, and political poems and feuilletons. The left Bolsheviks Bogdanov and Lunacharsky warmly supported the idea and promised articles, as did Martov and a friend of Plekhanov's called Vasilev. Plekhanov at first agreed to contribute, but he changed his mind when he discovered that Lunacharsky was involved, for Lunacharsky was beginning to show an interest in religious matters which alarmed many of his more orthodox Marxist colleagues. Still, Alexandra liked Lunacharsky and the friendship endured for many years. His numerous intellectual passions did not prevent him from writing with just the sort of simple enthusiasm she was looking for, and the first *Workers' Annual* (which came out later in 1906) contained a brief and lucid article by him on Mayday, the workers' holiday.[14] It also included her article "Who Are the Social Democrats and What Do They Want?" This was a popular and eye-catching piece, presented in short booklike chapters

124 | ALEXANDRA KOLLONTAI

entitled "An unjust system," "Can we remake the world?," "Where is the solution?," "Who are the socialists?," and "What are the Social Democrats demanding?"

Alexandra's main concern was that this publication should go a small step toward raising workers' morale and combating the disheartening effect she so feared of the Bolsheviks' boycott of the Duma. But her main anxiety, both in her agitational work and in her laborious advance toward some kind of organized women's work, was over the Bolsheviks' negative attitude toward the informal workers' clubs that had sprung up all through the past year in a distinctly "spontaneous" manner. It was in these clubs that she and her friends were planning to hold their first women's meetings.

Many male club members were less than enthusiastic about the idea of opening up what were often male sanctuaries to meetings for women only, and they found in the Social Democrats' general hostility to feminism a ready-made justification for their selfishness. They felt quite entitled, therefore, to combat "loathsome feminism" by locking up club rooms, tearing down information about meetings, going back on promises, and generally misinforming and confusing Alexandra and her friends with such wild hostility that they merely reinforced the certainty that separate women's meetings were sorely needed. Yet despite the enormous amount of extra and unnecessary work that all these confrontations involved, by March 1906, a month before the Duma opened, they were already able to hold a few women's meetings in the old workers' clubs beyond the Nevsky Gates, where Alexandra had taught her first evening classes eleven years earlier. Eleven years earlier, however, the Union of Struggle had regarded these small study groups as being of vital importance in raising workers' political consciousness and developing their skills in argument and negotiation. Now the Party was apparently too engrossed in its "urgent political tasks"; for "although in principle it recognized the usefulness of this kind of work, it did nothing to support the group's activities."[15]

Nor, much to Alexandra's disappointment, did Vera Zasulich, whom she visited for some advice on how best to organize a working-women's movement within the Social Democratic Party. As a member of the Land and Liberty Party in 1878, Vera Zasulich had captured the admiration of many women populists when, independently of all Party directives, she had calmly walked into the office of St. Petersburg's governor-general and shot him dead at point-blank range. Her action inspired many populists to carry out similar terrorist attacks and hastened their desire to organize the killing of the Tsar from within a new party, the People's Will. After her acquittal and her departure for Geneva, however, Vera Zasulich had soon been drawn to the longer-term Marxist perspectives of Plekhanov's Liberation of Labor group, as a member of which she had begun passionately to denounce the tactics of terror. By the time she returned to St. Petersburg after October 1905 she was also apparently renouncing the indignation she had so spontaneously expressed twenty-seven years before as a subordinate and a woman in the Land and Liberty Party. When Alexandra visited her in the spring of 1906, Vera Zasulich retorted that "she considered such an undertaking utterly superfluous, if not actually harmful";[16] for her, she insisted, as for all Marxists, there was no place for such sexually divisive ventures within the Party.

By the beginning of April the original planning group behind the women's meetings had expanded to include several craftswomen and servants, and more workers' clubs were overcoming their fears of feminism and granting the use of their premises. Alexandra was in close enough contact with the Party center to attend the numerous meetings that, in St. Petersburg and throughout the rest of Russia, were being called jointly by both Bolsheviks and Mensheviks. The Fourth ("Unity") Congress, which they were planning to hold jointly in Stockholm at the end of April, was eagerly discussed by party workers like Alexandra at meetings in the factories; she had high hopes that a newly reunified Social Democratic Party would emerge from this congress and she hoped to be elected as a Menshevik delegate. But the greater part of her imagination and energy in the spring and summer months went into assessing the proper political program to unite and expand the numerous small women's groups that were appearing in workshops and factories, eager for enlightenment. By the spring of 1906 Alexandra and her working women friends Maria Antonova, Marusya Burko, and Anna Semënova had successfully persuaded many women in these groups to attend women's meetings in the workers' clubs. With an almost complete lack of any Marxist literature on women in Russia (a lack which had been apparent to Alexandra since the mid-1890's), they relied chiefly on Nadezhda Krupskaya's booklet *The Woman Worker* (which had come out five years earlier) and elaborated together a rough and ready teaching program for these meetings, which they knew would be largely drawn up by the women workers who attended.

The first classes, which started in the spring of 1906, contained anything from twenty-five to thirty women and were "semi-legal"—which is to say that they would all gather at a union building or at a Sunday school under the guise of a delegates' assembly or a literacy class. Despite these precautions there was always at least one policewoman in the audience and sometimes two; so, quite apart from the complications of finding meeting places, it was necessary to verse the women in the risks involved in this continual police presence. But the greatest challenge, and ultimately the greatest strength, of the meetings came from the complete lack of suitable literature. Talks had to be spontaneous, political themes had to be quickly developed and graphically illustrated, and teachers had to concentrate on capturing the sympathy of their listeners. It was no wonder that for so many women who attended these classes and subsequently joined the Social Democrats, it was to the personal influence of Klavdia Nikolaeva, Maria Antonova, or Alexandra Kollontai that they attributed their political awakening.

It was not only working women who attended, however. Evgenia Fortunato—a conventional middle-class woman, like Alexandra in her thirties—was so moved by the excitement and spontaneity of her first meeting that she began to attend regularly. She had known Alexandra many years before when they both thought of little but society parties, dancing into the small hours, and secret raids on their families' libraries for the works of Ibsen, Sand, and Herzen. Hearing that her old friend was to speak at the Vorovaya Street workers' club, she went along and found her as elegantly dressed and coiffed as before, addressing her audience with all her old unaffected candor: "Believe me, I know the day is not too distant when we women will rule this country as the equals of our fathers, husbands and brothers. The main thing now is for us not to be isolated, not to hide from one another all the doubts and questions which together we can solve. Our unity is our strength!" She went on to talk of the strike movement of the past years, in which women had so thoroughly proved themselves the equals of men, and was greeted with applause so deafening that Evgenia anxiously searched the room for the police.

As they walked home together Evgenia Fortunato tackled Alexandra on the dangers of arrest. The dangers at such meetings were comparatively small, she was assured: police spies cared only for a woman revolutionary's hair and clothes, tended to snooze through meetings, and if the odd word did penetrate the haze of their ignorance, they generally interpreted it in the most conventional manner possible out of sheer laziness. They parted, but not before Alexandra had promised to keep her friend informed of every meeting she was to address, and from then on hardly a day passed when Evgenia Fortunato did not receive a note saying "this evening at Obvodny," "at Vyborg, both factories," "at the Vorovaya Street club."

She attended regularly, but she still found Alexandra's political transformation, her unstoppable energy, and her confidence quite mystifying. One foggy evening that spring as they walked home arm in arm from a meeting in a Vyborg factory she begged Alexandra to explain the process of her "rebirth." Alexandra reacted sharply against such an idea; she had cleared her mind in Zurich, she said, embarked on her socialist education much as they had gone about their secret reading as children, and still had to work hard to reshape her world and her consciousness.[17]

In February 1906 the Bolshevik-dominated Moscow regional textile-trade-union congress had passed an encouraging resolution: since women were less capable than men of defending themselves against the ravages of capitalism, delegates would ensure that all measures were taken to attract women on an equal basis with men into unions and all other workers' organizations.[18] Predictably there was no great rush to turn rhetoric into reality. But for hundreds of working women who had signed the feminists' petition, it inspired more hope than any resolutions that might come out of the First Duma, which opened that April and set to work abolishing some of the grosser inequalities of feudal tsarist law. Despite the fact that two thirds of the deputies were in opposition to the autocracy and in no mood to cooperate, women's appeals for the vote took a very low priority in their debates.

Appeals to conservative deputies' conscience and honor, such as were expressed in the Moscow Women's Union statement, issued in March 1906, were studiously ignored. "We women of Russia who have more than once demonstrated our undying love for the Fatherland . . . warmly protest against our exclusion from taking part in decisions which concern us . . ."[19] Such patriotism cut little ice with the rabid reactionaries of the monarchist parties. The Women's Union's petition to all the major parties of the First Duma, however, was taken rather more seriously, since it appeared above the signatures of hundreds of peasant and factory women: "We work as equals in the fields and factories, in science, literature, and art; in government, in public and private organizations as doctors and teachers; as rearers of the future generation. As taxpayers, workers, and obeyers of the law in the same measure as men, we need the right to make those laws."

The Duma was composed of 179 Kadets, an almost equal number of Octobrists, 94 Laborities (right-wing members of the Socialist Revolutionary Party), 44 of the extreme right, 44 representatives of various other nationalities, and 18 Social Democrats, all of them Mensheviks. After the preliminary draft of the main legal reforms had been agreed upon, one

Laborite stood up to make good his commitments to the 2000 signatories of the women's petition and proposed an amendment to include the demand for women's suffrage. He was supported by one Kadet and six other Laborites, and attacked by several other Kadet and peasant deputies. The extreme right jeered, the Mensheviks remained silent, and women's suffrage was pushed by a majority of votes into an inconspicuous package of paper reforms concerning religious, class, national, and sexual disabilities.

The Mensheviks' silence on this issue was only consistent with their policy of keeping their distance from all such half-hearted legislative games, and reserving their maximum demands and stunning rhetoric for the larger class demands of universal suffrage and an end to militarism. The "unity" congress had taken place in Stockholm three days before the Duma opened, and thenceforth most of the party organizations in Russia and abroad were, at least theoretically, under joint control. But any real hopes for unity had by December effectively been smashed, and it was only at the Mensheviks' insistence that the congress had been called at all. Although the Bolsheviks realized soon after the Duma opened that their boycott was quite needless, and although the Mensheviks' general tactics and conduct were hard to fault, Lenin urged his supporters to participate separately in the next Duma. They did not give the present one much longer, and they were quite right, for by July the Tsar had rejected its program and summarily dismissed it. At this the Mensheviks called somewhat optimistically for a general strike. But what followed were a number of strikes which attracted less than half the support of those of the previous year. Alexandra's women's meetings were inhibited by an ever heavier infestation of police, more and more revolutionaries were fleeing the country, and literature and propaganda were gradually being forced back underground.

It was precisely the kind of "semi-legal" political work in which Alexandra was engaged among the factory women that was hardest hit by this creeping repression of the post-1905 years. The political classes for these women which she and her friends organized in the workers' clubs had none of the party support or funds which could have helped out in a crisis; Alexandra's coorganizers had little experience of the caution with which any political propaganda had to be made, and the pupils themselves were all too likely either to risk arrest by expressing themselves too openly at meetings, or to lose heart altogether and stop attending. She certainly did not, like many Mensheviks defeated by the growing repression, advocate abandoning the illegal priorities of the Social Democratic Party, but two months after the classes had opened she was already beset by the difficulties of combining her commitment to them with her commitment to work for the Party, and of integrating this small but growing proletarian women's movement into that party. Beside these difficulties the differences between the Bolsheviks and the Mensheviks paled into insignificance for her.

Throughout the summer Alexandra had the chance to discuss these questions with Nadezhda Krupskaya, whose booklet *(The Woman Worker)* was being so eagerly read by her women pupils. But Nadezhda, traveling almost daily to St. Petersburg from Finland, where she was living in exile with Lenin, was more preoccupied with the Bolsheviks' election campaign to the next Duma than with women's work. By the late summer of 1906 most of the women's clubs, even including some of those attached to the Women's Union, had been closed by the police. It was hard to imagine how any sort of women's work might go forward without a firm guarantee from the Party to provide not only formal support but speakers, premises, literature, and money. It was only in September that Alexandra began to imagine this as a possibility.

6

Heckling the Feminists

Since the Duma first assembled in April 1906 Alexandra had been traveling frequently to Finland in order to attend meetings of the Finnish Social Democratic Party and to keep the Finnish Social Democratic deputies to their parliament, the Seim, in contact with the Menshevik Duma deputies. It is possible that the trip she made to the little Finnish town of Kuokkola that September was to visit the Lenins in the ground-floor flat they shared in the pleasant Villa Vaaza with Bogdanov, Zinoviev, and Kamenev, Lenin's old friends in the underground. It is more likely, though, that Alexandra had heard that Rosa Luxemburg was staying in the nearby *dacha* of a woman painter and was writing an article on the Russian revolution for the Hamburg Party paper.

Although Rosa Luxemburg had relied on Lenin and the Bolsheviks for most of her information, she was not very interested in the faction fighting within the Russian Social Democratic party and had repeatedly warned the SPD not to put its trust in either faction. She was confident, however, that the breach between them would eventually be healed, and she was also deeply excited by the very high level of working-class organization evidenced by the Russian strike movement; she was beginning to envisage the possibility of a truly revolutionary party growing out of a fusion between the Russians' spontaneity and the Germans' organizational methods. When Alexandra met her in the autumn of 1906 she was recovering from a recent prison spell in Poland and drawing on her experiences of the recent events in Russia ("the happiest months of my life") to write a report on the mass strike to present to an SPD congress later that month in Mannheim. Why didn't Alexandra go too? She could discuss some of her problems with Klara Zetkin and a number of other women in the SPD, who had organized their own congress, to take place shortly before the main Party congress.

Alexandra had always thought fondly of Mannheim in connection with her favorite poet, Schiller. (It is now of course an industrial town of such surpassing ugliness that it may be difficult to reconcile the reality with the place which existed in Alexandra's mind: the place perhaps for a sentimental rather than a political, pilgrimage.) But apart from a couple of surreptitious visits to SPD meetings in Berlin just before her marriage this was her first encounter with the awe-inspiring German Party and its exemplary women's section, whose membership in the years 1905 to 1907 alone leaped from 4000 to 11,000. By 1906 ten years' work by Klara Zetkin and a handful of friends was at last showing results; the principle of a division of labor within the party was now generally accepted, and fifty women SPD members (plus Alexandra and four other foreigners) were gathering to plan the first international socialist women's congress, which was to coincide with the seventh congress of the Second International in 1907 in Stuttgart. For Alexandra this meeting in Mannheim provided the inspiration which was to guide her in her approach to women's work when she returned to Russia.

First on the agenda at the Mannheim women's meeting was the crucial issue of women's suffrage. On this issue, as on so many others confronting the SPD, numerous Party members, terrified by the chaos of recent events in Russia, were abandoning their former militant demands; ominously large numbers of women in the SPD had been convinced by Bernstein's revisionist journal, *Sozialistiche Monatshefte (Socialist Monthly)*, to defer their struggle for the vote—a struggle which had until 1905 been officially integrated into the Party's campaign to enfranchise all workers, men and women. Articles in this journal had recently been suggesting that a working women's suffrage struggle was not in the best interest of the working class as a whole—that any separate women's organization went "against the nature of women and of mankind as a whole."[1] These views, which expressed the official revisionist line, found support among numerous women SPD members. But those like Klara Zetkin who opposed them, arguing that the SPD's universal suffrage campaign *must* embrace both men and women, had the Party's long traditions on their side, and they were in the majority.

This suffrage campaign, which had taken root thirty-one years before in response to the grossly discriminatory voting rights of the Reich (under which women and virtually all workers were disenfranchised), was both the precondition of the Party's existence and the key to most of its contradictions. Excluded from the vote, women who were socialists had naturally combined their own suffrage struggle with that of the similarly disenfranchised workers. It was in 1903, when the SPD had thrown an unprecedentedly large number of candidates into the Reichstag elections, that Bernstein and the revisionists had openly declared that women should abandon their struggle for the vote. "Stirring, not voting" was how they saw women's role in the election campaign, and it was thanks very largely to women's administrative and general "stirring" work that the SPD scored such an astounding electoral success that year. Along with the view that women should defer their own suffrage demands until universal manhood suffrage had been achieved went the conviction that they should campaign for factory reforms, insurance laws, and freedom of association, and generally learn how to practice some kind of equality in their everyday lives. The most eloquent proponent of these views was Lily Braun, whose book, *The Women's Question,* had so impressed Alexandra and was very well regarded in Germany. Shortly before the Mannheim congress Klara Zetkin had prohibited her from writing for *Die Gleichheit;* the debates between them were extremely acrimonious and did not bode well for a united German position at the Stuttgart congress.

In the intervals between sessions at the Mannheim women's congress Alexandra managed to talk to some of the organizers. From Luise Zietz, women's representative on the Party's executive, she learned about the women's section's agitational campaigns among peasant women and domestic servants. A former worker, Luise Zietz was one of the few Party radicals who was not an intellectual. When word had spread beyond her native Hamburg of her remarkable abilities as an agitator and organizer she decided to let her husband support her (which was considered highly unconventional) so that she could work full time for the Party's women's section. Alexandra also talked to Ottilie Baader, who had been active in the women's sections of the SPD since its formation and was guided in her work—as were Klara Zetkin, Luise Zietz, and Alexandra herself—by the works of Bebel and Engels. It was at this congress in Mannheim that Ottilie Baader was elected as central *Vertrauensmann (sic)* for German women (the congress tried to change the anomaly of her status by specifying that the word be used in its sexually neutral plural, *Vertrauenspersonen.*) With Klara Zetkin, Alexandra discussed the agenda of the main Party congress, which was to start in a couple of days' time, and at which Zetkin, as a member of the prestigious Party Control Commission and thus the voice of the women's movement, would have a considerable radical influence.

What Klara Zetkin did not tell her, however, was that a highly secret pact had been concluded between the Party and the unions, agreeing on parity between them on "all matters of mutual concern," and so investing the unions with the power to veto any of the Party's actions. In the wake of the Russian revolution the unions, flinching at the possibility of a repetition of these events in Germany, managed to turn the general strike into an unmentionable topic; the Party's previous support for strike tactics was reversed, and poor Rosa Luxemburg, the philosopher of the mass strike, arrived in Mannheim to find her enthusiasm for Russia branded as "anarcho-syndicalism" and her article mysteriously lost.

Germany had experienced strikes of such enormous scope the previous year that the mass-strike tactic—the main issue dividing radicals and revisionists—for a while overwhelmed all other topics of discussion in the Party. With half a million German workers withdrawing their labor in 1905 alone, the unions and their party representatives shuddered at the prospect of imminent revolution and refused responsibility either for organizing a mass strike or for supporting one with strike pay. The Party then declared itself prepared to do so "under certain conditions"—in other words, conditions of such total capitalist collapse that the workers would be required merely to deliver the death blow—and the whole topic, veiled in vagueness, was thus removed to a comfortably distant future.

With such a timid view prevailing, Alexandra's first experience of the mighty SPD was seriously disillusioning. After so many bland generalizations about the strike movement it came as no surprise that the past year's events in Russia were hurriedly passed over, and Rosa Luxemburg (who had not participated in the women's congress) was, much to her bewilderment, virtually denied the floor. At the many other workers' meetings in the town, however, Russia was an extremely popular topic. As soon as Rosa Luxemburg appeared outside the congress hall, formal agendas would be dropped and people would beg her to tell them about Russia, for from her work in the Polish Socialist Party after October 1905 she had derived a clearer and more positive insight into events in Russia than had any other member of the SPD. Her political work in Warsaw had been curtailed in March 1906 during the wave of repression there which accompanied the repression in Russia, and she had been thrown into jail. She was released five months later only to discover that another prison sentence hung over her in Germany for seditious remarks she had made at the SPD's Jena congress in 1905. Hence her retreat to the more secure hiding place of Finland, where Alexandra had met her.

Rosa Luxemburg's very great personal courage continued to exert an inspiring influence on Alexandra. Her assessment of the stages through which Russia's revolution passed between 1905 and 1906, although it made no mention of the activities of women, also evidently appealed to Alexandra. The pamphlet she wrote on Russia in Warsaw in 1906 *(The Days of the Revolution: What Next?),* however, was certainly closer in spirit to Lenin than to the Mensheviks:

> In the first phase of the revolution the army of the revolutionary proletariat assembled its forces and brought together its fighting potential. In the second phase this army achieved freedom for the proletariat and destroyed the power of absolutist rule. Now it is a question of removing the last shreds of the tsarist government; to get rid of the rule of violence which hinders the further development of proletarian freedom.[2]

"The Russian proletariat must be our example," she urged workers at meetings in Mannheim during the Party congress, "not for its parliamentary action but by its resolution and daring in putting its political aims just as high as the historical situation permits."[3]

The only other person with whom Alexandra was able to discuss events in Russia, and particularly the issue of participation in the Duma, was Karl Liebknecht, himself a Reichstag deputy and sensitive to all the anomalies of his position. She met his Russian wife, Sophie Borisovna, who had been studying in Berlin, and between sessions she managed to take time off to walk with him in the nearby Heidelberg hills and discuss Russia; for "of all the leaders of the German Party only he was able to discuss Russian questions in full detail, and he was always informed about our doings."[4] He was also one of the few men in the party who managed to treat women without a hint of the condescension evidenced increasingly in recent years by so many SPD members toward the women's sections and their leaders. (Much vilification of Liebknecht and his radical politics centered on the fact that his two chief associates on the Party's left wing were women—Rosa Luxemburg and Klara Zetkin.)

The most usual attack on the women's section was supported by the exasperatingly inconsistent argument that their theory and agitation were not justified by the small number of women recruits and that women's position could not be so bad if such excellent spokeswomen as Klara Zetkin and Ottilie Baader could be found. "The nervous excitement of our women is easy enough to understand if we remember that despite years of exhausting work they have had only a minimal success and the few who have to do the work become bad-tempered," said Ignaz Auer at a Party congress in 1900.[5] Alexandra, accustomed to cruder types of merriment at the expense of the women's movement, was a stranger to this kind of impeccably bourgeois insult, in which bad temper was considered proof of bad politics.

Liebknecht was happy to hear Alexandra's views on recruiting young people into the Party. He felt that the best way to attack militarism was to open up the Party to people young enough to be radicalized before they could be conscripted, and he had organized a youth congress which was to start in Mannheim a few weeks after the main congress ended. His campaign made him a remarkable number of enemies. Bebel accused him of "undermining the Party executive," and most members considered that to attack the army was quite beyond the present powers of the Party. It was Klara Zetkin who suggested some link between the Party's fear of the young and their growing distrust for women's party work. She reminded them of Engels's words that revolution must be made by converting the soldiers. "Young people are the most reliable force to keep us in continuous intellectual and moral development, to prevent us from rusting and resting," she said. "At the side of us adult fighters whose duty is to weigh and consider, there must be younger elements too, with the will to risk and dare."

"An inward impulse drives me from repose, impelling me on to achieve my work . . ."—with these lines from Schiller's play *The Maid of Orleans* running through her mind, Alexandra left Mannheim. Eighteen months of isolated struggle had been rewarded by gratifying evidence that the work of the women she had just met was committed to defend revolutionary perspectives against all forms of narrowness, whether of the sexist, or the trade-unionist, or the nationalist variety. She was confident that her comrades could be persuaded to accept the German way of working—"the fusing of the male and female halves of the working class in the Party organization, while retaining autonomy of agitation among women of the working class."[6]

This was the theme both of an article she wrote on the congress for the Menshevik journal, *Contemporary World,* in the winter of 1906,[7] and of the talks she addressed to the men and women who attended the workers' clubs. But the persuasive passion she brought back from Germany fell on deaf ears. Her proposals for a separate women's organization were enthusiastically welcomed by almost every working woman she met, but it seemed as if no amount of enthusiasm was going to urge the older male Party members out of their indifference, skepticism, and even downright hostility to such a scheme. Their fears about her "dangerous deviation to feminism" made argument difficult and overwrought, and although she was arguing virtually on her own against the entire St. Petersburg Party committee, this did not prevent a great many hostile and unforgivably underhand maneuvers against her in the following months.

After much prevarication the Party committee agreed to let her hold a working-women's meeting at which the idea of some special women's bureau in the Party would be discussed. Arriving at the hall, however, they found to their distress that it was locked up and a message pinned to the door saying: "Meeting for women only postponed—Meeting for men only tomorrow." The worker accompanying them there was an old friend of Alexandra's called Silnov, from the Nevsky factory; deeply embarrassed by this unfunny prank, he invited them to hold their meeting in his room. But the tactic had its intended effect. The women decided they were too few and too weak to set up their own organization, and when Alexandra went to the Party committee to ask for some rather more positive support, she left with the assurance that they would not offer any resistance—or any support either. They were not at all bothered by her arguments that not only had the Party failed to provide any real base for working women but that it was losing numerous women students and intellectuals to the feminist organizations; the feminists' petition to the Duma had received enough attention from the Laborites to draw large numbers of women Social Democrats and Socialist Revolutionaries to the Women's Union.

However, many working women were beginning to find a more satisfactory alternative to the Women's Union in the St. Petersburg workers' clubs, which Alexandra and the small group of women organizers continued to address. Each of these generally included no more than about a dozen women among their 600–900 male members, but already a sizeable number of working women in Moscow and other towns were plucking up the courage to join similar male-dominated workers' clubs.

In shared work and in the steady struggle to make Russian workers and their Party conscious of the needs of working women, Alexandra was to find her closest friends and allies, between 1906 and 1908, in working women organizers like Marusya Burko, Anna Semënova, Maria Antonova, and Comrade Solovëva. Among the small number of women in the Social Democratic Party, most of whose emotional allegiances were to the male majority, Alexandra was an exception; among women of the middle class, where she apparently had few friends, she was equally exceptional. Her struggle against both her party and her class was therefore a particularly solitary and difficult one. In her anxiety to give Misha some sort of stable and loving home life she must have felt her isolation most deeply; if the

Social Democratic Party had shown itself so indifferent to the infinitely more intolerable burdens placed on working women, how much less sympathetic must they have been to the pains and anxieties of unsupported middle-class mothers.

Early in 1907 Alexandra's group of working women friends was joined by a number of others. Anna Osipova was a Bolshevik textile worker; there was also a Bolshevik nurse called Efremova, of whom Alexandra was especially fond; then there was young Klavdia Nikolaeva, a typesetter, who had joined the Bolsheviks at the age of fourteen in 1905 and later rose high in the Party, as did two other friends (former Bestuzhev students), Konkordia Samoilova and Praskovia Kudelli. These two women Bolsheviks, possibly Alexandra's only middle-class women friends in 1907, had been teaching for some time at workers' evening classes. They took enthusiastically to their teaching assignments with women at the workers' clubs and became extremely popular (Konkordia Samoilova under her Party name of "Natasha"). Throughout the winter of 1906 and the following spring these women saw a great opportunity for expanding the scope of these classes by bringing them to the attention of the Social Democratic Duma deputies, who were beginning to arrive in the capital from their constituencies all over Russia in preparation for the opening of the Second Duma in March 1907. For Alexandra and her friends in both Bolshevik and Menshevik factions, there were innumerable jobs for these deputies to do.

There were 65 Social Democratic deputies altogether, 36 Mensheviks, 18 Bolsheviks, and 11 unaffiliated Social Democrats. By February 1907 most of them had arrived in the capital. They were harassed by the police as soon as they got there, isolated and restricted in whom they saw and where they went, and their difficulties were further complicated by the fact that they had all (young intellectuals to a man) classed themselves as peasants in order to satisfy the Duma's class requirements. Contacts like Alexandra enabled them to keep in touch with their constituents and to contact workers in the capital in the month before the Duma opened. Alexandra delivered messages to Party branches about the times of meetings, she was involved in carrying a highly illegal direct appeal to the barracks urging soldiers to form their own revolutionary cells, and she took messages of support to the deputies' headquarters, intercessions from workers' clubs, and even the demand from some women in these clubs that the Social Democrats specifically include women when calling in the Duma for universal suffrage.

Such demands, Alexandra realized, could not, however, hope to match the second immense campaign launched by the Women's Union for their admission to the Duma. Of the 26,000 signatories to their second petition the vast majority were working women. The Women's Union had by now found massive support among working women for their "sacred cause." It became increasingly clear to Alexandra that the hard-line speeches which the Bolsheviks were preparing to address to the Duma would win them few supporters among those women workers whose interests the Women's Union claimed to represent. On the complicated issue of how the Duma could best be used as a propaganda platform, Alexandra was in full agreement with her fellow Mensheviks and could only deplore the Bolsheviks' intransigent tactics.

Formally the two factions were agreed to act as a united party within the Duma; in fact there was little agreement between them about how to conduct themselves most effectively in this pseudo-parliament. The most extreme of the left Bolsheviks, who had initially held out for a boycott of the whole procedure, were eventually overridden by the Bolshevik majority, who drew some tactical advantage from this intransigence; the extreme group became known as "ultimatists" for their advocacy of a stiffly worded statement, to be read without expression and followed by a walk-out. The Mensheviks did not question the need for this extreme sloganeering, but neither were they going to pass up the opportunity for an argument; they wanted to use the Duma to create as much debate as possible.

The two factions' responses to the feminists' petition illustrated these differences quite clearly. The 104 Laborites, 98 Kadets, 37 Socialist Revolutionaries, and 16 populists to whom the petition was sent managed not to mention it once. It was the Menshevik deputy, Saltykov, who stood up to urge that women be admitted. The Bolshevik Alexinsky then gave the subject the ultimatist treatment—declaring that "the women's question will only be resolved with the final victory of the proletariat," and walking out. Fortunately Alexandra was saved the ordeal of further arguments with the ultimatists, for by the spring of 1907 the Bolshevik majority on the St. Petersburg Party committee was sufficiently alarmed by the feminists' petitioning powers to give their support to a series of women's meetings organized by Alexandra's friends in the Menshevik-dominated St. Petersburg textile union.

Two years after the revolution, factory inspectors were attributing the greatly increased numbers of women in the textile industry to their industrious, submissive behavior and the fact that women were less likely to drink and smoke. Although it was certainly true that women rarely asked for equal wages (and some strike demands included an explicitly lower wage for women), large numbers of women were joining the unions in the hope of gaining more urgent improvements in their working conditions. In the town of Ivanovo-Voznesensk near Moscow, for instance, where something like half the textile union members were women, strikers in 1907 demanded that women should get half a day off every week so that they could do the laundry. It was just this sort of practical matter that women wanted to discuss at the meetings which started up that April under the auspices of the Party.

Alexandra and other seasoned Party agitators would present twenty-minute talks on maternity care, factory hygiene, or workers' clubs in England to a rapt audience in the sumptuous mansion of the philanthropic Nobel family. It was only in the final minutes of their talk that they would quickly develop the themes of oppression and revolution; if on any occasion the police seemed particularly zealous, they would rely on a single word or nuance to make their point:

> The atmosphere was electric, the large hall was full to overflowing. Members of the textile and needlewomen's unions, typesetters and workers from the many enterprises on the Vyborg side were among those who attended . . . The feminists, significantly, did not dare send representatives; the dividing line between them and the growing women workers' movement was now more sharply drawn.[8]

Many in the audience, including the police, learned for the first time about the revolutionary Party's hostility to the feminists. For the police this presented quite a problem. After a couple of years' experience of feminist meetings they had grown restrained at women's gatherings, and it was rarely and reluctantly that they ever closed meetings at the Nobel house. The uneasy peace was soon broken, however, when one of the meetings coincided with a strike at one of the Vyborg factories, and the audience poured out into the street to put the speaker's precepts into practice. There were no arrests in the ensuing confrontation with the police, but from that day on meetings were banned, and the Party committee eventually decided to support the legal women's meetings at the workers' clubs.

But as the Social Democrats continued with considerable courage to harangue the tsarist Duma throughout March and April 1907, even these legal activities were gradually driven underground. In May all fifty-six of the Social Democratic deputies were arrested in a spectacular and highly ominous round-up: charged with organizing a military section of the Party to bring about an armed insurrection, being in contact with criminal societies, calling for the violent establishment of a democratic republic, and possessing forged passports, they were imprisoned under the harshest of conditions. For six months fifty-five of them (one turned informer) languished in prison refusing to talk, and at their closed trial there were violent scenes, shouted protests, and revolutionary slogans; they received long terms of imprisonment at hard labor in conditions so foul that many went mad and a few killed themselves. Alexandra and a number of other Social Democrats contacted Karl Liebknecht, who campaigned for their release for the next seven years with a group of foreign socialists in the Second International. After she left Russia for exile in 1908 Alexandra was to commit herself more actively to this campaign.

In Russia the possibilities for legal political work were dwindling daily. Alexandra looked forward to some encouragement from the International congress in Stuttgart in August, which she was to attend. As the only Russian delegate to the first International Congress of Socialist Women, which was to precede it, she wanted to be able to secure from the Russian Party a serious commitment to support a special women's section of the Party on the German model; they no longer needed to be convinced of the benefits of the women's clubs, also modeled on the SPD women's self-education circles. Alexandra and her friends were now intervening at feminist meetings with the approval of the Party, and these troublemaking activities were becoming quite popular among the bolder spirits. But all this was of little direct help to the masses of "gray" women, unenlightened by politics, and that spring she wrote her first article explicitly calling for a women's section of the Party. "What Is Done in Russia to Protect the Labor of Women Textile Workers?" was not published, however, until the early months of 1908, perhaps because she wanted this audacious demand to follow on the resolutions passed at the Stuttgart congress, to which she had been invited by the women she had met in Mannheim.[9]

Alexandra was the only Russian delegate at this gathering of fifty-eight women from the socialist parties of fourteen countries. The main organizer of the women's congress was Klara Zetkin, who invited both Alexandra and Rosa Luxemburg to stay in her home. The delegates had only two days, from August 17–19, 1907, in which to work out resolutions on women's suffrage and the establishment of an international women's bureau that they could present to the main International congress in Stuttgart. They set to work with great enthusiasm and speed:

In contrast with women's usual meek and mild ways, here the atmosphere was charged with excitement—quite unlike the somewhat lifeless efficiency of the main socialist congress. That bulky organization [*about 900 delegates attended*] imposed the need to observe a whole range of formalities which cooled the enthusiasm of the representatives of the socialist world; only in rare moments was this enthusiasm allowed to show itself and seize the minds of the audience.[10]

The previous year all the parties in the International had been polled on the question of women's suffrage. Although most of the replies had been positive, they had been given grudgingly; the fifth clause of the International's universal suffrage program—"without distinction of sex"—had not yet entered the flesh and blood of social democracy. It was Klara Zetkin, in her opening speech at the main International congress, who urged that "there are principles which the working class cannot, in its own interests, sacrifice; there are slogans which the proletariat cannot change, to gain greater results at certain moments, without seriously harming itself."

Alexandra spoke to support Klara Zetkin, and most of the sixteen women in the German delegation also voted to stipulate that the International give high priority to women's voting rights in their universal suffrage campaign. But a large number of women opposed them for various (but essentially similar) reasons. The seven Austrian delegates and their popular working-class leader, Adelheid Popp, spoke on behalf of a powerful women's movement in their country, whose journal, *Arbeiterinnen Zeitung,* had for the past year been urging its 10,500 readers not to violate the laws which forbade women from attending meetings or to engage in the women's suffrage struggle, but to join mass demonstrations against inflation and unemployment. With a timidity which Alexandra 'found appalling, they all but repeated the words of Adler, the Austrian Party leader, who had persuaded them that since votes for men now seemed a real possibility, women's suffrage demands were "untimely." The Belgian delegate and the three French delegates also accepted deferment of their political rights until men had won theirs, justifying this faintheartedness by pointing to the ever-present Catholic Church and its power to call a halt to any more radical demands. With them voted Lily Braun; despite her renegade revisionist views and her many enemies in the German women's movement, Alexandra got to know and like her, responding to the warmth of her "striking and original personality."[11]

Another friendship she made in Stuttgart was with the English Marxist Dora Montefiore, who had joined the Women's Social and Political Union when it first formed in 1903. Under the leadership of Emmeline Pankhurst the WSPU aimed to get the Independent Labour Party to put votes for women into its program. In the ensuing defeats for their cause in Parliament, the members of the WSPU left the ILP for their own independent campaign, accepting that only when propertied women had won the vote could this right then be extended to all women. Their campaign of demonstrations, heckling, and confrontations with the police was to earn them the name of "suffragettes." Dora Montefiore, a member of England's supposedly Marxist Social Democratic Federation, was outraged by the hostility to women's rights expressed by Hyndman and most of its other leaders, and to counter these views she fought within the SDF to integrate into its program the demand for all women to be enfranchised. The result of her labors was the small SDF-sponsored Adult Suffrage Society, committed to winning the vote for women of all classes (she apparently gave Alexandra a rather over-favorable impression of this small group as a revolutionary Marxist alternative to WSPU feminism). The only ASS delegate in the nineteen-strong English delegation, Dora Montefiore was the one person to dissociate herself from their argument that the property qualification would lead to the eventual enfranchisement of all women. She dissociated herself also from their bitter attack on the German delegation's "intolerant attitude" to feminism, a criticism warmly endorsed by the French.

The Finnish delegate, Ida Terssinnen—a deputy to the Finnish parliament (the Seim) and an old friend of Alexandra's—voted with the Germans, as did the representatives of the Hungarian and Swedish women's movements. For these less vociferous delegates the main points of interest were the German proposals for an international women's bureau, which was to keep the socialist women's organizations in touch with each other and keep them informed on the progress being made by various countries involved in the women's suffrage movement. Fear of the charge of separatism colored Alexandra's later defense and description of this bureau's function. It was not to enable women to "fight separately for their political rights . . . but to expose from within the Party how it oppressed them, and to force their comrades to take up the cudgels on behalf of proletarian women, for whom the question of becoming involved in political life is becoming increasingly urgent with every year that passes."[12]

The fear of separatism amounted to near paranoia, however, in the case of the Austrian women: in order that women might avoid accusations of "isolationism" for the sake of an extra and unnecessary organization, they proposed that one member of each national party be charged with keeping foreign socialist newspapers informed of any events relevant to the women's movement. This weak proposal was outvoted, plans for an international bureau were accepted, and *Die Gleichheit* was accepted as the paper of the international women's movement.

Speaking on women's suffrage, Klara Zetkin had said, "We are not so naïve as to demand that the workers' parties of all countries make it the cornerstone of their politics; how far they take the issue depends on the conditions obtaining in each country." The issue was in fact placed at the end of a crowded agenda at the main International congress, which reflected the Stuttgart delegates' overriding anxieties about the threat of war. The question of militarism naturally took first place, followed by the contentious issue of the relations between parties and unions. Women's suffrage and organization was to follow a discussion of the colonial question and the closely connected problems of the immigration and emigration of labor.

Klara Zetkin had consistently used the pages of *Die Gleichheit* to attack the growing military might of the German Reich and the squalid imperialistic attempts of both Germany and France to govern Morocco; she had also pointed out, in speeches and articles, that the Algeciras conference of the previous year had ranged England, Italy, Russia, Spain, and France against Germany and Austria for a war that seemed increasingly likely. As an organizer of Liebknecht's campaign against militarism and of the Socialist Youth congress which was to follow the International in Stuttgart, she was able to speak in the main debate. It was as urgent, she said, to free women from their slavery as it was to save the young from being slaughtered in war. The proletariat would never win their battles without women: the women of the Socialist International could play a vital part in attacking the European arms race which was making war appear increasingly inevitable.

In Stuttgart Alexandra joined Trotsky, Lenin, Martov, and various other Russians in the united Russian delegation. None of them spoke at the congress. Lenin was satisfied that Rosa Luxemburg could represent his views better than he could—and since every party was under extreme pressure to define precisely its obligations in case of war, conciseness was essential. The French tended to the syndicalist view that the socialists could actually avert war and that the moment of its declaration could be synchronized with a vast and crippling strike. Bebel weighed in with a lengthy call for the working class of each country to prevent war by all means possible, including strikes at armaments factories and refusing war credits.

Rosa Luxemburg had not joined the women's congress. She had saved her genius for cogent argument to compose a brilliant synthesis of the French and German positions. In the name of both Polish and Russian delegations she proposed an amendment which was finally adopted: "Agitation in case of war must be aimed not only at ending that war but at using it to hasten the general collapse of class rule." It was not until seven years later, when it was tested by the catastrophic reality of the 1914 war, that Alexandra's emotions prevailed for a while over her reason and she flinched at the terrifying militancy of that resolution.

The congress itself was quite remote from the realities of her life in Russia. When Trotsky's friend, the English delegate Quelch, was expelled from Germany for his insulting references to the Reich, Trotsky was reminded of a schoolroom "where a rude boy is told to leave the room and the rest remain silent. Behind all the SPD's power in numbers one discerned all too clearly the shadow of its impotence."[13] Valuable time was wasted discussing a proposal from the Dutch and Germans on the "possibly progressive nature of colonialism under socialism," and Alexandra found the spectacle of the "kings of eloquence" sharpening their weapons a disheartening spectacle: "Experienced in all the fine points of parliamentary battles, it was probably for just that reason so many of them sounded so very cautious."[14]

And it was not only radicals who would be contrasting the cautiousness of this congress with the militancy of the women's congress preceding it.

> However radical the men's speeches, whatever "insane" resolutions they might have adopted, the bourgeoisie could always be consoled by the knowledge that one sure resource was available to them: to break the opposition of the "hotheads" and replace them with submissive women workers. But then look what a surprise! From all corners of the earth women representatives of the working class got together . . . And if only recently the bourgeoisie sought comfort in the isolation of the female half of the proletariat, that sweet hope was dashed after the Stuttgart congress.[15]

She spoke from experience, for shortly after returning to St. Petersburg at the end of August she was summoned to police headquarters to answer some questions about the purpose of her trip abroad. Fortunately she was able to speak to them in the imperious manner appropriate to General Domontovich's daughter and, incredibly, convince them that she had visited Germany to order gowns and toiletries for the winter season. Incapable of challenging such an alibi, the police let her go. But Stuttgart had raised far more exciting prospects than toiletries. With the Party now officially committed to supporting legal women's work (and any idea of illegal work had been virtually out of the question since the dismissal of the Second Duma that July), Alexandra and her friends in the textile union began with great excitement to make plans for a women's club.

The first thing was to find suitable premises, and that autumn they found the ideal building in Predtechenskaya Street, near Ligovka, where the textile union had its headquarters. It was out of the question to ask the Party for any financial support of course, and Alexandra and her friends spent a great deal of time arranging benefit concerts and lectures to get it started. They had great and expensive ambitions. It was planned to turn one of the club rooms into a cheap buffet, so that women working in the area might drop in for tea and sandwiches and stay for the lectures. Another scheme was for the club to sponsor a summer camp to enable those who all too rarely had a holiday to get away from the city for a while. When all these plans were well advanced, Alexandra approached the St. Petersburg committee, secured their support for this "non-factional" venture, and in the winter of 1907 they were ready to open up their club under its disarmingly innocuous and hospitable name, the Women's Mutual Aid Society.

Though membership was open to men, only women were to be involved in the running of it, and on the opening night the club room was packed with women. Alexandra was in an exceptionally buoyant mood, and even Vera Zasulich, apparently regretting her previous hostile views toward the scheme, turned up and liked what she saw. The club was open every evening, and it was not long before some 200 women and 100 men were regularly coming along to use the library, meet friends in the canteen, and attend lectures on various subjects, ranging from the theory and history of socialism to the practical needs of women at work. Especially popular as a speaker was a friend of Plekhanov's, Dr. Vasilev, who had collaborated with Alexandra on the *Workers' Annual.* She and the women in the organizing group were also very popular, so much so that they were soon receiving more invitations than they could accept to speak to meetings in other parts of the city.

In the winter months of 1907, as Alexandra saw one club after another closed down by the police, comrades arrested, friends' flats ransacked by the police, and large numbers of friends going into exile to avoid arrest, almost all legal work had to be coordinated with the Social Democrats—Bolsheviks and Mensheviks—in the recently opened Third Duma. All meetings she addressed were conducted in an atmosphere of terrible strain, and not a day passed when she did not fear arrest and its painful consequences for Misha. She made many new and lasting friendships among the factory workers of the city and was able to use her experience of the feminist meetings to encourage them to speak up and argue at the workers' clubs. But that winter she had more particular reason to fear arrest. It seemed only a matter of time before the police confiscated her pamphlet, *Finland and Socialism,* which had appeared the previous year and in which she had described the reverberations of Bloody Sunday in Finland and given a highly optimistic assessment of the Finnish workers' fighting forces in their inevitable confrontation with Russia. It was on the basis of this and her previous writings on Finland that she was invited by a group of Social Democrats in the Duma to join a special commission on Russian-Finnish relations. For the next few months her trips to Finland would be followed by meetings at the Tauride Palace, where the Duma held its sessions.

Once again she saw how Bolshevik and Menshevik attitudes to the Duma were reflected in their attitudes toward women's organization. Even though unity in the face of the enemy demanded that deputies present the same slogans, a very considerable number of left Bolsheviks were now for withdrawing from the Duma altogether, and these "recallers" urged on the others (most of them "ultimatists") to an even more drastically uncompromising style of delivery. By the spring of 1908 the St. Petersburg committee, acutely sensitive to its own compromised stance in the Duma, was ready to see the Predtechenskaya Street club as the thin end of a feminist wedge in the Party. Meetings were increasingly disrupted by angry slanging matches between various Social Democrats and a group of working women who were so sick of these political recriminations that they demanded that all "intellectuals" be banned from attending. Alexandra tried in vain to point out that this would leave the club without any library, treasurer, or discussion program, but after many fruitless attempts to make the peace she found the whole conflict too draining to be worth her while and withdrew from the club that spring to embark on another plan to involve women in politics—a campaign no less fraught with conflicts.

As early as 1902, seven years after its formation, the Mutual Philanthropic Society had received permission from the Interior Minister to hold a congress in St. Petersburg. For the next three years the plan was obstructed by a series of excuses and delaying tactics, and by June 1905, when it was at last set to go ahead, the new minister had decided it might be an encouragement to "dangerous ideas" and it was banned. By the time the revolution had been beaten back at the end of 1907, however, the authorities looked much more kindly on the venture, and permission was eventually given for the First All-Russian Women's Congress to open on December 10 of the following year in the magnificent Alexandrovsky Hall of the Tauride Palace. It was to be a formal, ticket-only affair attended by about 1000 feminists and various sympathetic politicians and professors who would discuss the results of the past years' campaigns and lay broad and general plans for future work against alcoholism and prostitution. There would be a report on the suffrage campaign and the various attempts to improve factory conditions, and the whole proceedings would take place under the slogan "The women's movement must be neither bourgeois nor proletarian, but one movement for all women."

By the spring of 1908 there was so much talk of this congress among the feminists' servants and nannies, very few of whom were invited to attend, that Alexandra determined to use its slogan to rally working women to challenge, through some organized intervention, the notion that any movement could unite women whose class interests were so diametrically opposed. She found general support for the principles of this scheme from Lyubov Gurevich, Olga Volkenstein, and Morgulis, the same socialists with whom she had attended the Women's Union's first founding meeting in 1905; she was also supported by Ekaterina Kuskova, whose unorthodox (and somewhat "revisionist") interpretations of Marxism had long ago led her away from the Social Democrats. With this support Alexandra did eventually manage to extract grudging permission from the St. Petersburg committee for work to go ahead. But there were many in the Party who regarded any such contact with the feminists in a period of such appalling reaction as deeply corrupting; her most vociferous opponent was a militant young Bolshevik woman named Vera Slutskaya. However Alexandra could rely on the enthusiastic support of the women in the textile union, and since the Party denied them premises for meetings, she and her friends Antonova and Solovëva organized a series of preliminary meetings in her flat. Discussions were soon advanced enough for her to leave them to work out at club meetings how their intervention could be made most effectively while she started work on a fierce and lengthy (400-page) polemic intended to arm the group against the feminists.

This work, *The Social Basis of the Woman Question*, was hardly suitable as an agitational handbook by the time she finished it in September 1908, and by the time it was published it was too late to serve its original purpose and the feminists had lost much popularity. Nowadays many may question her assumption that once women had fought their way into the Russian Social Democratic Party, they would then be able to attack the sexual prejudice of its members from within and inscribe their own demands into its program. But in expounding the philosophy that was central to her whole life's work—that it was only in the fight for socialism that women would achieve equality—she remains cogent and convincing to this day. "Certain specific economic factors have brought about the subjugation of woman; her own natural characteristics [i.e. her role as mother] have played only a *secondary* part in this. Only the disappearance of the economic causes and the transformation of those economic modes which have enslaved her can fundamentally change her status."[16]

In a convoluted and passionate style redolent of three years' thwarted work, three years' accumulated bitterness toward both feminists and Social Democrats, Alexandra insisted that only the working class was capable of maintaining morale amid all the distorted social relations of the modern world. It was the woman of the working class who would "prepare the ground for the free and equal woman of the future." And although the path to her liberation in a new world of labor was fraught with danger and sadness, yet it was along this path that the working woman would "learn to discard the slave mentality that has clung to her, and step by step transform herself into an independent worker and personality, free in love."

She was also sensitive to the position of middle-class women, large numbers of whom were leaving the Women's Union but had not yet found any political alternative.

> Surely [the middle-class woman] cannot but see how little the general women's movement has done for proletarian women, how incapable it is of improving the working-class living conditions. The future of humanity must seem bleak and uncertain indeed to those women fighting for equality who have not adopted the proletarian world outlook or developed any firm faith in the coming of a more perfect social system. While the capitalist world remains unchanged, liberation must seem incomplete and partial—what despair must grip the more thoughtful and sensitive of these women.[17]

And Alexandra did not reserve all her sympathies for the politically awakened and the proletariat, as a new friendship she made in the summer of 1908 makes clear. Tatiana Schepkina, a well-known writer and translator, had never been a revolutionary and never would be, yet their friendship endured for very many years. Tatiana had accompanied her lawyer husband, Polivanov, to the Tauride Palace to meet some deputies after a session of the Duma. As he pointed out all the speakers to her they all fused hazily in her mind until her attention was caught by a striking woman in a green dress engaged in lively conversation with a group of Social Democrats. "She was clearly not an actress, for she was too bold, too simple, and without any flirtatiousness." Polivanov could only imagine she must be a journalist. They were introduced, and Alexandra was delighted to meet one of her favorite writers. Stories like "Ordinary People" and "The Insignificant of the Earth" had been popular with radical women for many years, and in the novella *One of Those* Alexandra had recognized many of her own dilemmas in leaving Vladimir. They often met after that. Tatiana liked her wit, her "somewhat masculine way of thinking—precise, clear, rather severe—in such great contrast with her exceptionally feminine appearance," and she urged Alexandra to make use of her house if ever she were in trouble with the police.[18]

Immersed in her writing throughout that summer, Alexandra had addressed few meetings and so avoided the police. She had caused a stir earlier on in March, when at a students' meeting in Dorpat she had delighted her audience with a talk on "the family question."[19] Working people's lives, she said, offered "emphatically more suitable grounds for the working out of new sexual psychology than those of the bourgeoisie." She took as her inspiration the factory woman newly arrived from the village, who did not hesitate to "follow the first call of love, the first heartbeat." "The heart cannot wait for conventional marriage": this conviction, which suffused Alexandra's book *The Social Basis*, could only be proved when socialism had made women independent and free love a reality—which would only happen when the socialist state made proper provisions for child care, provisions which she was to elaborate further in her subsequent works.

By September she had finished *The Social Basis* and began to look for publishers. But "it was not to everyone's taste," she discovered. The Mensheviks to whom she showed her handwritten manuscript wanted her to delete all those passages where she most sharply rejected collaboration with liberals. As the Bolsheviks were now firmly set against attending the All-Russian Women's Congress in December and were trying to obstruct the preparatory meetings, they were hardly going to be more favorable; she decided instead to send it off to Maxim Gorky, who ran the progressive publishing house, *Knowledge,* and was living on the island of Capri.

The anxious months before the congress in which she waited for Gorky's response were made additionally tense by the issuance of a warrant for her arrest. Charged with calling for an armed uprising in Finland, agitating among members of the textile union, and belonging to an illegal party, she faced a long prison sentence if she did not immediately go underground. She said good-bye sadly to fourteen-year-old Misha (who probably went to stay with his father), liquidated her small flat, put some belongings into a small suitcase, and for the next three months slipped in and out of the houses of her various "legal" friends. She accepted Tatiana Schepkina's offer of accommodation, and in the large crowd of writers and actors for whom Tatiana kept open house was able to pass unnoticed into the little back bedroom which was always kept ready for her.

The threat of arrest did not, however, significantly curb her activities. Hardly a day passed when she did not attend a meeting. In order to avoid the police, many of these meetings were held under the innocent guises of name-day parties or sewing circles; over the pies and herrings or embroidery the forthcoming congress would be discussed, and Alexandra would rehearse the forty-five members of the "labor group" in the speeches she had prepared for them to make at the congress. Thousands of women who had never attended meetings before were drawn into a campaign of mounting intensity. Domestic servants, women from the cardboard, rubber, tobacco, and footwear factories all became filled with enthusiasm to "scandalize" the feminists, and increasing numbers of them attended feminist meetings to heckle and hiss. "That horrible Kollontai" was anathematized by every feminist. Poor old Anna Filosovova, an organizer of the congress and a long-standing and highly respectable philanthropist, had to pray before her icons to exorcise Alexandra's evil spirit when she discovered that Alexandra had visited a meeting in her home. One woman Kadet demanded her money back when she discovered that she had inadvertently given a donation to subsidize Alexandra's "hooligan" activities.

Between October and December 1908 Alexandra worked to ensure that every working woman in the capital knew of the congress. She spoke to fifty-two meetings in those months, most of them advertized as lectures on innocuous topics like the health hazards of corsets or hygienic methods of child care. There were several narrow escapes; one large meeting at the

Nobel house was broken up by police searching for her, and she only managed to escape by covering herself in a shawl and running out the back door.

It was in November, all too late in the day, that the St. Petersburg committee was sufficiently impressed by these activities to delegate Vera Slutskaya (who had previously been so hostile to the idea of attending the congress) and a man named "Comrade Sergei," to lead the labor group. But their participation created as many problems as it solved. They turned their first talk to the labor group into an object lesson in "ultimatist" tactics by delivering a short speech on women's role in the *zemstvo* and then walking out. The labor group was thrown into confusion. The Bolsheviks among them wanted to adopt this style of delivery at the congress; Alexandra and the Mensheviks wanted to stay after they had spoken, and argue, and the majority of them were too nervous about the whole business to be able to concentrate on anything more than getting their lines right.

Late in November Alexandra heard from Gorky. He apologized for the delay (the manuscript had gotten lost en route to Capri), but would be delighted to publish it. This was a considerable relief as Alexandra had not kept a copy of it, but the work would clearly be too late for the congress. The night before the congress was due to open the poor women in the labor group were thrown into even greater confusion when the feminists swept into their homes in their rustling silk dresses, showered them with sweets and cakes, and warned them against the dangers of attending. Highly alarmed at the idea that all their elaborate preparations were about to be sabotaged by inarticulately hostile heckling from this group of skinny, badly dressed workers, the feminists sternly warned them not to be duped by the Social Democrats and the "German influence" of Alexandra Kollontai.

They were equally daunting the following day, arrayed in their brilliant gowns on the platform of the ornate, flower-decked Alexandrovsky Hall. Alexandra saw how, despite the months of preparation and the bold red carnations they wore on their thin cheap dresses, the labor group was quaking with fright. A textile worker friend called Volkova, one of the more confident of them, was to read Alexandra's report on the socialist women's movement, as Alexandra dared not risk arrest by speaking. She stayed at the back of the hall with her friends as the congress opened, and as the first speaker urged all "dissidents" to leave she watched their courage grow.

As each issue on the agenda was discussed—women's suffrage,

women's labor, women in political parties—a member of the labor group would step up and with increasing boldness read out her own stiff statement. The statement on sickness benefit caused quite an uproar, with women on the platform hissing and stamping, and the labor group jumping up to shout "What do you know of our lives, bowling along in carriages while we get splashed by the mud?" When one feminist retorted that it was precisely because bourgeois women did not have to endure such wretched lives that they were best qualified to fight for equal rights, Alexandra could not resist taking the floor to argue.

Her appearance created a furor. It was no longer safe for her to appear in public, and at that moment the fear of arrest loomed far larger in her mind than the catcalls of her feminist opponents. Slipping out of the Alexandrovsky Hall by the back door, she ran back to Tatiana's house, packed her bag, collected her passport, and prepared to leave Misha, her friends, and Russia. Tatiana got together a small farewell party for her. They recited Nekrasov's poem "Russian Women," the composer Vasilenko played one of his piano pieces, people sang folk songs, and they all recited their favorite poems from memory before taking Alexandra off to the Finland Station and putting her on the first fast train to Berlin.

Shortly after the congress opened the following day, the hall was swarming with police, and the irreproachable ladies of the Mutual Philanthropic Society and the Women's Union were subjected to the humiliations of a body search. The congress marked the demise of the feminist movement in Russia, and the reactionary press welcomed the event with glee. The rabidly monarchist and anti-Semitic politician Purishkevich likened it to an "assembly of whores," others followed suit, and the suffrage struggle sank without trace for the next six years.[20]

That evening, as Alexandra waited apprehensively in the bitter cold of the Lithuanian border station for her passport to be checked, she had little idea how long her exile would last. She was divided between sad anxieties for Misha and the anticipation of a new, legal life abroad. The uniformed official returned her passport with a click of his heels, five minutes later she was in Germany, in the neat and brightly lit station of Eidkunen, and the next day she was in Berlin, ready to start a new life in exile.

7

Exiled in
Workers' Europe

It is both a measure of her independence and a clue to her future isolation in the Russian Party that in December 1908 Alexandra moved not to Geneva, where the Mensheviks were based, nor to Paris, where Lenin and his coterie were living, but to Germany, the mother and father of all socialist parties and the home of the Second International. For the next eight-and-a-half years Germany, or rather the German Party, was to be her home, from which she visited England, France, Sweden, Norway, Denmark, Switzerland, Belgium, and the United States. In exile she became known as a popular journalist and a public speaker of considerable power, frequently compared to the great French socialist orator Jean Jaurès (she became known as "Jaurès in skirts"). It was in exile, too, that her sentimental faith in the international brotherhood of the working class matured into an unshakable confidence in the "creative capacities of the proletariat as a class"; experience turned her into a convinced internationalist.[1]

The threat of arrest was the first check to Alexandra's uninhibited revolutionary activities and one of countless such episodes in the whole downward turn of Social Democratic fortunes throughout Russia. Party membership, as high as 100,000 in 1907, was estimated with wild haphazardness by Lenin as anything between 30,000 and 10,000 by the end of 1908. No more than five or six Bolshevik committees were operating in Russia, and the Party could no longer protect its members in their illegal activities. The Social Democratic Duma deputies were forced to concentrate all their work on legal Marxist clubs and trade-union newspapers, and Alexandra and her Menshevik friends were all tarred by the Bolsheviks with the same brush as the "liquidators" who wanted to abandon underground work altogether. The charge was clearly wide of the mark in Alexandra's case, for immediately after the congress many of the women with whom she had worked were forced underground. Many more were arrested, and the large-scale reaction to the women's movement reflected the savage reaction throughout Russia to the defeated revolution.

The Empress Alexandra, whose mystical convictions had a considerable influence on the policies of her husband, Tsar Nicholas II, had no doubt that if the autocratic Russian state were to survive, women's traditional role in the family would have to be preserved. She sponsored an anti-feminist group "for purely Russian women" of the aristocracy which held a congress early in 1909 to offset the feminists' congress of the previous year. The Women's Mutual Aid Society was raided by the police and closed down, and thirteen members of the labor group were arrested. Shortly after Alexandra arrived in Berlin, she received a letter from one of those arrested, Marusya Burko, who wrote from Siberian exile in Archangel to assure her that the struggle would continue.

Few revolutionaries can have felt so optimistic. The past years' struggles were taking their toll in a wave of suicides and nervous breakdowns, and among the young people in the cities it became fashionable to practice a particularly brutish and distorted version of "free love." Artsybashev's novel *Sanin*, which had come out the previous year, intoxicated hundreds of men who tried to model their behavior on its sadistic and incestuous central character and claimed to have inherited the traditions of the nihilists of the 1860's. "Saninist" sex clubs sprang up, rapists prowled the Nevsky Prospect, prostitutes were murdered—and in the opulent apartment of a wealthy St. Petersburg official the "Temple of Eros" held saturnalias with children. When *The Social Basis of the Woman Question* appeared in Russia shortly after Alexandra left, it was all but buried in a mass of fourth-rate novels and manuals glorifying this revolting sexual rage for incest, pedophilia, lust, and suicide.[2]

Although she attempted in her book to distinguish the ideals of free love from the distorted sexual practices that went on in its name, it was in her denunciations that she was most passionate. She rounded on "those gentlemen owning and administering industrial enterprises who force women in their workforce and secretarial staff to gratify their sexual whims, threatening them with dismissal to get what they want . . . And those masters of the house who rape their servants and throw them out on to the streets when they get pregnant—are they not all adhering to the formula of 'free love?' " As for promiscuity, she said, it could offer little more to women than the same old endless search, only intensely more painful, for the ideal partner—a search from which she had managed to free herself in the past years only by living alone.

Her book was little more audacious than either Bebel or Engels and could scarcely have shocked even the most conservative of Social Democrats. There were other reasons why it provoked so little comment in the revolutionary press when it was published. For Lenin and many other Bolsheviks in those troubled days any investigation of sexual matters was all too suspiciously akin to the various unorthodox reinvestigations of Marx which were to provide Bolshevism with its first official "heresy."

Germany had a special attraction for younger revolutionaries and "seeking Marxists." These "seeking Marxists" looked to the German party for all the exciting ideological innovations transmitted by the philosophical ideas of William James and Henri Bergson, who emphasized the distinction between people's active lives and their other lives, that realm of contemplation which arises from memory. The "seeking Marxists" were more guarded in their enthusiasm for Freud, who for the past fifteen years or so had been elaborating and practicing in Vienna the principles upon which he based his psychoanalytical science. By 1908 Freud had already published numerous works in German, including essays on dreams, *The Psychopathology of Everyday Life, Three Essays on the Theory of Sexuality, Fragment of an Analysis of a Case of Hysteria, Obsessive Actions and Religious Practices, On the Sexual Theories of Children,* and *"Civilized" Sexual Morality and Modern Nervous Illness.* None of these had yet been translated into Russian, however, where his ideas were selectively grasped and all too often vulgarized and abused. The philosophical and historical method of Marxism alone was so irresistible that Russian revolutionaries were slow to make any synthesis between the two new sciences. But in exile, as Alexandra reflected more deeply on the failures of the first revolution and the possibilities of a second successful one, she began to question many of the assumptions of Marxism and was evidently fascinated by the discoveries of Freud and of those women in Germany who, under his influence, were advancing a more enlightened sexual psychology.

It was late on the evening of December 12, 1908, when she arrived in Berlin. Traveling out to the lushly wooded suburb of Grünewald, she found a small, hospitable boarding house on the Hübertusallee, which like so many taverns and hotels in Germany was run by people sympathetic to the SPD and was filled with people like herself of average means— journalists and doctors, women writers and translators. She had a comfortable room on the second floor, small and inexpensive but light and quiet, and with a table and enough bookshelves to make it ideal for writing. She grew to love this tranquil little room, screened from the outside world by the massive chestnut trees outside the window. For the first month she lived here "in solitude," as she wrote to a friend. She improved her German, a language which she had read fluently since her childhood but in which she had still had little day-to-day practice in speaking. (Judging from her later success at public speaking in German, she worked very hard at it, as she was to work at the Scandinavian languages when she began to learn them some years later.) She read the latest socialist literature and she took plenty of walks. She had no idea how long her exile would last, and while clinging to the hope of a speedy return she struggled simultaneously to make some sort of independent life for herself in circumstances that were far from easy. Her finances were limited; she was still supporting herself, paying for Misha's education, and planning for him to visit her every year during his summer holidays—all out of her uncle's allowance, which would not last indefinitely. She did not yet feel proficient enough in German to support herself as a journalist and Party agitator. In these years in which virtually the whole Russian Party was in exile and the powers of endurance of every revolutionary were stretched to their limits, those without families were particularly prone to depression and drunkenness. Lenin and Nadezhda Krupskaya in Paris, and Martov and Plekhanov in their Geneva "commune" were often the unwilling victims of wretched revolutionaries in search of some family comforts. "If only you knew how difficult it was to leave," she wrote to Plekhanov in January, "especially now when it seems there are a few cracks for some fresh air to penetrate."[3]

By the end of that month, however, she was writing more cheerfully to a friend named E. Sokolova whom she had evidently known in St. Petersburg, and appeared to be leading a more sociable life: "I'm meeting a lot of interesting people, rushing frantically off to meetings. I'm joining in the discussions too—quite successfully! And with my German! However, I've decided not to give any talks yet as I want to be fluent enough not to grate on people's ears."[4] Russian exiles were always popular at the rowdy SPD meetings at *Bierstuben* and taverns, but Alexandra soon discovered that six hours a day spent drinking and arguing left little time for writing and reflection, and quickly wearied of the endless inconsequential talk. "It was inconceivable to leave any argument unsettled. Politics, literature, and art were discussed by young people with inexhaustible energy until closing time, and they would continue in their flats, winding up the evening with the loud singing of revolutionary songs."[5]

She found a more sympathetic atmosphere in the house of Karl Liebknecht, and it was here that she met a crowd of Russians bound by personal friendship, militant comradeship, and an extreme anti-statist philosophy derived from Rosa Luxemburg and the Dutch revolutionary Anton Pannekoek. Karl Radek, Nikolai Bukharin, and Adolf Joffe, revolutionaries in exile from Russia, would visit from Vienna where they were based; Lenin's old underground Bolshevik allies, Grigori Zinoviev, Lev Kamenev and Nikolai Semashko, would pass through from Geneva and Paris, and all of them would attend the regular Friday-evening meetings at the Rheingold Restaurant arranged by Liebknecht. An endless procession of Russians would appear at Liebknecht's door with no money, a false passport, and a shaky knowledge of German, and thanks to "Comrade Karl" they would soon be fixed up with a loan, a job, or a speaking tour. Alexandra felt ashamed at the way his good nature was exploited by some of her wilder compatriots; this good nature had led him to take up the cause of one émigré who had abandoned these gatherings for the Buch mental hospital, where he was feigning violent insanity. The squalid case of the Bolshevik bankrobber Kamo was a source of deep embarrassment to both Bolsheviks and Mensheviks, and a major cause of the increasingly strained relations between the German and Russian Parties.

In the summer of 1907, when the Bolsheviks were still giving their support to expropriations, Kamo and his Georgian bandit comrades had bombed a convoy that was taking 250,000 rubles to the Tiflis state bank. The proceeds were sent to Lenin in Kuokkola, but since the money was in marked and unusable notes, it was sewn into the shirts of Bolshevik couriers and smuggled into Berlin, where Krasin, the intellect behind this venture, was living. However it was no easier to dispose of the money there, and eventually the highly disapproving control commission of the SPD took charge of it. Although Lenin tried various unsuccessful ploys over the next five years to get the money returned to Russia, by the time Alexandra arrived in Berlin the Bolsheviks had made it widely known that they condemned expropriations. But they had already lost many friends. Rosa Luxemburg minced no words about this "Tartar-Mongolian savagery," and Plekhanov and most of Alexandra's Menshevik friends dissociated themselves completely from the Bolsheviks from that time on. Most of the SPD, although unenthusiastic about returning Kamo to tsarist Russia, felt that Liebknecht's well-meant campaigning efforts tended to romanticize the whole sordid business, which merely proved to them that no real party in the Marxist sense had emerged out of the 1905 revolution.

When Alexandra joined the SPD early in 1909 and enquired about the possibility of working as a party agitator, she learned that was the anti-Russian feeling so great that Russian speakers were generally allowed to address audiences only in the most remote provinces. This prospect daunted her a little, but by the spring her German was good enough for her to look forward to leaving Prussia for her first speaking tour.

By this time she had considerably widened her circle of friends and correspondents. She developed a great affection for Georgy Chicherin, who as secretary of the Russian Party Foreign Bureau, based in Paris, was constantly traveling through Europe, raising funds for impoverished exiles, arranging meetings, and providing links between separate groups of émigrés and their permanent political leaders. "Every worker who arrived abroad knew Comrade Ornatsky," she wrote. (Ornatsky was his underground name.) "And everyone who came to work with him in emigration retained for the rest of their lives the memory of this crystal-pure person." Like Alexandra, he had a messianic faith in the value of work, an encyclopedic knowledge, and "a rare capacity for self-sacrifice."[6] But many of the more down-to-earth Russians considered that his life of Tolstoyan asceticism atoned rather excessively for his aristocratic background and his former position in the tsarist foreign ministry. Not only was he a teetotaler and a vegetarian, but he had also renounced poetry and music, dressed in rags and lived amid unmade beds, half-eaten food, and piles of literature in a style infinitely more squalid than most of the poor exiles he helped to support. Since the "unity" congress, his Foreign Bureau had been ostensibly run jointly, like all foreign organizations, by both factions. But since the Kamo affair, which he had been responsible for investigating, he had had particular reason to dislike the Bolsheviks, for they had put a stop to the enquiry and then accused him of being a disrupter and "wrecker." From that time on he regarded them as human monsters "whose existence constituted an abnormal phenomenon."[7] Although he was closer in spirit to the Mensheviks, he tended, like Alexandra, to regard factional arguments as irrelevant to the main business of preparing and supporting workers' organizations, and he was very friendly with Karl and Sophie Liebknecht and other SPD radicals, as well as with leftists in most of the European socialist parties.

Apart from Chicherin, Alexandra made few other friends in the Russian émigré circle. It was at some point early on in her long years of exile, however, that Alexandra's sexual solitude came to an end, and at the age of thirty-six—most people took her for ten years younger—she embarked on her first love affair. It is possible that she had first met her lover at Stuttgart the previous year. He was probably Russian and a Menshevik, definitely married, and the affair was evidently illicit, for Alexandra was very reticent about its circumstances and duration. It seems certain now that the man was Petr Maslov. An economist who had been writing since 1889 on agrarian questions, he had become by 1906 the Mensheviks' chief spokesman for the theory that the land should be "municipalized" in the first stage of the revolution rather than nationalized outright as the Bolsheviks advocated. It was from his lengthy and wide-ranging book, *The Theory of the Development of the National Economy*, however, that Maslov had acquired his considerable reputation as a scholarly economist. Alexandra reviewed the book, but apart from a reference in a letter to a friend in Russia a few years later to "sorrows of a romantic nature which seemed very important to me at the time" (which would suggest that the relationship brought her more unhappiness than pleasure), there are no other explicit references to it in her writings of that period—just a brief remark about a "colleague" of hers named Maslov in a review article of hers in 1910; one can only note a certain quality of sexual exuberance which runs through her autobiographical book, *Around Workers' Europe* (published in 1912), in which she describes her years in Germany.

It appears that Maslov was one of those socialists who believed that social revolution would be directed, in an orderly fashion, by the enlightened leaders of international social democracy; later she confessed her disillusionment with this man, whom she had first met and worked with some years before in Russia and whom she found intellectually so fascinating and such an "ardent socialist." Maslov was married to a sickly wife and had five children. He offered on several occasions to divorce her and marry Alexandra, but she was haunted by the feeling that his interest in her was merely sexual, that he was incapable of treating her as an intellectual equal, and that he did not satisfy her need for spiritual closeness. She felt unable to accept the rightness of his abandoning his wife, or the responsibility of caring for his children should his wife die.[8]

It was not until she wrote her autobiography in 1926 that Alexandra described in rather greater detail some of the emotional burdens which weighed on her during the course of this relationship:

> I am far from being one of those "new women" who take their experiences as females with relative lightness (one might even say superficiality), and whose feelings and mental energies are directed at all other things in life but sentimental emotions of love. After all, I still belong to that generation of women who grew up at a turning-point in history.

> Love, with its many disappointments, with its tragedies and eternal demands for happiness, still played a very important part in my life.[9]

The women friends she made in Germany shortly after her arrival were also to be an important part of her life. As soon as *The Social Basis* came out in Russia it was enthusiastically reviewed in *Die Gleichheit;* she had several businesslike and very friendly meetings with Klara Zetkin and reestablished contact with Luise Zietz, Ottilie Baader, and others in the SPD Women's Bureau whom she had met at Mannheim and Stuttgart. In discussing *The Social Basis* with them, she began to question her assumptions about the reactionary "law" of Malthus and to reconsider the whole issue of birth control, which her book had not mentioned. Her main concern then had been with the creation of new life and the possibilities of making birth easier for all women. In *The Social Basis* she had quoted the ideas of the Swedish feminist Ellen Key who in 1900 had elaborated a program for abolishing the double standard and granting all women, married or not, the right to sexual enjoyment and the bearing of children. Although Alexandra had taken issue with Ellen Key's emphasis on motherhood as the center of a woman's life (an emphasis which was enthusiastically greeted by many feminists in Russia) and felt that sexual love was generally more ennobling for a woman than maternal love, she certainly wanted to make motherhood a joy by lightening its burdens with state benefits.

In Germany and England, unlike Russia, large numbers of the middle classes and the more skilled workers were adopting some rudimentary form of contraception by the turn of the century,[10] and many women in the SPD were cautiously questioning the understandable hostility to Malthus which prevailed among most socialists. In so doing, they had to make very clear their differences with the large number of middle-class German feminists who by the first decade of the twentieth century were pointing out that if the state did not considerably improve the facilities it granted to mothers, only the poorest workers would reproduce and the race would decline; these views rather tended to confirm the German government's fears that feminism would lead middle-class women to a "birth strike" dangerous to Germany's military and economic ambitions. The socialist movement in Europe was deeply confused by the seemingly mutually exclusive philosophies of the early Malthusian social engineers and birth-controllers on the one hand, and those, on the other, who claimed that all women should have the right to enjoy the pleasures of motherhood. For on this issue the technology of contraception was gradually outmoding all previous Marxist teaching on the women's question. The socialist women's movement in Germany expressed more clearly than anywhere else its awareness of this confusion but failed to realize the particularly significant interconnection between women's control over reproduction and workers' control over production. Unconnected, these issues were to contribute to the rise of a racist and fascist ideology in Germany.

One such organization whose progressive and utopian ideals were gradually to become engulfed in racist ideology was the Motherhood Protection League, formed in 1904 in Berlin. Its founder, Helen Stocker, had derived her bold ideas on free love and motherhood from Nietzsche and Freud, and was convinced that women could only be economically free if they took the initiative in teaching men not to tyrannize, putting an "end to the capitalist domination of men," and restoring the matriarchy; sexual love, Stocker believed, was to be sublimated into maternal love. Numerous women involved in the campaign against prostitution began to chafe at what they regarded as the sexually repressive moral code of this campaign, which demanded that the double moral standard be replaced by a single standard of sexual temperance for men and women. Many women in the SPD too, including revisionists like Lily Braun, were drawn to the Motherhood Protection League.

The league combined philanthropy (it established counseling centers for unmarried mothers), visionary utopianism (it founded motherhood colonies run on communal lines), and moral literary propaganda to spread the view that since monogamous marriage could no longer encompass the sexual needs of the nation, women should be able freely to bear children without necessarily marrying. The progressive core of Helen Stocker's ideas made a great impact on Alexandra, as was evident in her next theoretical work, *Society and Motherhood.* But the league was fiercely distrusted by most radical women in the SPD, and its supporters were mainly revisionist Reichstag deputies, "academic socialists," and various socialists and psychologists in Austria and Switzerland, including Freud and the Swiss psychologist Forel.

Another of the league's supporters, who revealed many points of contact between the SPD and the older generation of liberal women reformers, was seventy-year-old Minna Cauer, with whom Alexandra became friendly. Twenty years earlier Minna Cauer had launched the militant Women's Welfare Association, which had aimed to use demands for a variety of social reforms as a means of developing a broader criticism of existing society, as well as pioneering new ideas on social and family life. Even Klara Zetkin recognized the valuable work of the association in radicalizing many feminists of the 1848 generation, and in 1894 Minna Cauer had led the majority of its members into the new Progressive Women's Association, which favored tactical cooperation with the SPD. By 1902 most feminist organizations were working with women in the SPD in the campaign for the vote and for the abolition of the remnants of Bismarck's 1878 Anti-Socialist Law—the combination laws—which banned women and young people from joining political groups or attending meetings. In Russia, where women's organization was at such a rudimentary level, such an alliance between socialists and feminists would have been inconceivable.

The women's congress in Stuttgart in 1907 had been held in defiance of the combination laws. Alexandra's decision to go to Germany a year later was prompted by their repeal, which meant that as a woman she could now address meetings without fear of arrest in most parts of the German Empire, except Prussia, where reform had foundered on the hostility of the Junkers. The laws still applied, however, to young people under eighteen, who found themselves in a highly ambiguous position in the Party, as Alexandra was to discover. Women's separate organizations and study circles (initially imposed by official restrictions) continued, thanks to their radical and eloquent organizers who insisted on the necessity of small consciousness-raising groups. But Klara Zetkin and Karl Liebknecht had to fight a great deal of trade-union opposition to their work with radical young apprentices and future soldiers who, they insisted, also badly needed a separate youth organization in the Party if only to give them the sort of practical guidance and support they needed if they were to avoid the rigors of arrest and the persecution of the state.

It was not only the combination laws that prevented Alexandra from speaking in Berlin, for almost any mention of the Russian revolution was considered by the powerful unions, whose support the Party so needed at the polls, as tantamount to a call for arms. "Let those who have such a surplus of revolutionary energy go back to Russia, instead of propagating discussions about the general strike from their summer resorts," one union leader had said in 1905.[11] It was the unions' interest in the existing order, transmitted to the Party after 1905, which ensured the Party's increasingly antirevolutionary views.

Alexandra had first met Kautsky in Geneva in 1901 and had seen him again at Mannheim and Stuttgart. She met him again in 1909 and liked him. He spoke a little Russian, and he and his wife Luise were anxious to make Russian exiles feel at home in their neat little house in the Berlin suburb of Friedenau. But reading his book *The Road to Power* she realized what a bewilderingly unsocialist world she had wandered into. It had appeared in 1906, the first statement of the SPD "center" and an open admission of the Party's separation of its distant revolutionary goals from its practical tasks of factory agitation. Revolution, said Kautsky, could neither be stimulated by socialists nor hindered by capitalists, for it was inevitable, and four major factors made it imminent: people were demoralized by the army and the bureaucracy, workers were hostile to their employers, an organized Party existed in irreconcilable opposition to the government, and the rulers were in moral decay. The entire dynamic of the revolution, it seemed, was to be provided by the ruling class, and he assigned such a remarkably passive role to the workers that their Party apparently needed only to retain its integrity in opposition until the fateful day when it could assume power.

The real prison wardens of the SPD, however, were the horde of unimaginative functionaries who turned it into the great bureaucratic institution for mass control that was subsequently taken over with such ease by the National Socialists. Typical of the party officials who emerged after 1905 was the SPD secretary Fritz Ebert, whom Alexandra met later. More reminiscent of a business manager than a revolutionary, he had by 1909 all but achieved his ambition of implementing "the uniform management of our administrative affairs." The executive's energies were fully taken up with exhaustive surveys of the population's social position and voting habits, full-time secretaries were appointed from above for all forty-three regional organizations, and the SPD was on the way to becoming a smoothly constructed voting machine, a party to compete with other bourgeois parties at the polls. As these party functionaries tended to retreat from all political debates, they also tended to thwart any revolutionary initiative as "divisive." By 1909 the revolutionary program was kept alive only by leading intellectuals like Rosa Luxemburg and her radical friend Franz Mehring, who taught workers at the Party's Marxist school; by the women's cultural societies and education groups, from which the radical line filtered through into the entire women's organization; and by the efforts of Karl Liebknecht and a few other radical Reichstag deputies to campaign against militarism and bureaucratic inertia.

While trying to find her feet in the German Party, Alexandra was also writing a large number of letters to friends in Russia and was anxious to keep in regular correspondence with old party comrades: "Naturally I did this in such a way that I demanded from the Party that it espouse the cause of women's liberation. But I did not always have an easy time of it. Much passive resistance, little understanding, and even less interest for this cause obstructed the path time and again." "For me, what I am was always of less importance than what I can"—this was the motto of her indefatigable campaigning life.[12]

The women from the labor group (those not arrested) reassured her from home that their work was going on in the clubs and factories, and when she heard from the woman who had read out her report at the feminist congress in her absence she felt encouraged "not to abandon our work but commit myself to it even more passionately. I read your letter to our comrades here and we discussed it," she wrote to Volkova. "It's such a pity you're so far away and not with us, for we constantly feel the need for your presence."[13]

By the end of March, Kautsky and the SPD Reichstag deputy Würms had arranged a three-week speaking-tour for Alexandra in the industrial towns of the Rheinland-Pfalz; her first stop would be Ludwigshafen, the main town of the area and center of the chemical industry, with a population of 50,000. The prospect of huge audiences (the town boasted 1800 party members and 6000 in the unions) filled her with dread, but she prepared to translate into images as clear and striking as her German would allow her firsthand experiences of the Russian revolution and the clubs and papers that had sprung up in its wake, as well as her ideas on women and the family; she was also to speak on Tolstoy, who in the 1880's had been such an inspiration to Russian populists, but who by 1905 was already supporting the far less radical claims of many liberal landowners and was vociferously opposed to the liberation of women.

In the first week of April she left Berlin and travelled 800 miles south. The local party chairman met her train. Ludwigshafen was just over the river from Mannheim, but as they walked through its dismal, dingy streets to the offices of the local party paper, she was struck by the depressing contrasts it presented; when she arrived at the offices, the editor did little to allay her unease. He scrutinized rather than welcomed her, announcing that as she was an "attraction" she would be paid 20 marks for each talk rather than the usual 15; and when she protested that this was the first time she had spoken in German, he coolly announced that he had advertized her talks for the next three weeks and his plans could not be changed. The reasons for this coolness were later explained by the more affable Party secretary, a revisionist, who was worried by the inflammatory effects that a Russian speaker might have on the young people in the audience and anxious that she should dwell on the dangers of anarchism for their benefit.

Alexandra left the editorial offices to visit one of the many Russians in the town, who worked in the dye factory and lived, she was horrified to discover, just like a petty bourgeois, with knickknacks in his sitting-room. Returning to her hotel, she stopped in at the party headquarters to try and get a copy of Kautsky's *Christianity and Socialism,* which she had agreed to review for a Russian paper and which nobody there had heard of. At eight o'clock that evening she arrived at the tavern where she was to address her first German meeting.

In Russian meetings formal barriers were dissolved by the illegality of the occasion; in Germany large quantities of beer fulfilled a similar function. Most of the wealthier union and party buildings were licensed to sell beer and relied on its revenues, and a network of socialist beer-lovers ensured that almost every town had its socialist tavern where meetings and discussions could be held. Alexandra arrived to find 800 people, mostly men, formally dressed and waiting for her with intense curiosity, clasping their mugs of beer. A policeman sat at a side table, as was customary when any Russian spoke. She was introduced and stepped forward to speak in a state of acute anxiety:

> *"Genossen und Genossinnen . . ."* The first words are thrown into the hall, but my head is cloudy, my thoughts won't flow coherently but jump about as if defeated by this foreign language. Only an unexpected out-burst of clapping restores my self-confidence, and only then does my voice stop ruling me. My head is filled with an extraordinary amount of nervous activity, thoughts, images, comparisons spring up with fantastic speed . . . *"Sehr richtig!"* resounds around the hall when I compare life in Russia with Prussia. Friendly laughter. As if thousands of eyes are fixed on me, waiting for a miracle to deliver them from the burden of their colorless lives. The last phrases are flung into the hall and seized respon-sively . . .[14]

"Don't say that's the first time you've spoken in German," said the party secretary, leading her to the table where party officials and their corseted wives were drinking beer. After three mugs the jokes became ribald. "Arthur, you should know!" the chairman's wife shouted when Alexandra asked her about the Party's proposals for maternity protection. The secre-tary began telling her about the local dye factories, in which thousands died annually from dropsy and all energy went into the struggle for the nine-hour day, and was just inviting her to inspect a factory for herself when he caught his wife's furious look of jealousy and dropped the subject.

The next day, however, he did manage to take her to speak at a chemical factory and tried to convert her to "revisionism" on the way. His words made her very clearly aware of the facile tendency of the SPD to dismiss as "revisionist" workers' demands for any practical improvements in their lives; the distinction between revisionists and orthodox Marxists was not nearly so clearcut as it had been in the Party's early theoretical debates with Bernstein in 1896. "I drink this cup every day," said the secretary. "It wasn't agitational speeches that pushed me into the struggle but life itself." She found the truth of much of what he said reflected in her audience at the factory, and she spoke badly. Bent-backed and blue-skinned from their exposure to dangerous chemicals, the workers wanted to sit, drink, and daydream, she felt, not listen to rousing speeches. Taking the tram back afterward, she glimpsed the distant Rhine, smelled the cherry and apricot trees, and saw another good reason why the hall was half empty.

Her next meeting, in an SPD stronghold known as the "red nest" of Speyer, was more lively. She was met at the station by the local secretary, who led her through the medieval town and past the cathedral, and from there they went to the industrial quarter with its thundering trucks, petrol fumes, and gramophone music wafting out of stuffy bars. The audience was large and radical, and included many women, who sat apart as if in church. The chairman introduced Alexandra and recalled the appearance of Wilhelm Liebknecht (Karl's father) in the town many years before and his own friendship with Engels. After her talk there were the usual rounds of beer at the separate party table, but she managed to talk to some older unemployed workers supporting large families on inadequate unemployment pay, and to some women strikers at a pen factory. Just as she was leaving, she was besieged at the door by a crowd of boys begging her to tell them about Russian prisons, bombs, and Cossacks, the hanging of women and the shooting of workers, and whether fifteen-year-olds were allowed into the Russian Party. They were all off to a fireworks and gymnastics display organized for them by their elders.

At Landau the party chairman was a breezy tavernkeeper and former builder who hectored her on the difference between the bourgeois radicals and revolutionary class politics and told her to make an election speech —and to avoid gossiping about party members' personal alliances. Most of the 200 people in the Landau meeting were building workers, but there were twelve women who sat in the front row; as she cursed the liberals and condemned any pact with them the women laughed particularly loudly. One of them, Matilde, small, lively, and dark-eyed, told her afterward that as women were so discouraged from meddling in politics, she had applied to Ludwigshafen for a special woman speaker. She invited

Alexandra back for the night to her tiny attic flat which she shared with "handsome Hanz," her husband, and that evening told her about her life. A vegetable-seller and washerwoman, she had learned politics working in a dress shop patronized by the idle rich. She discovered *Die Gleichheit,* went without shoes to buy it, and gave it to the other workers; and when her boss tried to beat her, they all went on strike, and the police were called to drive them back to work. Matilde left her job, starved, swept floors and took in a lodger ten years younger than she, whom she converted to atheism and socialism—and that was how she married "handsome Hanz."

The following day in Zweibrücken Alexandra learned of a strike of non-unionized, non-party women at a burner factory. The strike was in its fifth day, there was no money, the party chairman had told them to consult the metal-workers' union, and the union refused to listen. Alexandra was visited by one of the strikers, who begged her to intervene with the Party and to organize some special women's meetings; after a lengthy consultation with the party officials it was decided that a Russian agitator would be quite unsuitable for such work, and that evening she talked instead about the struggles of factory women in Russia. She heard a few days later that the strike had been lost and many of the women had lost their jobs.

As she approached the end of her first tour she left the soot and grime of the Pfalz for the small agricultural town of Grünstadt, and as the train sped through fresh cornfields and past small gardens nestling behind lilac bushes she was delighted by the beauty of the Rhenish countryside. She was met by a "comrade" in a panama hat who reeked of perfume and chatted amicably as they walked the two miles from the station to the town. He ran a small chemist's shop, he explained, and although he was not in the Party, he had offered it for the meeting "since she was a lady." Many of the peaceful, broad-shouldered peasants in the audience that evening had walked ten miles to hear her speak, and she was immediately reminded of the peasants of Finland. They warmed to her talk about serfs in Russia and the peasant uprisings of the past years.

Early next morning as she walked back across the fields from her hotel to the station she felt such a sudden, overwhelming happiness that her tour was over that she lay on the grass looking up at the skylark above:

> The fields were filled with that ringing silence of a summer day that you only find in the country. Woodbeetles and bees droned, butterflies circled, the high corn danced, the white camomile nodded. How wonderful

to stretch out and look up at the racing clouds and listen to the clamorous voice of that tiny black spot. How good not to have to hurry, to belong to myself again. Those twenty-one days of constant work already seemed like a distant dream. Images flashed past . . . the worn pale faces of the women, the hopeless apathy in the eyes of the men, depressing factory towns, noisy party offices, gloomy workshops . . .[15]

But her work was not over. Returning to Ludwigshafen, she was urgently requested to visit a leather-manufacturing town known as "Red Offenbach," where a recent wave of Russian Jewish immigrants had provoked a number of violent racist incidents. The large and prestigious union was fueling the prejudice, and everywhere in the town Russians were being assailed as locusts, filthy rivals, and thieves with no proletarian feelings. She set off to confront this daunting task, and arrived at the Offenbach party offices to find party officials filled with the same hostility. Her talk had been arranged for the previous evening, they told her, and new arrangements could not be made. The editor of the party newspaper eventually organized another meeting, and he explained that these Russians were the victims of a lockout in Vilno. They knew little Russian, less German, and had nobody to represent them. She had to shame the Germans out of their chauvinism and generally arouse some fellow-feeling.

The meeting was to be in the opulent union building, where she arrived to find a group of officials discussing how she could be prevented from speaking. These inexcusably bad-mannered *lumpen* Russians constantly crowded the union building with their crying children and endless demands—they should be expelled from the town, they said. She approached the meeting with terror, and addressed her whole speech to one very old woman in the front row. She felt utterly inadequate to describe the struggles of 1905, the unemployment, the lockouts, the pogroms, the tortures of the pale (the "residential provinces" in Poland and White Russia in which the Jews had been forced to live since the late eighteenth century), the despair of the Jewish people, whose persecution had become almost a hallowed institution in tsarist Russia. (They had been barred in 1886 from working in the government administration and in the legal profession, their admission to universities and schools was severely restricted, and forced conversions of the Jews in the late nineteenth century were followed by savage pogroms which continued even as Alexandra spoke.) How, she felt, could she possibly raise any hopes from the devastating picture she had presented by talking of the aspirations of the proletarian International? She had never been received with such hostility. "Find yourself a husband!" one man shouted. "You're a Menshevik!" said one of her compatriots. "And an opportunist!" yelled another. "After the women's congress we expected better of you!"

Shaken and sad, she left this meeting for her hotel to prepare a speech for another meeting at a tobacco factory. But try as she could to compose some statistics on child mortality in the "uninsured class," she could not concentrate. A letter from Misha had suddenly made her all too aware of her world beyond the remote factory towns of the Pfalz, and she lost all sense of time in replying to him.

Her thoughts were still on Misha that evening after the meeting when a delicate boy on crutches approached her and, bashfully admitting that he was not yet twenty-one, invited her on behalf of the women of his hamlet to address a meeting there the following day. At this audacity the party officials at their separate table sat up. He had no right to ask her, on four counts: such a suggestion should first have been put to the local party sub-group for discussion, the sub-group's decision would then have been passed on to the group's committee, "and only with their approval might I have been approached. His youth only added to the gravity of his crime."[16] Alexandra was delighted to accept.

She arrived at the hovel where he lived and was welcomed by his sister and her friends, crippled and prematurely aged by their work in the factory and by the real work of their day which began after they came home. Yet never had she met such a lively group of people. On the walls of the little hovel there were huge posters of Marx, Bebel, and Lassalle, and on the table, instead of the usual beloved knick-knacks, there were books. As she spoke in the small hall, "my little friend beamed all over. His eyes met mine and told me that in this hell of proletarian existence 'hope in the future' was the bright message which had replaced Dante's dictum."[17]

By the time she left Ludwigshafen at the end of April 1909, the local press had widely reported her speeches, noting her wit, her directness, and her ability to play simultaneously on people's thoughts, sensitivity, and will to act. As she stepped out onto the platform to change trains on her way back to Berlin, the traindriver ran after her and asked to shake her by the hand. He had driven her from Ludwigshafen, heard her speak at Zweibrücken, and wanted to send greetings to comrades in Russia.

She arrived back at her Grünewald boarding house to find an invitation from Klara Zetkin to join her in England. Dora Montefiore (whom she had met at Stuttgart) had asked the International Women's Bureau to support the Adult Suffrage Society in some organized intervention at a large congress of the feminist International Women's Suffrage Alliance (the IWSA) in London at the end of April. She was greatly taken with the idea of a second visit to the country of her childhood dreams, and she left immediately.

Since Dora Montefiore seems to have been her only contact in the English socialist movement, Alexandra can have known little of the attitudes within the two socialist parties, the Independent Labour Party and the Social Democratic Federation, toward women's liberation and the suffrage movement. But she had gathered that although the women's movement flourished at the branch level within the SDF, Dora Montefiore was fighting a lonely battle against the pedantic Marxism of its leaders. Maurice Hyndman, for example, felt that the struggles of individual men and women could play only a very small part in bringing about a social revolution. Belfort Bax, another SDF leader, was also convinced that socialists only had to wait for the inevitable crisis which would destroy capitalism and bring them to power. A member of the Men's Anti-Suffrage League, Bax argued that since it was men and not women who had the responsibility for supporting families, women could not possibly be oppressed; women's brains were smaller anyway—that should be the end of the discussion.

The ILP, although more responsive than the SDF to individual issues concerning women, did not have the radical courage to integrate women's economic and political needs into its non-Marxist program, and among its leaders there was also a considerable amount of antifeminism. Among various prominent independent socialists, too, there was a strong fear that any discussion of women's needs and sexuality would make a laughing stock of socialism. Robert Blatchford, editor of the socialist newspaper *The Clarion,* felt that people should defer their talk of such matters until socialism had been achieved.[18]

What did strike Alexandra most forcefully about England when she arrived in Dover in late April 1909 was the absence of uniforms and the pleasant lack of officiousness there. On the train from Dover to London, everything she saw—the castle on the hill, the ivy-covered cottages, the straw-hatted shepherdess sitting by a pond—reminded her of her childhood picture books. She took a room in an inexpensive boarding house in Greville Street, near the British Museum and near the Herzen Club in Charlotte Street, and then wandered about the streets of London.

Nowhere outside Russia had she seen so many poor people on the streets and such painful contrasts between undisguised poverty and blatant wealth. And the impression was confirmed next day when she walked along the Thames to Dora Montefiore's house in the Upper Mall, Hammersmith. She was enchanted by the riverside cottages and the apple trees in high-walled gardens, but as she passed William Morris's Kelmscott she reflected that only in England could a prophet of such beauty as the author of *News from Nowhere* have written this in the midst of such atrocious poverty as that of nearby Hammersmith. Dora's house was quite as much of a historical landmark as Kelmscott, Alexandra discovered. Twice seized by bailiffs (since Dora Montefiore refused to pay taxes, first in protest against the Boer War and then in order to demand universal suffrage), it had become a center of the small, militant Adult Suffrage Society, which was supported by a haphazard collection of SDF members, ex-suffragettes like Dora, and liberals like Charles Dilke. Apart from a few names, including that of its president, Margaret Bondfield, Alexandra had little idea of the society's scope and membership.

She arrived at Dora Montefiore's house to find Klara Zetkin already there, writing. After a brief discussion about William Morris and Dora's favorite author, Oscar Wilde ("such tastes would have been unthinkable for a German socialist"), she made some cautious inquiries about the ASS. She feared that apart from its general catalytic role on women's matters within the SDF its interests were more appropriate to theater than politics, and Dora did little to reassure her. "Energetic cries of 'Down with the House of Lords!' will create an atmosphere sympathetic to democratic slogans," she said as she outlined her plans to disrupt the IWSA congress; Klara would then hold forth on the international suffrage struggle, and Alexandra would talk about women in the revolutionary party in Russia. It all sounded very haphazard, and certainly very alien to the way socialists worked in Russia and Germany. "The English have their own logic, different from ours," she observed in *Around Workers' Europe.* "They are able to accept the facts, and they try only to make the most beneficial use of them for their own cause."[19]

That evening the visiting agitators were welcomed at a large party held in a building near the Law Courts, and the moment she observed "a working woman in a plain blouse and shabby slippers engaged in friendly conversation with the frock-coated man beside her," Alexandra felt at ease. Klara Zetkin and an emotional Finnish woman discussed the suffrage struggle; Alexandra talked about "socialist sensibility." The talks were followed by chamber music—Schumann, Sibelius and Rachmaninoff, in tribute to the three speakers' countries—and Alexandra was approached by a group of workers from Birmingham and Bristol. Self-educated socialists, they badly needed "more theory" and urged her to do a speaking tour of England. Her time was not her own, and she referred to "personal reasons" (possibly connected with Maslov) which forced her back to Germany; she regretfully had to refuse the invitation, but she left the party deeply impressed. "Never before had I sensed such social self-control. Public opinion there certainly creates fine manners."[20]

The ASS meeting which she and Klara addressed the following day was a more dispiriting occasion. Hyndman, the idiosyncratic leader of the SDF, joined them on the platform to address the small audience, as did the SDF member Harry Quelch, a working woman, and the liberal MP Charles Dilke—who cracked jokes about "barbarous" Russians with their serfs and nihilists and bombs. (The Duma deputies were expected to arrive any day in London, hence his antagonism.) Dinner at Hyndman's afterwards was all too reminiscent of her first visit to the Webbs in London, and she and Klara left infuriated by his quirkiness and colossal (male and national) chauvinistic vanity, which struck Alexandra as quite pathological.

Next day was an even more bizarre example of British socialism. She and Klara addressed a women's meeting organised by the SDF, which was followed by a display of Scottish dancing by a stout lady in a kilt who explained that she had dedicated herself to the working classes and was anxious that the workers should take more exercise. After this there was a meal in a smart, mirrored grillroom where elegant London drank tea after the theater and where Alexandra felt acutely uncomfortable.

She spoke to the Russian colony at the Herzen Club, in the same modest Charlotte Street room where in 1848 persecuted revolutionaries from all over Europe had first met to form the League of the Just. She was pleased to find that Russian exiles in London were less interested in factional arguments than in "Saninism," political clubs, and the women's movement in Russia. She attended a meeting of metal workers discussing a defeated strike at a wire factory, roamed about the London streets with a lively Irishman called Shaw whom she had met at the ASS meeting, and finally came to the purpose of the visit, the IWSA congress at the Albert Hall. This occasion, a triumph of organization for the IWSA leaders and its main speaker, Carrie Chapman Catt, was a severe anticlimax for the small Adult Suffrage Society delegation which had set out with such determination to heckle. In this vast, decorous assembly of 10,000 (mostly middle-class) women from Europe and America there were numerous women trade-union representatives too. Dora's plans to intervene foundered badly; this was clearly not the time or place to raise the demand for universal suffrage without any property qualification. "That's not rubbish you see on the streets, that's the unemployed!" Shaw shouted at one point, but his words were lost to the audience.

Her last day in England was May Day. It was a Saturday, and 50,000 people flooded the Embankment near the Westminster meeting-point. Inspired by the immense WSPU demonstration of the previous year, there were large contingents of women, among whom Alexandra had her first glimpse of the unemployed women with whom Sylvia Pankhurst was carrying out her political work in the East End of London. Since 1907 the WSPU, faced with the hostility and contempt of many members of parliament who had formerly given their tentative support to women's suffrage, had adopted a policy of seeking allies among middle-class women who had some social prominence. It appears that Alexandra was unaware of the powerful current of socialism which, despite Mrs. Pankhurst's increasing conservatism, was nevertheless still strong within the English suffrage movement; her experiences of feminist politics in Russia evidently made it difficult for her to imagine that any feminist organization could represent anything but the interests of middle-class women.

Singing and carrying red banners, Alexandra and Shaw moved off with thousands of trade unionists and children from the socialist Sunday schools in the two-mile-long procession to Hyde Park, where the ASS had a platform. The platform turned out to be a table, surrounded by a crowd of rough teenagers who were mercilessly heckling first Dora Montefiore and then Klara Zetkin. "You want to laugh?" said Alexandra, stepping up with some trepidation. "All right, let's laugh"—and managed to save her skin with a series of jokes. She and Klara then went on to the *Clarion* wagon, where various international socialists were to speak before a thick blue line of police.

As the sun set on Hyde Park they left, and Alexandra prepared to return to Berlin. England had "made a magical impression." In that week she had addressed six meetings in English, "and I confess the success rather intoxicated me. I was sorry to leave." She also missed her friends in Russia. "At times I miss you so unbearably," she wrote to Misha, "despite the fact that these last months I've been living a life of such heightened intensity and interest. The most contrasting pictures appear, new and interesting faces flash past—silhouettes of people, you might say —and in short, I've been living with every fiber of myself. And yet at times I would so love to be at home and working among my own people."[21]

In the mail she found waiting for her in Hübertusallee was a letter from the textile workers of the northern industrial St. Petersburg region, mandating her to represent them the following summer in Copenhagen, at the eighth congress of the International and the accompanying women's congress. She wrote two articles for the Menshevik paper, *Social Democratic Voice,* on women's organizations and prepared for her second speaking tour that autumn in Dresden, where she hoped Misha would be able to join her. On May 19 the English women's trade-unionist paper *Woman Worker* bore a highly posed full-length photograph of Alexandra Kollontai dressed, like most women interviewed in this paper, with extreme elegance, in a tightly-fitting black dress. In her interview this "sensitive mother, whose eyes brimmed over with tears as she talked of her country" described the activities of the Women's Mutual Aid Society: as more and more men were fired in Russia, and women replaced them at half pay, she said, it was now up to women to initiate strike action and lead men step by step to socialism. She had clearly wasted none of the theatrical propaganda opportunities offered by her visit.

More significant, and of great importance to the formation of her ideas, was her reading in England of Havelock Ellis. In his book *Man and Woman,* published in 1894, and his lengthy *Studies in the Psychology of Sex,* the final volume of which appeared in 1910, Dr. Ellis described the sufferings and ailments endured by women who were sexually deprived. Entreating men to have the courage and sensitivity to stop regarding women as a cross between "an angel and an idiot," he wrote:

> . . . we have to imagine a lock that not only requires the key to fit it, but should only be entered at the right moment and, under the best conditions, can only become adjusted to the key by considerable use . . . The grossest brutality may be, and not infrequently is, exercised in all innocence by an ignorant husband who simply believes that he is performing his "marital duties."[22]

Ellis, himself impotent and prone throughout his life to finding sexual excitement in the sight of other people urinating, had a boundless sympathy for the sexually deviant and repressed. For this pioneer sexologist, the complete equality of men and women was not only social and political but had much of its basis in the findings of sexology; people's biological variations, as well as their code of sexual and social behavior, were, he stressed, accessible to scientific investigation.

Alexandra discovered in Ellis, and in her fleeting acquaintance with the debates in England which his works prompted, a more congenial approach to the subject of sex and marriage than she had encountered in Germany. Moreover, it seemed to her that he raised questions relevant far beyond his own class and country, questions of erotic potential and sexual convention which the socialist movement had not even developed the vocabulary to discuss. Her own experience urged her that socialism must now tackle some of these questions and that if necessary she must be the first to do so in the Russian revolutionary press.

In the autumn of 1909 she left Berlin and arrived in Dresden, where she found even tighter police restrictions on Russian agitators. But it was with the Dresden Party that she first met with conflict. At her first meeting she talked to a large group of young people who were ostentatiously drinking lemonade and begging her to speak out against alcoholism and its corruption of the proletarian personality. She did so and trampled on a great many inebriated SPD sensibilities; her next meeting in a small town near Dresden was cancelled. This was for rather a different reason, though, for among the striking workers at a local brick factory there were numerous Russians, and it was feared she might be expelled by the police.

It was in Dresden that fifteen-year-old Misha visited her for a few weeks in January 1910. He had grown as tall as she in the year since she had left him, but he still had the sweet childish face of a schoolboy. The Party organized a group trip to Meissen in their honor, where in their winter coats and galoshes they "shuffled around halls, each more fabulous than the next. The inventions of builders intoxicated by images of eastern courts, the musings of crusaders, the knightly honor, the intrigues, the bishops, and religious excesses, all obligingly turned themselves for our benefit into poetic legends."

All too soon Misha had to leave. Alexandra now spent some time with a new friend, a women's organizer called Frau G., who shared her anxieties about involving women in party work. No sooner had women returned home after a ten-hour working day than " 'we ask them to drop everything, the children not in bed, the dishes not done . . . Should we call them to meetings and blame them for not caring about husbands and housework? Or should we rejoice when the children are dirty and hungry and roam the streets while their mother dreams of Party congresses?' "23 One solution to this everlasting problem was the "reading evening"; Alexandra was taken to a gathering of thirty women who shyly discussed Gorky, Zola, Liebknecht, and Kautsky, and in the process aired their grievances about the horrors of washday and considered the possibility of setting up communal laundries.

The next town she visited was Chemnitz (now Karl-Marx-Stadt), where she was taken around the awe-inspiring union building with its meeting-halls, canteen, bathhouse, and library. From Frau G., the energetic union organizer, she learned that prostitution was rampant in the town, and so she addressed her large audience with a depiction of the ways in which in capitalist society the institution of marriage, by enforcing women's economic dependence on men, was also indirectly forcing them onto the streets. The men's laughter was quickly silenced by their wives, and she felt encouraged to share with them some of her ideas on the purified and refined sexual relationships of the future. Afterward she sat drinking tea in a café with a revisionist shop assistant deeply critical of these idealistic attitudes and anxious that she should see for herself how easily girls were lured into casual prostitution in Chemnitz; Alexandra eagerly accepted her invitation to visit the local dance hall.

The following evening they both sat watching young couples stiffly taking the floor under the stern eye of the dancing master while at the tables shy factory girls who had starved throughout the week for their seedy Saturday waltz were wined and flattered by older men. This was the "beginners' class." The next dance hall they visited was filled with such joyless, garish, drunken degradation that Alexandra felt nauseated and they had to leave; her friend was quick to emphasize the simple "revisionist" truth that if the Party organized dances for young people, such dance halls as they had just seen would lose business and prostitution would be cut.

When Alexandra returned to Berlin that summer, she wrote to Volkova with this experience in mind, urging her and the labor group to intervene at a large feminist meeting called for July to discuss ways of fighting prostitution. From the article Alexandra wrote on the meeting, organized by the philanthropic aristocrats of the Russian Society for the Protection of Women, it would appear that she helped to draft the labor group's interventions.[24] But in the event the organizers managed to silence Volkova and her friends as they demanded equal pay ("too general!") and the unions' involvement in the campaign ("too political!"). Alexandra wrote more optimistically about a simultaneous meeting on prostitution held at the Nobel house, attended by 700 working women, and shortly afterward she received an invitation from Gorky to speak at the workers' school he was organizing in the Italian town of Bologna. Here was the very opportunity she had been looking for to elaborate before an audience of workers and intellectuals some of the ideas she had been considering recently; she planned to examine the ways in which people's instincts, feelings, and sexual ideology were shaped by the conventions of marriage, prostitution, and the family. That summer she left Berlin for

Italy, eagerly prepared to address the Bologna school on questions of proletarian morality.

This school, like Gorky's first school in Capri, was supported by many left Bolsheviks excited by the strange philosophy he had constructed on the disappointments of the failed revolution. "Godbuilding" (the notion that miracles would be made, God would be "built," by the combined faith of the people)—this was the "religion" that had sent so many left Bolsheviks and "recallers" (such as Alexandra's old underground comrades Alexander Bogdanov, Anatoly Lunacharsky, and Vladimir Bazarov) so terrifyingly off-balance in 1908 that Lenin felt impelled to enter the philosophical battle with his unreadable *Materialism and Empiriocriticism*, expel the "recallers" from the Bolshevik Party, and denounce the heresies of their journal, *Forward*. As a desperate expression of hope against hope and a comfort in troubled times, the appeal of "godbuilding" to intellectuals in the Party was understandable, although Alexandra was no more tempted by this religion than by the more usual variety. But, rather as radicals of the 1860's had been excited by the "subjective" ideas of the socialist philosopher Lavrov and by his insistence that populists could only contemplate working for revolution when they integrated into their party the principles of democracy and personal sincerity, she, like most later revolutionaries (including Lenin's, initially), was deeply impressed by Bogdanov's writings on the genesis of social relations in revolution.

Following the ideas of an obscure philosopher named Mach, Bogdanov described reality as experience—organized relations interpreted by the human mind. Society—experience organized on a *social* level—was an organism possessing psychic solidarity, based on the pleasure of holding together, and capable of being transformed into ever-higher forms of cooperation. Bogdanov did not, as Lenin claimed, reject the Marxist vision of economic production as an objective social force but asserted the equal importance of individual creativity (the ideas formed in people's minds) and regarded economics as one element in the whole environment shaping human institutions and behavior; no social or political group (and here was the real heresy) had any objective reality apart from the people who composed it.

The Bologna school was run communally, with teachers eating and sharing the housework with the twelve students. (Bogdanov, however, was observed to shirk his share of kitchen work, which he left to his wife.) Trotsky visited Bologna briefly to speak on organizing illegal presses. He had been arrested along with other leading members of the St. Petersburg Soviet in December 1905 and had been imprisoned in the Peter and Paul fortress, whence he was transferred in January 1907 to a distant place of exile in Siberia. On the way there the prison convoy stopped in a little village in the Urals, and from there Trotsky made his escape, hiding under some straw in the reindeer sledge of an expansive drunken peasant. Crossing the snowbound hillside to the nearest railway station, he made his way back to St. Petersburg, which he left, via Finland and Stockholm, for Germany. In the middle of 1908 he settled in Vienna with his wife.

Lunacharsky, who was then living in Paris, took workers through the museums of Bologna. There were courses on printing, propaganda methods, and codes. Stanislav Volsky, a weaver and philosopher from Ivanovo, taught classes on ethics and socialist sensibility; Mikhail Pokrovsky, a Duma deputy and later a noted historian, taught history; Pavel Polonsky, a psychologist and educational theorist well known in the 1920's, talked about free education; Alexei Gastev and Nikolai Kerzhentsev, Bolshevik workers and poets also famous in the 1920's, popularized their ideas on the scientific organization of labor; Lunacharsky lectured on philosophy, Menzhinsky on law, Gorky on religion, and Alexandra on sexual relations and the family and the Finnish workers' movement. The only full report of the school's activities was contained in a St. Petersburg police dossier; one of the students was a spy and ensured that all the others were arrested on their return to Russia. Alexandra sped back to Berlin as soon as the school ended, so as to prepare for the forthcoming International congress in Copenhagen in the summer of 1910.

8

The Collapse of Internationalism

With so little solidarity or agreement within the SPD the whole notion of international solidarity was beginning to seem increasingly unreal. While the "center" endlessly debated the unions' role in the class struggle the unions themselves were making their own alliances with the state. While the Bavarian Party was joining forces with the liberals, Rosa Luxemburg was urging the leaders to steer as close as possible to revolution by encouraging a continuous series of strikes, and Liebknecht and Klara Zetkin were pointing to the current wave of strikes and lockouts paralyzing the docks, the oilfields, and sections of the building industry as evidence enough of imminent revolution. In the face of all these revolutionary portents the "center" caved in; they forbade any mention of the general strike in the party press, and even as taxes were increased battleships were built and the European arms race assumed terrifying proportions, the SPD leaders continued to scorn the possibility of war. For had not Kautsky's *Road to Power* assured them that the Party was too powerful to allow such a thing?

For Alexandra there were evidently other more personal preoccupations increasing the tension she felt as she prepared to leave for Copenhagen. From certain oblique and veiled remarks she made in her description of this congress, it is clear that she was to meet her lover Maslov, presumably a delegate of the Russian Social Democratic Party. He emerges as a shadowy figure in her autobiographical account of this period, and it was only in her autobiography of 1926 that she shed some light on the conflicts arising out of this and later love affairs:

> The question arises whether in the midst of all these exciting labors and party assignments I could find time for intimate experiences, for the pangs and joys of love. Unfortunately yes! Unfortunately, because these experiences entailed all too many sad anxieties, and because all too many energies were pointlessly consumed. Yet the longing to be understood by a man down to the secret recesses of one's soul, to be recognized as a striving human being, repeatedly decided matters . . .[1]

That said, we can only speculate about the personal significance which the Copenhagen congress was to have for her.

The Danes who entertained the 900 socialist delegates from August 24–29, 1910, also seem to have regarded the congress as primarily a social event. The sun was setting as the steamer bearing Alexandra and her Dresden friend Frau G. pulled into Copenhagen, and they hurried straight from the docks to the party newspaper offices to learn what arrangements had been made for the women's congress. The offices were deserted, the leaders of the Danish women's organization were nowhere to be found, and when they finally found Klara Zetkin and Dora Montefiore, together they all deplored this lack of organization. But their tempers were restored in the friendly atmosphere of a party that evening at which the hundred women delegates got to know one another and resumed old friendships. Alexandra met her old friends from Finland and was introduced to Angelica Balabanova, who had left her native Russia to work in the Italian Socialist Party, as well as Kathe Dahlstrom, the much-loved leader of the Swedish socialist women's movement. She also met various members of the forty-strong Swedish and Danish delegations —working women whose livelihoods depended on their working at night and who were opposing the majority in trying to obstruct legislation in their countries which was about to ban women from doing night work.

The following day at the women's congress when this emotive issue was put to the vote, Alexandra regretfully cast her vote against them with Klara Zetkin and the majority, who insisted that night work benefited only the more skilled women workers. But she voted only with her head. "Logic was against them, but my heart was on the side of these young pioneers."[2] Another major issue was, of course, women's suffrage. The only women to oppose the Stuttgart resolution had been various members of the English delegation, including Mrs. Despard, who was wheeled in for the occasion. Charlotte Despard represented the ILP-sponsored Women's Freedom League, a women's suffrage organization which, despite its connections with various trade-union organizations and the Workers' Educational Association, officially adopted a very cautious attitude indeed toward socialism. Mrs. Despard and the other members of the English group argued so listlessly that they aroused little sympathy among the other women, and all of them finally walked out on a point of order. On these first two issues Alexandra had sided with the German Party and the majority. It was when the question of maternity benefits was discussed that she and a small number of Finnish delegates took a solitary stand against Klara Zetkin, insisting that these benefits should be extended to all women, whether married or not.

> It is important for this conference to stress that motherhood should be recognized as an independent social function which is not dependent on whatever form a woman's or family life might take. This recognition would help to clear the way for the new moral norms which are now arising in the working-class environment.[3]

A general fear that such widely available maternity benefits would encourage promiscuity led most women at the conference to reject her motion. Nonetheless Alexandra was elected to the International women's secretariat and, as "Helene Maline," joined the regular contributors to its official paper, *Die Gleichheit.*

At the main congress the following day the women's bright dresses merged with the dark jackets of the 900 delegates, the crowds of foreign journalists, and the bevy of Berlitz School interpreters. It was an infinitely more cumbersome affair, with socialists from sixty countries (including thirty Russians of every conceivable socialist coloration), few of whom understood each others' languages. Alexandra was in a particularly emotional mood as the congress opened with a moving revolutionary cantata and speeches of welcome, after which the delegates poured out onto the streets for more speeches, dancing, confetti, and drinking. The debates the next day were far more subdued.

Even though the workers of England and Germany were equally burdened by warships and taxes, their parties were in no mood to agree, and the mighty International, charged with the task of coordinating the world socialist struggle against war, wasted hours of fine rhetoric on the first point on its agenda—the unification of the Austrian and Czech union movement. Lenin busied himself radicalizing the commission on cooperatives, an issue which left Alexandra cold. "Even among the problems of socialism there are some that induce the deadliest boredom. Or is it just my own idiosyncratic feeling about the cooperative movement?"[4]

As the proceedings dragged on, Alexandra was approached by Anna

Danielson, the eternally mourning widow of the Swedish Socialist Party leader. There evidently was something about her, with her "sad blue eyes like our quiet Finnish lakes," that corresponded to Alexandra's own feelings; Alexandra agreed to speak at an open-air antiwar meeting in Malmö after the congress. She spoke to several meetings in Copenhagen, and her presence was noted by the crowds of reporters who filled the city and were pleased at the chance of some glamorous copy. "Slender and dressed in black, when she spoke her eyes blazed with revolutionary enthusiasm as she summoned up all her stirring inspiration, her indefatigable energy, and her infinite passion; and when she fell silent, such stormy applause was heard that one imagined it would topple the Tsar's throne itself," serenaded the Swedish socialist paper *Politiken.* [5]

She joined delegates on a steamer trip up the river to the watering place of Klampenburg, danced, sang, swam, and sat in cafés listening to music, and did not return until late at night. She had not been so sociable for a long time, and when she walked into the lavish party organized to end the congress, she felt as if she were at her first ball. The wine flowed, Vandervelde (the leader of the Belgian Socialist Party) flirted, Ottilie Baader urged everyone to dance, names and addresses were exchanged, and at a non-stop meeting in a side room Lunacharsky spoke in French, Jaurès in German, and Alexandra made three consecutive speeches in English, French, and German. Lunacharsky, much the worse for drink, then pounced on poor Jaurès and with the help of some Bulgarian comrades began to toss him into the air.

Alexandra's boisterousness seems to have been concealing a far greater sadness. The words in which she later described wandering out on to the balcony and looking up at the stars are so charged with sad emotion that we can only assume that she was saying good-bye to Maslov. Possibly she was saying good-bye to him forever, and he was returning to his wife; more probably it was her own feelings which were impelling her to end the affair, for her writings on women and sex after that time are filled with an honesty that could only have come from her own experience. She had given herself body and soul to him, and he had been unable to treat her as anything more than a sexual object; she had believed him to be a sincere socialist (she was always apt in this way to interchange moral and political judgments) and he had seriously disillusioned her by his vacillations. Looking back, much later, on this and similar sad endings which followed, and which also reflected her conflicting needs for the autonomy of solitude and for a more collective life, she wrote:

> The man would only see in me the feminine element, which he tried to mold into a willing sounding-board to his ego . . . Repeatedly the moment arrived when I had to shake off the chains of our relationship. Then, with an aching heart but a sovereign uninfluenced will, I would once more be alone. And yet the greater the demands life made of me, the more important the work waiting to be tackled, the greater grew my longing to be enveloped by love, warmth, and understanding. And so all the easier began once more the old story of disappointment in love . . .[6]

It was in this melancholy mood that she took the boat from Copenhagen to Malmö with Jaurès, Vandervelde, Anseele, and Keir Hardie, and she addressed her first anti-conscription meeting in Sweden with the nervousness of a condemned person ("After Jaurès me! Good Lord!"). But she managed a rousing speech, and afterward Keir Hardie invited his "dear Russian friend, whose name I can't pronounce" to visit England that winter. (In a way she found particularly English, he failed to add any more details to this invitation, which was dropped.)[7]

Alexandra traveled back to Berlin with Molkenbühr, the prominent SPD member, Reichstag deputy, and party expert on social services. He slept all the way, just as he was to sleep through the first volleys of war two years later. She slept not at all. "An agitator can have her own grief and pain, even after such great and rousing experiences."[8]

In Copenhagen she had again met Mikhail Pokrovsky, with whom she had taught in Bologna, and another Social Democratic Duma deputy, Poletaev. She corresponded with both of them for the next few years, and that autumn and winter she buried her personal sadness in a campaign against the brutal treatment of the imprisoned deputies of the Second Duma. Liebknecht, Oscar Cohn, the lawyer, and Minna Cauer were among hundreds of people in Germany who organized protest meetings and collected signatures; by December Social Democrats in the Third Duma had successfully demanded that the administrators of the Vologda and Zerenburgsky prisons, where inmates were starved and tortured, be replaced. In January Alexandra was writing to Pokrovsky that the whole German press, 110 Reichstag deputies, and 122 deputies to the regional parliament, the Landtag, had taken up the cause. To Tatiana Schepkina she described her own efforts: "In three weeks I have not belonged to myself. However, my dear, it seems we have been successful in rousing 'Europe' and changing 'public opinion' . . . They laugh at me in my boarding house and call me 'European public opinion.'"[9] As she attended meetings of the Reichstag with Liebknecht, the chief of the tsarist foreign police, Krasilnikov, reported back to St. Petersburg: "In the Berlin group of the Russian Social Democratic Party, A. M. Kollontai is considered one of the most prominent and active members."

Alexandra wrote a report of the Copenhagen women's congress for the Bolshevik paper, *Social Democrat;* and for Gorky's journal, *Life,* she wrote an article on "The Fate of Humanity and the Population Question."[10] Birth control had been a subject of discussion and speculation among educated Russians since 1905, but the vast majority remained in ignorance. When in 1910 a German doctor published an illustrated catalogue of contraceptive methods, its circulation was inevitably restricted, and although many progressive feminists were inspired to attack the social pressures forcing women to bear unwanted children, Alexandra could only fear the Malthusian implications of this new interest. A woman's solution to the problems of unwanted pregnancy could only be personal—a matter of individual conscience, not legislation; this was the tantalizingly inadequate conclusion of her article.

In February 1911 she visited her friend Frau G. in Dresden and from there embarked on a speaking tour of villages and towns of Saxony. She often had to walk miles across slushy fields to reach the more remote villages, but she loved these places where no agitator had ever been, for it was like "opening a crack into a new world, where people's souls are nourished by one living word in the brief time they have between work and sleep." And as spring touched the fields she tramped along rough tracks following the course of the distant misty Elbe and was reminded of the more primitive parts of Russia. She was reminded of Russia too when visiting a village where sickly women made paper flowers for the elegant Berlin department stores. "Everywhere the same desolate picture —a feeble struggle for a joyless existence. Everywhere listless children with an adult wisdom written on their sharp faces, and everywhere piles of those soft violets flattering the eye with their bright green stalks and flowers which spoke of spring. How I hate those soft fragrant flowers now . . ."[11]

Wearied by the endless procession of experiences and meetings throughout that month and never knowing where she would next lay her head, she was always finding new energy from chance encounters. At a daytime meeting in the village of Grödel, a revisionist described the mighty task of socialism in terms of the fight against rising meat prices, and was so roundly and inspiringly attacked by the young (vegetarian) secretary that Alexandra felt unwilling to follow his speech. She did, however, agree to explain to the women present, many of whose husbands had deliberately not told them about the repeal of the combination laws, the benefits of joining the Party.

At a packed meeting in the small industrial town of Riesa, near Chemnitz, she talked to some women textile workers, chatting unaffectedly and drinking beer with the men. A trade unionist on a whistle-stop recruitment tour gave a pallid speech and was sarcastically and brilliantly attacked by the women's organizer. Alexandra was bombarded with questions about women in Russia and how they coped with their husbands, and her story about a textile worker she knew who had organized a system for sharing the housework with her husband delighted them so much that one woman suggested the scheme there and then to her disconcerted husband. (This, incidentally, was one of the very few times when Alexandra tackled the problems of housework and the reallocation of tasks.) In the tavern afterward Alexandra suggested they introduce each other by saying how they became socialists. One woman said through reading Bebel, another said through working for the 1903 election campaign, but for most it was a family tradition and foregone conclusion.

The dying town of Grossenhain was more dispiriting. "We have taken in class hatred literally from our mothers' milk," the aged party secretary told her, "for we are only the fourth generation to be under the power of capital." His tone changed sharply when she enquired about women's activities. When women worked, men suffered, he said. "The house becomes a pigsty, the children die . . . And what does a woman *look* like when she works in a factory? You expect love to survive when a man's wife looks like a witch?" A crowd of women gathered around her after the meeting and took her to the station. "Silly old fool," they said. "We're stronger than he knows."

The next month women were indeed to show their strength as they came out on the streets of Austria and Germany in some of the largest suffrage demonstrations ever seen there. At Copenhagen it had been decided to mark March 8 as a day of international celebration for women, and Alexandra hurried back to Berlin at the end of February 1911 to help the Women's Bureau to organize demonstrations and meetings. They exceeded all expectations. Alexandra addressed a huge gathering of women in Frankfurt, and in every town and village there were similar meetings, many broken up violently by the police. "Men stayed at home with the children for a change, and their housebound wives went to meetings. This day set the tradition for a working women's day of militancy."[12]

But all the militancy and meetings were not leaving her time to write. Pokrovsky and Poletaev had asked her to draft a paper for the Duma on maternity protection, and she was expanding this into a full survey of maternity insurance throughout Europe. She also wanted to expand her pamphlet *Notes of an Agitator* into a book on her experiences in Europe. She decided to accept the open invitation of her old friend Georgy Chicherin, secretary of the Russian Social Democratic Foreign Bureau, to speak to the large Russian colony in Paris, where she knew few people and could settle down to some writing. Her talks would raise money for her compatriots, thousands of whom lived in the most desperate poverty in this center of the Russian emigration, often alleviated only by Chicherin's tireless fund-raising activities.

Arriving in March 1911, she took a room in the mansard of a reasonably cheap pension in Passy near the Seine, and for the next ten months this was her base. It was here, "in fits and starts," that she wrote *Around Workers' Europe,* a diarylike record of her experiences over the past two years.* Here too she embarked on her vast book *Society and Motherhood,* on which she was to work for the next three years, and she wrote two articles in which she first proposed some of the ideas by which socialists might integrate into their analysis of class relations a more systematic investigation of the rules of human behavior. Her thoughts on these topics had matured over the years she had spent in exile, when she had traveled so widely throughout Europe. It is difficult when assessing this wandering and somewhat rootless life of hers to say which events and people had the greatest influence on the formation of her views; the people she met, who may sometimes have appeared in the foregoing pages as a somewhat bohemian set of revolutionaries, were in fact some of the most important thinkers of the era.

Since in these articles she became the first person to insist on the political importance of changing sexual relationships and the intimate connection this had with the changing economic structure, she was beset by problems of vocabulary and style which anyone struggling for words to express new ideas will readily understand. Her solitary position within the German Party, her isolation from the various movements inside it which were challenging the old patterns of sexual behavior, her ignorance of the new methods of psychoanalysis and its attitudes toward sexuality, her awareness of the degrading depths to which the reaction in Russia had

---

*I have borrowed copiously from her intimate insights into the working of the German Party.

reduced the slogan of sexual freedom, and the consequent hostility of many Russian revolutionaries to all such questions—these were some of the difficulties she confronted in trying to express her pioneering ideas adequately. This was why she put the ideas of her first article, "On an Old Theme," in the form of a review of Grete Meisel-Hess's book, *The Sexual Crisis*. Not content to accept the views of Engels and Bebel—that humanity merely had to be freed of property relationships (as the working class already was) for prostitution and the double standard to disappear and for everyone to enjoy the level of sexual freedom they said was already enjoyed by the working class—Alexandra felt that a far more profound reshaping of the human psyche was required than these socialists, with their talk of social and economic transformation, recognized. Describing Meisel-Hess's book as the "thread of Ariadne" which gave a way out of the intricate maze of jealous traumas and sexual hypocrisy in which people's needs were trapped, she argued that its insights were of fundamental importance to the socialist movement.

Monogamous marriage could no longer fulfil people's sexual needs, she said, endorsing Meisel-Hess; it failed to resolve all the sexual and emotional conflicts which inevitably grew up between two people living in close proximity and exhausted the tenderness that had originally united them. The conventional squalid outlet for this marital incompatibility—prostitution—"suffocates the love in human hearts; from it Eros flies in fear of fouling its wings on a filthy bed," she wrote (her first use of the "winged Eros" in her writings). Moreover, prostitution reinforced the selfishness whereby men deprived women of sexual satisfaction. Prostitution "distorts our ideas," she wrote, "forcing us to see in one of the most serious moments of human life—in the act of love, in this ultimate accord of complex spiritual feelings—something shameful, low, coarse, and animal." Prostitution, by turning women into mere objects for men's sexual gratification, allowed men, "with startling naïvety . . . to ignore women's physical experiences in the moment of the most physical act."

"The normal woman seeks in sexual intercourse completeness and harmony," she continued, "whereas the man, reared on prostitution—which destroys all the complex vibrations of the sensations of love—follows only his pallid, monotonous physical inclinations, leaving sensations of spiritual hunger and incompleteness on both sides."[13]

For women who rejected the erotically unfulfilling prison of marriage and the consuming self-centered passion of the "free union," there was an alternative to sexual loneliness—something that Meisel-Hess described (somewhat unfortunately) as "game love."

In "erotic friendships" with men, women could satisfy all their longings for intensity and tenderness without drowning their ego or suppressing their independence, and could learn the art of a new kind of love that required "attentiveness, sensitivity, sharp awareness, and a profound penetration of the partner's soul, rather than the eternal smiles and roses." Love need not be suffering, it could be bright and joyful so long as it was not based on money or blood ties. The human psyche would become increasingly sensitive and complex as it passed through successive monogamous relationships and an infinitely wide variety of new emotions and relationships, and so developed its capacity for a "great love" which was purified of jealousy. In the future, when society assumed responsibility for the care of mothers and children, "there is no doubt," she wrote, "that love will become the cult of humanity."

"But in the meantime," she stressed in the second article she wrote in Paris in 1911 ("Sexual Relations and The Class Struggle"), "people have to sit in the cold with their spiritual loneliness and can only dream about the 'better age,' when all relationships between people will be warmed by the rays of the sun-god": attempts to achieve freer sexual relationships outside marriage and to live more communally aroused hopes that could not possibly be fulfilled while people still lived under the burden of spiritual loneliness born of property relations. It was not until seven years later, when these articles were republished in the Soviet Republic, that her ideas were found acceptable and fully discussed. They will be touched on later, because in 1918 the same articles in a different context had a rather different resonance.[14]

In Paris, Alexandra addressed crowds of enthusiastic Russians in a number of speeches along similar lines. But rowdy anarchists also occasionally burst into the drafty barn on the Avenue de Choisy which Bolsheviks and Mensheviks in Paris used as a meeting place, where they heard Lunacharsky talk about the erotic sculpture of Rodin and Alexandra storm against bourgeois morality. In Paris she also met Lenin, Nadezhda Krupskaya, and various members of their Bolshevik entourage (Inessa Armand, Grigori Zinoviev, Lev Kamenev, and Nikolai Semashko) who were all teaching that spring and summer at the workers' school they had organized at the nearby village of Longjumeau to offset the deviant experiments at Capri and Bologna. Cycling into Paris every day to attend meetings, they radiated such health and confidence in the slowly expanding Bolshevik Party that many errant "godbuilders" and "recallers" were rejoining their ranks; Alexandra could not but be impressed.

As a later novel of Alexandra's indicates, she was also deeply impressed by the great love that Inessa Armand and Lenin had for each other, which apparently did not conflict either with their affection for Nadezhda Krupskaya or with their political work. Although Alexandra was never a close friend of Inessa Armand, she must have felt drawn to this talented and original woman, whose charity work with the prostitutes of Moscow in the 1890's had led her to the more militant politics of Russian social democracy. Along with her five children she had left her husband in 1904 to live openly with her brother-in-law in Moscow, where she had joined the Social Democratic Party. She had taken part there in the December uprising of 1905 and had shortly after that been forced to leave Russia to avoid arrest. In 1910 she met Lenin in Paris and moved in with him and Nadezhda Krupskaya. It was then that the love between her and Lenin developed, a love which was to last until the 1917 revolution. This love cannot have done too much harm to the friendship with Nadezhda Krupskaya, for while the two women were teaching at Longjumeau they began to plan together how they might best work with Russian women in Paris.

Alexandra based the perceptions of her 1923 novella, *A Great Love*, on the distant glimpses she had in 1911 of this revolutionary menage. At the time there were other writing commitments which demanded almost all her energy. She would break off this writing only to address meetings, or to spend a few stiff evenings with Paul and Laura Lafargue at their Draveil mansion. She also embarked on an agitational trip to some of the industrial towns north of Paris, and in the summer she set off for the south of France to do a fund-raising speaking tour at Chicherin's request.

Her stay there was cut short by the news that housewives in and around Paris were demonstrating in force against rising food costs, and she hurried back north in September to join the marches and demonstrations. She spoke in street markets (where stalls were smashed and merchants attacked by angry women), in squares, in large covered markets and food halls, and in dark, crowded restaurants. Many of the "slaves of the hearth" she met had been converted through desperation and poverty into fine organizers and speakers; she praised their courage in an article ("The Housewives' Movement in France") for the Menshevik journal *Our Dawn*, published in Paris. By the end of the month the women could claim a partial victory, as cheap meat began to be imported from Argentina in response to their demonstrations.[15]

By September waves of homesickness and loneliness were assailing Alexandra. She had not seen Misha for over a year and had few friends in Paris. She wrote to Tatiana Schepkina from Passy:

> I feel so drawn to Russia, especially now. I can so clearly see you all gathering mushrooms, and the interminable rain falling, and the smell of the leaves, and the brilliant dew on the ripe red rowan trees . . . Oh, how I loved Kuusa in September—I think it was my favorite month, with those cold moonlit nights, the smell of the pine trees, the spiders' webs and the dewy haze of the mornings . . .[16]

The evenings she spent at the Lafargues were too formal for any close friendship between them to develop, as a note from Laura indicates: "Be good enough to dine with us next Saturday (September 16)," she wrote to Alexandra. "Catch the 3:30 train from the Gare de Lyon and return to Paris by an evening train." Yet two months after dining with them she was sincerely grieved to hear of their suicide and joined the thousands of people accompanying their coffin to its civil burial at the Père Lachaise cemetery. Both she and Lenin spoke briefly at their graves.

At the end of 1911 she went to Belgium to speak to the Russian colonies in Liège and Brussels, and this went so well that she was almost immediately invited back by the Belgian Socialist Party to address meetings in the industrial and mining regions of Turkuan and Borinage. She spent three weeks traipsing from one wretched village to another. The miners were angry and longed to strike, but they were demoralized and inexperienced: "Here one had to prepare their mood cautiously but firmly."[17] At every village she was welcomed with a great deal more politeness than she subsequently found in the Belgian leaders. One group of workers offered her a bag of stale rolls to eat after the meeting, and when her galoshes were stolen at another village, several muddy miles' walk from the nearest road, the organizers were so distressed that they collected five francs which they sent on to her with an apologetic note. This represented three days' wages for them, and she was so moved that she found her visit to the Brussels mansion of the Belgian Socialist Party leader, Vandervelde, quite unbearable.

After walking from the station to his house, she was greeted disdainfully by a liveried footman who refused to take her muddy coat and made her wait in the hall. When she was eventually received into Mrs. Vandervelde's ornately furnished drawing room, filled with artistic and literary celebrities, she was haunted by her recent experiences of poverty and slave labor. "Where was the contact, the comradely leadership?" she asked herself as she took her leave of these socialist dilettantes.

"My tour went excellently," she wrote to Tatiana from Paris in December 1911:

Everywhere audiences of a thousand and more people. Only the clerical newspapers thundered against "this Russian woman being taken around from one public hall to another," and demanded that it was high time to expel me. They even talked of trying to arrest me too, but of course that only drew more attention to me. I'm rather tired from traveling—do you realize, I made nineteen speeches in twenty-one days! All I want to do now is to sit here quietly and get on with some writing.[18]

For the next month that was what she did.

The Belgian press had also described her as a revolutionary on the run, preaching women's emancipation. She made good the charge by writing an article on Belgian working women's lives for the legal Bolshevik paper *Factory Life,* published in St. Petersburg.[19] She also had some tentative discussions with Inessa Armand and Nadezhda Krupskaya about the possibility of launching in Paris a Bolshevik paper for women. In those ten months in Paris she had started to move closer to the Bolsheviks, and when she returned to Berlin in January, she began to find Bolshevik militancy increasingly attractive, for she could no longer fully share the Mensheviks' confidence in the SPD.

In the months she was away, the Party had failed lamentably to deal with the first threat of war. When, in June, Germany had sent a warship to Agadir to protect Germany's interests in Morocco, France had retaliated by sending 50,000 troops into the capital, Fez, and Spain had speedily dispatched its own troops to back them up. Five days later Huysmans, secretary of the International, had invited the socialist parties of all countries to meet. The French and Belgians agreed immediately. But Molkenbühr (Alexandra's traveling companion from Copenhagen who had snoozed all the way to Germany), who was now temporarily representing Germany in the International, did not feel at all anxious about the situation. He reminded Huysmans in a secret letter that the German arms magnates Krupp and Thyssen had large interests in French mining; the Moroccan affair could only be a government ploy to divert attention from the Reichstag election, in which the SPD expected to do phenomenally well. There was no International meeting.

Rosa Luxemburg printed a version of Huysmans's letter and Molkenbühr's reply in the *Leipziger Volkszeitung,* and between the June incident and the elections in January 1912 Klara Zetkin traveled around Germany speaking on the dangers of war and the possibilities for resistance; *Die Gleichheit* remained faithful to the revolutionary left opposition. But all crucial positions in the Party were gradually passing to the reformists as the Party entered into a secret alliance with the liberals, and the radical control commission on which Klara Zetkin sat was dissolved.

Alexandra returned to Berlin in time for the election results, which gave the SPD a staggering 4,500,000 votes; its alliance with the liberals ensured that an extra 125,000,000 marks was voted for the naval and military budget. Bernstein persistently described war as one of those "occasional interruptions" in the progress toward international understanding and the arms race as a "non-organic parasite on the tree of modern economic development." Kautsky regarded the arms manufacturers as a "small clique" who should be brought to heel at an international meeting of the great powers.[20] But his words were lost in the wind. Even as he belatedly supported Liebknecht's campaign for anti-conscription agitation in the public schools the revisionist majority was clamoring for improved military training schemes. As strike followed strike and Rosa Luxemburg and the increasingly isolated radicals hoped against all hope for the day when the great lumbering Party would be engulfed by revolution, Kautsky repeated like a schoolmaster that the Party would support a mass strike only when one could no longer be restrained. Never before had the SPD "center" so clearly expressed its function—to thwart revolution. Agitation was out of the question, and it was with great relief that Alexandra accepted an invitation from the Swedish Party to embark on a three-week speaking tour in April and address a large antiwar May Day rally in Stockholm.

She arrived in early April to a warm welcome from Hjalmar Branting, leader of the Swedish Socialist Party, and the young radicals Frederic Ström and Zeth Höglund, whom she had met in Malmö. Posters everywhere announced her arrival. For the next seventeen days she addressed meetings in Ystad, Varberg, Göteborg, Lervik, and the factories of Bohus, comparing the 1905 revolution, which had been prompted by the sufferings of the Russo-Japanese War, to the rising anger in Sweden at the new conscription law. The same red specter now haunted Europe, she said (speaking in German, with Dr. Janes Sheld translating for her), for every strike was a protest against war. Thousands of people packed the Erde field in Stockholm for the May Day meeting organized by the revolutionary wing of the Swedish Party, and Alexandra shouted and shook her fist in a speech which gravely alarmed the conservative Swedish press. "The Tsar knows from experience that his war plans are threatened by the red specter of revolution. War on war!"[21]

She wrote to Tatiana after the tour was over:

> I would so like to be able to share my experiences with you, but for the
> time being I'm sending you this poster, which appears on the walls of
> fifteen towns and villages here . . . It's given me a feeling of huge moral
> satisfaction, for I was consciously and visibly speaking for the radical wing
> of the Swedish Party as a whole, not just the women's section, although
> I hope I gave something to the women too . . . There was tiredness of
> course, and a great deal of discomfort, but this was all nothing beside the
> warmth, generosity, and consideration of everyone I met here . . .[22]

She was seen off at the station by a huge crowd of women and young
socialists, and looked forward to returning.

Alexandra arrived in Berlin to find a letter from Kautsky formally
terminating their friendship; several cold letters from former German
friends followed. People who had opened their hearts and homes to her
as a friend had discovered that they had been nourishing a viper. She had
exposed their most intimate secrets in her book *Around Workers' Europe,*
which had recently been published in Russia.[23] Few of them had read it
—even those like Kautsky who could read Russian had not actually bothered to do so—but they were extraordinarily quick to see it as the work
of a "Russian chauvinist" out to make a spiteful mockery of the Party and
satirize its leaders. Acutely depressed, she begged Liebknecht to plead her
case before the Party's central committee, but there were no concrete
charges against her, only the deep hostility of almost all her old friends
in Germany. From Russia, though, she received a rather more cheering
response. One political prisoner wrote from Riga to tell her that the book
had been smuggled into the prison and was giving great pleasure to the
inmates, and Gorky and his companion Maria Andreeva wrote to sympathize with her in her isolation. "I congratulate you and shake your hand,"
wrote Maria Andreeva. "So many times when reading it I wanted to burst
into laughter and tears simultaneously."[24] Chicherin too was full of praise
for her honest insights into the German Party, and Liebknecht tried to
persuade her to regard the whole episode as political rather than personal.
But Alexandra was inconsolable, for "no suffering can equal that of seeing
one's comrades turn their backs and speak ill of one's efforts," especially
when those comrades included Klara Zetkin and others in the Women's
Bureau.

Zoya hurried out from St. Petersburg, where she was working for
various art journals, and stayed with her for a few weeks in Grünewald,
for despite all the times when life separated them and their friendship was
sustained only by letters, they were still extremely close to one another.
Although Zoya was never a political activist, she shared with Alexandra

both the political idealism which they had discovered together as children, and the strength and self-reliance to make an independent hard-working life for herself as a writer. (She was apparently unmarried, and little is known of the details of her personal life.) After Zoya left, Alexandra moved out of Berlin to the small metal-workers' town of Zeiten, telling very few people her address and soon burying herself in her writing. Here she worked ten hours every day compiling her research materials for *Society and Motherhood*, her stern routine broken only when Misha visited later that summer. "Spread out all around me are laws, financial reports, memoranda," she wrote to Zoya. "I've hidden from the world, shut the door, and am not giving my address to anyone. The weather is getting colder and we burn a stove. By early evening I'm already in my huge cold bed, and first thing in the morning I'm at work again . . ."[25]

In 1911 Lloyd George, England's Liberal Chancellor of the Exchequer, was inspired by the German National Insurance Act to pass his own National Insurance Act, which allowed women to contribute to a fund for four weeks' paid maternity leave. In an article she wrote in the summer of 1912 for the Menshevik journal *Our Dawn;* Alexandra welcomed this Act as a "blow to hypocrisy," which "cut through the path of routinism and conservatism," even if it was intended primarily to protect the child rather than its mother. She was careful, however, to stress her differences with the German women in the Motherhood Protection League, who were agitating for motherhood to be a freely available option, aided by state benefits, for all women. The ideas of Ruth Bree and other League members she dismissed as mere "utopian ravings"; there could be no doubt in her mind that the English and German governments were passing maternity laws in this period of growing military confrontation between them merely to ensure a greater supply of "cannon meat". Capitalists throughout Europe had every reason to fear that as women entered the workforce in large numbers to boost arms production they would inevitably tend to assume a greater control over their fertility: in Alexandra's opinion this fear of a "birth strike" was behind Lloyd George's Insurance Act. However, it was still to be welcomed for the undoubted benefits it offered to working women, and Alexandra referred contemptuously to the workers' insurance bill just passed by the Russian Duma which, in "typical Black Hundreds spirit," had omitted any mention of women.[26]

She may have sent a translation of this article to the trade unionists she had met in London; in any event it was probably this article that prompted an invitation to the TUC congress in September 1912 in Newport, Cardiff. She set about getting a mandate from the St. Petersburg textile union to attend.

When she arrived in Wales, however, her mandate cut little ice with the cautious Labor MP, Arthur Henderson, and the TUC organizers of the congress, whom she found desperately anxious to curb any discussion of mass action against war. It was only thanks to the eloquence of the radical unionist Tom Mann that she was eventually allowed to attend. In Newport she met Margaret Bondfield, the trade union activist and president of the Adult Suffrage Society, as well as Margaret Llewellyn Davies, organizer of the Women's Cooperative Guild. She also met some young organizers of what she described as "communist universities," by which she probably meant socialist night schools for workers. "Despite the fact that these universities supposedly followed the Marxist school, the syndicalist spirit certainly reigned among these young people. You felt a decisive revolutionary boldness about them that was completely lacking in the older trade unionists like Henderson."[27]

From Wales, Alexandra traveled to London, and she stayed for the next two months in the Greville Street boarding house. Working steadily by day on her book at the British Museum Library, in the evenings and on weekends she led a sociable life with members of the Russian colony. Chicherin was then in London, working on another of his indefatigable fund-raising campaigns with an earnest ex-suffragette called Mrs. Bridges-Adams. Maxim Litvinov, who spoke English well and was established in Hampstead as "Mr. Harrison," ran the Herzen Club, at which she spoke a few times. Ivan Maisky, the future Soviet diplomat, was at that time living in such poverty that he often fled his cold room for the warmth of the British Museum and the "bright flame" of Alexandra's company. She gave a few parties in her room, but the group usually congregated in the Oakley Square flat of the Bolshevik Nikolai Kerzhentsev, who like Alexandra had been a teacher at the Bologna school and was now married. On Saturdays and Sundays when the weather was fine they would go to Hampstead Heath, and their little encampment on Parliament Hill became quite a feature of the landscape. There they would spend the day playing chess and singing, running about with their children, talking, and sleeping. And there, according to young Maisky, who was to become a close friend of hers several years after the 1917 revolution, Alexandra was always the center of the liveliest conversations. Once at the end of a long September day spent on the Heath they all raced down the hill in couples, and as she sped down the hill, the setting sun behind her and her wide skirts floating about her, it seemed to the smitten Maisky that she was on fire.[28]

She was well out of Berlin. While she was away in the autumn of 1912 an anonymous review of *Workers' Europe* appeared in a trade-union paper, announcing that she was a Russian chauvinist and darkly hinting that she was a Russian agent. Legien, the touchy architect of the German union movement, summoned her to an interview; Liebknecht went in her stead, publicly denounced the review and added his signature to those of Gorky and Lunacharsky in a formal protest to the Party. In October, when Montenegro, Serbia, Bulgaria, and Greece joined forces in military action against Turkey, the SPD at last recognized the terrifying fact that the unhinged Russian Tsar seriously regarded the capture of Constantinople as the "great national hope." With anti-Russian feelings raging, the Germans agreed to an extraordinary meeting of the Second International in Basel to discuss the imminent war in the Balkans.

As delegate of the St. Petersburg textile union, Alexandra attended this last, tragically empty gesture of international social democracy. In a huge and splendid display of powerlessness and confusion 16,000 people demonstrated in the town of Basel and, led by children and young girls dressed in white, walked silently to the cathedral, offered for the occasion by the church council. The bells tolled, the red and white banners poured into the doors, the organ peeled out Beethoven's *Hymn to Peace,* and 550 delegates cried "War on War! Peace on Earth! Long Live the International!" It was impossible not to be moved, even though moved to despair.

"The meaning of the demonstration was read as a prophecy on the palace walls," wrote Alexandra to the women in the textile union. Anseele, the Belgian secretary of the International, presided, and in speech after rousing speech the socialist leaders of Europe proclaimed that the mighty International could still avert war if the workers of the world confronted their murdering capitalist oppressors and refused to fight. There were more speeches on makeshift platforms in the cathedral square. "I spoke as your delegate," Alexandra wrote to the women textile workers, and she spoke too at a couple of meetings organized the next day by the Swiss women's movement and the Party's youth group. She stayed on for the next few months in Switzerland, speaking at the invitation of the radical Swiss socialist, Fritz Platten, mainly at women's meetings. After a "mad gallop" across Switzerland to Lausanne, Winterthur, and Davos, she took a short holiday in the Alps with Platten and his friends, after which she helped to organize an antiwar demonstration to mark Women's Day.

Then in March she went again to Paris, where she addressed a few antiwar meetings organized by Russian émigrés, and from there to Belgium, where her old friends from Turkuan had arranged some antiwar meetings.

When she returned to Berlin in the autumn of 1913, her heart was troubling her, and she had to take to her bed. For the rest of her life increasingly crippling attacks of angina would overshadow her more stressful days, and from that time on she never traveled without her bromide and valerian tinctures. Ill and alone, she immersed herself in fiction—Flaubert, Rolland, Colette, Shaw, Schnitzler—and relating their attitudes toward women to her own ideas and those of several lesser-known German, Scandinavian, and Russian writers (including Tatiana Schepkina), she began her essay *The New Woman,* which appeared the following year.

Republished in 1918 along with *Sexual Relations and the Class Struggle* and *On an Old Theme,* this essay gave imaginative amplification to the ideas expressed in her previous two articles. The new type of single woman celebrated in fiction by innumerable writers had her counterpart in the single woman of the cities; for millions of women working by day in the offices and factories were living alone by night in their tiny rooms and surviving without marriage—free, resilient, soberly dressed, and self-reliant. It was capitalism which had created this new "species" of woman, forced by the "scourge of hunger" to struggle for her existence and so to enter directly and actively into the struggle of her class. It was her toiling life which forced her first to challenge and then to reject the conventions of bourgeois morality. For in learning through a life of hard-working independence how to assert her own personality, her "ego" no longer demanded exclusive possession of her partner in a sexual relationship. Whereas before the burden was always on the woman to build all her emotions around men so as to ensure the continuity of the marriage relationship, "the new woman assumes a rejecting or indifferent attitude to the firm bond, and is altogether in no hurry to pursue her love relationships in any particular fixed or determined form. The state of being in love —of passionate love—are but transient periods in her life." Struggling to harmonize her inner freedom and self-reliance with the "all-consuming passion of love," the "new woman" knew that it must be through work, not emotion, that she would finally and fully develop her social personality. And in this personal struggle of hers she would become intimately and directly involved in the class struggle, for it was in the collective effort to adjust to new economic conditions that she would find that her own developing psychology corresponded with that being evolved by the entire working class in its own interest. Social ideas, science, her calling, her creativity—it was by these things that the "new woman" lived: "asserting her individuality instead of naïvely attempting to absorb and reflect the alien nature of the 'beloved,' insisting on her right to earthly happiness instead of hypocritically donning the mask of virtue, and finally, putting the expression of love in a subordinate place in her life." It was in this process that she would develop to the point where "before us stands not a mate—the shadow of a man; before us stands a personality—a whole and human woman."[29]

Alexandra's thoughts were also turning to International Women's Day, and in letters to the women textile workers of St. Petersburg she was urging them to organize demonstrations to mark the occasion. Learning from them of a club which had opened in Moscow under the auspices of both Bolsheviks and Mensheviks and which already boasted some 900 members, she felt this would be an ideal place for their propaganda to be centered, and her hopes were rewarded when thousands of women poured out on the streets on March 8 to protest against the hardships of their working lives. A huge women's meeting in St. Petersburg at the Kalash-nikov Stock Exchange was soon swarming with police, who made numer-ous arrests, and similar meetings in Tiflis, Samara, and Kiev ensured that the Moscow women's club was soon closed. But the occasion had been fully covered by the socialist press. The Bolshevik newspaper, *Pravda (Truth)*, launched the previous year, carried pictures of women fighters, greetings from women abroad, and an article by Alexandra celebrating Women's Day in Russia as a "welcome sign that the Tsar's prisons and gallows are powerless to kill the workers' spirit."[30]

Her own spirits were still at a low ebb, and in the autumn of 1913 she left Berlin for London; she had not finished her work at the British Museum and needed to be revived by London's friendly social life. She spoke at several meetings organized in defense of the wretched persecuted Russian Jew Beilis. An impoverished laborer whose only crime was to live outside the Jewish Pale in South Russia, Beilis had been accused in a particularly horrible trial of organizing the gruesome ritualistic murder of a Gentile boy. His case was taken up by socialists in Russia and abroad, where a great defense campaign eventually managed to secure his release from his long and brutal prison sentence. Alexandra spoke at a large defense rally in Trafalgar Square, at which she eloquently attacked the tsarist government's bestial treatment of Jews. With her friend Ida Ter-ssinnen, the Finnish socialist, she also attended in London some meetings at Bebel House on maternity insurance.

When she returned to Berlin that winter, she found effusively apologetic letters from all the German leaders; *Workers' Europe* had been translated and passed around in manuscript, and had been found to be not so very offensive after all. But in a way the SPD leaders' first fantastically touchy response only confirmed the truth of her book's criticisms of the workings of the Party; "in every ironic reference to any old Schulz or Meier they saw clear evidence of a 'betrayal of socialism.' "[31]

Klara Zetkin was the first to write, apologizing unreservedly and warmly begging to resume their old friendship. She invited Alexandra to join the organizing committee for the women's congress of the International the following August in Vienna, at which it was planned to discuss women's suffrage, maternity protection, and how to demonstrate against rising living costs. (All three points Alexandra discussed in an article in the *New Workers' Paper.*) By the end of 1913 she had joined the International's Women's Bureau, and the head of the St. Petersburg secret police was writing to the tsarist police chief in Berlin to warn him of her renewed activities in the German Party.[32]

In the new year Inessa Armand joined the women's bureau as Bolshevik representative. Earlier tentative discussions about a Bolshevik women's paper were now showing positive results, for the *Pravda* Women's Day issue had prompted more letters than it could possibly print. Plans were swiftly made to bring out in St. Petersburg the first number of *Rabotnitsa (Working Woman)* on Women's Day—and the government, much to the Bolsheviks' amazement, gave its permission. Half the women on its editorial board—Praskovya Kudelli, Konkordia Samoilova, Lyudmila Menzhinskaya, and Lenin's older sister, Anna Elizarova, with whom Alexandra had worked between 1905 and 1908— were in Russia. The others—Inessa Armand, Nadezhda Krupskaya, Lilina Zinovieva, and Lyudmila Stal—were scattered about their various places of exile. Alexandra was in touch with several of the editors, but since she was still formally a Menshevik, she did not work on the first issue of *Rabotnitsa,* which despite all odds, and the arrest of the St. Petersburg editorial board after their second meeting, did come out on March 8, 1914 (produced single-handedly by Elizarova) and at once sold 12,000 copies. New editors were found who did sewing jobs to scrape up the money for a second, third, and fourth issue. The new offices were deluged with letters, and thousands of factory women gratefully paid out their four kopeks and ensured that *Rabotnitsa* survived in spirit long after it was closed down by the police in late June 1914 for the subversively accurate reporting of its fifth issue.

The success of *Rabotnitsa,* coinciding with the ineffectual appearance of the Menshevik paper *Women's Voice,* may have worsened Alexandra's already strained relations with the predominantly Menshevik Berlin community. When Lunacharsky accepted an invitation to give a couple of talks there in the winter of 1913, only she and Mikhail Uritsky protested at his extradition by the Prussian police. Her criticisms went further than that, however, for she saw "a little group forming in the community, composed of the leaders and the led," the leaders excluding from any responsible jobs those without "conspiratorial experience." Since most of the hundreds of Russian workers in Berlin inevitably lacked this experience, the Party had been reduced to a small intellectual clique, and Alexandra was accused of "demagoguery."[33]

But most of her time was taken up with preparations for the women's congress of the International, and she prepared documents, held meetings in her boarding house, and wrote a series of articles on the women's movement for the Russian press,[34] as if in frenzied work to repress the fear of war. "Would you be so good as to tell me in which year Sablina's illegal pamphlet appeared?" she wrote to Nadezhda Krupskaya in Krakow ("Sablina" was Nadezhda's underground name; her pamphlet, *Woman Worker,* came out in 1900):

> We need it for our book-stall. And have you any other illegal pamphlets or leaflets specially dealing with women? If anything comes to mind do get hold of it and send it to the socialist book stall for the International congress. Do please lean on your comrades and get them also to send me as much as they can, for I want this stall to be very well equipped. Comradely greetings, A.K.[35]

Nationalistic chauvinism had not yet touched the friendly inhabitants of the Hübertusallee boarding house, and Alexandra rarely left Grünewald that spring as patriotic demonstrations filled the center of Berlin and the Party dared not and did not try to match them. At the end of April some socialist women from Holland, France, and Scandinavia gathered for a two-day meeting at her boarding house to plan a large women's antiwar demonstration in Berlin that July. By then, however, the police were already out to arrest Alexandra, plans for the congress had disintegrated, and she had to leave the demonstration without reading her speech, which was circulated under the pseudonym of Davydova.

She left at once for Bavaria, and shortly afterward the police searched the boarding house for her. In the spa town of Kohlgrub, where nineteen-year-old Misha joined her, she doggedly worked away with one part of her mind on her congress reports, and watched people dance and gossip as if nothing were happening. But the letters she was receiving from home gripped her with an icy panic. "Why do none of my Russian comrades write about the war, only about the strikes, the barricades in St. Petersburg, and the revolution in the air?" she wrote in her diary[36] as Russia prepared to enter a war for which she had neither communications, nor guns, nor popular enthusiasm. Russia's war goals were self-contradictory and insane. While seeking world domination via the Black Sea and the Dardanelles, the Tsar could choose his targets only at the convenience of the superpowers, Germany, Britain and France, and was therefore merely paying for the right to be a privileged colony and ally, and to import capital and pay interest. The whole country was convulsed by strikes and demonstrations, and during the state visit of President Poincaré barricades were thrown up and there was fighting with the police. Throughout all these upheavals the Tsar's court and government were reminiscent of a madhouse, controlled by a mad "man of God," the monk Rasputin, whose apparent healing powers over the hemophiliac Tsarevich had given him and his innumerable charlatan associates a limitless power to dictate tsarist policy. Controlled by Rasputin and the mass of weird superstitions he introduced into the Tsar's family, Nicholas II was only too grateful to seize at the chance to proclaim the old virtues of "Autocracy, Nationalism and Orthodoxy."

Yet the Mensheviks, it became distressingly clear to Alexandra, were failing to make any propaganda against the mobilization. As the police department reported, "The most energetic and audacious elements, ready for tireless resistance, are the people concentrated around Lenin."

At the end of July she wrote: "Several Bavarian holidaymakers have decided to go home. Nobody believes there will be war. Everybody you talk to describes it as insanity . . ." Desperate for news, she and Misha decided to leave for Berlin. She bought *Vorwärts* in Munich, and learned that the SPD had organized an antiwar demonstration at Unter den Linden. But "again that excessively abstract tone . . . It says 'our country' does not want war. What does 'our country' mean? Why not simply say the workers won't allow this war? If they want Russia to avoid war, it's because they're afraid of its inevitable consequence—revolution."[37]

9

War on War!

Alexandra and Misha arrived in Berlin on August 1, 1914, and, escaping the gangs of rowdy patriots on the streets, found Grünewald as peaceful and friendly as ever. There was still hope: in France huge demonstrations continued, and in the SPD there was still a group of radical war-resisters. But hopes ebbed with the daylight hours, and as dusk fell a gray car traveled slowly along the Hübertusallee scattering leaflets: war had been declared on Russia. "Can't stop trembling," she wrote in her diary. "Suffering as for the death agony of a loved one. So this is war! When we first conceived of it, we imagined that at once the shadow of the red specter would spring up from behind its shoulders. But this submissive bewilderment, this silence from the Party, is enough to drive one mad."[1] By evening an atmosphere of such hysterical and suspicious chauvinism had crept into the boarding house that the landlady begged Alexandra and Misha to keep quiet for fear of an anti-Russian pogrom. As the boarders drowned their anxieties and belted out patriotic songs Alexandra and Misha fled to the SPD offices to ask Haase how soon the International could be convened; finding him extraordinarily vague, they went on to the Women's Bureau on the Lindenstrasse to discover what directives the International had issued. Luise Zietz there greeted her without a hint of her former warmth. Klara Zetkin was in a state of nervous prostration, she said, and was preparing a special issue of *Die Gleichheit*. There was no news from the Party, but, Luise said uneasily, she supposed that Germany must fight to free Russians from tsarism. "I looked her in the eye and realized that I'd never come to any understanding with her. I had the impression I was no longer a comrade but a Russian."[2]

The next day huge crowds of patriots assembled at the Unter den

Linden to be addressed by the Kaiser, and to cheer him with ovations and war songs. In "russified" St. Petersburg (renamed Petrograd), Tsar Nicholas returned from Germany to be greeted by thousands of his people singing the *Te Deum* on their knees outside the Winter Palace. Only in France did people continue to demonstrate, their rage surviving the loss of their most devastating orator: when Alexandra visited the Liebknechts, Karl (who had returned from France that day) vividly described Jaurès's murder in a Paris café and the frenzied demonstrations that followed his death. "The most frightful thing was that despite the great and terrible loss of this man, yet what a pale and petty incident it was against the nightmarish background of war," she wrote.[3]

Liebknecht was in a state of constant frantic activity. As he dashed about "like a cloud in the sky, pockets stuffed with notebooks, arms full of papers he would never have time to read, covered in street dust and smiles,"[4] he became increasingly isolated in the Party, and increasingly regarded by his colleagues as mad. Alexandra described his cheek twitching as he signed papers and answered the telephone, and almost all her conversations with him—virtually her only German friend during those terrible summer months of 1914—took place on trams and buses. Accompanying him one day to the center of town where he was to attend a Reichstag session, she learned that the SPD Reichstag faction was to meet the following evening to draft a united statement on the government budget, in which a staggering five billion marks were being demanded in war credits for the giant arms manufacturers, Krupp and Mannesman. The party majority felt that any protest would appear so insignificant that people would feel dispirited and future antiwar work would be undermined. Liebknecht and thirteen other dissident radicals were to have their protest incorporated into a statement which Kautsky had the unenviable task of wording.

Alexandra forgot her old differences with members of the Russian colony. As the taverns filled with cannon fodder and the streets thronged with shouting patriots Radek and other Russian hotheads "dashed around like madmen, cursing the Party for its failure to give the signal even for some demonstrations. The most pessimistic feared that the SPD might abstain, but not even the wildest pessimist imagined it might vote for the war credits."[5] That evening several Russian and German friends gathered in Alexandra's room:

> There we all sat, not daring to put on the light, as the men from the bakery below had threatened to organize a pogrom against all the Rus-

sians in the boarding house. The landlady asked us to keep very quiet. Now everyone has gone back to their rooms and Misha is asleep—but sleep escapes me. I look out of the window at dear familiar Grünewald, the sky and stars are so magnificently clear, and yet all I can hear is shooting, groans, women weeping, and I feel this terrible time will never end . . .[6]

By dawn her sleepless mind was still refusing to comprehend this war in which millions of people from twenty-eight countries were preparing to fight. At six in the morning sixteen policemen arrived to take her and Misha to the Alexanderplatz police headquarters, and after some rough questioning they were locked in a large empty cell guarded by police. Orders were given for her room to be searched, and she thought with horror of her mandate to the International congress. That mandate was to be her talisman. The next day, after another sleepless night, the door opened to reveal a fat policeman, who smilingly held out the documents and told her she could go—a revolutionary agitator could not possibly support the "Russian barbarians." It was eloquent testimony to the International's impotence. "That document which a week ago would have warranted my arrest now opened the doors of the Alexanderplatz to me."[7]

Alexandra went straight to the Reichstag to mobilize some support for Misha and the entire imprisoned Russian community, and on the way picked up a copy of *Vorwärts*—not even the most token protest against the Russians' harassment, no hint of international solidarity in theory or practice! Nor could she discover any clue as to how the SPD was to vote that day on the war credits. Her heart sank when she met Kautsky in the Reichstag corridor. Aged and distracted, both his sons called up for the Austrian army and his wife in Italy, he answered her questions vaguely: " 'In such terrible times everyone must bear his cross.' His cross? Has the old man gone out of his mind?" As one socialist deputy after another passed her in the corridor, many in uniform and accompanied by volunteer nurses, the horrible truth sank into her shocked consciousness that they really were going to vote for the government's war credits and so subsidize the monstrously powerful German arms magnates. Old friends hurried up, brimming over with incomprehensible patriotism and urging her that the war would defeat tsarism ("What, with the Oberkommando [the general staff] and the sword?" she riposted). Even the young stars of the Party, Frank, Wendel, and David (with whom she had spent an occasional evening at Josty's Café, a popular meeting place for young radicals), were now flaunting their uniforms, cursing *Vorwärts*, and declaring that the bullet was the answer to all arguments now. Her old friend

Stadhagen had also caved in: "If a robber attacks my house, I'd be a fool indeed if I started nattering about 'humane feelings' instead of shooting him!" As the deputies filed into this momentous session she managed to catch the attention of Hugo Haase, who shared with Liebknecht the chairmanship of the SPD. He assured her that the Party was in such favor with the government that he would personally intercede with the chancellor for the Russians' release. She bought a ticket for the visitors' gallery and went in.[8]

The gallery was packed and tense as the deputies listened respectfully to the chancellor, Bethmann-Hollweg, launch into a lengthy speech blaming Russia for the war. There were murmurs only as he mentioned the possibility of an invasion of Belgium (which was in fact already planned to start that evening). In the second session the SPD would deliver its statement promising not to abandon the Reich in its time of need.

During the afternoon recess Liebknecht, who was only too pleased to leave the oppressive Reichstag and his hostile colleagues, accompanied Alexandra on a long crowded busride across town to Oberkommando headquarters to demand the release of the Russian prisoners. They were subjected to a long wait by "dimwits in military uniforms, carrying out as precisely as machines their instructions from above."[9] Liebknecht grew increasingly agitated, pointing out to Alexandra the press office where telegrams about foreign spies and German victories were manufactured; and when they did at last see an adjutant, Alexandra was told that it would take three weeks for Misha's identity to be checked. In the meantime she could apply for permission to visit. They returned to the Reichstag just in time for the second session at five o'clock.

Haase read out the SPD statement and was greeted, even from the conservative benches, by a storm of patriotic applause. People jumped up, cried, shook hands, and Liebknecht walked out. He was immediately surrounded by a crowd of socialists reviling him as a traitor and a raving maniac. Rushing distraught into the corridor, Alexandra was met by Würms, who had arranged her first speaking-tour in the Pfalz and who now told her she had no right to be there. She and Liebknecht made their escape; as most buses had already been mobilized for war service, they walked through the Tiergarten, banishing despair by pondering on how leftists in the SPD and the International might be regrouped to fight the mobilization. Liebknecht still believed it would be only a matter of time before the Party was liquidated and they could then come out in open revolutionary opposition to the war. (It was precisely this faith—that the largest socialist party in the most industrially developed country of Europe could still be saved—that made the oppositionists so scattered and lacking in cohesion.)

That evening, as soon as news of the vote was out, Rosa Luxemburg called a meeting of close friends and sent telegrams to 300 known radicals urging them to come to Berlin for a vital conference. Klara Zetkin was the only one to send unreserved support; the few others who bothered to reply did so unenthusiastically. A few days later a letter disclaiming the SPD's vote and signed by Rosa Luxemburg, Klara Zetkin, Liebknecht, and Mehring appeared in two Swiss papers. On August 5 *Die Gleichheit's* leading article similarly denounced the vote and encouraged its readers to take part in antiwar demonstrations.

The next day, August 4, 1914, England declared war on Germany. Sophia Liebknecht was held at pistol-point while police searched the house, and Alexandra was ordered to leave the country. By this time she had no money for food or rent and was sick with anxiety that Misha might be kept in prison indefinitely. There was constant harassment from the police and chauvinists in the boarding house. "It was like lying with bound hands in the middle of the road. Horses are frenziedly galloping closer, they're on top . . . And nobody notices, for what do people matter now?"[10]

Yet another dawn knock on her door—but this time it was not the police but Misha, who had walked all the way from Deberitz prison, the second Russian released. Their tearful reunion was interrupted by the inevitable visit from the police, who checked their documents and once more ordered them to leave. A few days later, more Russians were released—Larin, Bukholz and Chkhenkelli, all of them hungry, harassed, and afraid to meet. The *Vorwärts* offices proudly displayed a poster exhorting people to catch Russian spies. "Life's cares sometimes shield one from world events," conceded Alexandra. "But now that the credits have been voted and people are befuddled by the slogan of 'saving the fatherland,' to what depths has the chauvinism of our German comrades sunk!"[11]

Misha wanted to "shake hands with his hero Liebknecht." Shortly after his release he accompanied Alexandra to a dinner party, a friendly but oddly assorted gathering of socialists opposed to the war. Luise Zietz was there, to Alexandra's surprise and delight, as was Eduard Fuchs, author of a number of erotic books on art history—a bohemian, who entranced her with descriptions of his visits to Egypt and his fascination with the Northern Lights. A brief blessed escape from the cold, unfriendly boarding house, here it was "all brightness, children and food. No sensation that you are an enemy, no anticipation of a pogrom . . ."[12]

But the evening had a more serious purpose. All were preoccupied with the German onslaught on Liège, particularly poor Sophie, whose brother was a student there. It was from just such gatherings of political outcasts and émigrés that the group of revolutionary internationalists emerged within the SPD who in 1918 would adopt the name of the Spartacus League.

As the SPD steadfastly refused to make any protest against the persecution of Russians, Alexandra, Bukholz, and Chkhenkelli all visited Hugo Haase to ask how the Party could ensure the release of the prisoners, save from reprisals those who were already out, lend them some money, and help them return to Russia. *Vorwärts* was restricted by the same war censorship as the other papers, Haase said, but as he enjoyed the confidence of the chancellor, he would arrange a suitable protest. As for their pressing desire to return home, did they really imagine that their Russian friends were preparing to exploit this moment to launch an armed uprising? Alexandra disliked the implication that Russian revolutionaries were working at the Kaiser's right hand, the other two argued earnestly that patriotism could be converted to revolution, and Haase dismissed them coldly. Shortly afterward Russians were offered permanent asylum in the SPD headquarters, and as a token of the Party's internationalist sentiments forty beds and washbasins were bought. Alexandra considered it outrageous that *Vorwärts* had still made not one protest against the chauvinism on the streets, but the others laughed at her for having her head in the clouds.

Enforced idleness, pointless meetings, the collapse of all beliefs, the struggle to keep afloat in the patriotic tidal wave that engulfed so many fellow Russians—all this sapped Alexandra's strength and added its own psychological burdens to the material horrors of her semi-imprisonment in Berlin. The only parties in Europe to vote against the war credits were the Bolsheviks, the Serbians, and a section of the English ILP. The Mensheviks in Berlin—ranging from a minority (like Alexandra) in intransigent opposition to the war to a majority of barely disguised patriots—reflected divisions in the whole Menshevik wing of the Party which would continue through the first terrible Russian losses right up until 1916, when no one but a lunatic or the tsarist court could seriously imagine a Russian victory. The resuscitation of the International would be a slow business. The SPD was dead, and Menshevism, as a political ideology more closely attuned to the SPD than was Bolshevism, was beginning to express for Alexandra all too many of the German Party's vile attitudes, which took their final form in patriotism.

"In the early days," wrote Alexandra in her diary on August 23, 1914, "I was so oppressed by the idea that the German Party was smashed":

> But now I feel that things are better this way. Historically better. Social democracy was at a dead end. Its creativity had dried up. All its activities were hackneyed, repetitive, congealed . . . There were no great new leaders, and this too was a sign of its stagnation. Those "promising young men," the Franks and the Stampfers, like the high priests of some decaying heathen culture, would sit around Josty's Café and talk scandal. Scandal and slander and contempt for everything "sacred" and "infalli- ble" in the Party . . . so petty, disdainful, and cynical, they only needed the Party as a springboard to government seats. Now German social democracy can no longer crush the workers' movements of the world with its unbelievably heavy bureaucratic apparatus, and its "model con- duct" which was beginning to stifle us . . .[13]

In the early days of the war, in response to urgent requests from the Allies, the Tsar had thrown a massive number of troops—the mythical "Russian steamroller"—into East Prussia and had thus helped to save Paris. By the end of August, Hindenburg had received his reinforcements and 300,000 Russians were killed at Tannenburg. And yet the SPD still crowed that this kind of mass slaughter would "liberate" Russia from tsarism. Alexan- dra was disgusted: "And this goes on in the heart of the Party which over the years has expended an unimaginable amount of energy in elaborating its 'pure socialist principles' . . . Now it can only spin fantasies about the total dissolution of all parties in an ecstasy of chauvinism . . ."[14] When *Vorwärts* sank so low as to reprint insulting comments about "barbaric Russian workers," Alexandra and some others hurried to the editors and demanded an explanation; they were told that the article had slipped in by mistake, which hardly seemed likely in a period of such harsh censor- ship. *Die Gleichheit* alone of all the socialist papers maintained its antiwar stance and consistently appealed to women to demonstrate against rising food costs and to support community relief organizations which helped women in childbirth, the sick, and the old.

At the beginning of September all citizens of Allied countries were ordered to leave Germany. There were sixty Russians in Berlin, most of them still in prison. In those difficult days Alexandra formed a close friendship with a Russian woman named Henrietta Derman and her husband. Few of the other Russians there opposed the war. One Bolshevik woman named Gordon was going to enlist as a nurse on her return to Russia—and the Mensheviks were no better. Alexandra invited Rosa

Luxemburg to her room in the hope of planning some illegal antiwar activities, but Rosa considered this plan premature and insisted that, in the initial stages, any antiwar work would have to be planned in the course of small, informal meetings. Her clear-headedness was heartening: "Her merciless sarcasm puts a great deal in its proper place."[15]

On September 13 a large crowd of Russians at the Berlin Town Hall were told that special trains had been arranged to begin the evacuation the following day. There was immediate and uncomradely competition for places, and Alexandra and Misha eventually managed to get tickets for the last train out, after standing in line at the police station for two days with their fainting, crying, pushing compatriots. Dr. Fuchs was there to provide the men with doctor's notes attesting that they were unfit for active service. Without these notes (or proof that they were bona fide students) every Russian man was liable to be called up, and it was a tremendous relief to Alexandra when Misha received his note, and she could be sure that he would not be conscripted. Fuchs was particularly well disposed towards Alexandra and Misha. He recommended that instead of sailing from Sassnitz to Trelleborg and then to Stockholm like the others, they should travel the much shorter distance from Trelleborg to Copenhagen, where he had friends. Misha could then take the boat back to Russia and resume his interrupted university studies.

The evening before their departure, Alexandra joined Larin and Chkhenkelli (the Russians released from Deberitz prison shortly after Misha) on a visit to the SPD central committee. With nothing to lose, they told them straight out what they thought of the SPD's stand on the war. Alexandra then said hurried good-byes to the Liebknechts and her other German friends, gazed for the last time at the falling leaves on the chestnut trees outside her window and, concealing her diaries in a small suitcase (for it was illegal to take any manuscripts out of the country), left for Denmark on September 16.

By 1914 the vast chain of communications planned by the Russians at the International congress four years before in Copenhagen by which revolutionary literature was to be smuggled from Lenin in Switzerland via Copenhagen (where postal services to the rest of Europe were good) to Sweden, and across the uninhabited expanses of northern Scandinavia to Finland and finally Russia was virtually perfected. Eduard Fuchs had many contacts in this "northern underground." Unfortunately in Copenhagen the export of literature was gradually becoming entangled with the far less wholesome export of black-market medical supplies and contraceptive rubber goods. Alexandra found the atmosphere there distinctly seedy and the Danish Party excessively cautious, forever checking their decisions against the historical precedents and the line laid down by the SPD.

With many misgivings she put Misha on the boat for Russia and steeled her nerves to attend some party meetings. Any hopes she might have had of doing antiwar work in Denmark dwindled rapidly. The socialists she met there either regarded national self-defense as a precondition of any class war or tended to an unconditional pacifism; although Alexandra joined the latter group, she realized quite well that the Danish Party had neither the prestige nor the organization to attach this pacifism to any program of propaganda. She shared her distress with Mikhail Uritsky, her old ally from Berlin. A friend of Trotsky's and a Menshevik since 1912, he was equally disgusted by the patriotism that had provoked even Plekhanov to call for blood and the Bolsheviks in France to enlist against the Germans. He was going to New York, where he hoped that Trotsky, who had just moved from Vienna to Switzerland, would join him. After a few weeks in Copenhagen, complicated by intense police interest in her activities, Alexandra too decided to leave, and at the end of September 1914 she traveled to Stockholm.

Alexandra knew she could rely on her old friend Hjalmar Branting, leader of the Swedish Socialist Party, and the young leftists Frederic Ström and Zeth Höglund for moral support and small loans of money (for now that her days as a paid agitator and journalist were over, she was desperately short of money). But in this newly divided socialist world where only the Bolsheviks immediately and unconditionally opposed the war, she was "wandering in the woods."[16] She took a cheap room in the Karleson Hotel on the Birger Jarla, opposite the King's Library, and it was here that she met and fell in love with another lodger who had recently arrived from Russia—Alexander Shlyapnikov. They were soon known to Swedish socialists and Russian exiles in Stockholm as lovers, and even Lenin was shortly to refer to Alexandra as Shlyapnikov's "wife." (Sweden was referred to in the letters that passed between Shlyapnikov and Lenin by its conspiratorial codename of "Spain.") Shlyapnikov was an old personal friend of Lenin's, a worker, a Bolshevik since 1903, and the resourceful organizer of the Bolsheviks' northern underground. It is possible that he and Alexandra had met and liked one another before—at the Copenhagen congress maybe, in Berlin, or elsewhere in Europe. For the past six years Shlyapnikov had been constantly on the move in Europe, working in factories (he was a skilled lathe operator) and helping to smuggle literature into Russia. They were the same age, and well matched. Both were generous, idealistic, tough, and highly moral, uninterested in power politics or factionalism. Despite poverty, insecurity, and frequent separations caused by Shlyapnikov's farflung underground assignments, they lived together very happily for several years.

A few weeks after war broke out, Lenin had written his famous *War Theses*. For the next three years all his efforts—incessant discussions, pages of articles, thousands of polemical letters—would go into defending the cause of turning the imperialist war into a revolutionary war. And for those years all Shlyapnikov's labors were dedicated to smuggling this literature into Russia. When the *Theses* reached him in Stockholm in early September, he worked tirelessly for the rest of that month, mobilizing every part-time underground postal clerk, fisherman, agent, and agitator in Scandinavia to bring Lenin's words into the factories and homes of Russia. By the time Alexandra arrived, the hotel had turned into the headquarters for leftists in the Swedish Party, who regularly met there to discuss Lenin's work and its implications.

Alexandra began to study the *Theses* closely as soon as she arrived in Stockholm and struggled to come to grips with its uncompromising message. Social democracy was dead—this she accepted. True internationalists must reclaim the name of communism by creating a new international communist movement. Lenin did not bother to go into the immediate causes of the war and who had started it, which pleased her. The Bolsheviks' concern was to analyze the class business of this war as a dynastic struggle for markets, launched to plunder foreign territory, to thwart the workers' revolution, and to "divide and decimate the proletariat of all countries by throwing the wage slaves of one nation against those of another to the profit of the bourgeoisie."[17] What Alexandra did not so easily accept was that in this crazed epoch of imperialist war and mass slaughter, there must also be just wars—those of serfs and slaves against their masters, those of national liberation, and those of wage workers against the bourgeoisie. She did not in other words so easily accept the realities of the class war.

However the *Theses* did spell out for the first time an antiwar program which she fully supported: socialists should demand that their parties vote against all war credits and withdraw from bourgeois governments; they should also establish illegal organizations where legal antiwar work was impossible, fraternize at the front, and encourage any kind of antiwar protest. Alexandra's first project when she arrived in Stockholm was to organize the sixty Russian women there into a demonstration. She described this in an article she sent to Nadezhda Krupskaya for the newly revived *Rabotnitsa,* but its editors were shortly afterward arrested, once more, and the article never appeared.

She became increasingly enthusiastic about the idea of working for the Bolsheviks, and by the end of October 1914, when Shlyapnikov wrote to Lenin that the *Theses* would be appearing in the Bolsheviks' Geneva-based underground paper, *Social Democrat,* Alexandra was inserting her own friendly note to him. Lenin's reply to her has not been kept, but to Shlyapnikov he wrote: "Heartily glad that Comrade Kollontai is on our side. Do you think she might push this manifesto in other languages?"[18] But she still had many pangs about joining the Bolsheviks and for many months remained in contact with the group of Menshevik and ex-Menshevik internationalists around Trotsky, who in the late autumn of 1914 had arrived in Paris; she also contributed to their journal, *Our Word.* Like them, she wanted an alliance with Lenin but could not accept his sectarian narrowmindedness.

Alexandra's reservations about Lenin's call for civil war and for wars of national liberation everywhere were shared by most of the young Swedish leftists who met at the "revolutionary club" in the Karleson Hotel. But although Lenin was exasperated by their "simple sentimental anti-militarism," he replied courteously to Alexandra's letters that autumn in which she aired her disagreements with him. "We hope that in struggling for peace, social democrats everywhere will confront their governments with their own demands, and that this will bring in its wake the 'civil war' which you consider the only correct slogan now," she wrote at the end of October. Never before had Lenin written so many patient, tactful letters as he painstakingly spread his message of revolution: "You are not, it would seem, in full agreement with the civil war slogan, but would assign to it a subsidiary (and very qualified) place behind the slogan of peace."[19]

Despite all her reservations, reading the *Theses* was "one of the most important moments of my life. I felt as though the wall against which I had been beating my head shattered and I stepped into the sunlight . . . able to see my way ahead once more . . ." Despite her irritation with Lenin's intransigence, she felt that "his extraordinary intellect enabled him to see what was inaccessible to the rest of us. It was then that I understood his moral and spiritual fearlessness."[20]

Alexandra translated the *Theses* into German, and for the first two weeks of November the "revolutionary club" discussed how best to transport the *Social Democrat* into Russia. (Shlyapnikov favored thick-soled boots, and the others deferred to his experience.) She incorporated Lenin's antiwar program into an article, "War and Our Immediate Tasks," for the November issue of the left-socialist paper, *Forsvarsnigilis-ten*. (Her Swedish was not yet up to writing articles and it was translated for her from the German.)

By the autumn of 1914 all these activities were already arousing a great deal of interest among the Swedish government and police, who began to discuss how best to disperse the troublesome Russian community in Stockholm. Shlyapnikov had managed to acquire the passport of a Frenchman named Noet, but although he spoke French perfectly, his false identity did not fool the Swedish police for a moment. However he had passed as a Frenchman in St. Petersburg, where in April of that year he had worked as a lathe operator in the huge German-financed Lessner industrial plant, been active in the metal-workers' union, struggled to explain to his friends on the shop floor the betrayal of the SPD, and helped to establish the Bolsheviks' headquarters at the *Pravda* offices. In escaping the massive arrests which followed the outbreak of war he had been joined in Stockholm by a number of soldiers and sailors from the Kronstadt garrison, and he was now enthusiastically writing to Lenin that the party center should at once be transferred there from the sleepy backwaters of Switzerland.

The Swedish government had different plans. Since 1911, when many workers and women in Sweden had gained the right to vote, support for the Socialist Party in the elections to parliament (the Riksdag) had considerably increased, and strikes and lock-outs had multiplied after the general strike in 1909. As all the major countries in Europe increased their arms expenditures, a growing body of conservatives and businessmen in the ruling Swedish Conservative Party began to demonstrate their support for Germany by demanding a larger military budget. They were opposed by the Social Democrats, on pacifist grounds, and by the Liberals, on chiefly economic grounds. At the beginning of 1914 there was an election which brought the moderate Conservative government of Hjalmar Ham-marskjöld to power. With the outbreak of war large numbers of people left the Liberal Party to join the Social Democrats, and Hammarskjöld's moderate policies were overridden by the pro-German majority in his party. Sweden, while retaining its neutrality, opted to increase military service and to build five new destroyers and cruisers.

Hammerskjöld's government, fearful of its Social Democratic opponents, therefore determined in late 1914 to disband the colony of Russian socialists in Stockholm. Shortly after Alexandra's article had appeared in the Swedish socialist press in November 1914, and after she had delivered a particularly stinging antiwar speech at a closed meeting of the Swedish Party, a warrant was issued for her arrest.

In the middle of November there was the anticipated dawn knock at the door. Leaping out of bed, she dressed, stuffed Shlyapnikov's address book and false passport under her belt, and opened the door, wearily resigning herself to moving on once more. She bit her tongue as the police scrutinized the map on her wall, but as they began a minute search of her drawers and shelves she exploded with anger: "I am a Russian revolutionary in exile, I have permission to stay here in neutral Sweden, and you have no right to search my things!" They continued their search and ordered her to prepare to leave—allowing her, however, to go to the lavatory, where she was able to hide Shlyapnikov's papers behind the cistern. Shlyapnikov came out of his bedroom just as she was being led away, and she managed to tell him in Russian where to find them. At the police station she was interrogated for many hours before being accused of spying for the Tsar and threatening the security of the Swedish state. She was taken to the Stockholm women's prison and there, in a clean bare cell, she sat in solitary confinement for a week.[21]

Shlyapnikov was desolated, and he embarrassed many of his calmer Swedish friends by the passion he devoted to campaigning for her release. Between him and Branting and some strenuous lobbying of the Riksdag, her extradition order was officially annulled. But she knew nothing of all this. The decision was calmly disregarded; she was transferred to the remote southern fortress prison of Klingsholm, near Malmö, and there she anxiously awaited deportation. After another week of suffocating prison solitude she decided to appeal to the conscience of a visiting pastor. It was not too hard to persuade him to carry a letter to Branting out of the prison, telling him where she was and begging him to mobilize the party congress, which was then sitting, to protest her deportation. Shlyapnikov made an emotional speech attacking the SPD, and for the next two months Branting tabled question after question about her case in the Riksdag. But the only answer he received was that Russians should not meddle in Swedish affairs. On November 26 Alexandra was escorted by the police back to Copenhagen, where Shlyapnikov at once made plans to join her. King Gustav, she was told, had ordered her permanent expulsion from Sweden.

Alexandra and Shlyapnikov led a miserable existence in Copenhagen: they were wretchedly poor, few boarding-house keepers were willing to rent rooms to Russians, and both of them disliked the northern underground's connections with Bolshevik supporters like the German revolutionary Parvus. Parvus, described by Trotsky (on whose ideas he had a formative influence) as "unquestionably one of the most important of the Marxists at the turn of the century," also had "something mad and unreliable about him": "in addition to all his other ambitions, this revolutionary was torn by an amazing desire to get rich. Even this he connected . . . with his revolutionary ideas. 'What we revolutionary Marxists need is a great daily newspaper published in three European languages. But for this we need money, and lots of it,' he would complain."[22] He was joined in this desire for wealth by a Polish revolutionary named Hanecki; basing themselves in Copenhagen, they had entered into various squalid arrangements with Danish businessmen in their negotiations for the northern underground.

Alexandra and Shlyapnikov received just as little support from the Danish party leaders as they had from the Swedish; they were urged not to attend meetings or write antiwar speeches. The police were constantly trailing them and checking their papers. The moment she arrived, Alexandra sent a telegram to the Swedish party congress thanking its members for supporting her, and on November 28 she wrote to Lenin:

> The conservative Swedish press has exploited this incident to persecute our Swedish comrades, especially Branting. They write that he has sullied his good name by his friendship with a Russian "nihilist," who makes antiwar propaganda at a time when Sweden must be "strong." It's very important, I feel, for our central organ to note that Swedish socialists . . . protest strongly against the expulsion of their Russian comrade . . .[23]

In his reply on December 14 Lenin continued to prod her into a more wholehearted commitment to civil war: "It's really quite useless to advance nice little programs full of honorable desires for peace, if you don't at the same time—and in the first place—advocate an illegal organization, and the civil war of the proletariat against the bourgeoisie." Her reply was addressed both to him and to Nadezhda Krupskaya, but from then on her letters were addressed to Nadezhda alone. Enclosing with her letter a statement from Russian women in Stockholm, as well as a leaflet she had received from England, she wrote: "Above all I'm glad we have some points of contact, which means we can work together in these disastrous times . . . when we are surrounded by such devastation, and it sometimes feels as though one was speaking a different language even from people who were recently friends."

"Dear and Honored Comrade . . ." ran Lenin's unusually florid (and equally critical) response. Reminding her that he was himself in touch with Litvinov in England and thanking her for the literature, he fully agreed with her that "revolutionaries should keep in closer contact with each other":

> But before bringing this about, I want to take advantage of your pleasant letter to continue our correspondence. I tell you frankly, I'm deeply afraid at the moment of such wholesale, unifying slogans as "war on war," because I consider it most dangerous and destructive to the proletariat. Did not Kautsky, after all, formulate the unifying theory to beat all in the pages of *Neue Zeit?*[24]

Alexandra's sadness in that terrible year was compounded by a personal sorrow which her cornered existence made it hard for her to comprehend fully. News came that her beloved sister Jenny had died. Her marriage to a man she had never loved had apparently collapsed, and as she traveled around Russia as an opera singer, Jenny's independent life had become increasingly lonely. She ended her days at the age of fifty-three in Yalta —alone, impoverished, and ill. The most painful thing for Alexandra was that in her frantic need to destroy all correspondence for fear of a police raid which might implicate her sister, "almost the day before I heard the news I tore up her last letters to me. Now it was as though I was without even that last shred of her soul . . ."[25] Although it was probably from her remaining sister, Adele, or her brother Alexander that she heard the news, she made no mention of any correspondence with them; her love for them had never equaled her love for Jenny.

She longed to leave hostile Denmark for Russia, and her heart began to trouble her again. She and Shlyapnikov managed to extract grudging permission from the Danish Party to attend a socialist conference of neutral countries in Copenhagen in January 1915, and they went armed with copies of *Social Democrat* containing Lenin's *Theses.* Most of the delegates still believed that their parliaments could be made to exert pressure on the warring countries, and the leftists from Holland and Scandinavia expended all their energy opposing them without advancing any sort of revolutionary program. "It was a lackluster affair," she wrote to Nadezhda Krupskaya. "I spoke privately to several delegates and was oppressively struck by the realization that all had a touch of nationalism about them. They have accepted the most legal path . . . The more I talked with them the more convinced I became of Vladimir Ilich's position . . ."[26] She was not convinced, however, to abandon her links with the *Our Word* group in Paris, and wrote an article on the conference for the January issue. The next three months' issues also contained articles by her.[27]

Police and poverty were making life in Copenhagen unbearable, particularly after the socialist deputies to the Fourth Duma were arrested that February. Shlyapnikov decided to leave for Stockholm to raise a few loans for transport work, as well as for his and Alexandra's daily needs. Shortly after he left, Alexandra thankfully accepted an invitation from women and leftists in the Norwegian Party to visit the capital Kristiania (now Oslo), where, they assured her, she would be unmolested by the police and warmly welcomed by the small and uncoordinated antiwar movement. After much harassment at the Swedish border, she managed to convince the police that she was only in transit. Shlyapnikov joined her, and together they traveled on to peaceful, hospitable Norway.

A half-hour train ride, followed by a stiff twenty-minute walk uphill, brought them to the hillside suburb of Holmenkollen. And there in the small red Tourist Hotel, one of several hotels and sanatoria scattered about the enchanting wooded hills outside Kristiania, they made their base between 1915 and 1917. "I immediately felt Norway was going to be right for me," she wrote in her diary:

> A quiet, gentle, solid town, with tree-lined streets and villas. Deep snow, deep quiet, cleanness, sledges, ringing bells—a world I've not known for a long time . . . Life seems to have stopped here, frozen into immobility like the snow-covered firs and ash trees. Yesterday was Sunday, and crowds of strong cheerful young people came out from Kristiania—it was so splendid! Deafeningly jolly shouts and happy laughter, a trail of toboggans streaks past, between the trees girls in red-and-blue-striped knitted hats flash past on skis, and the boys go red in the face doing risky ski-jumps down the mountain . . . What fresh healthy relationships these young people must have, living in this clean snowy place![28]

Yet, as she gazed down the hills to the fjords and the town below, she could not help an uneasy feeling that she was becoming too remote from the realities of the war and the struggle against it; she felt a creeping "unease that in the midst of this ghastly bloody nightmare I am living in a place of such magical beauty . . . I am having constant palpitations at night, first my arms then my legs go numb," she wrote to Tatiana Schepkina. "I really must try to regard this visit here as a rest cure, and stay for two weeks, no longer."[29] For the first week she did try to rest while Shlyapnikov went into Kristiania every day to meet new underground contacts in the town's smoky quayside cafés. There he reestablished contact with Anderson, leader of the transport union, and several of his fishermen friends, as well as many Norwegian comrades who knew the uninhabited northern regions and would take literature to the Finnish border on skis. Their common language was German, and Shlyapnikov spoke a little broken Swedish and Norwegian. His friend Egede Nissen, leader of the Norwegian leftists, visited the Tourist Hotel and helped to organize some meetings there, and with Frau Nissen Alexandra discussed plans for International Women's Day. March 8, they agreed, should be celebrated by the women of Kristiania not merely as a day of peace, but in a series of militant antiwar demonstrations throughout the country.

It was at Lenin's initiative that simultaneous plans were being made by Klara Zetkin and the Dutch secretary of the Women's Bureau, Helen Ankersmidt, for a joint congress in Bern for radical women from both neutral and warring countries. Alexandra was exasperated when she learned about this too late for her or her Norwegian women friends to get exit visas, and wrote reproachfully to Nadezhda Krupskaya (she wrote some twenty-two letters to Lenin and Nadezhda from Norway): "The Party is more radically inclined than in the other Scandinavian countries, and next month a nationwide antiwar campaign is being launched. I do think we should help them as much as we can, for although they are in excellent radical spirits there is often little basis or clarity to their activities."[30] Enclosed with this letter was a statement written by her and signed by several Norwegian women in support of Lenin's line. She also wrote an article on the Bern conference for *Our Word*.

But the only information she had about this event, stage-managed from the beginning by Lenin, was from Nadezhda Krupskaya's sketchy description of it. "I wish you had been here," she wrote to Alexandra afterwards. "I am sure we would have got on better with you than with Izolskaya and Angelica Balabanova."[31] (Irena Izolskaya, a Polish socialist, was a former associate of Rosa Luxemburg's.) Angelica herself wrote more explicitly about the clash between the majority of women who met that Easter week in Switzerland (including Dr. Marion Phillips, women's organizer for the English Labor Party, the prominent French socialist Louise Saumoneau, and Margaret Bondfield), who wanted to pass a simple pacifist resolution, and the small Bolshevik minority (Nadezhda Krupskaya, Lilina Zinovieva, and another former *Rabotnitsa* collaborator named Elena Rozmirovich), who demanded an immediate break with European social democracy, the establishment of a new International, and the transformation of the war into a revolutionary civil war. While Lenin sat drinking tea in a nearby café, waiting to be called in case of political difficulties, Klara Zetkin again and again appealed to the Bolsheviks to modify their resolution in the interests of a united statement; finally, sick with anxiety, she suffered a bad heart attack and was thought for a while to be dying. The Bolsheviks managed to pass their resolution, with some verbal concessions to the majority, and they went on to repeat the same splitting tactics at the youth conference that followed shortly afterward in Bern.[32] Women's Day in Norway was celebrated less acrimoniously with large antiwar demonstrations up and down the country.

As the snow thawed Alexandra's strength returned, and Shlyapnikov decided to go to England to earn some money. In April 1915 he left for London (where his skill as a lathe operator enabled him without any difficulty to find a job in the Wembley branch of the Fiat car factory) and joined the prestigious Amalgamated Society of Engineers (now the Amalgamated Union of Engineering Workers). His underground transport work he entrusted to Alexandra, who spent many hours in cafés meeting contacts and reporting messages in a code consisting of a group of three letters indicating page, line, and letter of Edward Bellamy's *Looking Backward* (a nineteenth-century *Utopia*). The password for new recruits was *"Grüsse von Olga"* ("Greetings from Olga"). The postal address for most revolutionary communications was the home of a chronically drunk and unemployed watchmaker and spinner of fantasies called Danielson, and his Russian wife Lyolya, whom Alexandra got to know well. As the weather grew milder she would pack a rucksack on weekends and take off for long walks in the hills with her friends. Few others in the Kristiania Russian colony played any part in this postal work, and Holmenkollen was generally regarded by the police as a tourist spot. She was greatly alarmed, therefore, to return from a long walk one evening to discover that the police had visited the hotel to interrogate the landlady about her and her Russian friends. She decided to hold no more meetings there, and to use the hotel merely for sleeping, eating, and writing, for she was now in the finishing stages of *Society and Motherhood*.

Six hundred pages long and four years in the writing, this detailed investigation of all the European governments' various medical and social schemes for helping working mothers reflected her fundamental concern for the laws needed to liberate women from the burdens of solitary motherhood. "Every mother must be convinced that once she fulfills her natural function and gives a new member to communist society, the collective will love and attend to her and her child."[33] After bearing her baby, breast-feeding it, and surrounding it in its first months with tender care, a mother had the right to regard her exclusive social obligation to her baby as over. Thereafter extending her maternal feelings to all children in the collective, she should have the right to choose, if she wished, to return to work, to entrust her baby to a nursery, in which she might work as a part-time assistant. She was to maintain as much of a special relationship with her own baby as she wished, knowing that it would be lovingly cared for by her friends in the collective. (After the October revolution of 1917, when Alexandra became Commissar of Social Welfare in Lenin's government, she was to be guided by her research for this book in her first two pieces of legislation—on the case of mothers and children —which reflected her major concern that women should be able to have children and be truly convinced that they would be cared for.)

Would it ever come out? she wondered, recalling the hours of work she had put into this book over the past four years. So many articles and letters had gone astray in her travels. What would happen to her diaries? Would anybody care about them in the future? Finally, she sent off the manuscript to Bonch-Bruevich, her Petrograd publisher, enclosing a letter entrusting all her diaries and letters to him should she die, and finally, in 1916, *Society and Motherhood* appeared in Petrograd.

From time to time during this period in Holmenkollen the sweet sounds of Grieg would waft in from the next room, and Alexandra's thoughts would turn to Jenny's death and her own frail heart. The next room was never let. It contained Grieg's own piano, and was opened only to his widow, who played his works with such exquisite delicacy that Alexandra would forget her writing and ponder on the memories that room must have contained. Although most revolutionaries felt impelled to renounce the joys of music, there were some—notably Chicherin and Inessa Armand—who were known to "break down" and play some Beethoven. For Alexandra, however, such ponderings were strictly confined to the pages of her diary.[34]

That April sterner tasks awaited her. Lenin had for some time been feeling that too many intellectuals were wasting their writing talents on centrist publications like *Our Word,* and Alexandra suddenly received a letter from Nadezhda Krupskaya conveying his admiration for her articles and tentatively enquiring whether she might like to contribute to a more militant Bolshevik publication. This was the opportunity she had been waiting for, for a "definite break" with Menshevism, and by May several articles by her were waiting in the editorial offices of the new Bolshevik paper, *Communist.* "Why Was the German Proletariat Silent during the July Days?" (signed A.K'ai) was eventually published in the first (September) issue of *Communist*, but not before Alexandra had received a series of letters from Lenin detailing her "serious political mistakes"—which were, according to him, "of two kinds."

For Alexandra, as for most revolutionaries—most notably Rosa Luxemburg, Nikolai Bukharin and Georgy Pyatakov (who had joined the Bolshevik organization in Moscow in 1905, like Bukharin, when both of them were barely fifteen)—socialism and national self-determination were mutually exclusive: nationalism had been rendered anachronistic by the imperialist war, and there was no sense in restoring governments which were being swept away to provide the territorial basis for a future communist society without classes or nations. "You say if it's imperialism we're fighting, then we don't need national self-determination or the arming of the people!" Lenin expostulated. "That really is the most glaring contradiction! For the social revolution against imperialism we need *both* one *and* the other." How could she believe, he went on, that on the eve of revolution the revolutionary class would oppose the arming of the people? "That's not fighting militarism, but merely a cowardly desire to avoid the great questions posed by the capitalist world. How can you say you 'accept' the class struggle without understanding that at certain moments it must inevitably be transformed into civil war?"[35] However much she disliked the hectoring (her subsequent ardent internationalism, and the fact that she did not comment on Lenin's criticisms, indicate that he did not convince her out of her first "mistake"), she was painfully compelled to admit that her resistance to accepting the concept of armed revolutionary struggle was illogical and emotional. Her article on the German proletariat —crushed, stupefied, and betrayed by their leaders—left the issue to be decided by the vanguard workers themselves, who, "at the necessary historical moment" of revolution, would be able to "boldly advocate all forms and methods of struggle which revolutionary creativity suggests."[36]

Alexandra learned at this time of an International congress which Lenin was planning for September in the little Swiss town of Zimmerwald. This was to be the first small but significant step toward a new communist International, and her spirited young Norwegian friends convinced her that a united radical delegation from Scandinavia should attend. That spring she joined them at their informal meetings in Kristiania with the more serious purpose of helping to prepare a militant antiwar statement which they could present at Zimmerwald. In May 1915 she traveled 300 miles north to Trondheim for a Norwegian party congress, where she urged the leaders to support preliminary discussions with radically inclined Swedes and Danes. She met there an old acquaintance, the

Finnish radical Carl Wiik, who had delivered a moving denunciation of the Tsar at the Copenhagen congress five years before; together they persuaded the Norwegians to send greetings to the imprisoned deputies of the Fourth Duma. The congress was just winding up in the best of spirits when the police moved in and arrested an outspoken parliamentary deputy called Tranmeil, who was thrown into solitary confinement on bread and water for ten days. Alexandra and several other delegates accompanied him to prison bearing soup and flowers, and her last memory of Trondheim was of the prison doors clanging shut behind him and of "wringing my heart as for a loved one."[37]

She returned to Holmenkollen, and in the light of Lenin's criticisms began to rework her article for *Communist*, into which she put great pains and an average of eleven hours' work a day. What she found so very difficult in this, her first article as a Bolshevik, was not only that she must try to explain the Germans' betrayal in terms adequately critical of the SPD, but also that she must spurn all the workers' "palaces," universities, and clubs that had so impressed her, which (as she now had to recognize) had broken the masses' militancy and made it impossible for them to develop any initiative or respond independently to the war without orders from above. She also embarked on a more ambitious project: a pamphlet in which she tried to convey the same hopeless sadness at the German betrayal and to suggest how this might be directed toward revolution. *Who Needs War?*—a simple, graphic appeal to soldiers and workers in the trenches and factories—belied the many laborious months she spent working on it; it did not appear until the following year.

In July 1915 she gratefully interrupted her labors to prepare for a visit from Misha. As she waited on the platform for his train to arrive her delight was mixed with anxiety and the constant terrible fear that he might be called up. But her fears were groundless, and on July 11, after his short visit was over, she wrote in her diary: "Just seen Mishulya off, my good, honest, sensitive boy. He is adamantly against the war—what joy! . . . Life is so hard for poor Misha, he is burdened with so many adult cares for which I or his father should have taken responsibility. In these last few days I learned to deeply respect this firm, sensitive, responsive person—and now he is gone."[38] She also learned a great deal from Misha about the morale of the soldiers and officers "under Nick's command" (as Misha put it). Officers continued to be promoted according to their seniority in the tsarist military bureaucracy and to treat with utter contempt the soldiers under them, who were rarely given any clue as to why they might be fighting. Regiments were surrendering en masse, and even police reports were admitting that "while the men have been clamoring for peace all along, never have they done it so blatantly; officers frequently refuse to lead them in attack for fear of being shot in the back." Nicholas II was universally loathed, living costs soared, speculation was rampant, and in the cities women were rioting for bread. "Everything is leading the workers to the limits of their endurance," Alexandra wrote. "When when will they say to their government: 'Stop! Enough!' and declare war?"[39] She had at last come to accept the justice of the class war.

In that same month, after Misha had left, Shlyapnikov returned from London full of confidence and with enough funds to resuscitate the underground postal route in Stockholm. Together he and Alexandra held several more meetings with the young Norwegians who were going to Lenin's conference in Zimmerwald. Carl Wiik, who was the crucial Finnish connection in the northern underground, joined this "magic circle" surrounding Alexandra and was equally lyrical in his praises of Shlyapnikov —"a wonderful man, quiet, good-natured, never boisterous, gesticulating or gushing, always clearheaded and absolutely indefatigable."[40] They sent off a proposed resolution on their opposition to the war (translated into Swedish) to Zeth Höglund and invited him to attend a meeting in Kristiania with his friends to discuss the congress. Lenin also received a copy and replied approvingly: "It's devilishly important to have a common internationalist statement from all left Marxists. Greetings, and once again congratulations on the Norwegians' decision."[41] The news that despite the imprisonment of Rosa Luxemburg and Klara Zetkin a militant antiwar group was still active in Berlin put new heart into Alexandra's work. "Barricades as the response to war," she wrote in her diary. "This is as it should be, this is what should have happened on August 4. Now I realize that the peace slogan is opportunism—and you won't find *Our Word* saying that."[42] She wrote finally to Martov, editor of *Our Word*, and broke with the Mensheviks.

On August 1, 1915, the anniversary of Jaurès' murder, she arranged a memorial meeting in Kristiania and wrote an obituary in the pages of the Norwegian *Social Democrat.* Two days later, with Warsaw about to fall to the Germans, Russia, with the utmost cynicism, granted self-government to her Polish satellite. Alexandra was assailed by anxieties for Misha. "The heart is frozen by so much blood," she wrote. "Every hour is drowned in this suffering."[43] Her thoughts wandered back to her old teacher, Maria Strakhova, who perhaps had not realized how deeply she had influenced Alexandra, as a child, to hate the regime. Had she become a patriot? she wondered.

With Klara Zetkin ill and in the blackest depression in prison, Alexandra prepared a women's statement for the Zimmerwald congress. Shlyapnikov left for Stockholm, and she resumed her work for the postal underground. Among the new people she met at this time were Egede Nissen (an elderly bohemian post office official, engaged in transport work since 1905) and a chronically sick woman called Ellisi Vessel, who lived near the Arctic Circle and was a great worshipper of Lenin's. Lyolya Danielson was also a frequent visitor to the hotel. "I'm so glad you don't live in the town," she once said. "I like to think of the mountains when I think of you." Alexandra thought it sad that this sensitive woman, who kept her soul alive by writing poetry (which she always brought with her), should have strayed after her marriage into the "dark kingdom of petty bourgeois existence"; her insights into Lyolya's struggling life led her to speculate whether this war could "hasten and lighten the 'transitional phase' in women's evolution. From all appearances it will. For woman is in all fields of work now, her labor power is necessary, her value has grown far beyond the confines of her family. And that is a definite plus . . ."44 Frau Dundas, a shop assistant staying at the hotel, had a birthday party one day on the grass outside; after serving hot chocolate and cakes to her friends, she packed a rucksack and set off on her own on a three-week hike over the mountains. For Alexandra, that day—August 3, 1915—was all too wretchedly memorable as the anniversary of the SPD's treacherous vote. Two days later Warsaw fell to the Germans.

10

Agitating for Revolution

On August 10, 1915, Alexandra received an invitation from Ludwig Lore and a number of other German radicals in the American Socialist Party to undertake a four-month speaking tour of the United States. Karl Liebknecht had suggested that they invite her, and her reputation as a speaker had made a considerable impression on them. Their invitation was supported also by a group of Russians living in New York: revolutionaries who sympathized with Lenin's position on the war but balked at his dogmatic narrowmindedness. These Russian internationalists (who included Nikolay Bukharin, V. Volodarsky, Chudnovsky and, in 1916, Trotsky) had since 1911 been issuing a weekly journal called *Novy Mir (New World)*. "The central headquarters of internationalist revolutionary propaganda," as Trotsky described it, *New World* attempted to spread its ideas beyond the confines of the American Socialist Party and into the ranks of the American working class, particularly the European immigrants.[1]

It was probably because of her enthusiasm for this publication that Alexandra, without a moment's hesitation, accepted Lore's invitation to visit America, where she was to speak to working-class audiences in eighty towns. After sending a telegram accepting, she began to wait impatiently for the money for her boat ticket to arrive. On the night of August 10 she was too elated to sleep:

> We are at a turning point in history. Capitalism has definitely reached its highest point . . . Maybe we are now only at the most rudimentary stage of the struggle, the negative stage . . . The mighty conflicts of the capitalist nations confront all civilized humanity with the dilemma of whether to destroy or to reorganize not national economies but the world

economy on the basis of socialized labour. If we thought "crises" produced this dilemma, we were wrong . . . The struggle has spread far wider
—this is the struggle for world domination. Capitalism creates the objective conditions for transition. The subjective historical push depends now
on the working class . . .[2]

She prepared to leave her beloved Holmenkollen, and early the next
month her friends, a Norwegian woman named Erica and a Russian
named Lyuba, organized a farewell party for her. They powdered their
noses, put on their best dresses, and all sailed down a fjord to the tourist
resort of Dronning. As they sat on a café terrace that clear, warm September evening and watched the sail boats like white butterflies against the
azure blue of the fjord, they teased her for her abstemious ways. She
neither drank wine nor smoked, and her only "vice" was an inordinate
love of cakes, on which she spent 50 öre (say ten cents), a sixth of her
frugal three-kroner daily food allowance.

The following day Höglund and Nerman left for Zimmerwald. To
enable delegates to return afterward without police harassment there were
to be no press reports of the congress, so Alexandra's impatience for the
money from America was mixed with an equal impatience to talk to them
on their return. Lenin wrote asking her to translate from German into
English his pamphlet *Socialism and War;* he wanted her to contact a
Charles Kerr in Chicago who he felt might be induced to publish it, and
to do as much fund raising for the Party as she possibly could: "It would
be a great pity if your trip to America was canceled after all this. We've
put so many hopes into it . . ."[3]

Finally on September 15 the money arrived, and she went into town
to buy a ticket for the steamer *Bergensfjord* which was leaving on the
twenty-sixth. The journey would take ten to fourteen days, "depending
on circumstances" and delays, since they had to travel via the Shetland
Islands to avoid the German war zones. Her old friend Zoya, with whom
Alexandra always discussed all her plans, wrote anxiously from Petrograd,
pleading with her to reconsider the journey. But Alexandra replied: "For
some reason I don't feel the slightest hesitation, not one iota of fear.
When you want something badly enough there are none of those feelings
to hold you back."[4]

"At last, news from Zimmerwald," she wrote in her diary the following day. And this news of a revolutionary nucleus emerging from the ruins
of the old International gave an added dimension to her trip to the States.
Although the majority had condemned the imperialist war, repudiated the

credits, and argued that the struggle against war meant the struggle for socialism, there was a sizable minority who supported Lenin's call for civil war; his most uncompromising supporters were the young Scandinavians.

Alexandra wrote forty good-bye letters (and spent a fortune on stamps), gave her manuscripts and diaries to her landlady to keep, packed ten copies of *Socialism and War* (which she planned to translate into English during her two weeks on the *Bergensfjord*), and, holding a small suitcase, said goodbye to Shlyapnikov and embarked for the new world.

The extreme discomfort of her third-class cabin, which she shared with three others, did not make translating the easiest of tasks, but she was comforted on her journey by a telegram from Misha in Petrograd and letters from Shlyapnikov in Kristiania. And she was able to share with a group of Russian immigrants to America a certain smug satisfaction at the excessive luxury of the first-class passengers, mostly Americans, who ate and danced the days and nights away. The journey was not disrupted by any dangerous confrontations at sea, and the ship docked in New York on October 8.

Alexandra was met by Ludwig Lore and a number of the other Germans who had invited her, as well as by a group of the radical Russian contributors to the Russian journal *New World*. They took her to her hotel on Union Square and outlined her formidable itinerary for the next two-and-a-half months, when she would be traveling to Racine, Milwaukee, Chicago, St. Louis, Denver, San Francisco, Los Angeles, Seattle, and Philadelphia. In each town she was booked to address several meetings in English, German, French, and Russian, and her daunting task was to try to recruit members of the divided American Socialist Party to the Leninist position on the war. The revolutionary *New World* associates of Bukharin, Chudnovsky, and Volodarsky felt that many of their exiled compatriots could also be brought round to accepting the left Zimmerwald platform. Alexandra suggested some subjects for her talks—national defense and the solidarity of the world proletariat, war and women's tasks, war and the International—and when they had all left, she steeled herself to prepare for her first meeting in New York the following day.

"I must devote all thoughts and feeling to the cause I'm working for now," she wrote in her diary. "I have renounced all personal life . . ."[5] To Lenin she wrote: "My trip to the United States is informed by the desire to spread as widely as possible the ideas you've so clearly formulated, the basis of revolutionary internationalism."[6] Trotsky, who arrived a little later from Paris (via Spain) to work for *New World* and met her fleetingly, described her trip in his autobiography with a more jaundiced eye:

During the war she veered sharply to the left, abandoning without transition the ranks of the Mensheviks for the extreme left wing of the Bolsheviks. Her knowledge of foreign languages and her temperament made her a valuable agitator. Her theoretical views have always been somewhat confused, however. In her New York period nothing was revolutionary enough for her. She was in correspondence with Lenin and kept him informed of what was happening in America, my own activities included, seeing all facts and ideas through the prism of her ultra-radicalism.[7]

Alexandra barely had time to take in the skyscrapers and garbage cans of New York City before going off to the first meeting Lore had organized for her. She spoke that evening to a small group of SWP members about the Zimmerwald congress, to help them produce their own antiwar statement; after a great deal of argument and shouting they all came out in support of the Zimmerwald leftists. *"Halt! Enough is Enough! Come and hear Alexandra Kollontai, distinguished lecturer of International reputation!"*—advertisements around the city blared out news of her meetings, along with biographical details and often the promise of music afterward. Nikolai Nakoryakov, editor of *New World*, first heard her speak at a large meeting of over 1000 people on October 12, 1915:

A very lively and emotional personality. She never dragged out her speech, which despite the apparent fiery improvisation was always beautifully organised and prepared, and made you feel there was a great deal of work and theoretical spadework behind it. She usually spoke no longer than an hour and always left time for questions, which she answered with great wit and animation. Her meetings were unfailingly successful, and even people unconnected to the socialist movement would rush to get tickets. Even the Menshevik leaders, who initially greeted her agitation coolly, had to confess that she destroyed a great deal of their influence like magic![8]

Out of that first meeting came a resolution supporting the Zimmerwald left.

Alexandra's contemptuous impression of the American Socialist Party leader, Morris Hillquit, whom she had first met at the Copenhagen congress in the benevolent role of peacemaker to the warring nations, was unchanged: "He's a great diplomat and a vile revisionist . . . takes the view that, with the help of trusts, the great powers' struggles can be 'softened.' He's terribly afraid they'll be excluded from the International . . ."[9]

She left New York for Milwaukee, where she was met by a group of Russians who led her off the train to speak to the Russian community there. Then there was another meeting in English, and soon she was off again on the train to Chicago—where she spent five hectic days and addressed ten packed meetings, defending Lenin against many angry critics. She managed to meet the publisher Charles Kerr, whom she found decidedly unenthusiastic about bringing out *Socialism and War;* and walking the streets of the city, she was oppressively struck by all the "ragged brokendown people, shuffling along in sullen silence."[10] She was reminded of Gorky's description of America as the "yellow devil." After her last meeting in Chicago, it was straight on to the train again for St. Louis, where she arrived at seven the next morning, and was met and shown around the town without a moment to herself to wash, rest or think. Then there was a thirty-mile car ride to a town in the Missouri hills, and she was back in her hotel by seven in the evening, with just enough time to wash her hands and comb her hair before the meeting.

Next day there were three meetings in three languages, before she was bundled into a train for Staunton. She cursed Dreyfus, who had organized this tour so as to squeeze every last drop of energy out of her and leave her not a moment's free time: "It's cruel and not at all comradely of him, and I blame him for economizing like this . . ."[11] All her letters to Lenin had to be written on the train or in moments snatched between meetings. "The German comrades have enlisted my services for a very good reason," she wrote to him on the train from Milwaukee. "Someone from Europe has immense authority here." Lenin replied, enclosing several copies of a Zimmerwald pamphlet: "Relying on you to distribute it everywhere in America (England's hopeless—it can be sent there from America). Please see local Bolsheviks *everywhere,* even if only for five minutes. Cheer them up and put them in touch with us."[12]

As the train traveled past the vast dull fields and two-story clapboard farmhouses of Illinois on the way to Staunton, she was reminded of the vastness of Russia. But her sharpest memory of Russia assailed her in East St. Louis, where the blacks lived. She was only too familiar with those "dusty streets, filthy ancient wooden houses, tasteless new brick buildings containing flats for the poor, a lot of saloons where no nice lady would go. And the only difference was that on the porches sat not our kerchiefed Russian *babushki,* but black women and their half-naked children."[13] She met the white pastor who worked there, and when she demanded why the schools were not integrated, he explained that this was out of the question as the black children "smelled vile". So deeply did he feel that this was a proper response to the problem that she felt not the slightest desire to continue the conversation. Unfortunately the pastor was her traveling companion to Staunton, Illinois.

Here at last, in this miners' community, she was welcomed with genuine hospitality. She was led off to the friendly City Hotel (where she had a simple room with a wooden bed and washbasin), and with a whole blessed evening to herself she could sit on the porch, write up her diaries, and watch the world go by and the sun set. The next day she left for the village of Mount Olive, scene of the historic 1898 miners' strike during which the bosses had opened fire on immigrant laborers exhausted by their fourteen-hour working day and wretched living conditions. Mount Olive was scattered with their graves, and the memories of that year lived on in the militant German mining family in whose cottage she stayed. But by 1915 most of the other German workers there had apparently forgotten the heroism of that great strike and were now staunch parliamentarians and patriots. Where in America, if not here, was there a basis for revolutionary agitation? she wondered after a meeting at which she was indifferently received. How could a new International ever take shape in the midst of such hopeless complacency? Nevertheless her experiences in America prompted some optimistic speculations about the future socialist society, "when all material cares are removed and people will finally be able to concern themselves with the science of the human spirit":

> Then we will learn the "laws" by which to attain its highest development, arouse its dormant forces, and discover all the things which still lie buried under the seven seals. Then perhaps we might also avail ourselves of the knowledge of the Brahmins, who without any scientific spiritual laws . . . have revealed in simple practical terms, by the path of experience, what the Human spirit is capable of, its nervous organization and power . . . And as an analogy, one cannot help wondering what colors, what diversity of form, what luxuriance can an experienced gardener produce in a garden which at present has little more than the *potential* for development?[14]

She arrived back in St. Louis at midnight, and first thing next morning she was on the long train-ride to Denver, Colorado. After two days and sleepless nights she arrived in Denver at six thirty in the evening and hurriedly prepared her speech for a meeting at eight. At seven the following morning she was on the train again for Salt Lake City, traveling with forty distinctly unproletarian delegates to an American Federation of Labor congress and a Chinese worker, garbed in blue overalls ("Now there's a proletarian!"). The view from the train "surpassed all imagination. What beauty, what clear skies, what air. And the stations too—what a delight, with their gardens of palms and cactuses . . . I've just realized how much I've been pining for the bright south. I should like to stop at these stations and not get back into the train. I should like to be an anchorite, for here one is so close to nature!" After breakfast of melon and other southern delights at the little station of Casa del Desierto, she rode for the rest of the journey on the observation car, captivated by the desert.[15]

This pure joy rapidly dissolved in San Francisco, where she managed to read the newspapers and their tormentingly inadequate news of the war. Arriving late at night, worn out by the journey, she was taken by two down-at-the-heel German workers to a hotel so filthy that she had to ask them to find something a little better. They saw nothing wrong with the hotel, did not have the money for the tram fare, and made her feel wretchedly embarrassed for her fastidious "ladylike" habits—hardly appropriate, they implied, for an agitator. But she had to catch up on some sleep, for she was to speak four times in as many days. She ended up in a 50-cent dormitory, equally filthy, cold, and mildewed; she sat there until six in the morning and then dragged herself across town to find another room. She spoke twice to the working-class Russian community, poor, illiterate, and too involved with their various religious sects to know very much about politics. But on at least one person, an old Siberian exile they called Grandad, her talks evidently had a great impact, for when she returned to New York she found a letter from him, begging her to put him in touch with the revolutionary movement in Russia. "You left, little sister, and you left behind you great rejoicing. The gray weary days of our exile drag on, but for many of us those days are no longer the same. When you came you stirred the stagnant mud in our hearts, and awakened forgotten images of another life . . . For some of us this may even be the beginning of a new life."[16]

She spoke in Los Angeles, and then traveled a thousand miles north through snowstorms to Portland and Seattle, where she arrived to find a large street demonstration of pale, hungry-looking workers mourning the death of Joe Hill. Joe Hill, a Swedish-born worker, was a member of the revolutionary union, the International Workers of the World (the IWW), and also a songwriter; many of his ballads were contained in the IWW's *Little Red Songbook*. Convicted for a murder he probably did not commit, he was executed by the Salt Lake City authorities and so, in a period when increasing numbers of IWW members were being arrested and persecuted, became the union's first martyr. In Seattle, which seemed so close to Alaska and Japan, and with the memory of this sad demonstration fresh in her mind, Alexandra felt overwhelmed suddenly by homesickness and longed to "pour out my thoughts in an angry speech of protest, not 'argue' against the war. Instead of philippics seething with rage, passionate, thundering, and threatening, I just keep turning out the same old 'discourse' against war and national defense, which is boring even me."[17]

"No, I definitely do have powers of prediction!" she wrote, on the long haul back from the West Coast via Minneapolis, Chicago, and Indianapolis:

> I knew this last part of my journey, from one small town to another, would be the hardest of this whole mad scramble through America. Short stops of four to seven hours, usually by day, sometimes in the brief evening hours . . . No social life, just a trail of comrades and organizers. An American working-class audience is warmer than a German one, more responsive. They react while you're speaking, not only when you thump them on the head with a pat joke, but at more subtle ironies and outbursts. And after you speak they always come up and make friendly remarks . . .[18]

In Chicago, at a meeting of the large Russian colony, she spoke on the same platform with that impassioned radical socialist, Eugene Debs, who quite outshone her. "Bold as a lion—even his eyes are worth something . . . I almost hugged him I felt so happy. Then the doubt stirred whether it was not merely the 'done thing' for such a great and generous heart to treat one with so much warmth, to show so much kindness . . . Well, I'm grateful anyway!" She also met Bill Haywood there, leader of the IWW, and they hugged like old comrades. "He's a real pillar—a storyteller and a romantic, but what a sincere fighter too, and with almost the whole of the IWW in prison or on strike!"[19]

After speaking at meetings organized by the German communities of Indianapolis, Louisville, and Cincinnati, she arrived back in New York, exhausted and ill, on December 22. There for the next twelve days she tried to recoup her strength. Suppressed memories and fears pursued her in dream-filled days and sleepless nights when she would awake gasping for breath, her heart palpitating wildly:

> This morning I dreamed vividly of snow-covered fields scattered with corpses and wounded. A crawling swarming crowd of groaning people, like that picture of Vereschagin's . . . [*Vereschagin, a noted Russian painter of the 1890s, had fought in the Russo-Turkish War of 1877; the experience inspired a cycle of war paintings quite exceptional for their*

brutal honesty] but at night—then the dreams are truly terrible. And to think such things are happening, they really are happening! How is it to be imagined!

She struggled to escape from these nightmares of anxiety by giving interviews to the American press and taking walks with Ludwig Lore, his wife Lily (who later translated one of Alexandra's novels), and their friends. Her worries that she had not heard from Lenin or received more copies of *Socialism and War* were relieved by a letter from him explaining that her letters had been confiscated by the French police: "I'm devilishly angry that 'noble' France has confiscated a series of registered letters from me to you in America."[20] And her constant fears about Misha were eased when she heard that he wanted to visit New York; two days after his letter arrived, though, she received a telegram which read "Staying in Petrograd. Misha."

Alexandra spent the next two months in America at a more leisurely pace, visiting Boston to stay with her friend Henrietta Derman, whom she had known in Berlin. Henrietta's husband, it was sadly obvious, had been turned into a physical and emotional wreck by his long sentence in a tsarist jail—"how frightful to think people are still languishing in those jails." As she traveled through the grimy desolation of industrial eastern Pennsylvania to address a meeting in Pittsburgh she longed for these perpetual travels to end. "I've had enough of adapting to this life on wheels, hastily brushing my teeth, gulping down some coffee, and dashing to the train. Enough of hot noisy American stations in provincial towns. Enough of the maddening din of locomotives. Enough of all those unproductive hours spent waiting on station platforms . . ."[21]

She spoke in New Jersey and in Philadelphia, where she met two young Bolsheviks, V. Volodarsky, and Gurvich, who had known Lyolya Stasova in St. Petersburg. After 1917 Alexandra was to work quite closely with Volodarsky—a poor Jew who had been politically active in his native Ukraine and then in St. Petersburg, since the age of fourteen. In 1913 he had left Russia for America under the threat of arrest, and was then working as a cutter in a Philadelphia garment factory. In addition to working actively in the International Union of Tailors, the American Garment Workers' Union, and the Socialist Party, he was in close contact with Chudnovsky and the other Bolshevik sympathizers working for *New World*. It was probably this contact which quickened the interest of the tsarist secret police in her antiwar speeches in America, for by February 1916 memoranda were flying back and forth between Petrograd and New

York. "I have herein to inform your excellencies that, according to information received by our office, on February 14 in New York's Arlington Hall about 500 Russians gathered to hear a speech by the well-known social democrat Alexandra Mikhailovna Kollontai," reported the chief of tsarist intelligence in New York. "Her entire speech was devoted to the question of how to arouse the international solidarity of the working class."[22] By the time she steamed out of New York harbor on February 21, she had a sizable dossier awaiting her in Petrograd.

She did not leave, though, without fulfilling at least a small part of her commitment to the American women's movement. She sat up the whole night before her departure to finish a pamphlet for March 8; *Not Life but Hard Labor* came out after she had left, under the unfortunate slogan "Workers' Wives Unite!" She had also written five articles for the socialist press. The conservative papers indulged in a series of bizarre fantasies to support their claim that she was a German agent, one writing that before her departure she had had a lengthy talk with the Swedish king and had offered him advice; another, that her husband was a German officer at the front.[23]

In the past four-and-a-half months Alexandra had addressed 123 meetings in four languages; America had left her stretched, changed, and exhausted. But the journey back to Bergen was not to be the rest she so longed for. At 6:00 A.M. on February 29, as the *Bergensfjord* neared England, British officers from a patrolling warship came on board and took the passengers as prisoners to the Orkneys, where the Germans' fate was to be decided. Alexandra and the other women were subjected to a body-search by a polite ex-suffragette volunteer; it was all too depressingly reminiscent of Russia: "The famous Habeas Corpus law of personal immunity has apparently become a mere empty phrase now in England."[24] One anxious day later the Germans were released and the *Bergensfjord* turned once more toward Norway; on March 6, 1916 she was back in Holmenkollen.

Shlyapnikov had just departed illegally for Petrograd, leaving Alexandra in charge of the smoothly operating postal service from Switzerland to Russia which he had perfected with the help of two newly opened railway lines from Tornio in Finland to Haparanda in Sweden. Alexandra had left America with a reputation as one of the most passionate of the left Zimmerwaldists, and this passion now flowed from her pen as she put the finishing touches to *Who Needs War?* This pamphlet, read by several million German and Russian soldiers, was one of her more enduringly popular works.

Who Needs War? was divided into small booklike chapters. The first, "A hero," described the crippled soldier returning to his devastated starving village; his tsarist pension is a pittance, he is a parasite on his family, and he cannot find work in the town. "What have we been fighting for?" was the next chapter, then "Who is guilty?" The pamphlet ended with a call for fraternization which evidently reached the hearts of many soldiers at the front:

> Comrade and worker of a foreign army, I know you are not my enemy; so give me your hand, comrade. Both you and I are victims of lies and violence. Our main enemy is in the rear. So let us turn our guns on him, our real common enemy. For my enemy is not one, like me, deprived in his own land of all rights, not one whose life like mine is crushed by capital and a struggle for bread. No, my enemy is at home, the enemy of the working class of all lands, and that enemy is capitalism! For it is that enemy which has made slaves of the working class!

She sent the manuscript to Lenin, who posted it off to Shlyapnikov in Petrograd, enclosing pages of detailed "corrections." He later wrote to apologize to Alexandra for not consulting her first about these changes; evidently he considered that this ambitious work was marred by her over-optimistic faith in international revolution (her old unrepentantly erring views on the "national question") and did not want an argument. In the summer of 1916 the Bolshevik Tkachev sisters worked day and night for a week on the press in their small wooden house in a suburb of Petrograd; shortly after they had dismantled the press and brought out *Who Needs War?*, they were both arrested. But by then the book was already in Bern, and the work of translating and distributing it had begun. Its first readers were Russian prisoners of war in Germany and the Austro-Hungarian Empire and, judging from the soldiers' letters received by the Bolshevik Foreign Bureau, its success was immediate.

In April 1916 the same socialists who had met at Zimmerwald met again at Kienthal in Switzerland and once again had clashed. But by then Lenin had considerably more allies. More and more socialists were renouncing the parliamentary path, breaking with the German Party, and joining the "ruthless struggle against imperialism." Shlyapnikov, as secretary of the Bolshevik central committee in Russia, kept the Petrograd workers informed of all such developments abroad; by means of messages filtering through from him to Scandinavia and Switzerland, Bolshevik exiles gradually reestablished contact with the revolutionary movement in Russia and began at last to anticipate the day when they might return there. But for Shlyapnikov, as for Alexandra and every other exile, it was far from clear whether that day would be in a year or in ten years. When Misha wrote to say that he had finally decided to go to America that summer to work as an engineer in a car factory in Paterson, New Jersey, Alexandra decided to join him there. She might after all, not see him again for a very long time. Shlyapnikov too had decided to go to America, to try to raise funds for the Party by finding a wealthy Jewish organization who might buy some unique documents he had on the persecution of Jews in Russia.

In August Alexandra entrusted all postal responsibilities to her Norwegian friends and, making it clear that she would not be doing any political work for a while, wrote asking Lenin to send a Russian replacement:

> But before talking business I must say how upset I was to hear of Nadezhda Konstantinovna's ill health, which has forced her to leave once more for the mountains . . . Dear Nadezhda Konstantinovna, I think of you so often, and not only in connection with "business." How infuriating to be separated by such vast distances, and to be unable to meet and chat . . . All papers will be kept by Widnes until Al [Shlyapnikov] comes back. And should any comrades come to replace Al, the password is *"Grüsse von Olga."*[25]

Shlyapnikov did not find the enthusiastic offers for his documents that he had anticipated. He spent all his time traveling around the country from one prospective buyer to another, and he and Alexandra rarely met. For two months Alexandra stayed with Misha in the industrial town of Paterson. She found it a dreary place. "We're living in the latitude of Naples, but it doesn't feel at all like the South," she wrote to Tatiana Schepkina.

> New York is completely surrounded by the sticks. I'm living with Misha on the edge of a town which is divided by straight little streets lined with maples. Along these streets stretch monotonously dull rows of little wooden houses with their inevitable porches, where rocking chairs are placed and where in the evenings American women, freed from their housework, gossip or simply sit. They seem so bored. At first glance the houses look comfortable, but then one becomes irritated by the complete lack of individuality in them and their furniture. I don't think you'd like it here at all. California, now that's a different story . . .[26]

The fact was that she herself was bored too, despite the pleasure she derived from Misha's company. She read voraciously—American literature and psychological studies—and looked back on the course her life had taken.

> Recently I looked back over my life and I realized that with all the diversity in it there weren't any long periods of satisfaction, there were no calm, bright, happy periods. The brightest time of my life was when I was a young girl, for that was a time of daydreams and hopes. The most deadly period was my marriage, the turning point. My life has been composed of so many small pieces, now bright, beautiful, captivating, now periods of dead emptiness, when suddenly all brightness is extinguished and a new phase of suffering and searching begins.
>
> Work has always been the center of my life, and in periods when I am working my soul is content and at peace; it doesn't cry, it doesn't rebel, it doesn't demand.[27]

It was this absence of any defined work program that made her so despondent in America on this second visit. She did however write a couple of articles for the American socialist press. By October she was already venturing into New York for meetings of the Society for the Protection of Child and Mother and for demonstrations against rising costs; she once again met her *New World* friends, the Bolshevik sympathizers Chudnovsky and Nakoryakov, who had now been joined by Bukharin and Trotsky and were creating a Russian federation of the American Socialist Party. Bukharin, who had been making strenuous attempts to induce the editors of *New World* to support the Bolsheviks, now seemed to have been successful. But Alexandra found Trotsky—who was still officially a Menshevik but willing to collaborate with Bukharin—a relatively unknown factor in this change of policy and considered that his line was far from clear. What did emerge clearly, however, at the long intense discussions held by the Russian community in New York was that Alexandra and Bukharin were the most vociferous proponents of the line that American revolutionaries should break with the American Socialist Party while Trotsky argued that, on the contrary, they should remain to fight within that party.

In December she was one of forty socialists, including the Japanese Sen Katayama, who met in New York to pledge themselves to a new communist International; and as the United States prepared to enter the war she drafted a militant antiwar manifesto for the combined Russian and German groups in the American Socialist Party.

A cheerful crowd gathered in the *New World* offices to see in the New Year of 1917. But as America began to mobilize, and maddeningly inadequate news of strikes and riots in Russia reached the Russian community in New York, they all longed for home. Shlyapnikov returned to Petrograd, and shortly afterward Alexandra left Misha in Paterson and started on the long journey back to Norway, where she arrived on February 28, frantic for news from Russia.

Women's Day was celebrated early that year in Petrograd. When Kayurov of the Bolshevik central committee was asked by a group of women textile workers for guidance on the day's events, he had strongly urged them to refrain from striking and to follow party instructions. Shlyapnikov later made it quite clear, however, that there were no instructions, no proclamations, because the party press was out of use. When workers were locked out of the Putilov armaments plant on March 7, 1917, the women of Petrograd began to take to the streets. The *soldatki* (the wives, daughters, and mothers of soldiers), previously as downtrodden and oppressed as prostitutes, demanded an end to their humiliation and angrily denounced all the hungry suffering of the past three years. Gathering strength and passion as they swept through the city over the next few days in food riots, political strikes, and demonstrations, these women launched the first revolution of 1917 and inscribed themselves firmly in the history of that extraordinary year. By midday on March 7 women were abandoning the breadlines and pouring into the center of the city: *"Bread!"* read their banners, *"Our Children are Starving!"* Soon housewives, *soldatki* and women workers from the homes and textile factories on the western side of the city near the border with Finland, were surging across the Neva bridges and thronging the streets. They were joined then by women workers of the Vasilev Island trolley terminus who first visited the neighboring barracks of the 180th Infantry Regiment to win their promise not to shoot if they came out on strike. By the following day the numbers on the streets had swelled to 197,000. Stones and ice were thrown at the police, and the soldiers in the Petrograd garrisons—raw recruits mostly, or family men—were determined not to go out. Their officers were no keener, and even the Cossacks lost their zeal. "The women go up to the officers more boldly than the men," wrote Trotsky (who, despite the fact that he was still in America, wrote one of the most vivid accounts of these days). "Taking hold of their rifles, they beseech and almost command: 'Put down your bayonets and join us.' "28

By March 10 women were invading the soldiers' ranks en masse and seizing their guns. Students were leaving lectures and joining the workers on the streets. The strike was general now, and there were no trams or papers. The poor working-class district of Vyborg was in the hands of its newly resurrected soviet, and the Bolsheviks, the only party to have consistently called for an armed rising, were called to account as angry workers demanded guns. With almost all the Bolshevik leaders in exile, it was now the Party that tried hopelessly to curb the violence; Shlyapnikov, as secretary of the central committee, lost many friends when he refused to arm this sudden spontaneous revolution. That night, with his habitual resourcefulness, he avoided the police as hundreds of revolutionaries and demonstrators, and the rest of the Bolshevik central committee, were arrested.

Without the Party to restrain them, the demonstrations became more violent, and several buildings were set on fire. The Pavlovsky regiment fired on the police, who were sniping from the rooftops at the crowds, and then returned to their barracks urging other regiments to follow their example. Next day 28,000 soldiers went to fraternize with the citizens of Vyborg, pledging their support for them and going on to rush the prisons. On that day, March 12 the released revolutionaries and workers proclaimed the Petrograd Soviet of Workers' and Soldiers' Deputies, and Bolsheviks, Mensheviks, and Socialist Revolutionaries went together to the Tauride Palace to arrange with the Duma deputies how to proceed with this new alternative parliament. Shlyapnikov, the only Bolshevik on its thirty-member executive, began the long struggle to convert this crucial organ of workers' control to the Bolsheviks. The Red Guards, the small bands of workers who had first appeared in 1905, now received official Bolshevik sanction and a code of conduct which Shlyapnikov drew up for them, and the first Red Guards to appear on the streets in 1917 were armed with guns provided by him.

On March 13 the last remaining troops still loyal to the Tsar laid down their arms. The tsarist government, at last recognizing that they could not compete with 160,000 mutinous soldiers and a city filled with "criminals," resigned "in the national interest." "Revolution by telegram" was how Trotsky described the way the news of events was borne across Russia as the new provisional government began to elect commissars to run the tsarist ministries and tried to restore confidence in the officer corps.

Only then, when Petrograd had lost over a thousand of its citizens, did the revolution begin to make headlines in the foreign press. Alexandra was returning to Holmenkollen from a meeting in town and was unable to buy a paper. It was only when she got into the train that she glimpsed the news over her neighbor's shoulder. *"Revolution in Russia!"* blared the headline. Yet the news was sketchy. There had been shooting on the streets, apparently, but now all was quiet. It must be a sensational bluff, she decided, and returned to Holmenkollen to finish off a lightly ironic (and ironically anachronistic) article, *Who Needs the Tsar?* The next day she read that the Tsar had "resigned in the interests of public order" and that the Duma had formed a provisional government to replace him— headed by Prince Lvov, a liberal landowner previously in the tsarist government, and including a prominent member of the Constitutional Democratic Party (Milyukov), a leader of the Octobrist Party (Guchkov), and Kerensky, who represented the right wing of the Socialist Revolutionary Party. The Petrograd Soviet had been resurrected, she also read; many of the Tsar's ministers had been arrested, and women had got the vote ("fairy stories! miracles!"). Her Norwegian comrades were jubilant, and when news reached Kristiania of a political amnesty, the Russian colony dashed around frenziedly buying tickets and worrying about their false passports.

As the Petrograd telegraph agency continued to bombard foreign countries with news of the revolution Alexandra was as prone to anxiety as the rest of the Russians in Norway, since she was desperately keen for someone to replace her in organizing postal work in Kristiania; she could not think of leaving before that. She wired Lenin (who was still living in Bern) for directives. "Fancy asking for 'directives' from here, where information is so extremely scanty!" he replied. "It's in Peter [Petrograd] where all the leading comrades of the Party are now . . . A week of bloody workers' battles, and Milyukov, Guchkov, and Kerensky are in power! Well, so be it. This 'first stage of the revolution,' born of the war, will be neither the last nor a purely Russian affair. Of course we still stand against national defense, against the imperialist war—all our slogans are the same." He urged her to stay on in Scandinavia to continue her work there, but this was more than she could bear. She did, however, agree to stay on for a week to receive his "Letters from Afar," which she was to arrange for *Pravda* to publish when she arrived in Petrograd. To the Norwegian colony as a whole he wired a terse and attenuated version of these letters: "Our tactics—absolute distrust, no support for the provisional government. Distrust Kerensky above all. No alliance with other parties. Wire this to Petrograd."[29]

The next week passed in one festive meeting after another, and the night before she left the Norwegian youth group of the Party organized an emotional gathering for her. "We've never seen such a packed meeting here," said an old sailor called Klinger with whom she had worked in the underground. "Greetings to Lenin!"

Thanks to her friend the Swedish socialist leader Branting the Swedish government had agreed to give her a transit visa, provided she did not travel through Stockholm, and on March 29 she prepared to leave. She wore her best dress and put up her hair in an elaborate style, confident that the best way to avoid harassment from the police along the way was to appear in the elegant dress and coiffure of a lady. Then, putting Lenin's letters into her corset and packing her diaries and a few clothes into a small suitcase, she took the train 800 miles north to the remote Swedish border town of Charlottenberg, on the first stage of her long, grueling journey back. A Swedish policeman in civilian clothes met her there and politely informed her that he would be escorting her across to Finland. The events of the past week had left her too dizzy and numb to care, and it was only as the train approached Finland that her spirits finally revived. Halfway across Sweden they changed trains, and Alexandra was met by a Russian called Khavkin whom a Copenhagen underground worker had assigned to help her on her journey. She stood until late that night in the train corridor, avoiding the police and listening to the garrulous Khavkin regale her with accounts of the past two months in red Petrograd. They reached Haparanda in Finland, and after a fairly lackadaisical body-search in which she had to remove all her hairpins to prove she was not carrying arms or literature in her coiffure, she waited with mounting impatience for the train from the Russian-Finnish border at Torneo. They ran forward to meet it as it steamed into view and were greeted by the drivers, former electricians commandeered to make these infrequent trips to Sweden, with ecstatic descriptions of the new regime. " 'All upside-down! In one blow! No more Tsar! The people are the boss now—you're not just a worker but a citizen!' they said. And with what pride that word was pronounced . . ."[30] They shouted and laughed and sang the *Marseillaise* all the way to the end of the line, where Finnish sledges of the kind she remembered so clearly from her childhood took them across the frozen river to the Russian border. "It was a harsh winter," she later recalled of this crossing into Russia.

> A white snowy shroud brightened the gloom of the polar swamps. But there was such joy in our jingling sledges as we crossed the frontier river into Torneo. Ahead lay the New Russia. It was still not ours, for it was still only bourgeois, but had not the workers' and peasants' desire for peace, and for a basic sweeping clean of the old Russia, been displayed in the creation of the soviets? Ahead was struggle and work, work and struggle. At that time, in March 1917, my soul felt as bracingly bright and fresh as the snow and the frosty air about me.[31]

Telegrams from the Russian government, as well as the Swedish police, had already alerted the Russian border guards to her arrival. Soldiers wearing red armbands crowded round, knowing her as the writer of *Who Needs War?*, to assure her that they were all friends of the Finns and had organized a demonstration to mourn the death of their soldier comrades there. Then more soldiers hurried up with news of more deaths across the border: "I feared that other mood. First it had been that Russian caps-in-the-air exuberance, but then it was all skepticism and bewilderment . . ."[32] She sent a telegram to Tatiana Schepkina asking to be met at the Finland Station, grabbed some newspapers from the station canteen, and settled into the train, which wound slowly past frozen Finnish woodlands and little stations crowded with smiling soldiers, heroes of the day in their red armbands; until at last they reached Beloostrov, the last checkpoint into "free Russia."

The guard proudly tore up the tsarist arrest warrant which had remained there since 1908, and half an hour later she was in Petrograd, racing forward to meet Tatiana and her husband on the Finland Station platform. Beside them stood an oddly incongruous coach and pair, the Petrograd Soviet's own cautious welcome to Alexandra as one of its most long-standing members and a prominent figure in the international social-ist movement. If the Menshevik majority in the Soviet thought to render the Bolsheviks there harmless by giving them coaches, she concluded as they all got inside and set off for Kirochnaya Street, they did not know their enemy; what she had yet to discover was that most of her Bolshevik comrades were committed to an alliance with the Mensheviks.

Her room was waiting for her as though she had never left it, and Tatiana left her alone there for a while to gather her thoughts; with Misha still in America and Shlyapnikov virtually her only close comrade in Petrograd, the new life she was embarking on was both promising and alarming.

That evening she joined Tatiana and her husband and a party of old friends in the great dark dining room of the Kirochnaya Street house. As they sat around the samovar discussing the events of the past month, the demonstrations, the shootings, and the government shuffles, Alexandra had to restrain herself from shouting, "You dear intellectuals, how can you say 'It's all over now, there'll just be meetings from now on?' "[33] Slipping away from the table, she telephoned the *Pravda* offices to announce that she would be bringing Lenin's letters the next day and asking to be accepted onto its permanent staff.

11
Militant Spring

The next day, after gulping down some coffee, Alexandra set off across town to the modest little offices on the Moika Canal where *Pravda* and the Bolshevik Party had their headquarters. From one end of the city to the other she passed people talking, arguing, hoisting banners, and milling about in an endless torrent of demonstrations that made the head reel; it seemed on that gusty March day as though the wind had driven the entire population of Petrograd onto the streets and hurled the last scraps of their partiotism and submission into the gutter. "Bolsheviks . . . Mensheviks . . ."—these were the key words on everybody's lips. But she resisted the temptation to stop and join them and quickened her step, for she had to deposit Lenin's "Letters from Afar" at the *Pravda* offices. A brief conversation there with Lenin's sister Maria, as anxious as she was for Lenin to return, left her in no doubt about the work to be done before the working class and its Party could create a new order of peace and justice in Russia.

That same day, March 19,* *Pravda* marked the return of Alexandra Kollontai, "noted writer and representative of the international social democratic movement." This less than ecstatic welcome for one of their more prominent revolutionaries reflected the confusion prevailing in the Bolsheviks' ranks. With their foremost leaders still in exile, radicals on the central committee like Shlyapnikov and Molotov were time and again outvoted by a majority too nervous and confused to dissociate themselves from the Provisional Government and to support the appeals for "revolu-

---

*We shall continue to use the old calendar, 13 days behind that of the West, which was discarded in Russia after the Bolshevik revolution.

tionary defeatism" contained in Lenin's letters—his postulate that soldiers must refuse to fight at the front in order to turn their guns on the enemy at home: that the imperialist war must in this way be transformed into a revolutionary war.

For the Bolshevik majority, more concerned with the overthrow of autocracy and feudalism than with the overthrow of capitalism, this "defeatism" was nothing more than a betrayal of the German working class; while the German soldier remained at his post, the Russian soldier must remain at his. This incomprehensible logic, dignified by its proponents as a policy of "revolutionary defensism," naturally led most in the Bolshevik party to ally themselves with the similarly patriotic Mensheviks and to declare their qualified support for the Provisional Government. Only two of Lenin's letters were published, and then grudgingly, in *Pravda*. For her first hectic weeks in Petrograd before Lenin returned Alexandra was to occupy her old familiar place in opposition to the party majority and, unlike them, in intransigent opposition to her old Menshevik allies.

None were more mystified by the apparently leaderless revolution than the government liberals—the Kadets, Octobrists, and right wing Socialist Revolutionaries—whom it had swept into power. Tsarist Russia no longer existed, but little else had been settled. The peasants were for the moment quiescent and the aristocracy demoralized, so that in March 1917 it was the two classes of the urban proletariat (represented by the Bolsheviks) and the bourgeoisie (represented by the Provisional Government) who were fighting for power. There could not possibly be any alliance between them, for the bourgeoisie, carried to power by the insurgent masses, was a class which in Russia, in contrast to the rest of Europe, had never succeeded in gaining any real power. Their weakness became most evident during the war, when Kadets, Octobrists, and many Socialist Revolutionaries had espoused the cause of national defense and the seizure of the Dardanelles. But conflicting with this patriotism was the awareness of the price that would have to be paid for it, in strikes and upheavals at home.

All through the riots of February the leading deputies in the Duma hoped against hope that the Tsar would put himself at the head of a more representative government and thus avoid the calamity of his abdication. One observer close to this liberal circle recalled the panic which the March Revolution induced in them: "Officially they were elated; they celebrated the Revolution, shouted hurrah in honor of the fighters for liberty, donned red ribbons, marched under red flags . . . But deep down and in private they were terrified, and felt like prisoners to hostile and dangerous forces." After the Tsar had abdicated, he went on, many liberals "started sobbing as soon as they got back home, had fits of hysteria caused by despair and impotence . . ."[1] Within the Provisional Government of the Duma only one deputy had the mildest of left-wing sympathies, and this was the thirty-six-year-old lawyer and Minister of Justice, Alexander Kerensky. But although Kerensky was a member of the Laborite Party (an amorphous petty-bourgeois organization formed in 1905 and vaguely affiliated to the right wing of the Socialist Revolutionary Party), his allegiance was always to himself and his own rhetorical powers rather than to any party or political principle; this became all too clearly obvious when he became Prime Minister in July.

Right from the outset of the revolution, however, Kerensky was regarded by Lenin with extreme distrust, a distrust intensified by the fact that as a member of the executive committee of the Petrograd Soviet, he was obviously trying to keep one foot in each of the two main political camps which from February to October controlled the situation in Russia. For he, like all the Provisional Government members, realized that it was the Soviet, formed in March on the model of its 1905 predecessor and containing deputies of workers and soldiers, Bolsheviks, Mensheviks and Socialist Revolutionaries, that held the real political power in Petrograd. It was the Soviet that had prevented the Duma liberals from proclaiming a constitutional monarchy in February and had forced Prince Lvov, president of the Provisional Government, to admit publicly that his government had "no real powers": "Its orders are not obeyed unless they happen to fall in with the wishes of the Soviet of Workers' and Soldiers' Deputies."[2]

And yet, in making that confession, Lvov was not actually conceding so much to this organization of workers' power. The Soviet, most of whose members were, as in 1905, members of the increasingly moderate Menshevik group and of the Socialist Revolutionary Party (which looked now for support among the liberal intelligentsia), had no intention of seizing power. It was quite content with this situation of "dual power," without recognizing that the organization of the bourgeoisie (the Provisional Government) and that thrown up by the masses (the Soviet) were in irreconcilable opposition to one another.

For the Mensheviks, the past month's events eloquently confirmed their faith that in this new government lay all the hopes of the revolutionary bourgeois regime for which they considered Russia was now ripe. They prepared to use the Soviet merely as a legal opposition to the Provisional

Government, even though that government only existed insofar as it was accepted and authorized by the Soviet, which retained all the real power through the army, the railways, and the post and telegraph offices. Most Bolsheviks felt that until they gained more seats there, they could hardly take a strong line either against the Mensheviks or against Kerensky's government, "so long as its actions corresponded to the interests of the proletariat."

When the tsarist police chief, in his last report before the abdication, blamed "propaganda" for stirring up the proletariat, he was in a real sense right. But for the men and women who had stormed heaven that month, economic misery and the horrors and humiliations of war spoke louder than could any agitation. This, as Alexandra recognized, was the source of the confusion with which the Bolsheviks in Petrograd greeted the death of tsarism and the culmination of twenty hard years of agitation and writing, persecution and exile. For now it was the people, "people in soldiers' uniforms and in civilian dress, who ruled the situation and whose will was imprinted on the face of the land."[3] From the revolutionary rehearsal of 1905 and her experiences as an agitator abroad, she was convinced that the successful revolution must depend on the Bolsheviks' capacity to listen to the anger of people deeply antagonistic to all authority and more enthusiastic about the idea of no government than of better government.

It was most probably from Shlyapnikov, active both on the factory floor and in the Party, that Alexandra learned something of the workers' frame of mind. (Shlyapnikov was no longer her lover—they had apparently drifted apart during her second trip to America—but he remained for many years a close friend whose political principles she trusted completely.) She discovered that even the most radical workers and soldiers in the steel plants and in the textile mills, on the factory committees and in the Finnish garrisons, were merely demanding that the government guarantee its promised reforms and waiting for the day when the German working class should rise against the Kaiser and demand an immediate armistice. Only then, they said, would the international revolution gather momentum. It was only now that the revolutionary leaders were returning, and now that the most skilled workers (called up first to the front as political troublemakers and killed there by the hundreds) were being called back to help get the factories going, that the Bolsheviks could begin to develop the flexibility, the fearlessness, and the inner-party freedom that would command the respect of the people who alone could make the proletarian revolution.

On that same day as her first visit to the *Pravda* offices Alexandra went on to the Tauride Palace; and there, in an almost surrealistic replay of the congress she had left eight and a half years before, the feminists were holding one of the largest demonstrations seen in Petrograd to press their claim for the vote. To the feminist organizations, virtually moribund since 1909, war had presented the opportunity to renew this claim and attach it to a patriotic program of war to victory; the Provisional Government had been sufficiently impressed by this patriotic fervor to grant women greatly expanded education and employment opportunities.

In 1907 an energetic thirty-five-year-old St. Petersburg doctor, Polixena Shishkina Yavein, had formed a new right-wing feminist organization, the Russian League of Women's Equality, composed of various members of Adriadna Tyrkova's Union of Women's Equality—the feminist group with which Alexandra had clashed after 1905. The league had faded out almost completely since then, and it was only after the February revolution that it began to attract a number of high-born ladies engaged in volunteer war work, as well as a large number of women intellectuals and Socialist Revolutionaries. Ekaterina Breshkovskaya (a long-standing and idealistic Socialist Revolutionary, called in earlier years the "grandmother of the revolution") joined the league, as did the former People's Will member, Vera Figner, whose courage had so inspired later revolutionaries like Alexandra; another member was the intellectual Ekaterina Kuskova, a Marxist unaffiliated with either Bolsheviks or Mensheviks. Alexandra watched in amazement as 40,000 women, maddened by a recent inconsequential meeting with Prince Lvov, poured through the town toward the Tauride Palace to present their demand for the vote to the Soviet. Their procession was headed by a motor car bearing the proud figure of Vera Figner—a sight fit to bring shame to any revolutionary. Alongside her clattered a group from the women's mounted militia, whose mainly middle-class members, although they did little actual fighting, nevertheless had considerable patriotic propaganda power.

Alexandra struggled to contain her exasperation as Vera Figner added her own speech to the patriotic pleas for national defense made by Dr. Shishkina and Ariadna Tyrkova: "What nonsense they're talking—out-and-out defensists. Shall I argue? No, not worth it, it's not the right audience."[4] Eventually Chkheidze, a leading Menshevik in the Soviet, was induced to come out onto the Tauride steps and address the assembled women with some vague assurances that the Soviet would struggle with them for their just rights. Then some soldiers leaped up, yelling that women should wait until the war ended to demand the vote. At this

Alexandra could restrain herself no longer. Running up on the steps, she denounced everyone who collaborated in the bloody horrors of the war. "All power to the soviets!" she shouted, and was promptly dragged off by one of the patriotic ruffians paid to keep order on such occasions. Outraged feminists rushed forward to attack her and several soldiers leveled their bayonets, but an equal number of women, as well as soldiers who had been in the trenches, knew what she was talking about and listened sympathetically. The patriotic pageantry of the meeting disintegrated in ferocious arguments, and Alexandra slipped out into the Tauride.

Several Bolsheviks who had watched the demonstration with some anxiety urged her not to belittle the achievements of the February revolution so blatantly. But she felt the Bolsheviks should appeal more boldly to the men who returned exhausted from the front and to the angry, starving women whom they bitterly joined in the breadlines and in protest demonstrations day and night throughout the town. As she left the Tauride she met a large crowd of soldiers and *soldatki* standing about outside, and as she wove a few slogans into a brief impromptu speech the soldiers lifted her onto their shoulders and all repeated the refrains: "Bread for our children! Down with war! Return our husbands! Long live the soviets!"

Lurking behind the appeals of Alexandra's Bolshevik friends for more caution was probably another reason; it was only a week earlier that they had sanctioned any special work among women, and on this issue the Party was as divided as it was on the proper tactics for ending the war and making the revolution. Vera Slutskaya, the Bolshevik with whom Alexandra had clashed over the 1908 feminist congress, was now secretary of the Vasilev Island regional Bolshevik committee and was using her interrupted medical studies to train factory women as *sanitarki*—medical assistants attached to the Red Guards in all the major cities of Russia. Known affectionately to her women friends as "our iron Vera," she had lost her old inhibitions about women's work and was considerably less antifeminist than many other women in the Bolshevik Party. On March 10 she had been put in charge of agitation among working women, and three days later at a party executive planning meeting she had tried to clarify this vague brief by recommending that the Petrograd committee include a woman's bureau, to which each district would elect a woman representative. The bureau would then be able to direct its energies towards reviving the women's journal *Rabotnitsa*, which had enjoyed such spectacular success when it first came out between March and June 1914, and writing and distributing leaflets "specifically directed to the proletarian woman question." All the bureau's work would be conducted only with the full agreement of the Petrograd committee; no separate organization was contemplated. This Vera Slutskaya emphasized for the benefit not only of most of her male comrades, deeply suspicious of any hint of separatism, but also of women like Konkordia Samoilova, who was the most vocal opponent of the scheme.

Tall, red-cheeked, with an intense gaze and a boundless capacity for work and organization, Konkordia Samoilova had been a Bolshevik since 1902 and was a formidable opponent. As the popular "Comrade Natasha," she had worked with Alexandra in 1907, and five years later she had been appointed secretary to the newly launched *Pravda* and had initiated the women's page. She was arrested as one of the founding editors of *Rabotnitsa* and had just been released from three years in prison. As with other *Rabotnitsa* workers (Lyudmila Stal, Praskovia Kudelli, Inessa Armand, and Elena Rozmirovich, for example) in Konkordia Samoilova an extreme anti-feminism combined, paradoxically, with a commitment to the concerns of working women, whom they all urged to integrate their needs for maternity insurance, electoral rights, and childcare centers into the Bolshevik program. Alexandra was caught in this contradiction too, of course, but not to anything like the same extent as Konkordia, who "could not endure anything that smelled of feminism, and regarded with deep reservations any organizational scheme which she felt might introduce a 'sexual division' into the proletariat."[5] When *Rabotnitsa* reappeared in May, it was considered by many party members to "reek of feminism." Although women's sections of the Party did slowly begin to develop, their work was sadly thwarted by this kind of sexual prejudice, and they were not ratified as the *zhenotdely* (women's departments) until three years later, when it was no longer possible to deny their recruiting achievements.

During her first evening back in Petrograd, Tatiana and her friends had warned Alexandra that the Bolsheviks were now haranguing the masses from armored cars. She was not cut out to be a street agitator, they insisted; her style was more appropriate to the drawing room. After her first day, during which she argued herself hoarse at two street meetings, she returned gratefully to Tatiana's house inclined to think them wrong. She stayed with Tatiana for the next four months, returning late at night from meetings and sessions of the Soviet, and leaving again first thing in the morning. (This was a convenient and hospitable arrangement which many returning revolutionaries, who had to make do with a more squalid and nomadic life, might have envied.)

The following morning she set out for the Party central committee to report herself ready for work. The most important task, the secretary, Schmidt, told her, was to increase the Bolsheviks' representation in the Soviet; she was to persuade a group or union of workers or soldiers to allow her to represent them and somehow get herself a mandate. Rummaging in a pile of documents from various unions, he at last triumphantly produced the address of the woodworkers' union, unaffiliated but apparently sympathetic to the Bolsheviks. With high hopes she arrived at the union's shabby basement headquarters and was admitted by a kerchiefed old peasant woman, the wife of the janitor. "Of course I tried to propagandize the janitor's wife and to discuss with her who had started the war, and why, and so on," she wrote later. "She didn't argue with me—she simply didn't show any interest. The expression on her face read very clearly: deliver me from idle chatter!" Two hours later, when the foreman returned from his business in the town and asked her if she wanted a job, her hopes were no longer so high. As she explained why she had come and who she was men gathered round, for they had read in the papers that she had been exchanged for German prisoners of war. "We don't betray our country, we're honest woodworkers," one said. The long argument which followed was guiltily interrupted as in walked another agitator, a Menshevik, who had been doing this beat for some time in the hope of getting the woodworkers to give him a mandate for the Soviet. Alexandra was bustled out of the door and left without her mandate.[6] However her speech to the soldiers and *soldatki* the previous day had not been lost on the radical Nikolai Podvoisky, who had organized the Petrograd military commission of the party with the purpose of recruiting soldiers to the Bolsheviks, and had invited Alexandra to visit him. She left the woodworkers with their Menshevik and went on to the commission's headquarters in the palace which Shlyapnikov had expropriated from the dancer Kshesinskaya, former mistress of the Tsar. The pools, baths, and ornate furniture of this courtesan's pleasure palace had now been turned over to the soldiers of the Bolshevik revolution, whose boots tramped day and night over the parquet floors and whose army greatcoats draped the silk upholstery. There she met Podvoisky, who asked her to speak to the soldiers the following week about reaction abroad to the February revolution.

On 21 March, the same issue of *Pravda* that contained Lenin's first "Letter from Afar" printed "Working Women and the Constituent Assembly," Alexandra's first article in Russia, prompted by the feminists' demonstration. The struggle for women's suffrage, she stressed, meant to continue the revolution and convene a new parliament which represented the people. It was not only hypocrites in the Provisional Government but also those wearing red armbands in the Soviet who thought to settle themselves more comfortably in power by opening the door to women of the middle class and excluding the *"babi"* who threatened to turn the state on its head. "Women will never be handed their rights on a plate," she concluded. "They themselves have to take them and fight for their own interests." Five days later *Pravda* carried a message from women at the Baranov textile mill who linked her article to their resolution to fight for admittance to the Constituent Assembly.

Lenin's article received nothing like the unanimous support she had anticipated, and she learned from Shlyapnikov that at a central-committee meeting called the day after its publication Kamenev and another long-standing but little known Bolshevik underground activist, Stalin, recently returned from Siberian exile, were using their seniority in the Party and their long experience of underground work to condemn the Leninist line. Lenin's description of the Provisional Government as an agent of Anglo-French capital, any support for which was an insult to the working class, they found deeply offensive. It was Kamenev's view that they should exert pressure on the government for a just peace with no annexations. This line, indistinguishable from that of the Mensheviks, was then carried by Stalin into the sort of compromising and wordy resolution which would later become so characteristic of him. It was probably Shlyapnikov who proposed at this meeting that Alexandra be elected to the executive committee of the Soviet. But until the Bolsheviks had considerably increased their power there, it was going to be almost impossible to air any radical views in *Pravda,* which followed Lenin's letter with the same sort of articles, advocating qualified support for the Provisional Government's defensist policies, that it had been publishing since February.

On March 23, the same day that Alexandra joined Elena Stasova, Nikolai Podvoisky, and Lenin's sister Maria at a demonstration on the Mars Field to mourn the hundreds killed by police over the past month, *Pravda* did, however, print her moving appeal (in an article entitled "Our Memorial to the Freedom Fighters") to continue the revolution:

> Our comrades all over the world are following us in spirit. Our victory will be theirs, just as our grief now is theirs. Now the first stage of the revolution is over, and we must get to work to build our memorial to those killed: a democratic republican Russia in which we can finally achieve the liberation of the working people![7]

A few days later Podvoisky introduced her to a large audience of soldiers at Kshesinskaya's palace who responded cheerfully to her speech. But they did not respond so cheerfully to the idea that they delegate her to the Soviet, and there were many embarrassed and outraged mutterings against Podvoisky's assurance that soldiers could be quite adequately represented by a woman. It took them a day to get over their shock. On March 27 she got her mandate, was automatically elected on to the executive committee of the Soviet, and joined the small number of women already sitting in this huge amorphous body which represented socialists of every conceivable social class and political and union affiliation. She was one of the few on the executive committee who had a mandate from the workers to represent them.

On that day Bolshevik delegates to the Soviet and members of other Bolshevik organizations gathered at the Tauride for a week-long meeting to thrash out the question of who would present the Bolshevik line at a meeting to be held jointly with the Mensheviks, which was due to convene a few days later. All that week Alexandra and Shlyapnikov, main speakers for the radical minority, argued themselves hoarse against Stalin, Kamenev and the Party "center," which was in a strong position to represent the Party at the subsequent meeting. Supported by the Moscow Bolshevik Party and thirteen provincial organizations, Alexandra angrily tackled Kamenev for his lifeless argument that now that the long bourgeois dictatorship had begun, the most the Soviet could aspire to was to "persuade" Kerensky to propose a just peace to the warring countries. During the proceedings there arrived another terse telegram from Lenin, who, thanks to Shlyapnikov's tireless negotiations with socialist leaders in the various countries between Bern and Petrograd, was already on his way back in the famous "sealed train." By late March, an arrangement had been made with the Imperial German government whereby thirty-two Russians, including Lenin and eighteen other Bolsheviks, were given permission to travel through German territory on condition that they did not communicate with anyone on their journey; an equal number of Germans were to be released from Russia.

"Our only guarantee to arm the workers," read Lenin's telegram. "No rapprochement with other parties. Last is *sine qua non*. We do not trust Chkheidze." This encouraged the radicals to pass a resolution praising the work of the Red Guards, and to describe the Soviet as the "embryo of revolutionary power" and the Russian revolution as the "point of departure for the revolutionary movement of the entire European proletariat." But they were hopelessly outvoted by the "center." Fifty-nine party organizations backed Stalin's insistence that the Provisional Government, "fortifier of the people's conquests," could be directed by the Soviet towards great and useful work, and that only when it had exhausted itself could there be any thought of Soviet power.[8]

Alexandra put some of her own impressions of this mood of empty jubilance into a letter to Lenin and Nadezhda Krupskaya in Switzerland:

> In the endeavor to create something new, the note of triumph rings a little too loudly, for the enemy is still in our midst and the working class (especially the executive committee of the Soviet) lacks firmness. "We're already in power!" they cry, and yet always the same cautious, indecisive attitude. People like Steklov, Sukhanov, Bogdanov,* and a host of other petty giants, have exploited the absence of our people in the heat of the revolutionary moment and have taken their seats on the executive committee . . . The Bolsheviks demand that all mandates be checked and the executive committee be reelected, but the majority are opposed to this . . . We dream of seeing you soon![9]

This dream was soon to be realized. By the time her letter arrived, Lenin, Nadezhda Krupskaya, Inessa Armand, Grigori Zinoviev (with his wife and small son), and fifteen other Bolsheviks had already left Switzerland. Shlyapnikov had managed to arrange their return to coincide neatly with the end of the Bolsheviks' meeting and the beginning of the joint gathering, and he put all his considerable propaganda skills into turning their arrival at the Finland Station into a festive welcoming demonstration of unforgettable ceremony.

On the evening of April 3, Easter Sunday, as troops and Bolshevik supporters were gathering on the square outside the Finland Station Alexandra traveled out with Shlyapnikov and other members of the Bolshevik central committee to the small Russian border station of Beloostrov. The train was very late, and the welcoming party sat drinking tea with a group of Finnish Bolsheviks in the station waiting room. Alexandra's bouquet from the Soviet executive committee was wilting by the time the train finally arrived. Lenin stepped briskly off, followed by his Bolshevik companions and an enthusiastic crowd of Finns. Then everyone was rushing forward to greet him, and the speech Alexandra was to have made flew out of her head. Shlyapnikov pushed her forward to present her

---

*Sukhanov was a leader of the Menshevik left wing; although somewhat erratic in his political allegiances, he left an invaluable record of the revolution. Steklov and Bogdanov (not Alexandra's old Bolshevik comrade from the 1905 revolution, Alexander Bogdanov) were lesser-known characters.

bouquet, saying, "Well, if you're not going to make a speech, do at least kiss Ilich." Then, after much embracing and shouting and after Nadezhda had pleaded in vain that all Lenin wanted was a cup of tea, they all got back into the train for Petrograd, Alexandra and Shlyapnikov joining Kamenev in Lenin's compartment. After cursing Kamenev amicably for his renegade politics (for despite everything, the two were close friends), Lenin anxiously sought their assurance that he would not be arrested on arrival.[10]

The train was by now very late, and the excitement of the waiting crowds was intense as Lenin, still clutching his withered bouquet with some embarrassment, hesitantly emerged onto the platform of the Finland Station. Alexandra fought back the tears as a soldiers' band struck up the "Marseillaise," and Lenin hurried through the ranks of welcoming soldiers and workers to the imperial waiting room. There the Menshevik Chkheidze delivered a distinctly cool welcoming speech on behalf of the Soviet, and then the dazed Lenin at last came into his own. Thrusting aside the bouquet, he turned in the other direction to his "dear comrades, soldiers, sailors and workers," and in language quite alien to the waiting crowds, declared that "the imperialists' piratical war marks the beginning of the civil war throughout Europe."

Searchlights mounted on armored cars illuminated strips of the station square—which thronged with people, whole regiments without their officers, a sea of red flags, and one bold red banner which dominated the rest: the banner of the central committee of the Bolshevik party. The crowds followed Lenin as he set off in an armored car for Kshesinskaya's palace and heard him again and again repeat the same words: the imperialist war must be turned into civil war. Again he repeated the same message to the startled crowds outside from the windows of Kshesinskaya's palace. Even the most radical of the Bolsheviks was stunned, even the most skeptical of them greeted his words with serious attention. None of them had expected this. Indeed many had assumed that he would at once call the Party to order, especially those most intransigently opposed to the Provisional Government. For Alexandra, the repetition of this familiar message had an immediately electrifying effect, and "knowing he was here, in this new upturned Russia, gave enormous confidence and stability. I was so happy too that those Bolsheviks who were still wavering would now be brought to order . . ."[11]

But when she arrived at the Tauride the following morning for the last day of the Bolshevik meeting, she could only ask herself in amazement whether the Leninist letters and literature she had helped to transport into Russia for the past two years had ever actually arrived. Her comrades were sitting around uneasily waiting for Lenin's arrival and complaining that his appearance later that day at the Soviet meeting, before a combined audience of Bolsheviks and Mensheviks, was premature. After a sleepless night of interviews and discussions and an early-morning meeting at the *Pravda* offices, Lenin finally arrived, and his opening words confirmed all their worst fears. It was but a dull caricature of Marxism, Lenin said, to claim that backward Russia should wait for the workers of Western Europe to launch the world revolution. The great honor of striking the first blow had fallen to the Russian proletariat; less class-conscious and less prepared than workers elsewhere, they would play a supporting role in the world revolution by which the war would be ended. A popular government would then tear up the tsarist peace treaties and invite the warring countries to conclude a democratic peace, renounce all conquests and reparations, and grant all peoples the right to self-determination. These bold terms, impossible for any existing government to accept, would seize the imagination of the people of the world, who would confront their governments and so turn the imperialist war into an international uprising.

If these words were greeted unenthusiastically by most of her Bolshevik comrades, Alexandra had little doubt as she passed through the Tauride corridors into the semicircular hall where the Soviet was sitting that his second speech would have a considerably more devastating impact. She passed Martov and a group of Mensheviks fulminating against Lenin and his schemes for a conspiratorial "Blanquist" putsch. No sane Soviet delegate would support him, Martov assured them; Russians did not like utopias. But few of the soldiers who packed the corridors shared Martov's views, and as their delegate, Alexandra was stopped and asked with incredulous excitement whether Lenin was really to appear. Hardly believing it herself, she joined the other Soviet executive committee members on the platform. The gloomy Chkheidze opened the session, and Lenin launched into the long speech familiar now as the ten *April Theses*. [12]

From an attack on the war he moved on to attack the Provisional Government and to conclude that only when the Bolsheviks had gained a majority in the Soviet could the revolution begin. Then all private property and the banks would be nationalized and the Soviet would gain control over production and distribution, and then would socialism at last be established. "It was impossible not to notice how swiftly people's expressions changed as the logical chain of Lenin's proposals unfolded.

The Mensheviks' leaders looked first distraught, then fearful and angry. By contrast, the faces of the rank-and-file deputies, the workers and soldiers, gradually cleared as if a door had opened . . ."[13]

To most deputies, however, including many Bolsheviks, Lenin's program of violent revolution seemed excessively abstract and utopian, an indication of his prolonged lack of contact with Russian life and the work of the Party. "It's obscene to applaud such rubbish!" shouted Bogdanov as Lenin was speaking. "These are the ravings of a lunatic!" Lenin managed to finish and sat down to scattered clapping (rather than the stormy applause that Alexandra overenthusiastically recorded). The old Menshevik Goldenburg then stood up to propose Lenin as candidate to the throne of the nineteenth-century Russian revolutionary, Bakunin, whose semi-anarchist ideas now seemed so much in accord with Lenin's. And one by one Mensheviks and Socialist Revolutionaries struggled for words to express their outrage. Lenin's supporters had produced no resolution of solidarity, and overcoming her habitual nervousness, Alexandra felt impelled to speak up for him—the only Bolshevik at that Soviet meeting to endorse the *April Theses* openly. Nadezhda Krupskaya and Inessa Armand, smiling at her from the front row, provided her only support. From most of the others present her words provoked catcalls and jeers, and in the bourgeois press her speech earned her the title of "Valkyrie of the revolution."

Lenin smiled gratefully after she had finished and took a brief nap while Chkheidze spoke. For Alexandra the congress marked the start of a new life of agitation, "for peace, for the power of the soviets, for fraternization at the front, and for the liberation and full equality of women . . ."[14] Lenin went on to defend his *theses* before an overwhelmingly hostile majority on the Bolshevik central committee and embarked on the long uphill struggle to woo its radicals, inspire its "center," and infuse the angry masses with enthusiasm for the Bolsheviks and their revolutionary program. Only now could Alexandra use the pages of *Pravda* to expose, with her article "Where Does 'Revolutionary Defensism' Lead?," the lie promoted by Stalin and Kamenev that national defense was somehow in the best interests of the Russian revolution. Their "revolutionary defensism" was a mere empty phrase, she declared, signifying nothing but the same patriotism promoted by the Provisional Government.[15] Soon there were few workers, soldiers, or *soldatki* in the capital who did not know of Alexandra Kollontai or had not heard her speak.

A few days after Lenin returned to Petrograd, Anatoly Lunacharsky, one of Alexandra's old comrades from the post-1905 days, arrived to join an independent organization within the Bolshevik Party called the Organization of United Internationalist Social Democrats (the "Mezhrayonka", or "Interdistrict" group). The political line of this group—composed mainly of former Mensheviks, members of the left Bolshevik *Forward* group, contributors to the internationalist journal *New World* (based in New York) and the Menshevik journal *Our Word* (published in Paris)—differed little from the Bolshevik attitude toward war and revolution; its members did, however, take issue with Lenin's notion of a narrow and exclusive Party, and they desired the maximum possible membership for the Bolshevik organization. It was these broad sympathies which made so many members of the "Interdistrict" group, joined over the following months by Karl Radek, Adolf Joffe, and Larin (all of whom Alexandra had known in Berlin), particularly effective as public speakers. In early May they were joined by Trotsky and V. Volodarsky when these two returned to Petrograd from America.

Throughout May 1917, as exiled revolutionaries flocked back to Russia, the Bolsheviks' following steadily increased, and Alexandra became, like Trotsky, Lunacharsky and her old Philadelphia friend Volodarsky, one of the most popular speakers in Petrograd. Speaking in Germany had taught her to give full expression to all her non-intellectual lyrical powers and to achieve a concentration of creative energy which can only be described as inspiration. There were moments when she felt "a strange lightness in my whole being, as if I was finding the right intonations and gestures without being conscious of it":

> Hypnosis! The audience is below and I am on the stage in one unbroken whole . . . You break off a train of thought and the current is broken . . . But then you throw out a living comprehensible word close to their hearts, and once again the crowd is one . . . And long afterwards, after we have all regained ourselves, the moment of merging into one, of losing one's "ego" in a common shared experience, leaves a sweet and exciting memory . . .[16]

Now before vast audiences in Petrograd she learned to harmonize with the stirrings of the "dark masses" all her emotions and thoughts, her logic and irony, her literary turns of phrase and incisive images. The theatrical impact of her powerful musical voice, her broad, generous gestures, and her striking appearance, was not lost on the bourgeois press. "When Lenin makes a speech, Kollontai makes a squeak"—with this sexually suggestive street ditty the papers tried to disparage her passionate defense of Lenin's *April Theses*. "It is plain," wrote the unpleasant scholar and observer of the revolution, Pitirim Sorokin, in his diary, "that her revolutionary enthusiasm is nothing but a gratification of her sexual satyriasis. In spite of her numerous 'husbands,' Kollontai, first the wife of a general, later the mistress of a dozen men, is not yet satiated. She seeks new forms of sexual sadism."[17] There were frequent comments in this vein, as well as allusions to her immaculate appearance and hints of wardrobes full of expensive clothes bought with "German gold." In fact her trunk had been stolen on her way back to Russia and she had only one dress, which she wore with her customary style. But she was kept too busy to be overconcerned with such innuendo, and it was only when a tramride across town turned into a skirmish with patriots that she regretted her new notoriety, or when her speeches in the Soviet, now sitting twenty-four hours a day, were brought to a halt with cries from the Mensheviks and Socialist Revolutionaries of "She's a Leninist! Down with her!"

If only a handful of Bolsheviks had greeted Lenin at the beginning of April, by the end of that month every factory and barracks was sending Bolshevik deputies to the Soviet. In one barracks after another, and soon in the garrisons of the Baltic fleet Alexandra's passionate speeches had an electrifying effect. Since it was "in the heat of the class war that the soldier, the worker, and the *soldatka* learned their political grammar on all the everyday practical questions so close to their hearts: falling pay, mass dismissals in the factories and rising living costs," it was just these questions, the hope and anguish which they generated, that she wove into her speeches.[18] But as she hurtled all over town, from one packed meeting to another, she was concerned that the *soldatki* had not yet been reached by this galvanizing party propaganda. Leaving the *Pravda* offices one evening with Lenin, Nadezhda Krupskaya, and a group of party colleagues, she complained about this indifference in words that would be repeated the following month in a *Pravda* article entitled "A Serious Gap."[19] The *soldatki* who read *Pravda of the Trenches* were hardly going to be receptive to the feminists' attempts to convert them to patriotism, she insisted; what was needed was a party commission to help them organize demonstrations throughout the country against living costs. Nadezhda quickly interrupted to stress that this would require no separate organization (Alexandra had proposed no such thing), and in the heated argument that followed most of the others denied the necessity of any special work among women. Finally Lenin proposed that she discuss the idea with other women party organizers and present some suggestions "on her own responsibility" at the party conference later that month.

Alexandra's idea was simply that every party organization should have its own women's bureau with one local member responsible for it. The response from her women friends in the party leadership was mortifyingly negative. It appeared that even passionate revolutionaries like Nadezhda Krupskaya, Inessa Armand, and Konkordia Samoilova, although recognizing that special efforts should be made to liberate women from their double oppression, were still inhibited by the fear that women's political backwardness and industrial "indiscipline" were threats to the revolution, and they showed themselves more ready to fight feminists than mobilize *soldatki*. Quite possibly they also distrusted Alexandra's attitudes toward the new morality and toward questions that had previously been raised only by bourgeois writers, and felt that this made her guilty by association with feminism. At any rate most leading women Bolsheviks in Petrograd scorned her plan outright, and even Inessa, who had just repeated Alexandra's intervention tactics at a feminist congress in Moscow, was in a minority there to defend it. With no support at all Alexandra could hardly raise the issue of women's work before the party conference. Three years later women's proven ability to demonstrate and organize forced the Bolsheviks to adopt the very proposals which Alexandra had made in April 1917. Even then, however, they could only justify appealing to women as a "separate group" on the paradoxical assumption that the Zhenotdel (the women's department) would convince them that they were no such thing.[20]

Without any encouragement from the Bolsheviks, then, Alexandra went ahead and organized a march of the *soldatki* on the Tauride to rival the feminists' demonstration of the previous month and to present to the Soviet the demand for their wretched monthly pension of seven rubles to be increased to twenty rubles. She made contact with several militant *soldatki* and on April 11 15,000 women assembled outside the Tauride to be greeted by the chairman of the Soviet—the Menshevik, Dan. Before the February revolution, by virtue of his unquestioned intellectual brilliance and broad revolutionary sympathies, Yuri Martov, the editor of *Our Word,* had been the leader of the Mensheviks; by March he had yielded this position to the very much more conservative and less imaginative Dan, who now appeared before the *soldatki* in the uniform of an army doctor. "Seek not more money but an end to war!" he appealed to the angry women. "That's strange, coming from a Menshevik!" shouted Alexandra involuntarily, and asked permission to address the meeting. "As a member of the Soviet executive or as a Bolshevik?" asked Dan, and when she said she was speaking for her party, he tried to break up the meeting, dismissing the women's claim as utopian and untimely. She did manage to speak, though, calling on them to send their own delegates to the Soviet and to take over the distribution of their rations and pensions.[21]

"It took months to make them understand that without silence and order you would not accomplish anything"[22]—so Nina Selivanova described the initial difficulties facing the meetings that launched this ambitious scheme. But thanks to the organizational talents of such *soldatki* as one Fëdorova, whom Alexandra mentioned admiringly, thirty-five women managed to form themselves into a union of *soldatki* in Petrograd, and there developed a network of similar women's organizations throughout Russia and the Ukraine. They could take heart, after all, from the maids of Petrograd, who since late March had been meeting in increasingly large numbers. "Comrade maids!" wrote one of them in *Pravda* after a meeting had overflowed into the street, "we need a bigger hall!" Restaurant workers had also formed their own union now, composed of two cooks, one waiter, and a waitress named "Comrade Katya," who had appealed in the *Workers' Paper* for support from "all women comrades working in the tearooms of Petrograd." Women at the Mignon chocolate factory had protested to the Soviet against their intolerable working conditions, those in the tobacco factories were demanding protection for pregnant workers, and in the Frolic textile mill workers were demanding 100 percent wage increases for men and 125 percent increases for women.[23]

Involved in all these activities, and more, was Alexandra's young protégée of 1908, the typesetter Klavdia Nikolaeva, whom ten years' work in the Bolshevik Party had turned into a bold and efficient organizer. From her Alexandra learned of the wretched underground existence of Petrograd's 4000 laundresses, who toiled for fourteen hours a day for a mere thirty kopeks (say, very roughly, four dollars in present-day purchasing power) in the city's steamy, squalid subterranean laundries, their lives plagued by rheumatism and swollen legs; they had at last been provoked beyond all endurance and had joined the city's bakers in the first strikes witnessed there since the February revolution. The Provisional Government had ordered them back to work and they had refused. In the new-found courage of women recently as despised and downtrodden as the *soldatki* Alexandra found inspiration, a savage rebuff to the Provisional Government and its vague promises of future reforms.

Invited by their leader, a Bolshevik named Sakharova, to address some meetings, she saw for herself the foul working conditions offered by the glamorously named Niagara and Progress laundries. We can only speculate about the many difficulties Alexandra must have experienced as a glamorous and educated woman in communicating with these women, for she makes no mention of any such difficulties in her autobiographical writings; we must assume that for the laundresses, as for the *soldatki,* her powers of sympathy and her eloquence made the Bolsheviks' promise of a better life seem a reality, rather than a mere component of government power.

The day after the demonstration by the *soldatki* Alexandra managed to catch hold of Lenin's sleeve after a meeting:

> "Just a moment, Vladimir Ilich, it's about the strike—it's spreading." "Strike? What strike?" He was immediately all attention. I summarized it as concisely as I could, but I couldn't help complaining; the laundresses were no different from the *soldatki,* and there were a lot of petty bourgeois reactionaries among them who were difficult to work with. "Lean on the proletarians," advised Ilich, "and the others will follow. And don't worry if the most downtrodden are the most reactionary. Their lives are hardest, and they'll be the first to understand what the Bolsheviks want."[24]

After that Alexandra attended almost daily meetings at the laundries and persuaded the women to add the Bolshevik slogans against the war and the government to their own demands for shorter hours, the municipalization and mechanization of all laundries, and the arrest of their owners. The editors of *Pravda* were induced to devote a page regularly to reports of the strike's progress, appeals for financial help, and lists of strike-breakers' names. On May 3 the laundresses won their battle for shorter hours and more pay. It was a partial victory but, as Alexandra wrote in a *Pravda* article, "In the Front Line of Fire," their struggle was that of the entire working class against the world of the bosses; no longer could these women be described as the "backward and unaware section" of the people.[25]

At the seventh conference of the Bolshevik Party, which opened on April 24, 1917, Alexandra cited the haphazard manner in which Bolshevik support had been gained for this strike to urge that some more systematic women's organization was needed. Again her suggestion was condemned by virtually all the women she talked to. Evidently for most of them the Bolsheviks' dramatically increased power and popularity promised more for them than they could achieve for themselves. Just three weeks after Lenin's return, the overwhelming majority of delegates now supported a resolution calling on the proletariat to make active preparations for the transfer of power to the soviets. Alexandra deferred her proposals, and toward the end of the proceedings she was elected to lead a delegation of Bolsheviks in convening a conference of Zimmerwald leftists in Stockholm that June.

It was after this conference that she embarked on her most hectic and demanding agitation, among sailors of the Baltic Sea fleet. Thousands of them had read her *Who Needs War?* and were now reading the Bolshevik naval paper, *Wave;* finding in the new government neither material benefits nor patriotic inspiration, they were going over to the Bolsheviks in such huge numbers that the Provisional Government had tried to disband the Russian garrison at the Baltic Sea port of Helsingfors, capital of Russia's Finnish satellite. After Alexandra's first meeting at Helsingfors, despite some heckling and jeering from misogynists and Mensheviks, she was able to report back confidently to Lenin that the sailors would soon be wholeheartedly theirs, and she was soon a regular and extremely popular speaker there. Although Lenin frequently urged her to write more, pointing out that pamphlets could reach a far wider audience than speeches, he rarely gave her time to do so—for no sooner had he spoken than he would pack her off to Helsingfors again. Four or five meetings a day were hardly conducive, she told him, to writing; as the Bolsheviks' most valued agitator on the fleet, her time was spoken for.

12

Peace, Bread, Land, and Justice

It was probably at her second meeting in Helsingfors, in May 1917, at the Alexandrov Theater, that Alexandra first met the man whom she was to love so passionately for the next five years. Pavel Dybenko, one of the most outstandingly brave men in the Baltic Sea fleet, was a Bolshevik—the "soul of the fleet," as Alexandra called him when, at the age of forty-five, she first met and began to love him. He had once thrown Kerensky over the side of a warship, and his popularity among his fellow sailors had been assured from that day on. In the months following their first meeting, at which they were so immediately attracted to each other, Alexandra's tender and almost maternal feelings increased for this impetuous and exceedingly handsome romantic, seventeen years younger than she, who had joined the Bolsheviks as an adolescent when he first left his poor peasant family in the Ukraine.

In many ways he regarded her as his teacher, for she encouraged him to read and to acquaint himself with the Marxist classics as well as with military theory. But she also encouraged him to express spontaneously his great power of feeling and his generous intuitive intelligence, which he had developed without the benefit of books or education—for this was what she loved most about him. As their affair blossomed throughout the following months they were to become known as the "most famous lovers of the revolution." Alexandra and Dybenko themselves were naturally more discreet; both of them were politically and emotionally reckless to some degree, and most of their comrades were probably more concerned about the obviously passionate, erotic nature of their liaison than with its more touchingly tender aspects. "I will not vouch for the reliability or endurance of women

263

whose love affairs are intertwined with politics," said Lenin a few years later, in a clear reference to Alexandra.[1]

The affair certainly damaged her political reputation as a Bolshevik —although there is no reason to suppose that, despite the inevitable conflicts between her independence and a whole-hearted commitment to her lover, Alexandra was any less committed as an agitator and writer during her years with Dybenko. If the life of an agitator left little time, as she complained, for writing, how much less time it left for the gradual exploration of hearts. As a character in one of Alexandra's later short stories declares (a "new woman," who seems to combine with the greatest of ease a series of love affairs with her hard-working life as a committed party activist): "You have to have *leisure* to fall in love—I've read enough novels to know just how much time and energy it takes to fall in love and I just don't have time . . . Of course, you sometimes have periods when you're less busy and then you suddenly realize that you like someone. But as for falling in love—there's no time for that!"[2]

For Alexandra, who was of an older generation than her young protagonist, Zhenya, the "great love" remained as an inspiring ideal, and one which she felt she had realized in her relationship with Dybenko. Yet they were never together for any longer than the brief moments they snatched from their party assignments, and they were constantly driven apart by their work. To these difficulties were added, for Alexandra, all the concomitant difficulties of the "great love" and its romantic, unrealizable hopes. Jealousy and misunderstandings, the unbridgeable class differences separating them, the difference in their ages, Dybenko's hot temper, and the uneasiness he felt in her company, which she would comment upon later—they rarely had the time to discuss all these problems which were to make their relationship such a stormy one. Throughout the summer and autumn months of 1917, however, before their incompatabilities and emotional difficulties had had time to accumulate and bring them such pain, their love affair lent an added passion to their work and gave a special excitement to Alexandra's frequent trips to Helsingfors from Petrograd.

Alexandra found rather firmer emotional support, and a haven from her stormy love affair with Dybenko, in her work with the Petrograd women who formed the editorial board of *Rabotnitsa,* and she combined her agitational work across the city with the lively campaigning life of the other editors. In order to keep their articles up to date, Konkordia Samoilova, Klavdia Nikolaeva, and Lyudmila Stal would spend their days traveling around Petrograd's shops and factories talking to women, returning at night to write copy. The new *Rabotnitsa* was reissued (weekly now, not monthly) on May 10 and immediately sold all its 40,000 copies. The press run was increased to 50,000, and its popularity was soon so great that mass *Rabotnitsa* women's rallies began to be held at the Cinizelli Circus and the Cirque Moderne, filled to overflowing in those days with crowds of people eager for the Bolsheviks' verbal pyrotechnics. "Who has not seen the Cirque Moderne has not seen the revolution," went the saying of the day, and Alexandra welcomed the theatricality of these gatherings, which brought women a little light entertainment and some relief from the cares of the factory and the breadline.

Now she was able to introduce into her speeches to the workers and sailors a bolder portrayal of the nightmarish ways in which war had burdened women—forty percent of the workforce—with rising costs and deteriorating factory conditions. Lyudmila Stal was describing the work of *Rabotnitsa* to sailors at Kronstadt; Nadezhda Krupskaya and Zhenya Egorova were addressing large mixed meetings in the Vyborg district; Anna Itkina (Alexandra's Soviet biographer) was talking to women in Narva; and Vera Slutskaya was organizing packed meetings on Vasilev Island. Praskovya Kudelli (a Bolshevik intellectual and one of Alexandra's old associates in the post-1905 years) and some other women who had been active in workers' clubs since 1905 launched a school for women revolutionaries in Petrograd; and, in Moscow Inessa Armand and Varvara Yakovleva organized similar activities around a small, primitively duplicated journal called *Rabotnitsa Life.* "Don't stand aside!" appealed Alexandra in her article "Our Tasks" for the first issue in May 1917 of the revived *Rabotnitsa.* "On our own, we're the straw any boss can burn; organized, we're a mighty force no one can destroy!"[3] Alongside this there was an article on Bebel by Konkordia Samoilova and a call to women, suggested by Lenin, to organize groups powerful enough to send delegates to the soviet.

In early June, Alexandra was sent to Helsingfors not as an agitator but as Bolshevik representative to the Finnish Social Democratic Party's Ninth Congress. With less than a day's notice and no speech prepared, she was sent off with vague instructions to exploit the divisions within the Party in order to persuade them to break with the Second International and adopt the revolutionary line elaborated in 1915 by Lenin and his supporters in the International at Zimmerwald. She was to stress the Bolsheviks' support for Finland's right to secede from Russia, exhort Finnish revolutionaries to fight their own native ruling class (now entirely qualified to run its commercial affairs without help from Russia), and point to the Provisional Government's failure to guarantee Finnish self-determination. After the first day of welcoming speeches in the Helsing-fors town-hall she joined her old Finnish friend Ida Terssinnen for a walk in the nearby woods, for she had not yet "breathed the grass" that spring. They took off their shoes so they could enjoy the feeling of sun-warmed sand and dry pine needles on their feet, but they had to turn back all too soon for a meeting on the town's cathedral square at which Alexandra was to speak.

The square was a sea of Russian sailors and Finnish workers, for crucial questions confronted this congress. The fight for Finnish independence, conducted against a series of changing governments after the disintegration of the old order in Russia, had been undermined when the Provisional Government dissolved its parliament and awaited new elections; many Finns considered it hopeless to attack a Russian government more interested in the bloody engagements in France and the collapse of its own battlefront than in the fortunes of its Finnish satellite. First to speak was Ivan Smirnov, editor of *Wave*—a revolutionary of thirty years' standing and an old soldier greatly respected for his courage, wit, and authority. He advised her to speak cautiously, as there were many defensists in the audience, but "caution was quite inappropriate to my fervor and my assignment from the central committee," and she went on to call for fraternization as the most practical way to end the massacre.

She then boarded a cutter which took her around the various warships stationed in Helsingfors, and one short meeting was brought to a halt by the hostile heckling of some officers, who ended up confronting their own men. At a gathering of the Helsingfors soviet that evening, she met an old childhood friend named Misha Bukovsky, who was probably the son of one of her father's military friends. Now an officer, he was, unlike many of his fellow officers, sadly bewildered by the enthusiasm of the Bolshevik sailors. All too rarely now did Alexandra enjoy the chivalrous courtesies of the old life: when he had helped her pack her bag, brought her some food, presented her with a bouquet of roses, and joined the crowd of Russian and Finnish revolutionaries who saw her off at the station, she wrote to him, "Mishenka, friend of my childhood, thank you my dear! You have warmed my heart."[4]

From Finland's clean simplicity she went directly to the ornate Cadet Corps academy on Vasilev Island for the first All-Russian Congress of Soviets, sitting from June 3–24. Of 1090 delegates, 105 were Bolsheviks. Patriotic feelings were running high, and the majority angrily attacked the Bolsheviks' plans for antiwar street demonstrations accompanied by the occupation of the post offices and telegraph buildings. She arrived in time to hear Lenin assure the delegates that Russia could exploit the war to accomplish a peaceful revolution, and she herself, speaking emotionally of her experiences in Finland, announced the Bolsheviks' unconditional support for all nations' right to self-determination to the point of secession. Seeing the unfriendly expression with which Plekhanov greeted her speech from the front row, "I became hot and flustered, attacking our opponents in quite unnecessarily insulting terms—always a sign of weakness."[5] The Plekhanov who had shaped her early days as a revolutionary was now dead for her, and they cut each other in the corridor afterward.

Never had the Menshevik majority in the Soviet been so out of touch with the rage of the Petrograd masses as in June 1917, when they approved the war plans of the newly reorganized Provisional Government —in which Kerensky was Minister of War—and urged them on against the Germans. While they were doing so, a leading trade unionist was reporting to the government that "we lack the strength to live under these conditions." With daily bread rations down to half a pound, workers began to requisition food and redistribute it fairly. Active in this work were increasing numbers of women, and a few days after the Congress of Soviets, at the first legal Congress of Trade Unions Alexandra presented a paper on the measures needed to protect women in the factories and to draw them into the work of the unions; it received unanimous support.

With chaos on the railways and in the factories the Bolsheviks began to publish statistics of Russia's annual industrial profits, and demonstrations reached massive proportions, each testifying to the misery and desperation of the exhausted people. On some days as many as 50,000 of Petrograd's 2,000,000 citizens thronged the streets until late at night; endless processions of peasants, women, soldiers, and sailors charged the city with such electrical tension and rage that strikes and lockouts increasingly turned into violent clashes with foremen and bosses as workers learned to avenge themselves for generations of insults and humiliations. In the countryside momentum built up as returning soldiers joined peasant soviets and committees, ignited the "red rooster" which burned and sacked the manor houses, and seized the land. Kerensky, speaking as a right-wing member of the Socialist Revolutionary Party, the party which supposedly represented the interests of the peasants, claimed to have the situation in the countryside under control. But apart from an ineffectual condemnation of land seizure he failed to produce any legislation to cope with the anarchy in the villages.

On Sunday, June 18, after Dybenko and his Helsingfors comrades had threatened that if the Bolsheviks did not organize a demonstration they would bring their sailors out on the streets of Petrograd, hundreds of thousands of Bolsheviks and large numbers of armed anarchists demonstrated with banners inscribed *"The Right to Life is Higher than the Right to Private Property!"* and *"All Power to the Soviets!"* These they bore peacefully to the graves of the February martyrs on the Field of Mars. Now each new casualty on the battlefield was bringing the Bolsheviks new recruits, for the Bolshevik program was seizing people's imagination and inscribing itself on their banners as *"Peace, Bread, and Land!"* They saw the Party's lucid and accessible leadership and genius for organization, and they listened avidly to its brilliant orators, Trotsky, Kollontai, and Volodarsky. Socialist Revolutionaries, Mensheviks, and hundreds of new women recruits all helped to swell the Bolshevik ranks, which had numbered 79,000 at the April party conference. That June, Alexandra addressed one women's meeting after another around the city and in the Cirque Moderne, for the unofficial Bolshevik women's sections were now drawing vast numbers of women into the Party. Many women, once introduced to the variety and novelty of political activism, were joining the most radical workers in pushing their demands so far to the left of the Party that virtually separate organizations sprang up in the Vyborg district and elsewhere, conducting the hard-line agitation that produced explosive demonstrations the following month.

The prospect of leaving the smoldering city that month for the Zimmerwald congress in Stockholm did not fill Alexandra with much enthusiasm. An endless procession of workers and soldiers was now visiting Lenin in the *Pravda* offices, begging him to call for an armed uprising before it was too late; she confidently anticipated returning to the barricades of a Bolshevik revolution.

Before leaving, she addressed the *soldatki* in an article based on a letter *Pravda* had received from a German woman describing the wretched lives of German prisoners in Russia. Then, when she finally heard that Branting had managed to secure permission from the government for her to visit Sweden, she moved out of Tatiana Schepkina's house and into a small boarding house in the Pesky district and, together with Vorovsky, her fellow delegate, went to the *Pravda* offices to receive instructions. Dybenko and a delegation of Baltic sailors were there, outlining to Lenin their plans for an open battle with the defensists, and she agreed to stop off at Helsingfors to address some meetings.

Without enough delegates to convene a proper congress, the Stock-

Alexandra Kollontai,
age 5

Alexandra Domontovich,
Kollontai's mother, 1877

General
Mikhail Domontovich,
Kollontai's father, 1899

Family and friends at the Kuusa estate in Finland, 1895

Alexandra Kollontai, age 16

Age 17, as a debutante in her
first ball dress

With her husband, Vladimir,
and son, Misha, 1897

Alexandra Kollontai (*extreme left*)
sitting beside Elena Stasova
at the Rubakin Museum

1905

At the Copenhagen Congress of the
Second International, 1910

London, 1913

Copenhagen, 1915

Alexander Shlyapnikov

Nadeshda Krupskaya

Lenin in 1897, shortly
before he left for Siberian exile

Inessa Armand
(about 1910)

Alexandra Kollontai surrounded by waifs in her commissariat,
Petrograd, early 1918

Alexandra Kollontai and Pavel Dybenko with a delegation
of Scandinavians, Petrograd, 1918

Alexandra Kollontai
(*top row, center*)
in a children's home
named after her,
during the evacuation
of Kiev, 1919

With Dybenko and his family in the Ukraine, 1919

Klara Zetkin

Sofya Smidovich

Klavdia Nikolaeva

Anna Artyukhina

Speaking at the Second
International Conference of
Communist Women, June 1921

On a business trip to London, 1925

In her office in Stockholm, 1932

January 1952, two months before her death

holm gathering of Zimmerwaldists was an inconsequential affair. The town had become the center of the Menshevik emigration, and despite the presence of Ström and Höglund, discussions soon degenerated into fruitless and angry arguments with the Mensheviks, who spoke for the Provisional Government and were supported by a majority who considered Russia too backward for revolution. Just how badly they had miscalculated became clear to Alexandra on July 5, when a dawn telephone call, possibly from Dybenko, told her that the barricades were up in Petrograd.

In a last insane offensive Kerensky had hurled thousands of Russian troops against the German lines. After a few days they were decimated. Five Kadet ministers resigned immediately from the government fearing that the revolution was imminent, and 35,000 workers at the Putilov armaments plant came out on strike, calling now not merely for control over production and wages but for the immediate transfer of power to the soviets. Their example inspired the machine-gun regiment, who decided that the moment had come to ask other units to join them, with their guns, on the streets. The Red Guards put in their first practice appearance on July 3, helped by several armored cars donated by the army and supported by large numbers of women medical assistants and fighters. Despite warnings from the Bolshevik Party that these plans were "uncomradely and inopportune," they then went ahead and contacted workers and sailors in Kronstadt and Helsingfors, and on July 4 their impromptu meetings outside the Tauride were swelled by the arrival of 20,000 sailors who had sailed down the river from Finland. Braving police snipers on the roofs and ignoring Lenin's advice to "stay calm," Dybenko and his comrades climbed through the windows into the Tauride and demanded a meeting with the Soviet leaders. "We trust the Soviet, but not those the Soviet trusts!" was their slogan, and "We want immediate confiscation of the land and workers' control over industry!"

It was Trotsky who argued calmly with them and managed to prevent skirmishes in the palace. Soon a battalion of the Izmailovsky regiment, still loyal to the government, arrived at the palace and dispersed the insurgents. The *Pravda* offices were raided, the Bolsheviks were "unmasked" as German agents working for Russia's defeat in the war, and orders were issued for the arrest of hundreds of Bolsheviks, including Lenin, Trotsky, and Kollontai.

As she dashed around Stockholm that day, snatching at every fragment of news from Russia, Alexandra longed to return. For here was final proof for the doubting Zimmerwaldists that the revolution was not merely the dream of a handful of Bolsheviks: "The working class itself was groping toward a new form of government now, adapting it in the period of their dictatorship to suit their own class interests."[6] By that evening the Swedish papers were referring to the Bolsheviks' "grave crimes against the state," and mentioning Alexandra in connection with her "special mission" to Stockholm. As she and Vorovsky struggled to follow the confused reports from Petrograd it became clear that Kerensky had put down the rebellion and had been appointed Prime Minister. Vorovsky advised her strongly to extend her visa and continue her work in Sweden, but she would not hear of it. The following day Zoya arrived in Stockholm from Paris, and Alexandra begged Vorovsky to lend her the money for her return journey. (This small loan, to be repaid by the Bolshevik central committee, gave rise to various stories in the Swedish papers suggesting that her journey back to Russia was paid for with "German gold" and that the entire July uprising had been manipulated by the German government.) A group of Swedes put Alexandra and Zoya onto the train as gloomily as if they were delivering them to Kerensky's prison, and an article in the socialist paper *Politiken* the following day (July 7) repeated the same fear. "But arrest was the last thing I thought about then, for it would have been quite impossible to stay away . . ."[7]

The war had brought floods of travelers to Torneo, Russia's only crossing point into Sweden. Apart from the spectacular white nights of summer, these barren polar regions seemed outwardly little different from when she had arrived there that March. But now there were no red armbands; the officers who greeted them confiscated their passports and led them off, accompanied by a secret-police agent, to a stately man in admiral's uniform, Prince Beloselsky-Belozersky, who arrested them.

Alexandra was a straightforward enough case: the Provisional Government, which was rounding up all its Bolshevik opponents and accusing them of being German agents out to sabotage the Russians' victory, could be well satisfied with the arrest of this prominent Bolshevik. But Zoya was listed on her arrest warrant as a man. She burst out laughing and threatened the angry officers with a fit of hysterics. For three days and nights, sitting upright on hard seats in their stuffy compartment, they crossed Finland, and at every small station crowds hurried up to inspect "Kollontai the spy." "Damned bloodthirsty bitch! There's that Bolshevik Kollontai! You deserve the gallows, along with all traitors to Russia! Long live Russia and her allies!" shouted the waiter in the restaurant car (since the death sentence had just been restored in Russia, his words were not so far off the mark). He also refused to serve them food.[8]

When they reached Beloostrov, the blinds were pulled down and their luggage was searched—to reveal two items of fatally incriminating significance. A pair of gray button boots which Alexandra had bought in Stockholm and some greasepaint Zoya had brought back for her actress sister were converted by the Russian bourgeois press into fourteen pairs of high boots and an arsenal of cosmetics, paid for with "German gold."

Dawn was breaking over the Neva as they arrived in Petrograd. They were conducted to Butyrki prison and interrogated separately by a colonel from the counter-espionage department, a cocaine addict with wandering eyes and disconcertingly violent habits. Dybenko had been arrested, he told Alexandra; if she gave information about a certain ensign she could go, otherwise she would be charged with encouraging disaffection in the army, assisting in the Russian defeat, holding relations with the enemy, and preparing an armed uprising. Zoya was charged with conducting a sinister coded correspondence with her. Take her telegram to Alexandra —"Can't leave, dental treatment, send sixty kroner or borrow from Vera." What did "dental treatment" mean? And who was Vera?

All the way to the Vyborg women's prison—Kerensky had prepared the political wing for a large intake of women spies—Alexandra harangued the soldiers accompanying her. They eventually abandoned the attempt to break her down by hinting that they had caught Lenin; but she well believed them when they told her that Lunacharsky, Trotsky, Kamenev, and another prominent Bolshevik activist named Antonov-Ovseenko were all inside the Kresty prison. Alexandra was to be held under harsher conditions than any of these however—in solitary confinement under a permanent police guard and allowed no visitors or letters. There she stayed for almost two months. Despite constant palpitations and dangerously high blood pressure, she was allowed to see a doctor only when her face and legs were so swollen that she felt too numb to get up.

An American dancer in the cell next to hers did pirouettes and complained loudly of the food; occasionally, when the criminal wing was full, the odd inmate would be thrown into a "political" cell, there to sob and scream all night. Otherwise it was silence and solitude for two weeks, until she was finally allowed to take a walk with the "criminals." She was lucky to escape without being attacked, for when they saw "Kalantaikha, the German spy" they all rushed forward, cursing her. She did manage to talk to the wardresses, though. One talked of her boyfriend, a Bolshevik, who did not want to marry her, and an older woman poured out her anxieties about her son in the army. "And from her grief we passed on to Bolshevism and the power of the soviets. Half an hour passed in a flash, but although we both finally agreed that nobody needed the war, she still locked me up that night."9 Then there were two long interrogations, in which the most serious charge they could apparently dream up was that of a love affair with Lenin. They were party comrades, she protested. "Ah, of course, you'd call it 'comrades,' " they leered, hinting all the while that a major case was being prepared against her. There were two more weeks of anxious and stupefying inactivity. She wrote in her diary:

> Night. Day. Night again. Today I wake up in an uncontrollably cheerful mood, and with a great feeling of *joie de vivre,* possibly because it's a sunny day. I tidy up my cell and wait for my walk, and when I'm out in the yard, I pluck up courage to talk to a wardress, who is carrying a knout. The little prison yard has been turned into a storehouse for firewood, and the smell from the fresh logs piled up is so resinous and refreshing that if you close your eyes you can imagine yourself in a forest. I return to my cell. But now I no longer feel the depression of my first days here. I feel as though I have summoned up all my internal strength, and I am resigned. Three years inside, well, so be it. Five years, so be it. But no, I'm sure it *won't* be so long! How can the Provisional Government possibly respond to the people's demands for an end to the war, for land to the peasants, for the regulation of industry, and for power to the workers? No, it will merely mark time: it doesn't understand that history demands a step forward to a new, socialist, future!10

She was at last allowed to receive parcels. The first to arrive contained some rolls, sausage, honey, butter, eggs, some precious digitalis for her heart, and more precious still a note: "Greetings to Comrade Kollontai from sailors of the Baltic fleet." Others followed from women textile workers, tram conductors and factory workers; their spirits were not broken, they all assured her; the defensists had not won.

Seven weeks after arriving in prison she was roused from bed one evening with the heart-warming news that Gorky and Leonid Krasin had raised 5000 rubles to bail her out and were waiting downstairs for her. (Krasin, a long-standing Bolshevik and organizer of the Party's bank robberies in 1907 had since that time worked as a highly skilled engineer in Berlin. Since his return to Russia early in 1917 he had been manager of the Putilov factory. It appears that he persuaded Alexandra's childhood friend Misha Bukovsky to intervene with the government for her release. There are many aspects of the chaotic "July Days" and the government talk of the Bolsheviks' "German gold" which are veiled in mystery. It was certainly true that many Bolshevik publications and connections in the northern underground were, thanks to the services of allies like Parvus and

Hanecki, indirectly subsidized by the German government, and that many in that government did feel that the surest way to engineer a German victory was to support the Bolsheviks.)

Alexandra fled room 58 in the Vyborg women's prison with immense relief and was soon traveling with Gorky and Krasin in a car toward Serpukhov Street. It was in a flat there that Vladimir had lived since their divorce. Alexandra learned the sad news that Vladimir had died while she had been in prison; nothing is known of the circumstances of his death. He was, like her, in his late forties. It was this, and the news of his mother's imprisonment, that had brought Misha (who was now twenty-three) hurrying back from America to Petrograd, where he moved into the Serpukhov Street flat with his step-mother, Maria Ipateva. They had both arranged for Alexandra to stay with them there until her health recovered.

From Gorky and Krasin, Alexandra learned of General Kornilov's part as Supreme Commander of the Russian army in putting down the insurgent masses during the July Days, and his attempt in the following month to seize power from the Provisional Government; his escapade had released a flood of sympathy for the Bolsheviks. She learned too that Lenin had not been arrested, as her interrogaters at the prison had assured her, but was safely hiding in the city, and that at the Sixth Bolshevik Party Congress, held secretly two weeks before her release, all 4000 of the formerly unaffiliated "Interdistrict" group had joined the Bolsheviks. She and the "Interdistrict" leaders, Trotsky and Lunacharsky, had been elected to the party's central committee, as had several other leftists, former anarchists, and Menshevik internationalists.

There was Kristian Rakovsky: Bulgarian by birth, Rumanian by nationality, French by education, and Russian by his associations, feelings, and culture, he was characterized by a subtle mind, a "profound nobility of soul" (as Trotsky put it), and a wide culture combined with great efficiency, little taste for violence, and a special regard for human relationships. A former member of Plekhanov's Liberation of Labor group in Geneva, he had been one of the moving spirits behind the Zimmerwald conference in 1915 and had finally joined the Bolsheviks after the July Days.[11] Also elected to the central committee was Adolf Joffe, one of Alexandra's former Menshevik associates in Berlin. The left Bolshevik Nikolay Bukharin joined them too, along with his old Moscow allies Osinsky and Vladimir Smirnov (editor of the Bolsheviks' paper for sailors, *Wave*), whom Alexandra had met in Helsingfors in May and June. Then there was a former anarchist, the brilliant Georgy Pyatakov; a Ukrainian by birth and a convinced internationalist by temperament, his vision of a socialist United States of Europe, forged by the international revolutionary proletariat, had led him after July to accept the Bolshevik line. Another person who joined the Bolshevik central committee was one of Alexandra's Berlin associates, Karl Radek; this passionate and unstable revolutionary has best been described as a "demagogic internationalist."

For almost ten years Alexandra was to be associated with these radicals, who after the Sixth Congress so changed the political complexion of the Bolshevik Party and after the revolution were to form the nucleus of the Party's "left opposition."

Alexandra was overjoyed to see Misha again and delighted to be able at last to make friends with Maria Ipateva, who had been such a devoted second mother to him. It was just as well that she was comfortably installed. For the day after her release (which was noted on August 22 in an *Izvestia* article announcing that "the invalid is resting with her son") Kerensky returned from the front; outraged that she had been released in his absence, he at once put her under house arrest until September under armed guards.

Kerensky's power was disintegrating with every day that passed. After his disastrous offensive the Germans had captured Riga and moved troops from the Eastern Front to serve elsewhere. The Russians had lurched off toward home, uninspired by Kerensky's front-line harangues, and this in effect was the end of the Russian army. Despite all Kerensky's propaganda against the Bolshevik "spies," their popularity grew. Hundreds of factory workers, armed by Kerensky to fight Kornilov's threatened dictatorship, now joined the Red Guards, which were augmented by women support troops, runners, and nurses *(sanitarki)*. The women who fought with the Bolsheviks over the next few months considerably outnumbered those who since May had been joining the women's Shock Battalions and Death Battalions, formed by the government (and supported by the feminist League of Women's Equality) to inspire the faint-hearted with their merciless resolve to fight the enemy to the death and to prove themselves the equals of men in battle. The Bolshevik papers printed various articles protesting against the way these women had been manipulated into helping to prolong the war, without questioning either their idealism or their capacity to fight.

Soon after leaving prison, Alexandra managed to break the strict house arrest which banned her from writing articles and smuggled out an appeal to the mothers of the girls who joined the Death Battalions, most of them young peasants, many of them Jewish, and all of them inadequately clothed, ill-educated, and unprepared for any real fighting. "Have we become so ungenerous that mercy means nothing to us?" she asked them in the sixth issue of *Rabotnitsa*. "That love and sympathy for those dear to us no longer prevail, but give way to an obscene and sordid blood lust?"[12]

By September 1 the Bolsheviks in the Soviet were strong enough to persuade a majority of delegates to call for all power to the soviets and the release of imprisoned Bolsheviks. Trotsky and Lunacharsky organized a riot in the Kresty prison and were freed without a trial. But the official prosecutors had a more ambitious case planned against Alexandra, whom they hoped to use later in a mass roundup of the entire Bolshevik Party. The task was quite beyond their powers, as she realized when she saw the twelve volumes of prosecution material against her at her first interrogation, and there was more material to come, they told her. Glancing briefly through the first volume, which contained a list of all her old Bolshevik associates and the various acts of espionage they were accused of, she declined to read any further. She wrote several open letters to *Pravda* and other papers protesting against the extraordinary powers of arrest which allowed Kerensky to detain her while the prosecutors were concocting these fantastic charges. She received many letters of support, including one from a worker in the Rozhdestvensky region. "Comrade!" he wrote to her. "That which snatched you so violently from the proletarian cause binds you still more firmly to us. Our paths are inseparable now, and we are with you always!"[13]

"We stand on the threshold of the world revolution," wrote Lenin, as mutinies and disorders brought unparalleled chaos to the armies of the warring countries. In Russia the crisis was ripe. On September 23, shortly after his release from prison, Trotsky was elected chairman of the Petrograd Soviet, the position he had occupied twelve years before; and while Lenin remained in hiding, he urged in one brilliant speech after another that all power should pass to the Soviet. The Bolsheviks, led by Trotsky and Lenin, were ready to seize power.

Therefore it was the more urgent, it seemed to Alexandra, to organize a congress at which the women of Petrograd could raise before the Party the issues of higher pay and prostitution, the problems of working mothers and their need for state-supported day-nurseries. Emerging from house arrest in the second week of September, she discussed this plan with her colleagues on the *Rabotnitsa* editorial board, Konkordia Samoilova, Klavdia Nikolaeva, and Emilia Solin. But although the party secretary, Yakov Sverdlov, readily agreed to defend their plan for a congress the following month before the central committee, there was some disagreement among them about what its purpose should be. Konkordia Samoilova argued that women were only strong insofar as their struggle excluded any separate demands and felt they should set themselves the more general goal of mobilizing women to support the Bolsheviks in the forthcoming elections to the Constituent Assembly; once again Alexandra eventually resigned herself to subordinating her more specific vision of women's needs to the Party's struggle for power. The congress would at least provide the opportunity for these needs at last to be openly discussed.

Hundreds of letters were sent out to party organizations all over the country, and Alexandra met daily with Sverdlov and the women organizers, deriving new passion and confidence from the numerous articles with which Lenin filled the pages of *Pravda* and which reflected his major and most radical work on state power, *State and Revolution.* Written in September 1917 and published the following year, this work came closer than any of his previous writings to Alexandra's vision of the decentralized new order, the "commune state." After taking power, the Bolsheviks would establish a peasant-proletarian republic, bridging the period between the bourgeois state and new classless society. Although this transition would last an entire historical epoch, it would, he stressed, be finite. And although the new state would be as precarious and beleaguered as the Paris Commune, the soviets would evolve an immeasurably higher, more democratic type of state apparatus, eliminating all the old hierarchies with popular elections, the full right of any group of citizens to recall their delegates, and the levelling of officials' salaries to those of the workers:

> Such a beginning, on the basis of large-scale production, must lead to the withering away of all bureaucracy and the gradual creation of a new order in which the tasks of supervision and accounting will increasingly be performed by everyone in turn, will soon become a habit, and will eventually die out as the specialized functions of a special stratum of the people.[14]

In the countryside the peasants' war was past the point of no return. In the cities the soldiers' demand for the Bolsheviks to take power could no longer be deferred. On the evening of October 10, decked out in the ornate hat and umbrella of a "lady," Alexandra walked to the St. Petersburg side of the town to attend the historic secret meeting at which the Bolshevik central committee was to plan the seizure of power. A party worker named Tatiana Flaxerman had lent her flat for the occasion, since it was relatively safe from police surveillance (her husband, the left Menshevik Sukhanov, grudgingly spent the night elsewhere). Most of those whom Alexandra joined around the dining-room table were in disguise, and Lenin, whom she had not seen since June, was unrecognizable in his gray wig. But there was no time for conversation as from ten o'clock that evening to early the next morning members delivered their reports. Soldiers and sailors in the northern region were prepared for action, the Moscow central committee had confirmed the workers' readiness to fight, the Helsingfors sailors and the soldiers of the Third Army were openly supporting the Bolsheviks, and the railway and telegraph workers were sabotaging Kerensky's lines of communication. Only Kamenev and Zinoviev now stood out against the seizure of power. "We have wasted a considerable amount of time since September, when the situation was ripe for power," Lenin retorted crisply. "What did those cowards want?" Alexandra wrote. "To gain power by the opportunist parliamentary path?"[15]

Dawn was breaking as the votes were taken; by a majority of ten to two, the central committee supported the resolution that "the armed rising has fully and inevitably matured." The tension broke. The conspirators were ravenous and exuberant. A samovar was brought in and they all gulped down hot tea and fell upon the extra supplies of cheese and sausage which had been set aside for this meeting. Next on the agenda was the formation of a special bureau responsible for the arming of men and women factory workers—so that just two weeks later every factory, barracks, and warship in every region of Russia was ready to take up arms for the Bolsheviks. Alexandra walked back along the unfamiliar early morning streets and canals in a daze of triumph and tiredness and, going straight to the Soviet, delivered a passionate speech calling for an end to power-sharing with the government, and all power to the soviets.

On October 16 there was another highly secret central-committee meeting at which a military-revolutionary commission, guided by the inspiring courage of Trotsky and headed by him and Podvoisky, was appointed to lead the insurrection. It was then that Trotsky, who, despite his immense intellectual and rhetorical gifts, had previously played a secondary role to Lenin, came into his own as the organizer and poet of the October revolution. Subsequent Stalinist falsifications of Soviet history would deify Lenin—at the cost of obliterating Trotsky's name from the historical record of that epoch-making event—but throughout October and the years which followed the revolution Trotsky was to be Lenin's closest ally. As chairman of the Soviet he addressed immense crowds of people, urging them in one inspiring speech after another to support the

Bolsheviks; he was everywhere at once, recalled Sukhanov. "His influence, among both the masses and the revolutionary leadership, was colossal; in those days he was the principal actor, the hero of that extraordinary page of history."[16]

The man who was later to boost his own importance in these events so ludicrously—Stalin—was also granted in that meeting of October 16 an important role as liaison officer between the Party and the military committee; joined by Yakov Sverdlov, the party secretary, and a new member of the Party and of the Central committee, Felix Dzerzhinsky, he was appointed to a new "military center," entrusted with the task of mediating between army and Party. To give the revolution the appearance of a planned and orderly transfer of power, it was decided that October 24, the opening day of the Second All-Russian Congress of Soviets, would be the most propitious date for the insurrection.

But events could not so neatly be timed by the Party. October 22, the "day of the Soviet," was marked by massive demonstrations at which Alexandra addressed one huge meeting after another, and on that day the government's military headquarters passed into the control of the Soviet. Failing to push the Cossacks into patriotic demonstrations, the lifeless government locked itself inside the Winter Palace as workers from the Sestroretsky ordnance factory armed the men and women of the Red Guards and the cruiser *Aurora* sailed down the Neva to aim its guns at the palace. Alexandra's plans for the women's congress could not so easily be timed either. After addressing numerous soviet meetings, she announced in a *Pravda* article that the congress would open on October 29 in the Forward Club on Malaya Bolotnaya Street. But that same night Kerensky ordered a company of Junkers (officer cadets) and a government commisar to raid the *Pravda* offices. All central-committee members were ordered to the Smolny Institute, now the headquarters of the Bolshevik general staff. The guard was strengthened, an extra supply of bullets was laid on, and Dzhezhinsky was directed to supervise the transfer of power on the railways and in the post and telegraph offices to the Soviet. At eleven that evening copies of *Pravda* were delivered fresh from the press; the Junkers had been dispersed by a group of Bolshevik sappers, and Alexandra saw her article in print after all.[17] But the congress obviously had to be postponed.

Alexandra spent the next three days and nights, sleeping on the floor or not at all, in the Smolny. With its dull gold barrack-like façade and smoky-blue cupolas, this Institute for Girls of the Nobility, established by Catherine the Great, had been converted into the headquarters of the

Bolshevik revolution. Outside, young soldiers and *sanitarki* in red ker-chiefs gathered nervously on the muddy cobbled streets alongside the Neva. Inside, the numbered signs on the doors of the young ladies' classrooms and teachers' offices had been covered with new signs advertiz-ing literature for sale, entreating "Comrades, for the sake of your health, please preserve cleanliness," and proclaiming the central committee of the Petrograd Soviet. Two canteens were set up to provide meager meals of cabbage soup, bread, and tea, and the polished wooden floors of the long vaulted corridors rang to the tramp of military boots as endless processions of soldiers reported to Trotsky in the third-floor office of the military-revolutionary committee. Only when talking proved useless, he told them, were they to use guns.

That night, as in the July Days, Dybenko and a company of sailors sailed into Petrograd, followed by three torpedo boats; and, as the prelimi-nary Soviet congress opened the following day he greeted the delegates with the assurance that the Baltic sailors were prepared to conquer or die. It was upon the enthusiasm of the sailors and soldiers that the Bolsheviks relied now, for the Mensheviks were still in a majority on the Soviet, even though the Bolsheviks checking the credentials of the arriving delegates insisted that a majority of those with mandates were Bolsheviks. Trotsky spoke that day to assure his impatient audience that "armed conflict, today or tomorrow, does not enter our plans. Stand firm," he said, "and there will be no civil war, our enemies will capitulate at once and you will take the power that belongs to you by right." Alexandra had no time for such assurances: "How can he say that 'armed conflict does not enter our plans' when the armed uprising is already a fact?"[18] Lenin was equally distraught over this inexplicable lenience: "I urge comrades with all my strength that everything now hangs on a thread, and that the issues before us won't be resolved by conferences or congresses (even the congress of soviets) but exclusively by the struggle of the armed masses," he wrote from his hiding place in the city. "We cannot wait!! We may lose every-thing!!!"

Even as he wrote the Ministry of Religion was being seized, one detachment was occupying the telephone exchange, another the state bank, and another the telegraph exchange. When Lenin finally arrived at Smolny at 2:35 A.M. on October 25 to address the Bolshevik central committee, the government had lost the support of all the major regi-ments; the landed, the wealthy, and the prostitutes who departed with them were packing their bags to leave Petrograd. Scattered rifle fire was heard as the Junkers tried to prevent workers crossing the Neva bridge from the Vyborg side; Kronstadt sailors were sent to defend them, and together they all marched to the Smolny. That morning a group of soldiers, sailors, and *sanitarki* arrived at the Winter Palace and, haranguing the Junkers and members of the Women's Death Battalions who crossed their path, began to force their way in.

All that day delegates had been arriving at Smolny. By evening the ballroom in the south wing, where the congress was to assemble, was packed to the ceiling with long-haired peasants, workers in dark shirts, and tough soldiers in greatcoats. Thick cigarette smoke served as a primitive sort of heating on that chilly October evening, someone had torn the Tsar's portrait from its frame, and the mud from innumerable boots covered the dancing floor. In all other respects the hall, with its plush curtains, massed chandeliers, and tall white marble columns, was more suggestive of the old order than the revolutionary regime which was to be born there. At 9:30 P.M. muffled shots were heard as the *Aurora* fired blanks to signal the collapse of the government; ten minutes later Dan rang the chairman's bell to announce, "Our comrades in the Winter Palace are under fire!" Lenin spoke then—his first public appearance since the July Days—and as he stood up Nadezhda Krupskaya confessed to Alexandra her fears for his life. But he spoke calmly, announcing that all power was now passing to the soviets, stepping down to an applause so deafening that it silenced even the *Aurora*'s cannons.

Most agree now that there were 390 Bolsheviks at that congress, 160 left Socialist Revolutionaries (the right Socialist Revolutionaries had walked out), and 72 Mensheviks. Whatever the accuracy of these disputed figures, at 2:30 the following morning, when the news arrived that the Winter Palace had been seized, that the ministers had been arrested, and that the inert Provisional Government had disintegrated, the new power legally passed to the Bolsheviks. In the name of the outgoing Soviet, the Menshevik, Dan, proclaimed the new government, which quickly elected its commissars.

Alexandra was not alone in her unwillingness to enter the new government. When Lenin proposed Trotsky as the obvious choice as president of the Soviet government—Commissariat of the People's Commissars—Trotsky opposed this so adamantly that Lenin finally agreed to take the post, Trotsky taking over the relatively insignificant Commissariat of Foreign Affairs. Antonov-Ovseenko, Krylenko, and Dybenko were entrusted with the military leadership, Shlyapnikov was Commissar of Labor, and Alexandra was put in charge of the Commissariat of Social Welfare, a jumbled and ill-organized ministry newly created by the Provisional Government. She had not expected the appointment, and it did not particularly delight her, but the pressure of work to be done was so great, and the amount of time in which to discuss matters so scarce, that she barely gave a thought to her immediate personal reactions.

It was hunger that finally brought Alexandra to her senses—and fatigue. Trotsky had collapsed the previous day; that afternoon, after three astounding days charged with an almost electrical tension and after a particularly heated argument with a Socialist Revolutionary, Alexandra was overcome by dizziness. She was prevented from falling by a Red Guard, who offered her a ruble for bread. She was grateful but refused, but he insisted on taking her address and later that evening crept into her flat, left some bread there for her, and crept out again before she could discover his name to thank him.[19]

That evening the new temporary Government of Workers' and Soldiers' Deputies appeared before the Soviet congress and asked for its investiture: the Provisional Government of the Duma was no more. When the roar of applause which greeted Lenin eventually died down, he announced, "We shall now proceed to the construction of the new socialist order." As he read out his "peace declaration to the peoples of all belligerent countries," peace was suddenly no longer a dream. He called on governments to start peace negotiations with the Bolsheviks and to agree to their demands for an immediate three-month armistice and an end to all secret diplomacy. The declaration was carried almost unanimously, and "suddenly, by common impulse, we were all on our feet mumbling together in the smooth lifting unison of the *Internationale.*" John Reed, the American journalist (who recorded these events so movingly in his book *Ten Days That Shook the World*) continued:

> A grizzled soldier sobbed openly and Alexandra Kollontai rapidly blinked back the tears as the immense sound rolled through the hall, burst out of the windows and doors and soared into the quiet sky. "The war is over! The war is ended!" said a young workman next to me, his face shining. And when it was over, as we stood there in an awkward hush, someone at the back of the hall shouted, "Comrades, let us remember those who died for liberty!" So we sang the *Funeral March,* that slow, melancholy and yet triumphant chant, so Russian and so moving . . .[20]

Lenin then went on to read the Land Decree, which he had scribbled on a piece of paper. All private ownership of the land was abolished forthwith; private property was to be transferred to the township committees and regional soviets until the Constituent Assembly met, and all land, which could not be leased, mortgaged, or otherwise alienated, would be allocated to individuals who wished to cultivate it.

As Alexandra wandered home through the streets of Bolshevik Petrograd that night, "extreme happiness, watchfulness, and an awareness of our responsibilities merged into a resonant choir of sensations."[21] Whereas the more pessimistic of the Bolsheviks saw their hold on the government lasting only a few weeks, Kerensky and his White generals were confidently hoping to smash it within a few days. While the disinherited clung to their hopes of peace and land and the promises of the Bolsheviks' decrees, the propertied classes embarked on a struggle to the death for their old privileges and against the new government. As she passed a modest wall-poster announcing the Bolshevik revolution, Alexandra noticed how little attention it commanded from people still more concerned with their place in the breadline than in changes of government. Two students, evidently Bolsheviks, chortled when they saw it, an old man shook his fist, and a debonair bureaucrat started to foam at the mouth. There was still hope for these enemies of the revolution, however, and wall space was hotly contested by the Committee to Save the Country. This committee represented an ominous new rival government, formed that day in the Petrograd Duma by liberals in the old government who were joined by the right Socialist Revolutionaries who had walked out of the first part of the soviets' congress. Their aim was to cripple the Bolsheviks by organizing civil servants' strikes to halt the new commissariats, the banks, all municipal services in the two capitals, and all stenographic records of the October revolution.

13

Cooks and Commissars

Already Kerensky's Cossacks were marching on Petrograd. Gatchina, twenty miles away, which had come under Soviet power by the end of October, had been recaptured by Kerensky's forces. Hundreds under Dybenko's command died defending the Bolsheviks in Tsarskoe Selo, only a few miles from the capital; among those who died there was Vera Slutskaya, killed by a shell as she tried to get medical supplies across the enemy lines. Haggard and red-eyed, Alexandra and the other leaders of the new regime appealed to workers in the local soviets and factory committees to dig trenches, build barricades, and reinforce the barbed-wire entanglements around the encircled city. And on October 28 tens of thousands of men, women, and children poured south and west through the shabby city streets toward the Moscow Gate, cartridge-belts over their working clothes, rifles, picks, spades, and barbed wire in their hands. Smolny was seething that day as Alexandra presented herself for assignment. She found the central committee huddled in a side room, newspapers covering the windows. Looking up affably from his work, Lenin begged her to take a car immediately and occupy the palace on Kazan-skaya Street that housed her commissariat.[1] She set off on her own, as terrified of the inevitable sabotage ahead as of the vast and nightmarishly ramshackle structure of her new responsibility.

Few can have felt so unsupported as Alexandra, so inexperienced and so lacking in the technical qualifications needed to run this new government in which every cook was to take a hand. The Commissariat of Social Welfare traced its origins to Catherine the Great's charitable Smolny Institute and the complex of institutions, scantily subsidized by the philanthropy of the imperial chancery, which had sprung up under her august successors. From her precursor in the Provisional Government, Countess Panina, Alexandra had inherited responsibility for educational institutes for girls of the nobility, sordid waifs' homes—"angel factories" as they were called—exalted by the names of their royal patrons, leper colonies, orthopedic workshops, TB sanatoria, almshouses; war victims and the elderly also depended on her for their pensions. It seemed conventional enough to choose a woman for this conventionally "feminine," nurturing ministry, which proved in fact to be such a heartbreaking one. The first of her responsibilities could of course be ignored. All the rest, crying out for money, were to be subsidized by the revenue which accrued from state-monopolized playing-card factories. But this money would of course be available only if the workers there supported the Bolsheviks.

As Alexandra arrived at the doors of the old palace to find her path blocked by a massive, braided commissionaire, she realized that she would not be laying hands on even the meager funds contained in the building without a fight. To her announcement that she had come to take control of the commissariat he merely repeated in leaden tones that visiting hours were over and she should present her petition the following day. After a mortifyingly ineffectual attempt to force her way past this human barrier, she gave up and went on to a meeting.

Committees and soviets were springing up so thick and fast now that every soldier, every schoolchild, every housewife, and every passenger on a long train ride was joining in the great feast of meetings which greeted the revolution, and forming their own soviets. The new government, the "soviet of commissars," was meeting daily for five or six hours—inspiring people all over Russia, in decree after ambitious decree, no longer to bow the head or take orders. Much of Alexandra's energy in those early days went into organizing the women's congress which had been delayed by the revolution. Only a week before she had been discussing with the other women organizers and Sverdlov how best to use this congress to prepare non-party working women for the armed uprising and to persuade the soviets to consider their needs after victory. Specifically and most importantly she considered these needs to be sixteen weeks' paid maternity leave, regular time off for breast-feeding, and the provision of nurseries and warm rooms in the factories where babies could be fed. These demands (first expressed in her 1914 pamphlet *Working Woman and Mother*, which had been reprinted in 1917 and was by now extremely popular) she wanted to discuss with women at the congress before presenting them to the government as the basis for their new maternity laws. She wrote a couple of articles for *Pravda* publicizing the event,[2] and with the other women organizers wrote hundreds of letters inviting women from all over the Petrograd region to send one delegate for every 500 women to Petrograd. The congress was to open on November 6 and would last twelve days. The former Urals cinema, now the First House of Culture, on the Vyborg side, was thought large enough to accommodate the eighty delegates they anticipated.

Despite hunger, looming civil war, the chaos of the new Soviet regime, and the never-ending pressures of work, Alexandra had never felt so happy as in the winter of 1917. The dusty two-room fifth-floor flat, inherited from a friend, into which she moved with Misha and Zoya, was more of a home to her than any of her former impermanent domestic arrangements. She was glad too to be living again with Misha, who at the age of twenty-three had returned from America, where he had worked in a car factory, determined to gain an engineering degree. He enrolled at the Petrograd Technological Institute and, with considerable firmness of purpose, declined a life of political activism and committed himself with great enthusiasm to his studies and his new student friends. Whether or not he supported himself by working part-time as an engineer is not known. Alexandra's salary of 500 rubles a month (the average qualified worker's pay)[3] was certainly adequate to her own needs, if not his as well, and as long as she remained healthy, she did not feel too deprived by their meager diet of gruel, bread, and tea.

On October 30, 1917, the revolution scored its first military victory: Dybenko, as Commissar of the Navy, ordered the White General Krasnov to have Kerensky arrested, and Petrograd was saved. He went on to turn his attention to the morale of his troops. A number of White generals and soldiers had raided the wine cellars of the Winter Palace and had distributed the contents among the Bolshevik soldiers, large numbers of whom had been roving around the streets after the revolution in a ferociously drunken state. Dybenko seized the wine barrels and hacked them open, so that for several days the gutters of Petrograd ran red with the wine of the Tsar. He also announced that any soldier found drunk would be shot—thus earning the undying gratitude of the government for the swift measures he took to ensure a sober October.

Dybenko and Alexandra met as briefly and infrequently as before, either in Helsingfors or in Petrograd, but they had other difficulties to contend with from certain members of the government, as Trotsky, in his memoirs of Stalin, recalled.

A day or so after the revolution, while Alexandra was visiting Finland, Trotsky and Stalin arrived early in Lenin's office in Smolny for a government meeting:

> From behind a partition we heard the thick bass voice of Dybenko, speaking on the telephone to Finland; the conversation was obviously of a tender nature. This twenty-nine-year-old black-bearded sailor, a jolly self-confident giant of a man, had recently become intimate with Alexandra Kollontai, a woman of aristocratic antecedents who knew half a dozen languages and was approaching her forty-sixth year. In some circles of the party there was undoubtedly much gossip about this. Stalin, with whom I had never before had a personal conversation, now came up with unusual jauntiness, and jabbing with his shoulder at the partition, said, leering: "That's him in there with Kollontai! He's in there with Kollontai!" His gestures and laughter seemed unendurably vulgar and out of place. I don't remember whether I said nothing or answered drily, "That's their affair," but I do remember the same glimmer of animosity on his yellow face which so many who crossed him so well recall.[4]

But Alexandra's pressured life hardly had time to assimilate such hostility: "We were hungry, we rarely succeeded in getting a night's sleep, there were so many difficulties and dangers, but we all worked passionately. We were in a hurry to build the new soviet life, for we felt that everything we did today was desperately needed tomorrow, even if it was rough and ready."[5]

Against the hostility Alexandra was to face from officials in her commissariat, Stalin and his sexist innuendo would recede into insignificance. Helped by the Junkers whom the Red Guards had magnanimously released when they stormed the Winter Palace and financially supported by the big banks, the Committee to Save the Country paid a month's salary to all officials working in the commissariats and confidently waited for them to come out on strike and for the new government to collapse. As in the commissariats of both Shlyapnikov and Trotsky, hundreds of office-workers inside the Kazanskaya Street building were on strike; the sight of Red Guards angrily marching clerks and high officials along the muddy streets was as common that wintry October as that of disapproving bourgeois bystanders who shook their fists at the rabble. "What a strange time that was! Although power was with the soviets, and the Soviet of People's Commissars was Bolshevik, the institutions kept chugging along the rails laid by the Provisional Government."[6]

Alexandra did not have to wait long for the incentive to confront once more the braided doorman and his fellow strikers. Early one morning she was awakened by a ring at the door to find her first petitioner, a peasant who silently handed her a scrap of paper on which Lenin had scribbled, "Give him as much as he needs for a horse out of Social Welfare funds." The story of this horse, requisitioned by the tsarist army, then followed. The peasant had been in the capital for two months, he told her, had visited every conceivable office in his search for compensation; he was on the verge of despair when he heard that the Bolsheviks had taken power and had promised to return everything to the peasants; all that was needed, apparently, was a note from Lenin.[7]

With her heart in her mouth, Alexandra took the first step toward breaking the strike by contacting a Bolshevik commissariat official and former Putilov worker named Egorov. He then called a meeting of the younger workers, the messengers, guards, nurses, boilermen, and book-keepers, who were in the technical union and sympathetic to the Bol-sheviks. They elected a council of workers (a soviet) and all set off for Kazanskaya Street, where they managed at last to get past the doorman; but as they charged up the stairs they were pushed out of the way by a torrent of bookkeepers and clerks, who were out of the building before they reached the top. There they were met by two solitary strike-breaking sympathizers. Everywhere else the evidence of the sabotage was all too sickeningly evident. Typewriters lay smashed on the floor, documents had been torn up and scattered about, the keys to the safe were nowhere to be found, and everywhere in the building they met large groups of desper-ate, bewildered petitioners.[8]

For the next week, from twelve in the morning until four, Alexandra and her small determined soviet struggled without money, equipment, or files to cope with waiting rooms crowded with crippled soldiers, many of whom had been persistently visiting the building for the past few months in the hope of compensation, their patience clearly about to break; with doctors pleading for the money for their orphanages; with peasants in need of compensation for floods and fires; and with a host of angry people whom they were quite unable to help. They summoned the striking officials then, many of them titled aristocrats, to beg them to return the keys to the safe, but they merely fell to accusing each other of walking off with them.

Eventually Alexandra could no longer bear the wrecked offices and inconsolable petitioners; sweeping up great armfuls of dead documents, she and her secretary, Alyosha Tsvetkov, took a car to Smolny. There they settled into a large room, bare but for a table and two chairs, hung a sign outside announcing the "Mobile Commissariat's" visiting hours, and awaited their first petitioners. Several robust young men soon walked in, not invalids but hungry nevertheless, and in no mood to be argued with: if they really were Bolsheviks, they must feed the hungry and cut the red tape. After Alexandra and Tsvetkov had dug a few kopeks out of their own pockets as "temporary assistance," the men demanded work; Alexandra sent them off to join the Red Guards, knowing at least that there they would be fed. They were followed by a one-armed war invalid, who wanted not a false arm but the money to buy knitting machines. His plan to establish knitting cooperatives for one-armed veterans had won Lenin's approval, and now he wanted the money. Told to return in a few days, he went out grumbling, to swell the waiting crowds of war cripples who already packed the corridor outside.

Exhausted, hungry, and desperate, these poor victims were now bitterly cursing the Bolsheviks and their empty promises. Like them, the old people in the almshouses had formed their own soviet and were threatening to riot on the streets. Alexandra still had not paid the workers in the playing-card factory. Nannies in the orphanages were threatening to run away with the babies. Alexandra could wait no longer—it was intolerable that the people most in need should be so betrayed. One night after Tsvetkov had left she stayed late in her office; the tears streamed down her face as she thought of the most vociferous supporter of the strike —who was not rich and was supporting his mother. But she reminded herself sternly that a revolution was not made with white gloves and steeled herself for some drastic bureaucratic measures; the next day a Red Guard detachment was sent to arrest the strikers and bring back the keys to the safe.[9]

That day Alexandra was at last able to compensate the persistent peasant for his horse, but any more substantial payments still had to be deferred. Alexandra's formidable feminist predecessor, Countess Panina, had made away with 90,000 rubles and had had to be packed off to the Peter and Paul fortress; there she continued to curse the Bolsheviks, refused to return the money, and exhorted her former employees not to break the strike. At the countess's trial one peasant woman told the American reporter Louise Bryant (who wrote an invaluable account of her experiences in Russia during the revolution) that "she really does like poor people, you know, for she thinks they're almost as good as other people."[10] This magnanimity had first shown itself over twenty years earlier, during the first great strike movement in 1896 in St. Petersburg, when Countess Panina organized the Society for the Protection of Women in an attempt to lead striking women out of depravity and into the safe pastures of sewing bees and religious peptalks. In 1905, along with Ariadna Tyrkova and most other members of the Women's Union, she had joined the Kadet Party.

Lenin, who had once spoken in her house, described the countess as "one of the cleverest defenders of capitalism." By February 1917 she had had considerable experience in the management of large charitable donations. She invited workers to the Kazanskaya Palace for lectures on their civic duties, recruited several women onto her staff, and aimed to make her newly created commissariat assume the functions of all the various inadequately financed and corruptly managed tsarist charitable agencies. The resulting chaos she had bequeathed to Alexandra. Her hatred of the Bolsheviks had provoked her to board the *Aurora* on the night of October 24 to persuade the sailors not to fire on the Winter Palace. Her hatred of her successor was particularly intense: "That absurd Kollontai!" she exploded to Louise Bryant, shortly after she had left prison. "She invites the servants to sit in armchairs at her meetings—such things cannot be! What do they know of social reforms or technical training? It is just putting the feet up and the head down, quite mechanically."[11]

In fact Alexandra had immediately abolished the old hierarchy, leveled the salary of every official and messenger with her own, and at regular meetings in Lenin's office with her young supporters she tried to reorganize the commissariat along soviet lines. Egorov recruited new workers, and by early November a hundred people were ready to open the commissariat building. Guided by Alexandra and an elected *collegium* of three men and two women, they worked in shifts around the clock to sort out the files, guard the typewriters, and defend the building. "The word 'sympathy' was a sort of professional term in our soviet, where all work revolved around those whom fate had cheated and disinherited," she wrote.[12] All agreed with her that one of their first concerns should be to convert the hellish "angel factories," which disgraced every town in Russia, into modern mother-and-baby homes. A number of women factory workers were persuaded that their experience and suggestions were needed for this work and joined the officials in a "social investigation team," which visited the small number of nurseries and children's clinics in the city to decide how they could best be reorganized.

The same practical goals of modernization guided the proposals Alexandra made to the women's congress that month. By November 6 a twelve-day program had been arranged, and food and accommodation had been provided for some eighty women. But as Alexandra stood outside the small Vyborg hall with Konkordia Samoilova and the others to greet the arriving delegates it became clear that they had greatly underestimated the numbers. Soon 500 delegates, representing 80,000 women from factories, unions, and party organizations not merely in Petrograd but in Moscow, Ivanovo, and Tula too had crowded into the hall. Sverdlov arranged extra food and accommodation; Konkordia and three other *Rabotnitsa* editors (Emilia Solin, Rakhilia Kovnator, and Arbuzov) were elected to the platform, and Konkordia Samoilova gave the speech of welcome.

Klavdia Nikolaeva spoke first to encourage women to vote for the Bolsheviks in the forthcoming elections to the Constituent Assembly: "for we, class-conscious women workers, know that we have no special women's interests, and that there should be no separate women's organizations. We are strong only so long as we are organized into one fraternal proletarian family with all workers struggling for socialism." After these arguable sentiments a well-dressed woman stood up at the back of the hall and, introducing herself as Dr. Doroshevskaya, explained that she was one of the nineteen candidates to the Constituent Assembly and wanted to speak for the League for Women's Equality. A volley of catcalls greeted her words and order was only restored when Alexandra, in a strange reversal of roles probably prompted by her reservations about the preceding speech, persuaded them to hear her out: The enemy was defeated, she said: They could afford to be generous. Dr. Doroshevskaya immediately assured them that she was not a social parasite but a single unsupported mother. "Everywhere women are subjected," she went on. "Everywhere they are still struggling for their rights. Women who visit us from America and England are in complete solidarity with us and wish us well in our struggle. Men cannot defend our interests, for they do not understand us." Alexandra's *soldatka* friend Fyodorova retorted that the league had never shown the slightest concern for working women and was merely out for their votes. The discussion trailed on for a while until the congress adjourned.

The next day two printers named Prokhorova and Vasileva and a worker from an optical factory called Fomichev read reports about women's working conditions, and Anna Itkina spoke of her work with women in the Narva district. Then Alexandra stood up, to gusts of applause. Look out for your own interests, she advised them, and send your own representatives to the Constituent Assembly, representatives who will raise the issue of equal pay, paid maternity leave, and the prohibition of long hours, night shifts, and all work damaging to women's health. Given the poverty and isolation of the new government and its tendency to overlook women's needs, it could not be expected to do any more initially than to give women *legal* equality—by introducing civil marriage, legitimizing all children born in and outside of marriage, and making it easier to obtain a divorce. Full equality in the workers' state would still have to be fought for, and this, she stressed, could only be done if women formed their own groups within the unions, factory committees, soviets, and party organizations. Again many of Alexandra's colleagues demurred at her suggestion. They considered that *Rabotnitsa* was quite capable of coordinating women's activities, as it had done so excellently before the revolution, despite the fact that a newspaper was a vehicle for propaganda rather than an agent of government. But her proposals for maternity protection were less contentious and won enough support for her to be able to turn them into law the following month.

Just as the congress was adjourning that evening news came through that the peasants' union had come out in support of the Bolsheviks; a woman was sent off to present the peasants with the delegates' congratulations. When they heard shortly afterward that Nogin, Rykov, Kamenev, and Zinoviev had resigned from the government after a coalition with the left Socialist Revolutionaries had been rejected, Alexandra decided to make some theater out of the occasion and arranged to take a group of delegates to see Lenin in Smolny. "That's some fighting force," he said in amazement when he learned of the thousands of women represented at the congress. "We're ready to give our lives for you," one of them said. "Not for me, but for the power of the soviets and the happiness of the working people," he firmly corrected her.[13]

The organizational plans and resolutions which emerged from this women's congress were only partially realized. The Constituent Assembly was dissolved the following year by the Bolsheviks, and the proposal for an All-Russian Women's Congress was rejected as untimely. The women who censored Kamenev and Rykov obviously made enemies in the Party, but then most party members could only regard women's liberation as of secondary importance to the crisis in the government, the civil war, and the imminent danger of a German invasion.

On November 8 Trotsky had handed a note to the Allied ambassadors, reminding them of the Bolsheviks' peace decree and asking them to regard this as an official proposal for an armistice and the prelude to negotiations. He received no reply. For five days the new government waited for some sympathetic sign of rebellion from the workers of Europe and clung to their conviction that world revolution would soon make all such diplomacy a thing of the past. When on November 13 Trotsky was eventually sent through the German lines to arrange for peace talks to start in Brest-Litovsk the following week, he still had high hopes of the propaganda value of the exercise. But as talks began against an ominous silence from the German workers, Trotsky's confidence in his own indefatigably brilliant Bolshevik propaganda dwindled, and the new government was torn apart by arguments over its own survival.

It was only later, in January 1918, when the Germans presented their punishing ultimatum demanding colossal indemnities and vast chunks of Russian territory, that Alexandra stood out against the desire of Lenin and the majority for a separate peace with Germany, and joined Bukharin and the left Bolsheviks. However these leftists' idealistic belief that the Bolsheviks should enter into a revolutionary war with German imperialism —their willingness to sacrifice the Russian revolution if necessary in the interest of the world revolution—was already partly reflected in her own pure revolutionary consciousness, even in those early struggling days. "The Bolsheviks will undoubtedly succumb," she told a French friend of hers, the revolutionary, diplomat, and army captain, Jacques Sadoul, "but before disappearing they will have sounded unknown words, new formulae which will never be forgotten! Even if we are conquered we have still achieved an immense amount in abolishing the old ideas; the really creative work of raising the world's culture will come first from the other countries."[14]

In the six months in which she had agitated for the Bolsheviks in Petrograd after her eight years abroad, Alexandra had met only the most advanced of the workers and soldiers, and Dybenko and his equally sophisticated sailor comrades had inspired her with confidence. Now her commissariat was introducing her to a Russia she barely knew—to the peasants, three-quarters of the Russian population, and to the masses of peasant women, who were at the very bottom of the social order in Russia.

In many ways the life of the peasant woman was still much as it had been in the dark ages of the tenth century, when Russia was Christianized and Byzantine notions of female spite and devilry had first begun to permeate Russian culture. The Tartar invasion of the thirteenth century had introduced a brutal Oriental attitude toward women which merely reinforced these notions, so that when the Muscovite Russian state was consolidated in the seventeenth century and serfdom was legalized, women's merciless exploitation by their husbands and fathers was officially condoned. The male head of the household was regarded as an agent of imperial power, with full authority over his wife, children, and dependents; he was expected to prove his love for his wife by beating her regularly, and in a church manual which appeared at that time there were panegyrics to the rod, which was to hang over the bed in every well-ordered household.

In almost all peasant families the birth of a son was greeted with joy; the birth of a daughter was greeted with weeping by her parents, whose first concern was to marry her off as quickly as possible. A woman had no voice in the peasant assembly, in which she was forbidden to sit even if she was a widow or head of a household. Nor did she have any rights of inheritance, or any say in her family's finances; the only property she was allowed to own was her trousseau and certain small domestic utensils. As field laborers women shared with the men all the heavy work of reaping, threshing, and vegetable-gardening, although they were traditionally excluded from certain jobs like bee-keeping and sowing. And to this labor was added the unremitting labor of constant pregnancies; in 1908 it was estimated that twenty-five percent of peasant women aged forty-five had had an average of ten pregnancies, a quarter of which were miscarriages. Peasant women's toiling lives—darkened by miscarriages, post-natal complications, and an appalling infant mortality rate, all of which were so common as to be rarely spoken about—brought them neither social status nor economic reward: "A hen's not a bird and a woman's not a person," went a popular peasant saying.

Although the peasant family structure varied widely in Russia and there was no "typical" peasant family most households consisted of two generations, and in general the wealthier the family, the larger and more extended it was. For the young wife this extended family brought its own tragedies, for she frequently had to undergo the horrifying ritual of sleeping with her father-in-law, particularly if her husband were forced to leave the village to fight in the army or augment the family earnings by finding seasonal factory work in the cities. Women, whose only influence was over each other, frequently tyrannized their daughters-in-law; it became common for young wives to set up their own cooking arrangements within the "extended" family.

By the early nineteenth century large numbers of the poorer peasant families who could not exist through farming alone were engaging in cottage industry, and in this too women were inevitably allocated the least skilled jobs. It was in the last two decades of the nineteenth century that women first began to leave the villages to work seasonally, like their husbands and fathers, in the factories. Increasingly large numbers of them began at that time to leave the villages for good, and from 1885 to 1911 the number of women industrial workers leaped from 7000 to 47,000. But countless other peasant women combined work in the fields with other kinds of seasonal work, and it was common for them to travel around the neighboring villages during the summer months, prostituting themselves at the local fairs.

At the end of the nineteenth century and in the first decade of the twentieth the great majority of peasant women working in the cities were employed as domestic servants. Their serf origins and the subservience they had learned from their families made them highly sought after, particularly by the rising merchant class, for their manners were so respectful and their needs were so wretchedly modest that they were rarely given anything but a corner to sleep in, miserably inadequate food, and subsistence wages. It was tacitly accepted, moreover, that the master of the house had the right to seduce these servants and then throw them out on the street when they became pregnant. As waitresses in the cities' tearooms, peasant women were treated little better by their customers and employers. And in the factories not only did employers welcome women workers as cheaper and more manageable but they also frequently operated a system whereby they could pick out the prettier women and sleep with them whenever it suited them.

The number of peasant women arriving in the cities to work in the factories leaped dramatically in the years of the Russo-Japanese War, and again during the First World War, by which time they represented forty percent of the labor force. But these women, many of whom Alexandra first met in 1906, were living in a different world from that inhabited by their peasant sisters. It was only in the spring of 1917 that she had met the more oppressed and downtrodden women who worked in Petrograd's laundries and tearooms, and the *soldatki*—who so soon after leaving their villages were demonstrating with such inspiring results their power to protest and demonstrate.

Now in her commissariat Alexandra was beginning to meet all the Tsar's most truly rejected subjects—men as well as women—who lagged so far behind the workers in the rest of Europe that it seemed inconceivable that their revolution could survive in isolation. In her years of exile she had had all the time in the world for reflection and doubt. Now that every second was so precious to the threatened regime, she accepted without hesitation that even if they perished before achieving socialism, they could at least express people's desire for equality. It was in this spirit that the government rushed through its inspiring volumes of new legislation on labor relations, social insurance, the nationalization of houses, the abolition of all titles and distinctions of class and sex, the legal sanctioning of civil marriage, and the recognition in law of all children.

The government regarded many of these new laws as a "description of its determination to bring about socialism," often more valuable as propaganda and inspiration than as reality, closer often to modernizing than to revolutionizing. Its first law, the marriage law of December 20, was of a quite revolutionary simplicity. Otherwise, as Alexandra remarked, it was "not essentially any more progressive than those existing in other progressive democracies . . . On the divorce question we are on a level with North America, whereas on the question of illegitimate children we have not even progressed as far as the Norwegians . . ."[15] On the last question she was referring to the sexual hypocrisy which still separated legislation from reality many years later, and to all the deeply conservative attitudes toward women and marriage, which this law barely affected. That December it was with a solid sense of achievement that she greeted this "razing to the ground of the bourgeois marriage laws," and the introduction of a new, simple marriage ceremony. "I feel that our generation has made a breach in the wall that only exists now in the colonial countries," she wrote to Misha (who was evidently out of Petrograd at the time). "And I feel that a part of my energies, thoughts, and struggles and the example of my whole life has gone into that great victory . . ."[16]

The law's greatest achievement, however, and the Bolsheviks' first pledge to women, was born of the lonely unnoticed struggles of her mother's generation, for now their daughters and granddaughters would have the right to initiate divorce and receive alimony. Any man of eighteen and woman of sixteen could marry (provided they were not already married, insane, or closely related), and had only to declare their intentions to the Department of Marriage Registration; in a codicil added by Alexandra the couple was given the right to choose what surname to use after marriage. When Dybenko proposed that they make an example of the new law by registering their relationship, Alexandra was not immediately taken with the idea. Misha protested ("You'll always be Kollontai for me"), and Zoya expostulated that to get married again would be both foolish and shockingly inconsistent of her. "Will you really put down our flag of freedom for his sake? You, who all your life have always fought against the slavery which married life brings, and which inevitably comes into conflict with our work and achievements?" demanded Zoya.[17] But Alexandra thought of all the times Dybenko had complained that she felt him unworthy of her, all the hours she had waited for him in fear and trembling that he might have been captured by counter-revolutionaries. As married people they would be less easily separated, and they might even be less gossiped about in the Party. She eventually agreed late one night, after sitting up many anxious hours waiting for him and on his return almost fainting with relief into his arms. They went through the simple ceremony, one of the first couples to do so, and the registry office promptly and symbolically lost all record of their union.

Their relationship continued on its old erratic course, her anxieties about Dybenko's daily skirmishes on the streets unbearably exacerbated by rumors that other women found him equally irresistible and were also falling into his arms. Their marriage caused something of a sensation in Russia, even in those sexually exuberant times. It was their age difference, according to the Swedish socialist Zeth Höglund (who visited Russia early in 1918), which created so much gossip in Russia. It was their class difference which so shocked *The New York Evening News* correspondent, Albert Rhys Williams, who wrote, "We were astounded to find one morning that the versatile Kollontai had married the sailor Dybenko."[18] Their marriage launched an endless series of rumors: there was one that the ceremony had been performed by a priest, and there was another curiously persistent rumor that the two of them had abandoned their commissariats immediately after their marriage to take a lengthy honeymoon in the Crimea. Few people stated explicitly what Alexandra had pointed out seven years before in her indictment of the double standard in *Sexual Relations and the Class Struggle*. A doctor could marry his cook, she had written, and a professor could marry his young working-class student, and neither would risk social ostracism and disgrace. But God help the woman writer or teacher who married *her* cook or *her* young male student—especially if he was handsome—for by so doing she was proclaiming to the world that she physically desired men.

Whatever the law's dubious personal benefits to her, however, it did provide the incentive she needed to expand the "social investigation team" in her commissariat into a department which could draft the necessary maternity laws and ensure that they were carried out in practice. Against the preoccupations of work and hunger her anxieties about Dybenko receded. In constant meetings with her investigation team and with other members of the government she often forgot to eat, even when two rounds of Dutch cheese arrived for her and Lenin from some Swedish well-wishers. She was painstakingly cutting this on newspaper into minute pieces in order to share it with Lenin's secretary and her commissariat workers, when she was called to a meeting and forgot all about it. She returned that evening to Lenin's office to find it gone. The guards at the door had changed many times during the day and each had taken one piece, assuming this crumb to be the day's rations. On this meager nourishment her work thrived.[19]

On December 19, 1917, the same day as the passing of the marriage law, Alexandra announced that her commissariat had opened a department which would reorganize the children's homes, help women throughout pregnancy, and reduce the rate of infant mortality. Guided by a six-person *collegium*, which included herself and her secretary, Alyosha Tsvetkov, and was directed by Dr. Korolev, who had had experience of working in children's homes under the old regime, the department produced its first decree on the protection of mothers: nursing mothers should work no more than four days a week and should be provided at their factories with nurseries and regular time off for breast-feeding. More advanced than this however, and in advance of every other European country, was the additional commitment to allow women sixteen weeks' paid maternity leave, and to entitle all mothers, whether married or not, to receive enough insurance to pay for a friend also to take time off from work and help with the birth.[20]

Since contraception was still inaccessible to most people and abortion was considered a dangerous operation, it was all too obvious that merely to recognize *de facto* marriage and to abolish the idea of illegitimacy would not go very far to help either the desperate women who were forced to abandon their babies or the countless young people who escaped as soon as they were old enough from the "angel factories" and inevitably turned into criminal delinquents. Long before the revolution thousands of these children had been roaming the streets of every Russian town, existing on little but what they could steal or prostitute themselves for. The poverty and marital instability produced by war, civil war, and revolution had spilled an estimated 350,000 homeless children, or *besprizorniki*, onto the streets. Savage with hunger, and often armed, they presented one of the darkest and most intractable problems of the Russian revolution—and, inevitably, of Alexandra's Commissariat, which they visited in their hundreds in the hope of money and accommodation.

The task of tackling the problem was beyond Alexandra's means. By 1921 the number of these children had increased to 7,000,000. Together with a number of children and various women Bolsheviks such as Nadezhda Krupskaya and Sofya Smidovich, Alexandra discussed various ideas for setting up foster homes as self-governing colonies, but until people could be trained to open them and the necessary food and money could be found, these remained unrealizable and only a very few managed to get started. Some of these children went to school simply in order to be fed, but now that lessons were turning into mass meetings, numerous teachers, many of whom were priests, were on strike, as were the civil servants who administered the schools; this meant that food was not ordered and so was scarce even there. The only hope, Alexandra considered, or at least a first radical move in the proper direction, was to ensure that mothers had enough support from the state so that they were no longer impelled to throw out their children. Just as the state must protect pregnancy as one of women's social functions, so it must also be directly responsible for the care of their children. This responsibility, spelled out in a second degree issued by her commissariat in November 1918 on the protection of children, would be guided by three main principles: the need to keep nursing mothers healthy so that they could breast-feed their babies adequately, the need to promote enlightened attitudes toward the evolving socialist family, and the need to create every possible outlet for children's emotional and physical development.[21]

As day after day for the next two months Alexandra tried with increasing helplessness to explain to weary petitioners in her office how little could be done in a country ravaged by war and paralyzed by strikes, none was readier than she to admit how partial these first decrees of hers were. Almost every experimental new step the commissars took in these early days was in determined reaction to some crisis; almost every new piece of legislation was created by the methods of bourgeois law (alternatives to which were only very gradually being elaborated) and built on the fiercely tenacious attitudes of the old tsarist culture. If Alexandra's subsequent lyrical hymns to motherhood ring somewhat false to the modern ear therefore, this may be because—although she realized and deplored how far Russia was from experiencing the liberating effects of universally accessible birth control—she was unwilling to explore the question of whether the more conservative party members might not actually *want* to inhibit women's sexual initiative and—by urging that Russia had to increase her birth rate—exploit their sexual ignorance. "As the soviets were the first in the world officially and legally to recognize motherhood as a social function, and since inevitably in the workers' republic women will always have this kind of 'labor conscription' imposed on them, it was from this point of view that I approached the problem of maternity insurance"—this was how she put it, equally ambivalently, ten years later.[22] It took several months for the decree even to become law.

Her decrees did offer certain practical possibilities for inspiring future work, however, and the general commitment to state childcare was accompanied by the more specific commitment to open palaces for mothers and children in Moscow and Petrograd. The first of these, in Petrograd, was to arise from the ruins of tsarist philanthropy and serve as the model for the mother-and-baby homes of the future. The Nikolaev Institute—a former "angel factory" on the Moika Canal where babies were still being scooped off the streets and dumped in baskets to live the rest of their childhood with no more identity than a number on the knuckle —would be abolished. The countess running it and the babies and nurses were moved into a side wing while for the next month Alexandra and a team of commissariat workers and weekend volunteers cleaned and brightened up the building. They put up curtains and moved in enough beds and cots to accommodate at least some of the pregnant women on their long list of applicants. Thanks to her commissariat colleague Dr. Korolev who had had several years' experience of the old baby homes, they made plans for a model nursery, a medical laboratory, a surgery, a dairy, and a library. Displayed throughout the building were illustrated posters on baby care and child development. The deposed countess had only to point to these posters, with their exhortations to mothers to share their breastmilk with others, to confirm many of the nannies in their worst fears: the Bolsheviks wanted to nationalize women and separate them from their children. For Alexandra the palace became a symbol of her battle against women's manipulated ignorance; for the enemies of the revolution her name became the symbol which launched a thousand rumors, including, for example, the tenacious belief among many women that she was forcing twelve-year-old girls to marry.

Despite all opposition, however, she had managed to get her commissariat going, and Lenin was sufficiently impressed by her achievement to call upon her one evening in December 1917 to use all her powers of persuasion to induce the striking workers at the central post office to return to work. Since the Junkers had seized the telephone exchange three days after the revolution, telecommunications had been slowly grinding to a halt. Alexandra arrived to find a large crowd of strikers enthusiastically applauding a Menshevik speaker and was almost shouted off the stage as she pointed out that no amount of workers' control or soviet power could replace the skilled labor needed to keep communications and industry going. Then she changed tack, talking to the women and persuading them that to wreck the revolution meant wrecking all the benefits it offered to them. To cheers from the women in the audience a group of anti-Bolsheviks rushed onto the stage and started to attack her, tearing the buttons off her coat and hurling her fur hat to the ground. A fight broke out as some men and women ran up to defend her. They managed to get her safely out of the building and accompanied her to Smolny, where Sverdlov warmly thanked her. Soon afterward news came through that the workers would be returning the next day.[23] This success prompted a mood of such optimism that, a few weeks later, Alexandra rashly embroiled herself in a confrontation with the most stubborn of all the moribund tsarist institutions—the Church.

By the end of December playing cards were evidently in great demand; money from the state-monopolized factories—virtually the only source of income for Alexandra's commissariat—was flowing in satisfactorily. She personally supervised all the accounts and the distribution of pensions, and presided over the self-managing *collegia* in charge of the commissariat's various departments. Work on the Petrograd Palace of Motherhood was progressing, thanks to the numerous women who sacrificed their Saturdays to sew baby-clothes and refurnish the building, and their example was being followed by women in other parts of Russia as well. But the thousands of the desperate and dispossessed who crowded the corridors and stairways of Kazanskaya Street posed a far more soberingly intractable problem. "People mercilessly trampled underfoot by tsarism had of course found no compensation from Kerensky. Mothers carrying babies, orphans off the streets, the blind, the old, the wretched and the poor, lepers, soldiers' widows and above all the cripples of war, those who had lost legs, arms, eyes . . . discarded like rubbish on the streets . . ."[24] All she could at first do was to raise the veterans' pensions, but as the weather grew colder they had taken to camping on the floor, had formed their own soviet and were demanding to be rehoused. By the end of December the commissariat workers decided to make their accommodation an urgent priority. Tsvetkov reconnoitered and soon found the ideal place—a place where there were hundreds of beds in small private rooms, canteens and kitchens crammed with flour, vegetable oil and tinned herrings, as well as enough firewood to last for two years. Several thousand veterans could be comfortably accommodated. The Bolsheviks were no strangers to appropriating palaces for the Party and dispossessing the aristocracy—the only disadvantage to this otherwise ideal building was that it happened to be the illustrious Alexander Nevsky monastery, and the revolution had no intention yet of disestablishing the Church.

However neither Alexandra nor Tsvetkov was too anxious about that, and Alexandra was doubtless encouraged to go ahead with her plan by Dybenko, whose own reckless method of taking direct action had proved so effective in the past months. After talking to the forty novices in the monastery, whose dismal existence was little better than slavery, Tsvetkov discovered how much they resented the fat bellies of their superiors; they were easily persuaded to open the gates the following day to Alexandra and her colleagues. They arrived to find the gates locked and the monks barricaded.inside. After breaking the news to the veterans—who immediately threatened to smash up the commissariat and riot on the streets— they agreed they could no longer afford to stand on ceremony: this would be the first monastery to be seized by the new regime. Tsvetkov prepared the eviction order, Alexandra telephoned Dybenko to ask him to come along with a detachment of sailors, and together they all strode off to confront the monks. But this time the monks were better prepared. As the expropriating party, led by a brass band, swung cheerfully into sight, the monastery bells tolled and from all sides local worshippers and provocateurs rushed to defend their holy landmark. Before anybody could tell who started it, there was an exchange of shots and several people died, in one of the most shocking skirmishes of the Bolsheviks' struggle for power.[25]

The fighting was soon broken up by a group of government representatives who ordered the plan to be dropped and summoned Alexandra and Tsvetkov for an interview with Lenin, who was as distressed and angry as they were. Quite unmoved by Alexandra's attempt to explain how excited the novices had been at the prospect of forming their own soviet, he retorted that the commissars had no business behaving so wildly and arbitrarily in this exceptionally delicate political matter. Until the Soviet state was formally ratified by the Constituent Assembly later that January, it could have no real power against the priests.

This fact the Church was, of course, quick to exploit. Alexandra and Tsvetkov were anathemized, in a solemn ceremony which consolingly linked their names in the minds of the religious with those of Leo Tolstoy and the seventeenth-century peasant rebel and "antichrist," Stenka Razin. The Kadet and Menshevik papers gleefully pointed to this as one more example of Bolshevik ineptitude, and of Alexandra's foolish attempts to replace skilled workers with cooks and servants. She received a large number of threatening letters after this incident but refused military protection and continued as before to go out unarmed and without a bodyguard. At least the veterans were found new accommodation (probably in one of the old tsarist charitable institutions). The Department of Veterans' Affairs, an under-funded organization surviving largely on workers' donations and formerly attached to the Commissariat of the Interior, was transferred to her commissariat.

In December and January the precarious new government, harassed and divided by the increasingly harsh line the Germans were taking with Trotsky and the Bolshevik delegation at the Brest-Litovsk peace negotiations, could ill afford such domestic crises. By December they had signed an armistice with the Central Powers, who undertook not to move any more troops to the Eastern Front or to interfere with the Bolsheviks' front-line antiwar propaganda within the German army. It was with this propaganda that the Bolsheviks hoped to trigger off the revolution in Europe, without which their revolution could not hope to survive against the capitalist powers.

The Russian army had fought its last battle in August 1917, when the Latvian capital of Riga had fallen to the Germans. Although it was the Bolsheviks' promise to call an end to this war which Russia had lost so disastrously and which had rallied people to support their revolution, it was not the Bolsheviks who ended the war; the entire nation, simply by refusing to fight, had made the Russian army nonexistent. A few weeks after they had come to power, the Bolsheviks had presented to the Allies their proposal to negotiate for an armistice with Germany. The Allies had furiously denounced the treachery of this "separate peace" and so, when the German government, eager to be finished with its Eastern Front, did finally sign an armistice with Russia on December 15, 1917, it did so with the full confidence that the isolated and precarious Soviet government would not hold out for its demands for no annexations or indemnities. The German military team which negotiated with Trotsky and his Bolshevik colleagues at Brest-Litovsk throughout December felt sure that they could argue the Bolsheviks into accepting their peace terms.

But when, in January 1918, the Germans did present their list of indemnities and territorial demands, they were far harsher than any of the Bolsheviks had anticipated. Many on the central committee derived enough confidence from the achievements of October to feel that revolution in Germany and Austria could not be too far away (and they were not disappointed, for throughout December and January both countries were swept by strikes). The toughest line against the Germans would, they felt, pay off. To negotiate with their sworn capitalist enemies meant the dishonoring of the revolution; to accept German peace terms meant its sure death.

As German workers came out in strikes and antiwar demonstrations throughout late December and January, the left Bolsheviks argued (with increasing hope) that without an international uprising a genuine "democratic" peace with the Kaiser was nonsense, contrary to all the policies of international socialism, and an endorsement of the worst kind of opportunism. The leftists who had joined Lenin that spring in agitating for the revolution were now prompted by these and a variety of other reasons to oppose, with varying degrees of passion, his desire for the best possible peace terms for Russia. Led by four delegates elected to the central committee in July 1917 (Bukharin, Georgy Pyatakov, Karl Radek, and Mikhail Uritsky) and joined, at first temperamentally and then explicitly, by Alexandra, they represented a great force on the central committee and won the support of both Petrograd and Moscow party organizations. Their guiding faith—shared by Dybenko and many army commanders— and the stuff of essential front-line propaganda, was in a revolutionary war against German imperialism. This slogan, argued Lenin, was mere showmanship, tantamount to the aristocratic code of "death with honor"; there was no sacrifice too great to preserve Bolshevik power, and there was no sense in discussing a confrontation on any terms with the Germans without a united party. 'We'll surrender imperial Petrograd and holy Moscow and retreat to the Volga—but I'll save the soldiers of the revolution and I'll save the revolution!"[26]

Eventually it was Trotsky's temporizing position of "no peace, no war," which the leftists chose to mean the former and Lenin to mean the latter, that won a majority of central-committee votes. On January 17 Trotsky was back at Brest-Litovsk, confronting this time a new delegation of questionable authority from the Ukrainian People's Assembly, the Rada, who were planning a separate agreement with the Germans. Undaunted, he announced the immediate mobilization of the Russian army and his government's refusal to accept peace conditions "which carry sorrow, oppression, and suffering to millions of people"—and walked out. The German delegation was sufficiently thunderstruck to spend the next two weeks closeted with the Kaiser and the General Staff. The December armistice was repudiated, and they prepared for their inevitable new offensive against Petrograd.

On the point, apparently, of being annihilated by their enemies abroad, the Bolsheviks dealt more briskly with their enemies at home. In early January, the "temporary government" drafted the Declaration of the Rights of the Toiling and Exploited People, which declared the establishment of the Soviet Republic and convened the Constituent Assembly for January 18, 1918.* The assembly, now the rallying point for the anti-

---

*The Western calendar, thirteen days in advance of the old Russian one, was not adopted until the end of that month, but it will be used here from the beginning of 1918.

Bolsheviks, met, predictably rejected the proposed constitution, and was promptly and unceremoniously dissolved by an armed Bolshevik sailor. Dybenko, bitterly hostile to any peace terms with the Germans, longed to leave for his native Ukraine to prepare the army there for the anticipated German attack.

As the Bolsheviks prepared their constitution—to be published later that year—by which the Church would be disestablished, the convents nationalized, and the monasteries turned into veterans' and waifs' homes, Alexandra looked forward to the time when her commissariat would share in some of the proceeds from the sale of religious artifacts. In the meantime she confirmed her anathema by publishing a decree in *Izvestia* on January 21 announcing that state payments to churches for religious services and the upkeep of buildings would be cut, and offering displaced priests and monks the opportunity to work in her commissariat. With all her dreams strictly subordinated to her commissariat's limited financial resources and the Party's urgent priorities elsewhere, she could at least look forward to her precious Palace of Motherhood's opening at the end of that month, and whenever she could escape from a central committee meeting she would race over to the Moika Canal. A particularly exciting project was for a Museum of Motherhood, dreamed up and labored over by a member of her commissariat's *collegium* for mothers and babies, Dr. Vera Lebedeva.

After Trotsky had walked out of the Brest-Litovsk negotiations on January 28, leaving the Germans to plan their counterattack, the Bolshevik central committee was thrown into two weeks of anxious daily eight-hour meetings. Despite this, Alexandra spent most of January 30 at the Nikolaev Institute with Dr. Korolev and the new staff there. With a solid sense of achievement she inspected the large airy bedrooms, the medical laboratory, and the library; then, hanging up a sign outside announcing that the Palace of Motherhood would open the following day, she went on to a central committee meeting. It was long after midnight when she returned home. Over some bread and tea that Zoya had saved for her, they talked for a couple of hours. It was four o'clock and she was just going to bed when Korolev telephoned her: the Palace of Motherhood was on fire, he said, his voice breaking.

She telephoned Dybenko at once, begging him to come with a detachment of sailors, and together they drove in dazed silence through the frosty streets, past the patrolling Red Guards, and towards the ominous red glow over the Moika Canal. Great flames leaped up into the frozen sky, lighting the blackness for miles around, and as they drew up she felt frozen with fear. The sign they had put up so confidently hung askew on the gaping doors, the entire central part of the building had collapsed, and the glowing snow was littered with beams, boards, and shattered glass. She and Dybenko's sailors helped the firemen already there to prevent the devastation spreading, and a young commissariat worker ran up to tell her what she had already realized, all too horribly clearly—it was sabotage. The fire had started in too many places at once —and on the very night before the Palace was to have opened—for it to have been caused by mere carelessness: the wing accommodating the countess, the nannies still loyal to her, and their infant charges was untouched. Alexandra's "baby," created through sleepless nights and hours of patient preparation and persuasion, was dead.

That appalling night it dawned on her with a sudden sharp clarity that unbearably deep fears had been aroused by the Bolsheviks and their family laws in the minds of countless women who had been forced to abandon their children during the war and were stricken with guilt forever afterward. Suddenly from out of the intact section of the building a strange dishevelled procession of nannies emerged, moving toward the smoldering rubble in their nightdresses, babies in their arms. "There she is, the Antichrist!" they yelled as Alexandra and Korolev made for the side wing. "She took the icons down! She wants to turn the orphanage into a brothel! The Bolsheviks are after the children's rations!" She helplessly tried to pacify them and talk to them. "She wanted to burn us with our babies!" they cried, hysterical and inconsolable, lining the stairs to prevent her from going up to the countess. One nanny leaped forward and tried to throttle her. The sailors pulled her back, herded them all into the side wing, and put a guard at the door to protect them. Alexandra's neck was covered with bruises for several weeks.[27]

Without any real hope of success she, Dybenko, Korolev, and another commissariat colleague, Egorov, set up a commission to investigate the causes of the fire. The countess, summoned to Smolny by a couple of sailors, imperturbably explained that the fire was a divine judgment on the throwing out of the icons, and on Alexandra's insults to the religious propriety of her establishment. And as for her sluttish Bolshevik nurses, who had sailors in to stay and left their cigarette-ends lying about, it was surprising they had not started a fire before. Enraged by this, Dybenko leaped up to demand that they arrest her on the spot. He only grudgingly accepted Alexandra's reminder that Bolsheviks needed more direct proof to arrest people: stupid words were not enough, even though the countess's air of smug revenge and holy hypocrisy marked her clearly as the culprit. A far more serious anxiety was the hold people like her had over simple women who were struggling to achieve some peace of mind in their war-torn lives and were only too quick to see this peace of mind menaced by heartless Bolsheviks plotting to tear babies from their mothers in order to have them reared by the state.

Adding to all the fears which beset her was Dybenko's fierce determination to leave for the Ukraine, and, with a flagrant and flamboyant disregard for party directives, to prepare the army to attack the Germans when they invaded, as they inevitably would. He left Petrograd in the early days of February, and since his work in the Ukraine was conducted in a strictly clandestine and underground manner, Alexandra had no news from him for three months. She was condemned to wait, powerless and anxious, for the disgrace which his insubordination was sure to bring him.

Alexandra's dark premonitions of the ideological and personal struggles ahead led her to an even more fervent compensatory hope for the revolution abroad. Just two days after the fire, the central committee nominated her to lead a truly desperate mission the following month to Stockholm, London, and Paris. With her were to travel her old Lithuanian Zimmerwaldist friend from New York, Leonid Berzin, and Mark Natanson, an elderly Bolshevik who in his youth in the 1870's had been a member of the People's Will. To try to persuade radicals in the European socialist parties to commit themselves to a revolutionary war on German imperialism was obviously a hopeless task; Alexandra, Berzin, and Natanson were rather to induce what friends the Bolsheviks had in Sweden, England, and France to endorse the Soviet peace plan and openly defend their revolution.

On February 17, when the Germans called an end to the farcical Brest-Litovsk talks and announced their new offensive against Petrograd, the hopes raised by this mission diminished drastically. Despite repeated calls from some leftists for Lenin's resignation and Lenin's own threat to resign, everyone realized that without any leader of comparable stature to replace him the Bolshevik regime would not survive; in the interests of party unity Trotsky agreed to accept the Germans' peace terms. Encouraged by these signs of Bolshevik disunity, Germany and Austria stepped up their territorial demands, and on February 23 Sverdlov read out their final ultimatum to the central committee. Never had the Bolsheviks been under such strain in the choices open to them as in those forty-eight hours in which they had to decide whether or not to accept this ultimatum. Having lost 2,500,000 people in the three and a half years of war, Russia was now to repay her aggressors with 34 percent of her population, 32 percent of her farming land, 89 percent of her coalfields and 54 percent of her industrial centers. For, in addition to vast indemnities and the demobilization of her army, she was to cede Latvia and Estonia and evacuate the Ukraine and Finland.

It was on this last cruel condition, and on this alone, she insisted, that Alexandra joined the minority of four on the central committee who voted against the seven Leninists and against the peace. There were two abstainers. In the most stressful moment of the Party's life, they waited in the hope that the revolution in Germany would materialize, before accepting peace terms that spelled disaster to all hopes for an international revolution. The Germans continued their advance, the prospects for revolutionary war receded, and as the Bolsheviks sent off their request for peace simultaneous preparations went ahead for the defense of Petrograd. German divisions had remained on the Eastern Front as a precaution against the Red Army, and it was all too clear that Germany did not trust the Bolsheviks' surrender and would remain mobilized to strike.

Formally the treaty was to be ratified by the Party and soviet congresses later in March; in fact it was signed on March 3, 1918—the first paralyzing blow to the Bolsheviks' international hopes which forced them gradually to scale down the vast ambitions of their international strategy to the more modest requirements of internal development. For Alexandra, Bukharin, Pyatakov, and other leftists the treaty meant not only the betrayal of internationalism but the reinforcement of German imperialism with large chunks of profitable territory. The final German demands, she felt, imposed a duty on the soviets to continue battle; inspired by the example of Dybenko, she pressed for a rapid reconstruction of the army in the firm hope that the Party and soviet congresses could be persuaded to reject the treaty. "We shall die, yes, but beautifully," her friend Jacques Sadoul reported her as saying, although these sentiments did not inspire her to accept his proposal to enlist in his volunteer Bolshevik army. According to his fevered imagination, she was in those days the "high priestess of the holy war, impelling the Red Army to shoot forth from the earth to defend the first conquests of the Russian revolution against its external enemies."[28]

On March 2, 1918, Alexandra left the beleaguered capital on her mission to elicit support for the Bolsheviks from socialists in Sweden, France, and England—expecting, as she had done the previous June, to return to the barricades. But in contrast to her mood on that occasion, she left with a heavy heart. As she, Berzin, and Natanson set off for Sweden, their crisp new Soviet diplomatic passports containing not one visa, the thought of missing the Seventh Party Congress, due to open four days later, preyed on her mind.

They travelled by train first to Helsingfors, where they spent a couple of days. At a meeting in the National Theater, organized to pledge support for the Soviet government, she could do little but reassure the Finns of the Bolsheviks' continuing help to the embryonic workers' government which had been born in the early days of the Finnish civil war in January. Their departure from Helsingfors was noted by the American ambassador, who wired home: "Kollontai [sic] and two other prominent Bolsheviks are leaving for Stockholm bent on international revolutionary propaganda: watch them."[29] Had he seen the small damaged steamer that was to take this desperate crew across the half-frozen Baltic to Sweden, he might have saved himself the bother of wiring. The tsarist naval officer in charge refused them an icebreaker, and had high hopes that they would either refuse to go or would sail off to their death. His hopes and their worst fears were justified as huge drifting chunks of ice collided with their fragile boat. By the time they reached the Åland Islands (which lie in the Baltic midway between Finland and Sweden and were then claimed by both countries), they were so badly shaken, and their boat was leaking so dangerously, that they decided to abandon it. That evening as they were eating in an inn gloomily, facing the prospect of being stranded there for some days, a young Finn in their party rushed in to tell them that the Germans had overrun the island.

He smuggled them into hiding, where they were eventually discovered by some Finnish White Guards who took them all into custody and ordered the two Finns with them to be shot. Alexandra and the others pleaded with them for a tense hour or two, and they at last agreed to release one, who was barely out of his teens. As the other was led off to be shot they turned wretchedly for home, their spirits quite broken.

They returned to find the Party preparing to move the capital from Petrograd to Moscow in anticipation of the German invasion. "An evacuation commission was moving the state jewels and the art collection from the Hermitage, and nobody seemed even to notice the return of our unsuccessful delegation. I was the only one among them who felt miserable, for I wasn't used to failing in any task assigned to me . . .," she told a friend.[30] However she had returned in time to speak at the Seventh Party Congress, which opened on March 6—a congress which marked the very high-point of free-ranging debate within the Party. After the Brest-Litovsk treaty had been signed on March 3 and the Germans had established a puppet regime in the Ukraine, the left Bolsheviks in Petrograd had brought out their own paper, *Communist*, in which they reviled the leadership for compromising its revolutionary principles. Lenin's pragmatic opening speech on March 6 did nothing to allay the criticisms of the nine left Bolsheviks on the central committee, including Alexandra, who over the next few years would bring the same limitlessly optimistic perspective to almost every aspect of life in Russia.

With almost half Russia's former territory—including most of White Russia, the northern Caucasus, and the Ukraine—occupied by the German armies, and with local counter-revolutionaries supported by foreign intervention already drawing blood in ominous anticipation of the civil-war carnage, Lenin argued at the congress that to continue the war meant passing the death sentence on the revolution. Without a revolution in Germany, inexplicably delayed but still inevitably certain, the Bolsheviks would perish to be sure, but in the meantime the Soviet state must survive as the best guarantee of international revolution. The leftists then presented their boundlessly encouraging vision of the Russian revolution as a global turning point at which the masses of the world would be drawn irresistibly out of the mire of compromising sophistries toward the banner of anti-imperialism. Bukharin attacked the peace as crippling the energies of the working class, and its defenders as concerned only with party unity. The fragile workers' state would not decline like the Paris Commune, he said, for it had a far greater capacity to experiment: "The organization of the struggle will develop in the very process of the struggle." He was supported in a series of anti-Leninist speeches by Mikhail Uritsky (the prominent leftist central-committee member), Andrey Bubnov, Karl Radek, Ryazanov, and Alexandra, all of whom repeated that Soviet power was worth nothing without an international revolution, and that no defeat was to be as feared as this "obscene peace." The leftists Pyatakov and Yakovleva threatened to resign from the central committee if Lenin's line was adopted; the Party was sailing closer to a split than it had been since 1903.

Alexandra's passionate support of the leftists must have been prompted partly by her anxieties about Dybenko's insubordination and about the physical dangers he must at that moment have been facing. She can have known little about his activities, beyond that he was working underground in the Ukraine with some detachments of Red troops whom he was recklessly planning to lead against the Germans. On the evening of March 7, as the second day of the congress was drawing to a close, she felt impelled to break her usual silence and bring to the discussion some of her own experiences on the Åland Islands:

> Revolutionary will is not hardened in times of peace, or through agita-
> tion, but through war . . . On the Åland Islands I saw German, English,
> Swedish, and tsarist officers all meeting together, and that was enough
> to convince me that the imperialists are uniting against the working class.
> The struggle in our transitional society must go underground to build a
> new army . . . If our Soviet Republic perishes, another will raise our
> banner to defend not the fatherland but the Labor Republic. Long live
> the revolutionary war! [*Applause*]

The government was not a mere receptacle of power, she continued, but
the initiator of experiment. Lenin's plea that the peace would give a
breathing space to the exhausted Russian people was unfortunately nonsense, as the Germans had already taken the Ukraine; it also gave support
to the most savage kind of imperialism, a "breathing-space," as Radek had
said, "only for capitalist investments."

Sentimental and suicidal words, retorted Lenin. So the European
revolution had dared to be delayed, so German imperialism had dared to
attack—all he wanted was some time to rebuild the Russian army: "If you
can't crawl on your belly in the mud, you're not a revolutionary but a
windbag." Faced with Lenin's threat to resign, and thanks also to some
rigging of the Leninist votes, the Brest-Litovsk treaty was formally approved; the Russian Social Democratic Workers' Party was acceptably
renamed the Russian Communist Party (Bolsheviks), and the constitution
was ratified. The leftists' attempt to mark the occasion with a call to arms
addressed to the whole European working class had failed. This congress,
the last to decide an issue by majority vote, took the Bolsheviks one step
closer to centralized one-party rule.[31]

Throughout these proceedings the government was being transferred
to Moscow as Petrograd, the "northern commune," prepared to defend
itself. The day after the congress ended, Alexandra was summoned by a
letter from Bonch-Bruevich, of the evacuation commission, to join other
members of the government on the platform of Petrograd's Nikolaevsky
railway station at ten the following evening. With little time to pack more
than a few things, she left Zoya to clear the flat and move on later, and
with a heavy heart said goodbye to Misha, who was adamant about
continuing his studies at the Petrograd Technological Institute. Misha
moved in with some other students, with whom he lived in communal
poverty for the following three years; Alexandra did manage to see him
every few months, as he visited her regularly in Moscow, often bringing
a student friend with him.

By March 11, 1918, Smolny had been evacuated and the government had moved into the bulky fortress of the Moscow Kremlin—still to be haunted by Ivan the Terrible and a blood-stained list of Muscovite tsars long after the hammer and sickle had replaced the eagle and the musical clock had been rebuilt to chime the "Internationale" instead of "God Save the Tsar." Alexandra and the other commissars were allotted rooms in the Kavalersky building, opposite the Kremlin.

With its thriving black market, its jumble of architecture, crowded streets, and proliferating government departments, Moscow became the center of the left opposition and their short-lived journal, *Communist.* And it was here that the Fourth Extraordinary Congress of Soviets was convened, from March 14–16, 1918, to ratify the treaty, or rather to ratify the Party's decision. All discussion was severely curtailed, the left Socialist Revolutionaries walked out *en bloc,* and Alexandra, who as a member of the Petrograd Soviet executive committee sat on the presidium, resorted to haranguing Lenin in an intermission. As Morgan Phillips Price (the *Manchester Guardian* correspondent fortunate enough to attend the congress) described it:

> Mme Kollontai, Commissar of Social Welfare, bitterly [accused] Lenin, whom she had buttonholed behind the tribune, of treason to the revolution in publishing his theses on the peace. "Enough of this opportunism!" she cried. "You're advising us to do the same thing you've been accusing the Mensheviks of all summer, compromising with imperialism." Lenin, calm and unmoved, stood stroking his chin and looking at the ground.[32]

The leftists were outvoted by 36 to 453, and shortly after this congress Alexandra resigned from her commissariat "on the ground of total disagreement with the current policy."

Apart from the acute distress caused by the Party's attempts to disparage the left opposition, Alexandra's much gossiped-about marriage was bringing her fresh anxieties of both a political and a personal nature. Three months after Dybenko had left for the Ukraine, her leftist views were being contemptuously linked by many party members with his risky adventures in the Ukrainian underground, which by April had come to light and were threatening to put him beyond the party pale. In that month he was arrested by the Soviet government and charged with high treason, a charge, as Alexandra learned to her horror, that made it very likely that he would be shot. He was brought to Moscow as a prisoner.

In this black period of her life she embarked on a frantic campaign to save him. It was a period of which she wrote later in her autobiography, "I cannot treat of [it] here, since the events are too fresh in my mind. But the day will come when I will give an account of them."[33] It was thanks largely to her passionate intercession for Dybenko that he was released in the summer of 1918 from prison after paying his own bail. To the scandals of their marriage, Dybenko's wild behavior in the Ukraine, and Alexandra's support for him was now added a new scandal: Dybenko jumped bail and he and Alexandra, without notifying anyone in the government, left Moscow to visit Misha in Petrograd. There were rumors that several commissars wanted them both shot for desertion, and this trip was most probably the source of the rumor about their lengthy honeymoon in the Crimea. Lenin claimed to have devised the most appropriate punishment for them: they should be forced to live together for five years. Their crime was not after all so great. But Dybenko was expelled from the Party, and for Alexandra, Dybenko's activities and her support of them brought nothing but the contempt and derision of most of the party leaders. Little by little she was relieved of all her party work. Angelica Balabanova recalled that "she was made the object of censure and ostracism and removed from every public post." Some of her duties were offered to Angelica (who refused them), and as she left the central committee her photographs were removed from all the party offices.[34] By the end of that year her commissariat had been absorbed into the Commissariat of Labor. From Petrograd Dybenko returned in the summer of 1918 to the Ukraine to pursue, with a quite indefatigably reckless courage, his campaign to prepare the Russian army to attack the Germans.

14

Civil War

In the months following the peace of March 1918 and in the lulls between the first skirmishes of the impending civil war the left oppositionists turned the same optimistic perspective they had brought to bear on the war with Germany to the problems of workplace democracy. In the spring of 1918 a system known as War Communism was set up with the two principal aims of nationalizing industry and providing the peasants with manufactured goods in exchange for grain (which had to be requisitioned). Production had been virtually destroyed by the war, and a great deal more than slogans for workers' control was clearly needed to hoist industry out of the sabotage and demoralization which had left hundreds of factories throughout Russia abandoned and inoperable. The Supreme Economic Council, headed by such leftists as Bukharin and the old Bolshevik and central-committee member, Ivan Smirnov, and chaired by Lenin, had been formed in December 1917 in consultation with factory committees, with the aim of encouraging people to return to work and getting industry started again. In the following months it laid plans to nationalize key industries and develop capital, to limit the powers of the market, and to hire some of the much needed specialized skills of the bourgeoisie. Many workers, seeing these first tentative steps toward nationalization as the long-awaited signal that socialism had arrived, then spontaneously launched nationalizations in the name of the government, which was as divided in its response to this initiative as it was to all the crises confronting it. Bukharin and the leftists on the Supreme Economic Council believed that the nationalizations should be recognized. Lenin pointed out that the government's precarious negotiations for foreign capital could all too easily be wrecked at this early stage and urged that

313

the capitalist structure of industry should be retained as long as possible, and that workers should merely curb the activities of private capitalists until the state could establish full control over the economy. After the Fourth Congress of Soviets in March 1918 Bukharin and three other leftists were removed from the Supreme Economic Council, which was then directed to induce workers with various wage incentives and fines to return to work and increase production. Late March saw an even greater limitation of workers' control with a government decree on the centralization of the railways, which granted dictatorial powers to the Commissariat for Communication, made it responsible for establishing "iron discipline," and subordinated all workers to its individual executives.

More government and trade-union decrees followed, and by mid-April the issues of workers' control and democracy subsumed all others. On April 20 *Communist* declared:

> To introduce labor discipline so as to restore capitalist management cannot increase productivity, but can only diminish proletarian class initiative. It threatens moreover to enslave the working class, and arouse discontent among the backward elements as well as the proletarian vanguard; to introduce such a system in the face of the prevailing hatred of "capitalist saboteurs" we would have to rely on the petty bourgeoisie rather than the workers.

As Bukharin pointed out, "It's all very well for Lenin to say that each cook should learn to manage the state, but what if a commissar is appointed to supervise and order each cook about?" Lenin reacted with his most vituperative attack ever—the left was a "disgrace"; with this notion that individual workers could control production, they had completely renounced communism and deserted to the petty-bourgeois camp. A party conference was called at the end of April 1918 to demand that the leftists discontinue their independent existence, liquidate *Communist,* and approve Lenin's *Immediate Tasks of Soviet Power.*

The experience of history, said Lenin, had shown that the dictatorship of individuals was very often the vehicle for the dictatorship of the revolutionary class. Development of large-scale industry, the very foundation of socialism, now called for an absolutely unquestioning submission to the leaders of the labor process. In this transitional stage to the new consciousness the new regime must make their priorities the orderly administration and control of both capitalist and nationalized industries, an end to wildcat strikes, and an end to anarchy. With the cooperation of workers and peasants, whose functions would be defined by a chain of command which elected managers and hired specialists, a network of producer-consumer communes would be established throughout the country. To increase labor discipline a great many measures would be needed, including bonuses and special bureaus which would establish the correct production norms for each factory and measure each worker's productivity and labor time with a system of work cards.

Describing itself in one of its last issues at the end of April 1918 as a "businesslike and responsible working-class opposition," *Communist* and its contributors denounced these state-capitalist measures, proposed full workers' control and the communal organization of farming, and rejected any arrangement with capitalism. But by May the left oppositionists, who were in a majority in the Moscow and Urals parties, were rallying to Lenin; as first Petrograd and then Moscow were circled by a ring of enemy fire, they suppressed their criticisms for a while to take on the propaganda work so urgently needed to rouse support for the Bolsheviks. Without any real leadership or consistent program, however, they continued intermittently for several years to attack the Party for its bureaucratic centralization and the commissars for stealing power from the soviets. After April 1918 the main focus of their criticisms was on the dictatorial expedients introduced into the newly formed Red Army by Trotsky, who had reintroduced the death penalty, saluting, and separate living quarters for officers, and had rejected as "politically pointless" the system whereby officers were elected by the soldiers. That summer, as the crisis of war demanded a quick transition to internal socialist policies, many leftists' criticisms were silenced when all enterprises worth a million rubles or more were nationalized. It was not until two years later, in 1920, that Alexandra and other leftists took up their criticisms again and extended them into the consistent and detailed program of the Workers' Opposition.[1]

In May 1918 the civil war began in deadly earnest, when Czech prisoners of war in the Volga region, backed by the British and French governments, rose against the Bolsheviks and signaled a wave of foreign-engineered anti-Bolshevik revolts throughout southeast Russia and Siberia. In the southeast large numbers of Don and Kuban Cossacks had been consistently opposed to the revolution, and the Bolsheviks had not extended their influence beyond such industrial cities as Rostov and Taganrog. By late November 1917 these Cossacks had found a leader in General Kaledin, who had assembled an anti-Bolshevik force several thousand strong. Similar armies appeared, particularly in the south and east of Russia, led by a host of former tsarist generals and admirals, the most prominent of whom were Generals Denikin, Kolchak, Alexeyev, Krasnov, and Lukomsky. These generals were allied politically to numerous liberal politicians, many of whom, like the former Kadet leaders Milyukov and Rodzianko, had held important posts in the Provisional Government.

The White Guards who assembled under the military and political leadership of such men to bring down the revolution represented a large and highly trained fighting force, fully capable of defeating the Bolshevik Red Army, and were supported militarily and financially by England, France, and Germany. By May 1918 the Germans were already occupying Poland, Lithuania, Latvia, west Russia, and much of Great Russia. Moscow was threatened by the Germans from the west and by White Guards from the east; White Guards connected the French and English armies in the north with the Volga, via Yaroslavl and Vologda. In order to survive, the Bolsheviks needed to appeal to people drained and confused by years of war, and enfeebled by their daily half-ounce bread rations, to summon up all their last remaining strength and defend the revolution.

There were other more personal reasons for Alexandra's exhaustion and despair in those first days of the civil war. She had so passionately defended Dybenko that she had cared little about the ridicule to which this campaign had subjected her, or about the mutterings of Lenin and other more conventionally married comrades on the subject of women who entangled their love lives with their politics. Now she began to suffer the painful consequences of her intercession for Dybenko. The charges against him had been serious enough, but they were now complicated by reports of his wildly insubordinate behavior.[2] Rumors about the numerous love affairs that had brightened his life since his departure from Petrograd also filtered back to her and added one more jealous torment to her afflictions. Her pleas that Dybenko, who had played such a heroic part in the October revolution, should be reinstated in the Party had met with little response when in May 1918 she received an assignment from the Party to embark on a speaking tour of the Volga region; this, it was clearly felt, would put a stop to her embarrassing activities on Dybenko's behalf. Besides, the Whites' advance on the Volga basin called for a Bolshevik agitator of her brilliance to inspire the terrified townspeople and the retreating Red soldiers with the courage to stay and fight the White invasion.

It was with a heavy heart that Alexandra took the train north, to Yaroslavl, at the end of May. She stayed there for a few weeks, working on the Bolshevik paper, *Don,* and joining a team of agitators who encouraged soldiers and civilians with literature, pictures, films, and all their powers of persuasion to stay on and continue the fight for the same principles for which they had made the revolution. She then sailed down the Volga on an agitation steamer, leaping ashore at every small town and village to exhort the threatened communities of Kalmyks, Bashkirs, and Tartars to defend themselves; for that summer, as the former tsarist general Kolchak moved his White forces up from Samara, the Bolsheviks were facing the greatest danger of the war. She seized every possible opportunity for a speech, whether jumping onto a peasant's cart to address a crowded market-place, or talking to smaller groups of sympathizers in people's houses. Arriving in Nizhny Novgorod in July, she heard that the German Ambassador, Count Mirbach, had been murdered—allegedly by the Socialist Revolutionaries in the hope of pushing Germany into declaring war on Russia and unleashing the revolutionary war. The truth of this Bolshevik allegation is now thrown into question by our knowledge of the vast sums which Germany was paying out both to the Bolsheviks (who, it was felt, would speedily reduce Russia to chaos) and to their monarchist and capitalist enemies in Russia, in whom the Germans saw the future leaders of a country which they would again be able to exploit economically once the revolution was defeated.

Whether it was the Socialist Revolutionaries or, as some now claim, the Bolsheviks themselves who organized the assassination, it prompted a series of uprisings on the Eastern Front; in July 1918 Bolshevik fortunes were at their lowest ebb. "We're actually dead," said Trotsky. "All we need is for someone to bury us."[3] Alexandra's front-line agitation continued at the same hectic pace, but experience now forced her to admit that a revolutionary war was nothing but a splendid illusion. The army could not possibly be expected to initiate any fighting, despite Trotsky's massive infusions of ardor and discipline—she had only to remember the wounded veterans in her commissariat to be convinced of this. Now all the hopes and desires for a new life which she poured into her speeches were for the reconstruction of her poor, wrecked country.

Leaving Nizhny Novgorod in late July, she traveled 200 miles south along the Volga to Saratov, then another 200 miles south to Tsaritsyn (now Volgograd) and the port of Astrakhan on the Caspian Sea. From there she took an agitation train, complete with slide-shows, literature, medical supplies, baths, and a theater group, which took her and the twenty or so other agitators with her to Penza. Then it was back to Nizhny Novgorod, and in August on at last to Yaroslavl—which they found surrounded by Kolchak's troops. Right until the very last moment, when a savage attack left hundreds dead and yielded Kolchak the town, Alexandra and her fellow agitators stayed to give heart to the defense forces. "We just about landed in the thick of it in Yaroslavl," reminisced an agitator, Vasili Kachalov, in a letter to her afterward. "It was lucky we managed to dash back to Kostroma and return safely to Moscow."[4]

Alexandra did not go directly to Moscow, however, but stopped at the small textile town of Orekhovo-Zuevo, thirty miles away, for she wanted to discover how women were coping on the home front. Women were already beginning to play a part, still tentative and erratic to be sure, in the civil war. On her travels Alexandra had seen them undertaking a variety of jobs, learning to handle rifles, joining women's regiments, and gradually being accepted in male regiments, doing combat duty in times of siege and police work in the towns during lulls in combat. Throughout Russia, and particularly in Odessa and Baku, educated women like her were taking readily to the most dangerous tasks of partisan warfare, and were highly valued—as infiltrators and disorganizers among the White forces—for their espionage work. It was as political workers, however, that such women were most valued by the central Red Army political section, which was coordinated from Moscow by Varya Kasparova, a Bolshevik activist (about whose background, unfortunately, little is known). Kasparova trained countless women to join the kind of agitation and propaganda (agitprop) teams on which Alexandra had worked. The obscene and often anti-Semitic jokes directed by the foreign press against these women had a lasting impact abroad, as Alexandra was to discover several years later when she arrived in Norway, preceded by a reputation for boiling her enemies alive with an icy coolness—a cigarette in her mouth, and a revolver at her belt.[5]

But what of the problems which the vast majority of women in Russia faced—and would still face, Alexandra realized, after the war was over?

> As the struggle became increasingly bloody much of what was happening was very alien to my way of thinking. But after all, there was still the unfinished task of women's liberation. Women, of course, had received all rights, but in practice of course they still lived under the old yoke: without authority in family life, enslaved by a thousand menial domestic chores, bearing the whole burden of maternity, and even the material cares, for many women now lived alone as a result of the war . . .[6]

Vastly greater numbers of them worked too, for although the workforce as a whole shrank during the civil-war years, in which so many thousands of workers were killed, the percentage of women workers increased. But these new responsibilities, potentially so liberating, had only added to women's burdens, and Alexandra knew only too well from her own painful experience how war tore men and women apart, bringing its own disruptive chaos into their family lives.

The women she talked to in Orekhovo formed over half the workforce in that town, housed in the same barracklike conditions that had been such a blot on the industrial landscape of tsarist Russia. There was no town hall or library, the shops were almost empty, and even though the soviet there was gaining strength, she was mortified to discover how little it had actually achieved. The main problem was distribution, and women were hesitant about putting forward their own demands. They had, however, managed to organize a children's canteen, and although they were anxious to do more and desperately needed more guidance from the Party, Alexandra was highly impressed by this first move toward communal feeding; she believed, like many of her colleagues in the Party, that the organization of consumption on a collectivist basis was both a precondition and a necessary attribute of the revolutionary way of life they were attempting to construct. She promised to return to Orekhovo, this time with the support of the Party, to help women organize more canteens and nurseries. She left for Moscow with the sad realization that "the revolution has brought rights for women on paper, but in fact has only made life more burdensome for them."[7]

With the exception of the sensitive and sympathetic party secretary, Yakov Sverdlov, who had helped to organize the Petrograd women's congress in November 1917, few other men in the party leadership had played any organizing or supportive part in the Bolshevik initiatives toward women. *Rabotnitsa* had been closed down in January 1918 because of lack of paper, and had been replaced by women's pages in the party papers; a proposed congress to celebrate Women's Day that year had been rejected as inopportune. Age-old male prejudice had seen Dybenko's crimes reflected in his wife, and since few other left oppositionists were subjected to the same censure, it is to be assumed that her opposition to the peace had been compounded in the Party's eyes by her espousal of women's liberation.

Nor had her tireless efforts on Dybenko's behalf induced him to take a more conciliatory attitude toward party authority. She returned to Moscow early in September 1918, prepared to renew with undiminished passion her campaign for his reinstatement, only to discover that he had left the Ukraine the previous month and had then traveled south to the Crimean town of Simferopol, where he had again embarked on an underground campaign to prepare an armed rising against the Germans. Betrayed by provocateurs, he was arrested once more, this time by General Sulkevich's German puppet government in the Crimea. He was thrown into Sevastopol prison, from which he tried to escape, and after this he was put in handcuffs and leg irons and transferred to another prison. Alexandra was greeted on her return to Moscow by the horrifying news that Dybenko was once again languishing in prison, under strict guard and the harshest of conditions. The horror of this news was compounded by her increased powerlessness to help him; she would not only have to intervene with the Party on his behalf but also persuade them to intervene with the Germans for his release. She managed at last, after many wearying days spent petitioning the central committee, to get an assurance from the party secretary, Sverdlov, that he would negotiate for Dybenko to be saved from death. She went on to plead for his full restoration to the Party, which, given his extreme intractability, did not seem likely.

Perhaps it was partly to remove her from this sour controversy that Sverdlov proposed that she make another agitational trip, this time to the textile towns of the Moscow region, where she would have plenty of opportunity to talk to women. In the middle of September, then, she set off once more for Orekhovo in a train filled to overflowing with men, women, and children who were going to buy flour for the winter months from peasants in the nearby villages. As long as Alexandra had submitted loyally to all the plans of the leadership she had been granted some scope in her autonomous work among women; now she put her hopes in the masses of women who were just becoming politically active, and whose lives were too heavily burdened for them to be deferential to the Party. She thought confidently of Orekhovo, with its history of militancy which went back to 1885 and the first organized mass strike in Russia, which had forced the Tsar to grant the first factory law. It was in textile towns like Orekhovo that women as early as the 1880's had formed such a large and increasingly militant part of the labor force.

She was taken from the station in a phaeton which had been expropriated from the millionaire factory-owning Morozov family and installed in their elegant mansion, now used to accommodate visiting party workers, actors, and opera singers. Her talk that evening on working mothers in the Soviet republic was poorly attended and greeted with a patent lack of enthusiasm, as if her words were only too obvious. As she ate an excellent meal in the workers' club afterward she talked again with the women she had met on her first visit—"Comrade G——va," for example, whom she mentioned in her account of this visit: "a woman of a com-

pletely new type, proud, conscious of her young strength and her rights
—a citizen of Soviet Russia." Fighters and nurses, many of these women
had narrowly escaped death; the woman who had organized her first
meeting had since been killed fighting in the Don region. The subject of
Alexandra's talk was not popular, they explained, because they wanted the
answers to more urgent concrete questions. Why, for instance, did thousands of people have to make pilgrimages for wheat? How, with distribution in its present anarchic state, were women to organize communal
canteens? As Konkordia Samoilova wrote later after working as a propagandist in this area, "Opening a nursery for working women's children in
Ivanovo-Voznesensk attracts far more women to us than ten speeches on
maternity protection."[8] A more puzzling problem for Alexandra was how
to appeal to those not in need of such help, like the elderly woman
working at the Morozov guesthouse, who clearly regarded the party workers who stayed there as usurpers and would have much preferred to serve
her old masters.[9]

From Orekhovo she traveled on to nearby Kineshma, and it was in
the house of a textile worker named Anichkina, over glasses of weak tea,
that plans for a national women's congress were first tentatively discussed.
By the time Alexandra returned to Moscow this plan, which had been
forming in her mind for some time, had matured. What better way could
there be for women from all over Russia to insist that the Party make good
its promises and involve them in the whole social and political life of their
country? She found equal enthusiasm for the idea from Konkordia
Samoilova, Klavdia Nikolaeva, and some twenty other leading women
organizers, who were markedly less hesitant now about her plan for a
separate women's bureau which would convene the congress and carry out
its resolutions. Through Sverdlov they conveyed their request to the
central committee. It was refused. The congress was not forbidden, but
"special women's apparatuses" were just not to be thought of. With
considerable perseverance Alexandra and her friends insisted that without
some sort of party-backed women's organization, local parties could not
be expected to cooperate in the congress. The central committee relented;
a central women's bureau was out of the question, but men and women
party members would be assigned to prepare women in the local organizations for the congress. Many women shared in the confusion which
Alexandra's seemingly modest proposal created. "What, will there be two
parties now, one for men and one for women?" friends of an organizer
called Vera Golubeva asked. Many of the more skeptical women felt that
the meeting was being organized from outside the Party and that the

Bolsheviks were only cooperating in order to expose it as "feminist."[10]

As plans got underway and a date was fixed in November Alexandra felt able to take a week off to visit Dybenko, whom she had not seen for five months. Although this was not the most opportune time to leave her work, personal anxieties sometimes had to take precedence over political responsibilities; she felt too anxious about his future to delay. Thanks largely to her intervention the Soviet government had entered into negotiations with the Germans for his release in exchange for some German prisoners of war, and in late September he had been released from prison in the Crimea. From there he had once again immediately set to work, traveling 600 miles or so north to Vorozhba, near Kharkov in the Ukraine, where he had formed a detachment which he led to Ekaterinoslav, where the fighting with Kolchak was at its height. There, according to one fellow soldier, he not only planned to defeat the Whites but "nurtured the idea of overthrowing the government by force." His truculent attitude toward party authority, which had intensified since his expulsion from the Party in April, worried Alexandra deeply, as well as severely limiting the scope of her own activities, but while she hoped to induce him to take a less intransigent attitude, she was determined to keep some emotional distance from his problems.

At the end of September she traveled 700 miles south to Ekaterinoslav with Podvoisky in his agit-train, and was kept busy writing articles for his army paper, which was distributed to soldiers along the way. She arrived to find the town "still living on its recent battles. The name of Dybenko was on everybody's lips." She managed to persuade him to apply for readmittance to the Party and reported back about the eight meetings she addressed in Ekaterinoslav. Those five days they spent together passed all too briefly, clouded as before by the same jealous torments and fears of separation. "Our meetings were always a joy beyond measure, our partings so full of heart-rending anguish. Yet it was precisely this power of feeling, this capacity to experience everything so fully, so ardently, that drew me to Pavel."[11] She then left for Moscow; Dybenko, transformed by the Ekaterinoslav victory into a hero, went on shortly afterward to Sevastopol as commander of the Crimean army; both resigned themselves to another long separation.

In the early days of the revolution when they had worked together, the conflicts between party work and her love for Dybenko had been exhilarating, for her pride in him as a comrade had been equal to her passion for him as a lover. Now she was feeling increasingly demoralized by her conflicting needs to support her wayward lover in his disagreements with the Party and to pursue her own important work within that Party, work which her support for him was making so very difficult. After she returned to Moscow, she tried to resolve some of these conflicts and find a little peace of mind; the first thing she did was to write to Lenin asking him to restore Dybenko to the Party, allow her to resume her old responsibilities as an agitator, and give his approval to the women's congress. He agreed to get Sverdlov to "cancel the sailor's expulsion," and welcomed the women's congress with a predictably cautious warning against any separate organization. "Thank you so much for your greetings," he concluded. "I for my part welcome your return to more active party work."[12]

Although she did return to more active party work in the autumn of 1918 and tried to push her conflicts over Dybenko into the back of her mind, she did so with the haunting awareness of how fragile their relationship was, how impossible it was for love to survive all the dangers and separations of war. His death-defying bravado which had caused her so much anxiety, the numerous women he had met in the course of his escapades, his tendency to dismiss with a flick of the hand her need to discuss her feelings—all these qualities which had so captivated her in the first year of their love, and had seemed such a sign of his strength, now threatened not only her work but the very basis of her rational world.

But there were other men in the Party besides Dybenko to contend with. By no means were all the leaders as open as Lenin to the idea of a women's congress, and it was bearing in mind the powerfully sexist opposition to the plan from such central-committee members as Kamenev and Zinoviev that she wrote a series of articles "itemizing" plans for women's liberation. In all of these (and notably one entitled "Among the Backward," which appeared on October 31, 1918 in *Communard*) she repeated the traditional arguments that women were the politically "backward section" of the population, in order to justify the struggle for women's liberation with reference to the more traditionally acceptable goal of mobilizing them to support soviet power. In her anxiety to win the Party's approval for the congress she even went so far as to describe Lenin's qualified words of approval for it as the basis of their work: "If the bravest fighter on the civil war front returns home and day after day hears nothing but complaints and grumbles from his wife, he'll see her as an opponent of the struggle for soviet power; her political unawareness can make even the fighter steeled in battle weaken, and if not go over to the counter-revolution, then at least give in to his wife and submit to her harmful influence."[13] Like most party members, she saw the key to women's oppression in household drudgery. But in her articles, and at the congress itself, she went much further than this to urge that if men were ever to be persuaded that setting up nurseries and communal laundries and kitchens required a political commitment to women's liberation, and to accept that this was a commitment worthy of their serious attention, then it must be the women who prepared the propaganda.

On November 16, 1918, red-kerchiefed delegates began to arrive at the small hall allotted to the congress in the Third Moscow House of Soviets on Sadovo-Karetnaya Street. Postal communications were disrupted in those days, and the organizers had received no more than a few hundred replies to their invitations. By that evening over a thousand women, dressed in sheepskin coats, felt boots, peasant costumes, and army greatcoats, had packed the hall and were still arriving. "I remember that when we applied for accommodation for a few hundred people—about three hundred—we were told, 'Don't bother, it's not worth it. You'll never get that many. Plan for eighty and no more,'" Alexandra wrote later. "In fact 1147 delegates came."[14] They also came from all parts of Russia and after long and often hazardous journeys across the war zones they were exhausted and hungry; by that evening voices were being raised against the inadequate food and accommodations. When Alexandra and the others applied to the central committee for extra provisions they were roundly condemned for their inadequate preparations. The rations were eventually increased, however, and the women uncomplainingly ate tiny plates of barley gruel, slivers of bread, and thin soup with minute pieces of dried roach floating on top. Permission was grudgingly granted for them to use the Hall of Soviets after Alexandra threatened that the women would riot and occupy it anyway, and they all moved on to the Kremlin.

The delegates, over a hundred of whom were peasants, settled back comfortably into the red plush seats, and the congress opened amid much cheering and shouting. Klavdia Nikolaeva took the chair, Sverdlov delivered the opening speech, and Inessa Armand launched into a passionate attack on pots and pans and domestic drudgery. She concluded with a call for more communal nurseries which provoked many an anxious cry of "We won't give up our children!" Alexandra stood up then to deliver her speech on the family and the communist state, which was later published as a pamphlet with that title in 1919. First reassuring the women that the new government had no intention of separating them from their children, she went on to insist that until the necessary economic level had been reached and women could be relieved of housework, they must be the ones to push the government into ensuring that the process of replacing the old family was not too painful for them. Although she used the word *communism* rather confusingly to describe both the present realities of the new regime and its future goals, she nevertheless dwelled on the continuing tragic conflicts women faced, torn between the desire to raise their own children and the struggle to realize their social personalities. The workers' state must assume responsibility for every woman, married or not, while she was breast feeding her baby, so that she could fulfil her need to be both a mother and a worker, without one job's detracting from the other.

In the past Alexandra had analyzed sex, marriage, and the family in terms of capitalist property relations, which degraded the "maternal instinct" into the mere reproductive instinct. In the workers' state, rent apart by a civil war which was making the disintegration of the family inevitable and the need for new citizens imperative, the private property of the landed and propertied minority had been redistributed among all the citizens of Russia, whose economic and social well-being now depended on the labor power of the masses. The only assurance of Russia's future prosperity lay in the future generation—the socialist equivalent of capitalist accumulation—hence her emphasis on the social duty of having children. But hence also the possibility of a future in which parents, freed from many of the burdens of childcare, would be able to enjoy not only the company of their own children but those of others too. Then it would be possible to envisage the "union of two members of the workers' state, united by love and mutual respect" in an idealized, purified form of the monogamous relationship, in which women were freed from their economic dependence on men and released from the burden of rearing their children without support from men or the state. The age-old jealous dramas of individual sexual love would, she realized, retain their hold on people long after the economic causes of male supremacy, the isolated monogamous couple, and the old deluded hopes of romantic happiness had disappeared. However Alexandra was honest enough to admit that it might take many generations of men and women to realize the generous and unselfish ideal of the "great love," so she did not claim that in the immediate future, as people struggled to establish more honesty and equality in their sexual relationships, these relationships must necessarily be either monogamously exclusive or long-lasting.[15]

In recognizing this, and thus acknowledging many of her own fears about her precarious relationship with Dybenko, Alexandra was trying to share some of these fears with the women at the congress. Countless women and men had learned to love each other in the early days of the revolution, and almost immediately afterward had been cruelly separated by war. But although for her, as for many others more unfortunate than she was, one of the most devastating effects of the war was the emotional burdens it placed on women, she wanted to assure women that they could learn a new assertiveness and resilience from their experiences. Alexandra's popularity ensured that her speech was warmly applauded, although it was followed by a number of other highly articulate speeches by women delegates who by no means shared her libertarian views on the new morality and would doubtless have preferred for her to have concentrated on the more conventional rights and duties of conjugal love.

Nadezhda Krupskaya, who was on the platform and had helped to organize the congress, kept Lenin informed of the proceedings, and on the third day he arrived quite unexpectedly as another woman was speaking. Failing to find himself an inconspicuous place in the hall, he was at once recognized and greeted with an applause so deafening and so prolonged that he smilingly held up his watch to beg for silence. His speech was unoriginal—a general statement of the Party's determination to abolish housework—but it gave those present such enormous confidence that they all broke into the "Internationale," and a final resolution was passed banning the offensive word *baba* ("peasant hag") from the language.

The proposals with which the congress adjourned were to provide the basis for women's work over the next three years. In order to avoid the dreadful suspicion of separate organization, it was agreed that a commission attached to each party organization would be responsible for conducting agitation among working women. These would be composed of delegates elected for a three-month term by every factory and village who would present women's demands to the local parties and report back their response. Supervising this work would be a central commission, based in Moscow and led by Alexandra, Inessa Armand, and Vera Moirova, the daughter of an Odessa laundress who had recently joined the Party. Their work would be discussed in greater detail at the Ninth Party Congress the following year.[16] *Pravda*'s report of the congress was headed "The Mobilization of Women for the Red Front"; Alexandra's vision, elaborated in "The Family and the Communist State," was rather broader. Her program for canteens, communal laundries, and clothes-mending centers would, she felt, allow women the free time they needed for reading and attending meetings and concerts.

Her new work on the Women's Commission involved many of the responsibilities she had carried as commissar. She worked with Nikolai Semashko, Commissar of Health, as well as Vera Lebedeva, head of her old commissariat's mother-and-baby section, which had been transferred to Semashko's ministry (the rest of her commissariat had been transferred to the Commissariat of Labor). Also working on the commission were Sofya Smidovich, a revolutionary of long-standing who was now more concerned with practical relief for orphans, delinquents, and unmarried mothers than with discussions of the new morality; Alexandra Artyukhina, an active trade unionist and former Petrograd textile worker who had been involved in Alexandra's first women's project, the Women's Mutual Aid Club, which had opened in St. Petersburg in 1907; and Lyudmila Menzhinskaya, an even older acquaintance, with whom Alexandra had worked on the Rubakin Mobile Museum when as populists and teachers in the 1890's they had both embarked on their first political activities. Lyudmila had been a co-founder of *Rabotnitsa* in 1914 and was now a journalist of some repute.

Most of their work involved persuading women that they themselves had to demand that the government provide them with day nurseries, and urging them that their best hope lay with the Bolsheviks. This "agitation by the deed," a guiding principle of the Bolsheviks' work among women, involved endless, exhausting meetings with women who were hungry, confused, and crying out not for more joyous motherhood but for legalized abortions. The filth, inadequate sewage systems, and rampant venereal disease, not to mention the scarcity of doctors and their resistance to performing this operation, all made abortion too dangerous to appear an easily acceptable option.

By December, Alexandra came to dread every new day with its endless round of meetings: "It was not people who were against us," she wrote, "but hunger and passivity." In general, though, women gave her a sympathetic hearing, and there were times (at Petrograd's Zinel printing works, for instance) when she managed to enflame their imagination. "Maybe they understand me because I feel their sufferings so deeply. But this daily struggle with people's moods exhausts me, and I sometimes feel I haven't the energy for one more meeting." She missed Misha constantly and feared that he was not eating enough. Some time at the end of 1918 she received a telegram from him announcing that he was going to pay her one of his brief visits: "He's a student and lives in a commune, and I'm sure he's hungry and cold, but I've nothing to send him and I find this quite unbearable. I'd so love it if we could live in the same town but he's very fond of his student life . . ."[17]

Her own room in Moscow's Hotel National, which housed party workers, was at least heated and lit; but that autumn, as the peasants refused to sell their grain (withholding it for their own consumption) and the most brutal and haphazard rationing started, she shared the universal daily diet of half an ounce of bread and a few handfuls of oatmeal. At least cooking apples were plentiful for a while, and these formed her staple diet. A friend told her that "if you put an apple in the teapot, cover it with boiling water, and leave it under a cushion for a few hours, it will be well cooked and not bitter at all. My secretary Maria Petrovna and I share lunch, some broth and occasionally a potato-peel cutlet, and the other day someone sent me some red caviar, which I shared with the others."[18]

Not everyone shared in this deprivation, as she commented sarcastically in two *Pravda* articles, "The Priests Are Still Busy" and "It's Time To Do Away with the Black Nests." Looking about the streets of Moscow, she wrote, "we see more and more of our own people," and only occasionally, "like some weird anachronism, a fugitive from another world, do we glimpse a warmly clad plump gentleman or a lady draped in furs; but even they look confused, as if asking the working people to forgive them for their existence . . ." How then did the churches continue to flourish, warm and brightly lit? How did the priests pay for their magnificent robes? How was it that trains loaded with flour, butter, eggs, and sugar arrived for them from southern Russia? She concluded that it was because the power of darkness and ignorance which continued to oppress people who had already been oppressed for centuries was still very great; the neutralization of the Church must be one of the most important tasks in making the new life, along with ending illiteracy, feeding children, and arousing women to the common task.[19]

Alexandra's most eloquent reply to those comrades who argued that such moral and ideological problems as these were "merely superstructure" was contained in the three essays that she chose to reprint that winter in one book, *The New Morality and the Working Class.* "Sexual Relations and the Class Struggle," "On an Old Theme" (republished as "Love and the New Morality"), and "The New Woman" no longer seemed so shockingly audacious as they had when first published in 1911 and 1913 (although they still strike us now, reading them more than sixty years later, as original). The crises she had described then were just as relevant to the transitional state of Russia in 1918, and they gave emotional amplification to the social problems and their solutions which she outlined in *The Family and The Communist State.* As she said in "Sexual Relations and the Class Struggle":

> There is no bolt, no defense against sexual conflict . . . The waves of the
> sexual crisis are sweeping over the threshold of workers' homes and

creating conflicts which are every bit as acute and heartfelt as the sufferings of the "refined bourgeois world" . . . One of the tasks confronting the working class as it attacks the beleaguered fortress of the future is undoubtedly that of creating more healthy and joyful relations between the sexes.

And, she continued, they *can* be changed; they can be "based on the creative principles of friendship and sharing, rather than on some mere blind physiological force."

Alexandra was speaking for the exhaustion of everyone in Russia. Industry—plagued by lack of raw materials and deprived of workers, devastating numbers of whom were called up to fight—was grinding to a halt. (Virtually the only functioning factories turned out war materials.) Yet it was precisely this crisis, and the threat of another starving winter, which intensified the urgency of attacking the domestic economy and making its socialization part of the government's entire economic program. Alexandra helped to improvise communal kitchens, applying to the central rationing committee for increased provisions of soup, fish, or meat; and at meeting after meeting she induced people to eat there rather than at home. By 1920 ninety percent of the people in Petrograd were eating communally, and sixty percent of the Moscow population was registered at the communal canteens. Although many of those could not actually be fed (because bad distribution all too often left the kitchens bare of food), this was at least a first step toward separating marriage from the kitchen—a shift as vital as the separation of the Church from the State. Alexandra was also hoping that canteen eating might encourage more communal attitudes in some of the cumbersome aristocratic mansions that had been divided up to provide horribly inconvenient, uncomfortable, and crowded living quarters for working people. Because people generally had to share their lavatories and makeshift kitchens with each other, and often had to share crowded rooms with complete strangers, many such arrangements were described, with some distaste, as "communal houses." In fact they were at best lifeless and uncooperative, at worst extremely squalid and filled with the sounds of angry arguments.

People's lives had been so atomized by capitalism, and they had had so little leisure that they were barely capable of loving, emotional experiences. But, as Alexandra wrote in "Love and the New Morality," "Any emotional experience which is not just the physical act enriches, rather than impoverishes, the soul." Any emotional experience could be "bright and beautiful" if freed from the degrading dramas of bourgeois society, where love is either tragedy or "vulgar vaudeville":

> And yet, when one speaks of sexual morality and the working class, one often meets with the shallow argument that "there's no place for this until the economic base has been transformed"! As though the ideology of a class were built up only *after* the completion of sudden about-turn in social and economic relations which assures that class of its supremacy! The whole history of experience shows us that the ideology, and also the morality, of a social group is created precisely in the course of this group's laborious struggle against social powers hostile to it.

Fundamental to the personal crisis experienced by everyone in Russia, and its most eloquent and painful legacy, was the end of private property (the dominant reason for all bourgeois sexual relationships) and the end of the myth that sexual partners could totally possess one another.

Few Marxists in Russia after the revolution would have disputed Alexandra's assumption, central to her thinking since she first read Marx, Bebel, and Engels in the 1890's, that capitalism had created a competitive ideology based on private property that the role of the bourgeois family was to preserve and transmit capital, and that that of the proletarian family was to reproduce the labor force which was the chief component of that capital. Nor would they have denied that capitalism had created a cleavage between socialized labor (in the factories, offices, schools, and other social institutions) which fell to men, and private labor performed by women in the home. Many in the Party seem to have been less willing, however, to recognize that to this "secondary" labor of housewives and mothers were added all the psychological burdens of maintaining the emotional bond of the marriage relationship; less willing to realize that although it was on the basis of private property that men of the bourgeoisie (and, to some extent, of the working class too) had defended their "individual rights"—their claim to unique possession of their wives—it was precisely this individualism, encouraged by capitalism, which had given rise in the early twentieth century to a new and searching scrutiny of people's personal lives.

Alexandra had recognized this important fact when in 1911 she based her first essay on the subject, "On an Old Theme" ("Love and the New Morality"), on the discoveries of the German writer Grete Meisel-Hess. Without attacking the ways in which capitalism divided and isolated men and women from each other, Meisel-Hess was nevertheless able to assert women's need to express themselves sexually and emotionally outside the confines of the rigid bourgeois family. Every sexual relationship, Alexandra maintained in "Love and the New Morality," must now be subjected to the most painful reevaluation. In 1918, just as in 1911, "the modern lover would sooner forgive any physical unfaithfulness than 'spiritual unfaithfulness,' and sees any emotion experienced even outside a 'free relationship' as the loss of his own personal treasure." Now that bourgeois morality, whereby women's personality was judged exclusively in terms of their connection to their sexual partner, was recognized as degenerate, the new morality must view sexual relationships from the viewpoint of the health of the partners and their possible offspring.

In a somewhat alarmingly confused passage in "Sexual Relations and the Class Struggle," Alexandra then took the argument on from the general area of the new morality to the "specific demands of the human race," envisaging the possibility of "bringing the selection of sexual partners in line with the interests of humanity." The missing link in her argument (connecting the specific present to the abstract future, the needs of the Russian people to those of the entire human race) can perhaps be provided by recalling that when Alexandra first wrote this article she probably envisaged more confidently a worldwide socialist revolution. By 1918 she can have had no illusions that Soviet Russia, isolated and impoverished, could hope to destroy capitalist property relations and the hypocritical morality they engendered; she realized too that the Bolshevik marriage law of November 1917, and the legislation she had helped put through for the protection of mothers and children, were but first steps in the right direction.

Her main purpose in this book was to condemn most of her fellow socialists' indifference to sexual problems, and to insist that there was nothing utopian in desiring a revolution of the human psyche; the proletariat was already evolving as one more ideological weapon in the class struggle its own radically new morality. Since the new marriage law it had become obvious that the great majority of men and women embarking on long-term sexual relationships were not bothering to register their marriages. Despite the immense psychological and material burdens these new freer relationships often imposed on women (and Alexandra herself felt tormented enough by her own feelings of jealousy and dependence in her relationship with Dybenko to understand these problems), she nevertheless felt confident that the old rigid and imprisoning marriage of convenience was at last being superseded by something better. Party activists like herself had much to learn from the working-class principle of comradeship, she felt: a principle which derived its power from a constant process of reeducation. It was through this comradeship, of which middle-class people were generally so ignorant, that untroubled "erotic friendships" developed, in which people's capacities for loving could themselves be developed. Only after a series of such early guilt-free sexual relationships (which had been common among the proletariat, in opposition to official hypocritical morality, for several decades and which must now be welcomed and encouraged) could people experience a "great love, completely free of any dark aspects."[20]

The optimism of this work evidently reflected much of the Bolsheviks' desperate optimism in the grim winter of 1918. Their tentative hopes for the international revolution were renewed briefly in November, when the German working class overthrew the Kaiser and Liebknecht proclaimed the soviet republic in Berlin. Following the collapse of the Western Front in September 1918 there was a mass of strikes throughout the country; the SPD executive and the Reichstag group of SPD deputies together stated their minimum demands for participation in any government, and the revolutionary shop stewards group issued an appeal to the population to rise up and overthrow their imperial rulers. By October the German government was visibly disintegrating under the demands of workers and soldiers for an end to the war, and the following month the SPD issued an ultimatum to the chancellor for the Kaiser's abdication. On November 9 there was a general strike in Berlin, and large groups of armed workers and soldiers thronged the streets. The chancellor, Prince Max of Baden, formally handed over his power to the SPD chairman, Ebert, and an armistice was signed with the Allies: the Russian February revolution was resurrected on the streets of Berlin, and the German radicals, like the Bolsheviks, felt that Germany too would have its October.

As the war ended Red Army fortunes in the civil war also improved, with the reestablishment of control of the Ukraine and the Volga region. Alexandra saw the New Year in as a guest at the Red Officers' Club, where her own activities as an army propagandist and her marriage to the much admired Dybenko (then still in the Crimea) had made her a number of friends. In the club, a former imperial hunting lodge filled with exquisite mirrors and chandeliers, the tables were laid with priceless soup bowls filled with thin watery soup. A small piece of cheese was served as a special rare delicacy to celebrate the occasion, and, particularly welcome to Alexandra's sweet tooth, each guest had one sugar lump through which they sipped their tea. The Red officers, many of them former officers in the Tsar's army, wore service jackets without shoulder-straps, and the women were wearing the kind of dresses fashionable abroad a few years before, with low waists and skirts narrowing to the hem.

Earlier that day the American journalist Louise Bryant had visited Alexandra, asking to be taken to meetings, as she wanted material for her book on the Russian revolution. In those terrible, hungry days Alexandra was as anxious as most others in the Party that foreigners should not witness the hunger, the physical exhaustion and the hostility to outsiders that were inevitable at all meetings. She reminded Louise Bryant of the similarly angry mood which had haunted all meetings during the American Revolution, and, hoping to present her with a rather sunnier picture, invited her to the officers' club. The evening concluded with a concert at which the popular opera singer Gzovskaya moved everyone to tears.[21]

Alexandra retired to the hotel exhausted. The tireless political work and unending personal anxieties of the past year had taken their toll on her strength. For the next three months she was confined to her bed, intermittently afflicted with a serious heart condition which was now diagnosed as angina pectoris.

On January 15, 1919, it seemed as though the fire of the international revolution had finally been extinguished. The German bourgeoisie, represented by the moderate majority in the SPD and leaders like Philipp Scheidemann, had proved very much more powerful than its Russian counterpart, and the remnants of the Kaiser's army had rallied to the support of the counter-revolution. The powerful right wing of the SPD, which had been in control of the situation since November, dared not risk a civil war which might endanger the young republic and allied itself to those former government and army leaders who supported the republic (provided only that it did not change the old social and economic order). By January the SPD majority—the "bloodhounds" of the counter-revolution, as they described themselves—began their attack on the revolutionary proletariat and its leaders.

Rosa Luxemburg and Karl Liebknecht, released from prison by the November revolution, were driven from their underground hiding places in Berlin and given short prison sentences, and then had their skulls smashed by rifle butts in a display of unbelievably savage revenge. Rosa Luxemburg was dragged half dead out of a police car and thrown to the bottom of the Landwehr canal; Liebknecht was shot at close range in the Tiergarten and dumped at the local mortuary.

The German left never rallied after the death of their most inspired leaders, but the Bolsheviks clung to their last remaining hope: the world revolution would take much longer to mature; they would have to play for time and take inspiration from the two who had dared with such inspiring courage to defy the majority in the SPD. Alexandra went into shocked mourning for the death of the German revolution and the bloodthirsty murder of her friends. Rousing herself from her sickbed, she wrote an obituary for Liebknecht—"the heart of the German revolution"—and Rosa Luxemburg—"its brains." The SPD had allied with the police and the Kaiser's army, and "those precious brains were spilled on the roadway . . . But around those graves, which the workers cherish so dearly, new fighting proletarian battalions are already springing up. The Scheidemanns won't succeed in trampling in the mud the revolutionary banner wrenched from the hands of Liebknecht and Luxemburg. Heroes will die, but the revolution still lives!"[22]

This devastating series of events must have considerably delayed Alexandra's recovery, prone as she was to palpitations and insomnia when under stress. She was presumably cared for by her secretary, Maria Petrovna, and Misha probably visited her from Petrograd, but it is unlikely that news of her illness induced Dybenko to make the 900-mile journey from the Crimea to Moscow. In February 1919 she had to undergo heart surgery, which confined her to her bed until March. She certainly did not lack visitors in her convalescence, and several women from the women's commission brought flowers and stayed to talk. An American journalist named Marguerite Harrison (from the *Baltimore Sun*), who later wrote a book about her experiences in Moscow, visited and found her "utterly chic and charming, in an exquisite boudoir gown of green velvet, trimmed with sable" (this was probably expropriated from some aristocratic wardrobe).[23] The Russian-born American anarchist Emma Goldman, also visiting Russia at that time, came too, casting a critical eye at the vase of roses on her dresser and noting that Alexandra's wardrobe appeared to have survived the revolution.*[24]

By March 2 Alexandra was well enough to attend the historic but sadly impotent first founding congress in Moscow of the Third (Communist) International, the Comintern. Without permanent staff or offices and lacking any serious support from the world communist movement, the Comintern in its early days in the spring of 1919 was still little more

---

*Apart from one essential piece of clothing, a fur coat, which she had been wearing for over ten years, and from which she had made herself a hat, Alexandra's wardrobe was not so very extravagant; most of her clothes she had probably received from friends or through expropriations.

than an idea in the minds of the Bolshevik leaders. Since the defeat of the German revolution its president, Zinoviev, had continued to broadcast from his base in Petrograd optimistic assurances to communists all over the world that the Soviet republic would survive, and that it would support the world revolution in every possible way. Hopes revived briefly, later in March, when the Hungarian prime minister resigned and was replaced by the Soviet protégé, Bela Kun, and the optimistic mood was sustained in April when Munich launched a short-lived soviet regime. But for most of those present in Moscow for the founding congress of the Comintern that March (the delegates represented the radical minorities of the various socialist parties), the Bolsheviks' assurances could not but ring somewhat hollow. The new government was hardly in a position to foster national revolutions actively, and its role was confined merely to moral support and encouragement. Alexandra delivered a short speech calling for more women's involvement in the Comintern.

She returned to the women's commission, after three months in bed, to find that Sverdlov himself was ill: women were now deprived of their most loyal support against the prevailing hostility to their work. During Alexandra's absence Inessa Armand had proposed a most enterprising method of encouraging women to become politically active and confront this hostility; at women's meetings that winter, attended by factory and handicrafts workers, housewives and seamstresses, delegates had been elected to serve for three months as "apprentices" in various Soviet and government departments. There they had learned how the government worked and how it could best work for women, and had become involved in all the numerous tasks of reconstructing their country.

On March 16 Sverdlov died, and with him went many valuable records of the revolution which he had stored in his brain. The monumental calm of this truly brilliant organizer, who had devoted himself for the past two years to the cause of party unity, belied a deeply passionate idealism, which was well expressed by the unhesitating support he gave to the women's movement. Alexandra and her friends mourned the loss of one of their firmest allies in the Party, and she recorded his death in a deeply appreciative obituary.[25]

It was symptomatic of the organizational mania of the Eighth Party Congress, which met two days after Sverdlov's death, that it was thought necessary to create an organizational bureau (the Orgburo) to keep the party records and supervise the staffing of party organizations, as well as a political bureau (the Politburo), which consisted of a small group within the central committee empowered to take urgent political decisions which would only later be reported back to the central committee. Zinoviev's bold words as the congress opened—"Any comrade who considers it necessary to steer the Party and Soviet ship in another direction can speak up; that is their right"—deceived almost no one: with these two new organizations it was now the central committee that would be firmly in control of all the assignments and policies of the Party. Few of those present, however, realized that the man nominated as liaison officer between the two new bodies—Josef Stalin—would in the years following build his own phenomenal power on the complicated political machine that was slowly beginning to take shape.

The left oppositionists, well aware that legislation was being engulfed by the executive powers of the commissars and party bureaucrats, proposed that the central committee be expanded from fifteen to twenty-one members and elevated into a truly proletarian collective. But neither these committee reshufflings nor the inspiration behind them were of any real consequence. Their proposal was accepted, and the central committee promptly developed its own inner circle, which retained and strengthened its power to make decisions. And since this inner circle was formed largely of conservatives such as Zinoviev, Kamenev, and Rykov, who had opposed Lenin in 1917, there was considerable support for Kamenev's argument that with the "trust" of the working class the central committee could grant itself dictatorial powers: "Each decision of the higher jurisdiction must be absolutely binding on the lower. Each decision must be fulfilled, and only after this is an appeal to the proper party organization permissible."

Revolution had raised the question of whether to run factories on the lines of the democratic autonomous communes envisaged by the leftists, or with the "scientific" management, labor incentives, and discipline proposed by the majority. That spring, as General Kolchak marched westward toward the Urals and the Eighth Congress met to discuss the emergency social and industrial measures now known as War Communism, the leftists deferred many of their previous idealistic aims. Bukharin and several others actually regarded falling production as a sure sign of the breakdown of the old system, and even welcomed the centralized industrial "chief committees" which controlled production: since these were run not by individuals but by administrative *collegia* of the type Alexandra had introduced into her commissariat, the committees, with their high level of trade-union participation, appeared to many leftists to signal the first transitional stage to the communist economy. It was against the bureaucracy in the Party itself that a newly formed group who called themselves the "democratic centralists" now inveighed. Their target was the local party committees, which had been transformed recently into "political departments" exercising rigid control over all the industries and military institutions in their jurisdiction.

All the party leaders except Lenin, Zinoviev, Bukharin and Sverdlov had had military tasks thrust upon them in the civil war, but few of them had shown such an eagerness to combine military and bureaucratic methods of work as did Stalin. Appointed before the revolution in October 1917 as liaison officer between the army and the Party, and assuming after the revolution the post of Commissar for Nationalities, this apparently modest and quiet man had by 1919 acquired more influence as the instrument of an increasingly centralized Party than most party members could at that time have imagined possible. The "political department" which he perfected in that year in the Donets Basin was the first and the best organized, and it was the model for the many other departments which were set up throughout 1919 to transmit propaganda downward, to curb opposition, and to improve production and military performance.

Attending the Eighth Congress as a delegate of the women's commission, Alexandra had planned in the main discussion of the Party's program to attack in its name these bureaucratic excesses and at the same time call more positively for the withering away of the nuclear family:

> Lenin read my amendment, and from his face I could see he didn't approve. "What do you mean by the disappearance of the nuclear family? Where is it stated what sort of family will exist under communism? A program now, that's something tangible. We've got to start with practical necessities—we have in fact to *save* the family and protect it from collapsing, especially now. What are you in such a rush for? We'll be able to settle all these problems when we've dealt with the Whites. Put away your amendment and write an article for the time being. We can discuss this properly later."[26]

Since a great many of the people she talked to at the congress were only too anxious to agree that her proposal laid too much stress on problems which must await Russia's economic development, she abandoned it, and instead based her long speech on the thousands of letters received by the Women's Commission from women all over Russia, begging for material help and support. The Party would have no success in recruiting women with general political appeals, she said; it must instead tackle all the burdens of family life which deprived women workers of the time and energy for politics. To make Soviet construction a reality and remove the debates of this congress from the realms of abstraction, the Party must give priority to drawing less active social groups into its program. "We have to conduct a struggle with the conditions that are oppressing women, and emancipate her as a housewife and mother. This is the best approach toward women—this is agitation by the deed."

She then added her own specific criticisms of the bureaucracy insofar as it threatened the women's organizations. There was no need for more bourgeois "specialists," for "there are already far too many petty-bourgeois elements who are alien to us." Only the politically educated working-class woman, with her healthy class instincts, could educate men to reform and rebuild the disintegrating family. In deference to Lenin, Alexandra avoided calling explicitly for the death of the family, urging instead that if communal living and eating were properly organized, they would soon prove so popular that the individual household would die a natural death; if it were possible to abolish the family overnight, she felt sure that most women would approve.

Her words were given serious attention, and her speech was circulated, along with some specific proposals for work among women: each party committee should ensure that its organizational meetings were attended by delegates from the Women's Commission, and political education courses for women should be set up.[27] The resolution which followed on this speech of hers committed the Party to giving every support and encouragement to the work of the Women's Commission.

Hovering over all these urgent discussions of future social and economic policies, however, was the crisis in the Ukraine. That winter the Germans had been beaten back and the Bolsheviks had established their own government in Kharkov. Fiercely opposed for a variety of political and emotional reasons by many Ukrainians, this government—and the related issue of Ukrainian independence—forced the Bolsheviks to assess the prospects of the international revolution once more. Many leftists argued for Ukrainian autonomy in the interest of the greater decentralization of the Party, but many others, including Bukharin and Pyatakov, insisted that the Ukrainians' struggle against capitalism was inseparable from the Russians'; Lenin's argument was that the Russian Communist Party must for the present try to retain control over all the former territories of the tsars. Toward the end of that month, as General Denikin's White armies fought for the towns of the Donets Basin and General Kolchak swept down from the Urals to the Volga, many sank their disagreements with Bolshevik policy in the desperate fight to save the Ukraine from the Whites.

At the end of March, Alexandra was sent off to the southern front with a number of younger party workers whom she was to train in the art of front-line propaganda. She was particularly happy to accept this assignment, since it would be relatively easy for her to travel from the Ukraine to the Crimea, where she might once again meet Dybenko after their five-month separation. She arrived in Kharkov, where she met Konkordia Samoilova, who had headed south to lead the first party-based women's movement in the Ukraine. Traveling up and down the Volga on the *Red Star* agit-steamer, Konkordia had become an extremely popular agitator, inspiring many women to support the Red Army by making bandages, nursing soldiers, and joining in volunteer defense work. Alexandra's popularity there had preceded her arrival, and it was gratifying for her to see her slogan—"Be a mother not only to your own child but to everyone's children"—on posters around the city. She worked with Konkordia Samoilova for the next two months, extending the focus of the Women's Commission to engage women in the war effort. She wrote several articles for the Ukrainian *Izvestia*, including "What Are We Fighting For?" and "The Struggle With Tsar Hunger," and she also addressed a number of women's meetings to persuade party members and unpaid volunteers to set up and staff women's groups. When numerous women complained that their work was constantly hindered by the contempt and apathy of their male comrades, she could only refer them to the resolution passed at the party congress.[28]

In May, Alexandra was presented with an impressive sealed parchment mandate from the Ukrainian Communist Party, and she set off south with her team of about twenty young agitators in an agit-train elaborately equipped with projectors and literature. No sooner had they left Kharkov than their journey was brought to a halt by skirmishes and sabotage. Their magnificent train was shunted onto a siding and connected to an immobilized engine, and they sat for a day in unendurable frustration as trains thundered past in the direction they wanted to travel. Their parchment mandate was powerless against the stationmaster's sabotage, and their threats to telephone the Kharkov government to order that he reconnect them were equally powerless against his insistence that their engine was overloaded; besides which, as they all knew quite well, telephones were barely working. Eventually they were connected to a slow freight train, and their journey continued on its laborious course south.

At every town and village along the way, many of which were just a few miles from the front, they stopped and talked, on platforms, in squares, and in meeting halls. They met rich peasants preparing to entertain Denikin and shouting "Death to the communists!"; they met anarchist communities "vying with each other in the democratic slogans they proclaimed"; and finally, passing through countryside devastated by Denikin's armies, they approached the smoke-blackened villages, immense factories, and furnaces of the heavily industrialized Donets Basin. It was in Kadievka and Makeevka, in the mining communities of Golubovka and Shakhty—there, where the miners' lives were one long infernal subterranean struggle—that Alexandra and her companions at last felt the real power of the resistance. It was there too that the fiercest battles were anticipated. After going down a mine at Golubovka, she was just launching into a rousing speech in the town when a Red soldier ran up and firmly ordered her to stop speaking. Denikin's forces were approaching, a train was waiting to take her and her team north, and the meeting dispersed as the sounds of gunshots approached the town. The guard who checked their papers doubted that their train would get through.[29]

The cumulative exhaustion of the past few hazardous weeks suddenly overwhelmed Alexandra. Her heart had been weakened more than she had been prepared to admit by her three-month illness, and she had not fully recovered her strength when she undertook this grueling campaign. Oblivious to the battle and everything but her own tiredness, she fell asleep. Their train collided with another, and she slept on. When the others finally managed to wake her, she looked out to see the tracks covered with blood and wounded people; they quickly lifted all the casualties into their compartment, discovered to their great relief that nobody was seriously hurt, and tore up towels to make bandages. Alexandra was able to give those in pain some of her own valerian and bromide heart-drops and then, reassuring herself that everything possible had been done for them, she fell back into a heavy sleep. She was awakened again at six the next morning. The peace of the fresh spring fields was broken by shouts and curses: the railway line was blocked by several trains going back and forth from the front, the stationmaster had disappeared, and the workers were ordering the passengers out to push the trains. Leaping onto the platform, Alexandra harangued the workers until the stationmaster was found. The line was eventually cleared, and they made their way back to Kharkov.

They arrived there at the beginning of June, just as the city was preparing desperately to defend itself; Denikin's troops, supported by the British and French, were drawing even closer. The Ukrainian Communist Party had been disbanded and had gone underground, and most party workers had returned to Moscow. Alexandra herself managed to get posted from the Ukraine to work in the political department of the besieged Crimea, where she would at last be reunited with Dybenko. In this same month, June 1919—a month after Denikin had swept away the Soviet Crimean Republic—the Bolsheviks proposed that the economic, military, and government organizations of the Ukraine, the Crimea, Latvia, Lithuania, and White Russia be directed by the Bolshevik government in an attempt to unite these republics in their struggle against the Whites. A new soviet government was formed in Simferopol, headed by Lenin's brother, Dmitry Ulyanov. Dybenko was Commissar of the Army and Navy there, and Alexandra, as head of the political department, was to be in charge of Red Army propaganda. Her journey from the Ukraine to the Crimea was fraught with dangers: "There are endless obstacles on our route," she noted as her train passed through the Crimean town of Melitopol, "which takes us through areas devastated by the Whites. You never know what's ahead, whether the enemy is lying in wait or has blown up the next bridge. Will we get through? I don't know, but our troops are holding up well . . ."[30]

It was in that short stressful month in Simferopol before Denikin landed on the Crimean coast that Alexandra and Dybenko rediscovered the happiness that they had first experienced together in the summer of 1917. Their work was harassed and hurried, their lives were threatened; but it was just such dangers, and the courage and comradeship they found within themselves to cope with them, that brought out the best in their relationship. Working closely with Dybenko, Alexandra used every means she could think of to inspire the Crimean people to struggle against the Whites, to continue the struggle underground if they were invaded, and meanwhile to engage in the practical work of setting up sanatoria and orphanages. Herself inspired by the campaigns for enlightenment and against banditry initiated in the Ukraine by Kristian Rakovsky (that brilliant and humane Bolshevik who had been president of the soviet government there), she organized political courses for soldiers, addressed countless meetings, wrote leaflets, and encouraged women to support the Red Army. Even as Denikin advanced she refused to admit the possibility of defeat.

Few, it seemed, shared her optimism, for "at commissars' meetings they discuss military questions and never get as far as discussing anything else. And at party gatherings, it's how to transfer party work to an illegal basis, how to save cadres, and how to save money. It seems it's not worth setting anything up now—it's just a question of how long we can survive."[31]

Convinced that not enough effort had been made to talk to people outside the big towns, Alexandra made a week-long propaganda tour of the spa towns along the Black Sea coast, explaining the policies of the Soviet government and contrasting these with the banditry of Denikin and all the other capitalist-backed armies. As a girl she had regularly taken the waters in these little spa towns, and she had particularly fond memories of Gurzut, where she allowed herself to take a short break. From the hotel of her childhood holidays she heard once more the splash of the sea and delighted again in the garden and its magnolia trees. But these pleasures were overwhelmed by a sudden sharp memory of suppressed mourning, for on the wall there was a photograph of her beloved sister Jenny and an obituary which described in unbearably painful detail the last ten years of her life as a singer. "It's five years since I heard of Jenny's death, but the wound hasn't healed yet and I don't want to touch it, for it's still so very painful . . . She died without us—oh, what a solitary, patient, touching person she was . . ."[32]

Alexandra returned to Simferopol to find the government preparing to evacuate. The night before Denikin landed, she was drafting an appeal in the name of the Soviet government urging people to work underground against the invaders and assuring them that they would eventually have their own government. At 5:00 A.M. on June 23, the government met to evacuate, for Denikin had landed. "We had no plans to defend Simferopol," she wrote in her diary. "The hour of evacuation had come, though we had held out to the very last moment. Dmitry Illich [Lenin's brother] left with us in our compartment—he had become very ill and his nerves were quite shattered."[33]

It took Alexandra, Dybenko, and the rest of the fleeing government a week to reach Kiev, and once there Alexandra was appointed Commissar of Agitation. Dybenko was made Commissar of the Army, and they moved with other party workers into Kiev's Hotel Continentale. Working happily together, they both enjoyed the magnificent opportunities for propaganda work offered by the Ukrainian Party, and made a number of trips around the region in two splendidly equipped agit-trains. When Alexandra had visited Dybenko in Ekaterinoslav eight months before, she had been there very much on his terms, as his wife, committed to supporting him and subordinating her own needs. In the summer of 1919 they worked and lived together as equals, and despite knowing that they would inevitably soon be parted again, Alexandra was happy.

Vera Moirova was in Kiev, sent south by the Moscow Women's Commission to organize women's activities there, and Alexandra embarked on a bout of voluminous writing. She started on a history of the Russian women's movement, published the following year in Kharkov, and wrote several articles for the Ukrainian press, including "Whose Will the Golden Harvest Be?," "Women Workers and Peasants and the Red Front," "Don't Be a Deserter" and "Be a Firm Fighter." These were turned into pamphlets which she distributed on her agitational trips around the countryside and at meetings in the city. "How happy I am to be doing creative work again," she wrote in her diary on July 7, 1919. "The soviets' power is going from strength to strength, even though Kiev is threatened."

It was in this contented mood that Alexandra and Dybenko greeted N. Ravich, a writer and journalist who visited them at their hotel— probably to discuss helping them to organize classes for the Red soldiers. They took him with them to the Kiev park, where they sat amid the ripening apple and cherry trees, gazing quietly down at the river Dnepr and inhaling the scent of the lilacs.[34] There were few such opportunities to forget the Whites' noose tightening around Moscow and Petrograd. As Denikin prepared to march on Moscow via the arms center of Tula, and Kolchak appointed his subordinate, General Yudenich, to march on Petrograd, Kiev prepared for invasion. This added new urgency to Alexandra's work in the city's newly opened and desperately overcrowded children's and orphans' homes, which were ably organized by a young Ukrainian Bolshevik woman named Valentina Dyushen. Her growing fears of the battles ahead were reflected in her pamphlet *Be a Firm Fighter:* reassuring men of the Bolsheviks' commitment to care for their families and citing the children's homes they had established, she entreated them to fight to the last drop of their blood, promising eternal glory to those who died for liberty and the power of the soviets, and eternal shame to the deserters.

Insubstantial promises perhaps, but one fourteen-year-old girl called Galina Serebryakova described later how the soldiers, hostile to Alexandra at first, were gradually won over by her "strong voice, her artistic diction, the intelligent and intelligible way she assured us of the value of all we had already accomplished, and the enticing picture she painted of the future, after the war was won."[35] She herself was baptized by this fiery rhetoric into the women's movement. Stopping Alexandra after a meeting to ask for literature on the women's question, she was invited back to drink carrot tea at the hotel, and there she was urged to read Bebel, Zetkin, Armand, and Luxemburg. "It's not enough just to win our full rights," Alexandra told her. "We've got to catch up spiritually with men."

By the end of August the Red Army was preparing to retreat from Kiev. Dybenko received orders to leave for the south to rout Denikin's army from the Caucasus, and Alexandra helped to arrange for trains to take 400 people, mostly women and children, out of the city. Equipping herself with a false passport and the uniform of a White Army nurse, she said goodbye to Dybenko and accompanied Valentina Dyushen on the laborious two week journey back to Moscow. The prospect of another long separation from Dybenko filled her both with dread and with relief. The thought of waiting once more for six or eight months for just one brief meeting with him made her groan. Yet she must have welcomed the prospect of being free once more to live her life without dramas. Before, she had imagined that she gave him strength to withstand all the days of pain, the fear, the fever, and the bullets at the front. Now she was beginning to know him better, and know that as he followed each new surge of the revolutionary battle it was for him like falling in love again. Each time they separated, he seemed to need her less than he needed some quiet loving wife to whom he might return in the brief time he snatched from the battlefield.

On the way back to Moscow she had little time to fret. The first part of the journey was a steamer trip 150 miles up the Dnepr river to Gomel; all along the route they stopped at one town after another, as Alexandra and several of her companions jumped ashore to explain, again and again, that the Red Army would soon be returning. The slow train from Gomel to Moscow made frequent stops, which provided the same opportunities for improvised speeches on station platforms; the Reds' retreat was only temporary, she repeated, they would return.

In September 1919 Alexandra returned to Moscow and her room at the Hotel Nationale, near Red Square. She spent most of her time that month at the headquarters of the newly established Women's Department, the Zhenotdel. Alexandra's speech, and the ensuing resolution, at the Eighth Party Congress in March had prompted such a flood of complaints from women that their work was being undermined and undervalued that the status of the Women's Commission had at last been elevated into a nationwide party-sponsored department, led by Inessa Armand, who had long been arguing (considerably more quietly than the flamboyant Kollontai) for a woman's bureau on the German model. It came as a surprise to many people that Alexandra had been bypassed as director of the Zhenotdel and had been assigned a subordinate position as the representative of delegates working in the countryside. This was a post which carried little responsibility, since the Zhenotdel had not yet elaborated any adequate program for the women of the peasantry.

The Zhenotdel, like the German bureau, had a centralized hierarchy; women workers in regional parties were assigned to work for it, and their activities were coordinated by the new journal, *Communist Woman.* One of its first jobs was to ensure that every group of factory inspectors included at least one woman, who could detect whether or not laws were being properly observed, higher standards of hygiene were being introduced into the factories, women were being protected from night work and overtime, and the needs of pregnant women were being adequately met. Its main task, in other words, was to enforce all existing Soviet legislation and extend the declared principles of sexual equality beyond the paper they were written on. Inessa Armand became ill, exhausted by the burden of her work with the party secretary, Krestinsky, with whom she arranged for the training of Zhenotdel workers. Women's conferences, she felt, could be an invaluable method of political education. The most reliable and energetic of the women who attended these conferences could be transferred to a soviet or government agency, and there, supervised by Zhenotdel instructors, they would be trained to take part in government. After a few months, such a woman might either move on to some government post or return to her old job, where she would be an example to her friends. In this way, she stressed, women would be involved in socially useful work as well as being released from the burdens of housework. But these ambitious aims were limited by the strict proviso that the Zhenotdel was to be a temporary organization and that where women's groups seemed spontaneously to be taking on a permanent character, they were to be disbanded.

The Zhenotdel delegate, with her red headscarf and shabby clothes, was soon a familiar and popular figure in every village and town in Russia, as she trudged from house to house, often taking abandoned children into her own home, and when necessary picking up a rifle and leaving for the front. Alexandra was responsible for many of the decrees issued in the winter of 1919–20 on the organization of Zhenotdel bureaus in the provinces, and by the time the second conference of provincial Zhenotdel organizers met in Moscow in March 1920, it was stated that bureaus had been established in virtually every province in European Russia. On her return to Moscow in the autumn of 1919 Alexandra was so inspired by the meetings which local delegates were organizing to discuss women's health problems that she proposed that the Zhenotdel seriously tackle the problems of prostitution and venereal disease, which had been exacerbated by the war; most of the women she talked to, however, in these days before penicillin, felt that the problem was beyond their capacity to solve. A commission was set up to study this issue, but it remained dormant until Alexandra revived it the following year.

In the autumn of 1919, as the civil war dragged on and party leaders urged again and again that the only hope for the Russian revolution lay in the international communist movement, a second Comintern congress was planned for the following June. Alexandra's main work after she returned to Moscow in September was to help Inessa organize a conference of Communist women which was to coincide with this congress. In the course of this work she and Inessa Armand came up against such depressingly negative responses from the trade-union leaders that she felt compelled to petition the political organization within the central committee—the Politburo—on the "pressing question of the relationship between trade unions and the women's sections, in view of the heated discussions which are disrupting our work."[36]

But work itself disrupted so much else. She had not seen Misha since the beginning of that year (and even now had not the time to visit him), and she was beginning now to look back on the past two years and realize with a new and painful clarity how hopeless and emotionally draining had been her struggle to find emotional security with Dybenko; each new meeting had raised her hopes, and each parting had dashed them and left her feeling emotionally bereft and vulnerable again. "Dear sweet Khokhlya," she wrote to Misha that September:

> I can't tell you how much I want to see you and talk to you. I wanted to take a few days off to dash to Petrograd and visit you, but no sooner did I arrive here than I was inundated by urgent work that had to be done for the First International Communist Congress of Women. It's the same old conflict all over again: my heart longs for you but work holds me back. And so I must button myself up tight so as not to let my desires disturb my efficiency.[37]

Twice evacuated in as many months, Alexandra shared much of the grief that the dangers and dislocations of war brought into so many people's marriages. Not only was it becoming increasingly obvious to her that she would never really be able to share her life with Dybenko; she was constantly haunted by her own feelings of guilt, by the uneasy suspicion that he wanted her to follow him, be a proper conventional wife to him, give him everything. She often felt too that he was overawed by her self-confidence and wide learning, for he was often jumpy and insecure in her company. It was probably at this time that she wrote the first of many (undated) letters to him in which she apparently tried to convince herself of their inevitable parting by first convincing him. "Now I realize that I can never make you completely happy. One part of you feels comfortable and happy with me, but another part of you feels oppressed. I'm not the wife for you, for I'm a person first and a woman second, and that's all there is to it . . ." Their relationship did not end in the autumn of 1919, but continued to disintegrate slowly and painfully over the next four stormy years.

By October, Inessa Armand and Alexandra were ill. Inessa continued to write speeches, send letters to delegates, and see to all the organization of the Comintern women's congress until she was too ill to know what she was doing. Alexandra was soon confined to her bed, delirious with typhoid. There she remained for several months, as the fever attacked again and again and was followed by a blood infection, acute recurring nephritis, and her old heart trouble.

15

The Crisis of
the Revolution

In the autumn of 1919, as Alexandra lay semiconscious, the whole of the Ukraine fell to Denikin; Orël was threatened, Petrograd was in mortal danger, Kolchak controlled Siberia, the British army had established governments in Estonia and Archangel, the French fleet was in the Black Sea, and independent Russian armies (the "Greens," for example) ran back and forth between the Reds and the Whites, eating the bread of both. But the greatest danger of all for the Red Army, deprived of food, boots, and hope in that terrible autumn, was the scourge of typhus, cholera, and hunger and the absence of any prospect of peace, after six unrelieved years of war. From 1918 to 1920 7,500,000 Russians died from famine and epidemic. The number of those killed by the Red and White forces is harder to calculate, but the Whites' mass killings of workers and Jews were almost equally balanced by the Reds' systematic attack on speculators, saboteurs, corrupt officials, the aristocracy, and the bourgeoisie. Alexandra estimated that of 73,858 women fighting in the Red Army, some 1850 were wounded, captured, or killed.

Nurses were in such acutely short supply that Alexandra is unlikely to have received anything but the most minimal medical attention, but she was probably visited by her many friends in the Zhenotdel and by Misha too from Petrograd. In contrast to her own bleak existence in Moscow's Hotel Nationale, how enviably secure the married life of so many of her comrades must have seemed to her. If before falling ill she had steeled herself for a separation from Dybenko, how much more she must have needed him in her illness. It is quite probable, however, that he neither received her letters nor knew of her illness, for shortly after they had gone their different ways in September, he had been appointed to lead the Thirty-Seventh Infantry Division on the southeastern front. Letters travelled slowly and were all too frequently lost, and Dybenko had thrown himself passionately into his new military responsibilities. For one reason or another, then, he did not visit her in Moscow that terrible autumn as she hovered between life and death.

The peasants' cautious and eventually hostile attitude toward the new government did not imply any consequent support for the Whites, and it was their refusal to feed and accommodate the White forces that, incredibly, began to turn the tide of the war in the Bolsheviks' favor. The industrial workers, despite starvation and indescribable suffering, did on the whole remain loyal to the Bolsheviks, and 700,000 citizens of Petrograd, under the passionate and inspired leadership of Trotsky, threw themselves into the defense of the city. On October 21 the battle for Petrograd was won at Pulkovo Heights, and everywhere Bolshevik defeats were turned into victories—at Voronezh, in Estonia and Siberia. Many in the government now began to hope that the precarious peace treaty which was being negotiated by the great powers at Versailles would collapse and that world revolution would break out.

Those involved in this victory knew better than any its devastating costs. Through the upswing in the Bolsheviks' military fortunes, Trotsky's focus shifted from the crises of war to those of the economy. Symptomatic of the tensions and divisions which the new economic plans introduced into the Bolshevik ranks in the winter of 1919 was a party conference (the eighth), which proposed a scheme to ensure the Party's majority in every organization and union, and a congress of soviets (the seventh), where some ninety percent of the delegates opposed such a measure and called for the Party's control over the factory committees to be lifted. In December Trotsky submitted his *Theses on the Transition from War to Peace*, which demanded a drastic, although temporary "militarization of labor." Lenin gave his support to this scheme, which amounted to party control over every material and personal aspect of millions of workers' lives and let loose an avalanche of protests. There was widespread hostility to Trotsky. But these protests were against the policy itself and were not formulated as a criticism of the party mechanism that allowed such decisions to be made from above.

The following month the "general regulations for universal labor service" were introduced; under the terms of this "labor conscription law," anybody could at any time be called up and assigned a new job in another town, to "deal with the consequences of public calamities." As the civil war ebbed away, the Party showed no inclination to soften the drastic measures of War Communism. On the contrary, labor efficiency was even more firmly equated, in true bourgeois fashion, with one-man management. Lenin even went out of his way to stress that this management was to be appointed by the ruling (i.e. working) class, although this was of course taken by most to mean not the working class at all, but the Party.

At subsequent major trade-union and Supreme Economic Council meetings opposition to the scheme gradually died away. A new group of left oppositionists and "democratic centralists" now gathered strength to support a demand for collective management which was advanced by a leading member of the Central Trade Union Council, Tomsky. The somewhat vaguely defined target in their attack on the government and the Supreme Economic Council was that body's burgeoning bureaucracy —responsible, in their opinion, for the unrest in the unions—which was to be removed by increased (and equally vaguely defined) inner-party democracy.

The Supreme Economic Council had been formed in December 1917, as a sort of economic cabinet representing all the commissariats and numerous workers' soviets. Its powers were, theoretically, immense. It had the right to confiscate and requisition property and food supplies, and to issue orders on economic affairs which were binding on everyone, the government included; it was responsible for the long-term organization and planning of state finances; and as nationalization of industry went ahead throughout 1918 and 1919, the various departments of the Supreme Economic Council took control of the nationalized sectors of the economy. But as this body had been established to guide and coordinate the economy not to organize production in the factories, it was only a few months after its formation, as we have seen, that it was coming into conflict with the unions and the government. By 1919 it had already sprouted so many subsidiary organizations attached to local factories and specific industries that the resulting bureaucratic chaos was described by one observer as little better than "administrative partisan warfare."[1] The chief object of the unions' criticism, however, was the important role within the Supreme Economic Council of the technical specialists. The vast majority of these "specialists," whose skills were so badly needed by the new government as it struggled against economic disorganization and collapse, had of course acquired these skills under the old regime. Most of them, bourgeois in origin and by temperament, had only with the greatest reluctance agreed to work with the new government and showed little concern for the day-to-day concerns of the workers, who bitterly resented their presence in the factories and their power over the government.

As opposition to this government crystallized around the issues of the power of the "specialists," one-man management, and the militarization of labor, an opposition movement more firmly based than any previous one gradually emerged as the Workers' Opposition, aptly named as the only genuinely proletarian response to Trotsky's proposals. Led by Shlyapnikov, now chairman of the metal-workers' union, and by other dissident trade unionists and democratic centralists, several leftists on the central Trade Union Council began to assert their authority over this council, and its authority over the Supreme Economic Council; their purpose was to turn the Trade Union Council into an independent center in which the unions could share power with the various party organizations.

This proposal was approved in late March 1920 at the Fourth Congress of the Ukrainian Party, which was to provide the embryonic Workers' Opposition with many of its members. It was at the beginning of that month, however, at the Ninth Party Congress, that it was first discussed in detail.

Lutovinov and Shlyapnikov, with the prestigious metal-workers' union behind them, were able to deliver their theses on the trade-union question with considerable force. Control of each branch of industry must lie with the production unions, nationally represented by the Central Trade Union Council, they insisted; more explicitly there must be a three-way separation of power among the Party, the workers' soviets, and the unions. These proposals were endorsed by the democratic centralists, who argued that since military, soviet, and union affairs inevitably fell within very different spheres of influence, to apply methods from one sphere to another could only produce a most painful clash of cultures. "Syndicalist contraband," retorted Lenin—nothing short of a proposal for a party within a party. The collective principle was "utopian, impractical and dangerous." At the previous party congress he had stated that the organization of industry must be in the hands of the unions. Now, he said, their task must be to explain to their members that only with a minimum of workers' participation in management could the shattered economy be rebuilt. Election must be replaced by selection. This provoked the old Bolshevik Smirnov to demand pertinently why the government did not in the interest of consistency go ahead and practice one-man management on itself.

Joining the defenders of workers' control with her own criticisms of the government and its authoritarian attitudes was a Zhenotdel worker named Martynova. Women's work was continuously obstructed by frivolous and contemptuous attitudes toward women. "When I raise this question at this serious party congress, it brings a smile to your faces; that smile indicates an attitude toward the organization of our work which will later affect its results." Specifically she criticized party workers' blind obedience to the Moscow center, which meant that Zhenotdel workers were generally selected quite randomly, without any regard for their commitment or competence, and with the sole purpose of fulfilling the formal directives from the party center on women's work. Trade unions and soviets had an equally cavalier attitude toward the subject, she added.

Martynova's resolution, calling on the Party to "turn the most serious attention to the work of the Zhenotdel," was approved. But since the Party considered the first priority of this and all other organizations to be the "tasks of production," the resolution hardly implied any radical commitment to improving the status of women, or granting the Women's Department any more democratic election procedures.[2] On the contrary the new nine-member Orgburo was now empowered by the Ninth Congress to transfer party workers from one job to another at its own discretion. The same message was repeated at a trade-union congress the following month by Trotsky, who was now Commissar of Transport as well as of Defense and had the full support of the Politburo (the other nine-member body established at the Eighth Party Congress) in any measure he wished to enforce.

Shlyapnikov left Moscow shortly after the congress for the Caucasus, where he organized a worker's school; the Workers' Opposition gradually took shape throughout that year, gathering support both there and all over Russia.

Encouraged no doubt by Shlyapnikov's criticisms, Alexandra now gathered enough strength to leave her bed. It is possible that Dybenko had by this time received her letters, and that fearing she was dying, he had left the Crimea in February in order to visit her. But it is more probable that he returned to the capital on his own business. After the army under his command had defeated General Toporkov's White Army corps in south Russia, his troops had then gone on to play a major part in the Bolsheviks' capture of Tsaritsyn. When he returned to Moscow in February, his heroism was rewarded by a new appointment, as commander of the First Caucasian Cossack Division. Before leaving to take up this new post in the Caucasus, he urged Alexandra to take a convalescent holiday with him in his native Ukraine, and although she was still very weak and thin, she agreed to accompany him to Ekaterinoslav. After leaving him the previous autumn, she had been resolved to end their relationship, but she was now too weak and unsteady to contemplate leaving this man who was so full of energy and hope and, despite all their differences, so very devoted to her.

She left Moscow in March, determined to leave behind her responsibilities and to rest. But it proved to be hardly the holiday she so badly needed:

> For some reason this always happens to me. I went to Ekaterinoslav for a holiday, but people were soon coming to visit me from all sides with their problems and requests. There were women from the local *zhenotdel,* and simply women who wanted advice about their divorce or their children; there were peasants with complaints about the requisitioning, and sick and wounded Red Guards petitioning for increased pensions . . .[3]

Her happiest memory of this holiday was of the studies she embarked on with Dybenko. Usually in the past it was she who had been the teacher, she who had carried so many of the emotional burdens of their relationship; on this occasion they both decided to acquaint themselves with the history and science of warfare. Alexandra found herself recalling the times when as a child she had so eagerly read her father's military manuals. "We immersed ourselves in various military textbooks, and became familiar with all the strategies, tactics, and concepts of war," she wrote. For a brief period they managed to bury the old suspicions and differences. But when Dybenko persuaded her at last to visit his family in the nearby village of Lyudkov, she became more painfully conscious than ever before of the contrasts in their backgrounds which made the class differences separating them so unbridgable. She resigned herself to the fact that "of such contrasts is my life composed"[4]—but recognizing this fact did not make it any easier to bear. Dybenko's mother, a simple, kindly woman now old and widowed, had worked as a day-laborer and instilled into all her seven children a thorough hatred of the landowners. She observed the saints' days and tended the icons in her bare whitewashed hut, and was evidently overawed by her new daughter-in-law. The moment they arrived a stream of peasants from the neighbouring cottages arrived to peer at Dybenko and his bride. They stayed no longer than a couple of days.

Alexandra then accompanied Dybenko to Kislovodsk in the Caucasus, where he was to take up his new post. There she met Shlyapnikov, who was organizing a Party school for workers. She was deeply impressed by the way these workers were being taught to articulate their needs and grievances, and throughout the spring and early summer of 1920 she taught a number of classes there. This teaching, which she combined with work for the local Kislovodsk Zhenotdel, enabled her to escape from the oppressive atmosphere of the house in which she lived with Dybenko. For it seems that with his important new army post he had been allocated a luxurious mansion in which she was expected to live very much on his terms, as his wife. A sanctuary for him, this domestic life rapidly became a prison for her, and her own feelings at this time reflected the broader fear that as the civil war drew to an end women in Russia would lose much of the freedom they had experienced in the past three years and would be forced back into the old isolation of the nuclear family.[5]

Three articles which she wrote in Kislovodsk appeared in *Communist Woman* in June 1920. The first was on the first women's conference of the Second Comintern Congress, then taking place, which she had helped Inessa Armand to organize the previous autumn before she fell ill. The other two, entitled "Labor Conscription" and "The Protection of Women's Labor," dealt with some of the issues confronting women as the civil war ended. Women, whose labor had been conscripted in the war effort and whose part in winning that war was recognized by all in the Party, now had to consider the best way of urging the government to consider their needs after victory. As increasing numbers of Red Army soldiers returned to swell the unemployment in the towns, women could all too easily lose everything they had gained if they did not insist that labor be reorganized to suit their needs. Alexandra realized how natural it was that people whose lives had been so tragically disrupted should long for some stability in their family lives. But she realized too that until Russia had the resources fully to collectivize women's labor in the home, this stability could only be gained at the terrible cost of reinforcing all the old traditions of the family as an institution in which men had authority over their wives and women were isolated and trapped in mindless drudgery.

Although admitting the necessity for some "capitalist techniques" in industry, Alexandra insisted that these be strictly subordinated to a central economic plan which granted men and women equal opportunities for work. This plan, as well as the "correct distribution of labor" (labor conscription, in other words), could only be fully realized when people's demands were organized collectively and the bourgeois family was replaced by more communal living arrangements.[6] Her chief hope, therefore, was that women's continued involvement in production would have a dramatic effect on their consciousness and confidence, and would help to free them from the vestiges of fatalism and ignorance which so tenaciously clung to them from the past. Women's release from the private family was not only an essential precondition of their liberation; of equal importance, in her opinion, was the fact that all the labor hours women spent on housework were unproductive and of no value to the economy. It was only when women contributed these labor hours to social production in the factories that the material conditions for creating socialism could be said to exist.

Alexandra struggled against continued exhaustion, insomnia, and palpitations to write these articles and to continue her work for the Zhenotdel. In June 1920 she gave up the struggle. She suffered a bad heart attack and remained in bed in Dybenko's house, too ill to consider working and too weak and helpless to struggle any longer against her feelings of dependence on him. Eventually she recovered enough strength to leave the Caucasus for Moscow, and the moment she arrived she went into the hospital for a second heart operation. Returning to her hotel room she suffered another bad attack of typhus, complicated again by blood poisoning. She did not leave her bed until September, when she emerged to speak briefly but passionately to the Ninth Party Conference on the issue of free speech and criticism.

"Comrades," she said, "there should be a guarantee that if in fact we are going to criticize, and criticize thoroughly, what is wrong with us, then people who criticize should not be sent off to a nice sunny place to eat peaches. For this does often happen, comrades, as we know." She went on to speak, from her experience at the Zhenotdel no doubt, of the local party officials who changed the orders they gave their subordinates without informing the party center, for fear of being accused of deviations from official policies. "Long live criticism!" she concluded, "but let us not have to eat peaches afterward!"[7]

Shortly after this congress, in October 1920, she attended two funerals. It was only after Inessa Armand's tragic death at the age of forty-six, only two years younger than Alexandra, that she and the other friends of this brave and uncomplaining woman learned of the sixteen-hour day she had worked at the Zhenotdel, planning almost singlehanded its work in the Moscow region and, against all odds and opposition, organizing the Comintern women's congress that summer; of her impoverished, lonely existence in one small cold room; and of her anxieties about her five children—the four eldest had been working in other cities, and the youngest, a fourteen-year-old schoolboy, had been staying with friends of hers in Moscow. Only occasionally had she complained about the cramped

Zhenotdel headquarters, running off to work in the unheated Rumyantsev public library to avoid the noise and clutter of the Vozdvizhenka Street offices ("Our comrades, especially in the Zhenotdel, do so love to chat"). Since Klara Zetkin was ill, she had drafted all the proposals for the Comintern congress and presented them, and by the time it was over she was so exhausted by her lingering illness that she had left Moscow with her youngest son to take a holiday in the Caucasus. There she had wandered restlessly about the mountains, a book under her arm, acquiring an obsessional desire for loneliness and a total incapacity to rest. It was there, in September, that she caught cholera from some evacuees and died.

On October 11 Alexandra joined the central committee and Inessa Armand's many friends at the Kazan Station, where the coffin was met and taken in procession to the soviet building. It lay in state for twenty-four hours. The next day her body was escorted to the cemetery by a procession of women and students, softly singing the "Funeral March." As the ashes were being interred at the Kremlin wall, Lenin appeared, his face almost covered by a thick scarf to conceal his tears. Many party members knew of the unconsummated and enduring love the two had had for each other before the revolution, but Alexandra, who had first met Inessa Armand in 1911 in Paris (shortly after she had moved in with Lenin and Nadezhda Krupskaya), had understood more clearly than most others the reasons that had forced her to move away from Lenin after they returned to Russia in April 1917 and assert her independence. "Lenin never survived Inessa's death," she confided to a friend seven years later, "and it precipitated the illnesses which were eventually to undermine him too. When they brought her body from the Caucasus and we accompanied it to the cemetery, Lenin was almost unrecognizable. He walked with closed eyes and we thought that at any moment he might collapse."[8] Alexandra's novel A Great Love, which was published in 1923, treated this passion, some claimed, with inexcusable imaginative invention.

That same month John Reed's ashes were also buried at the Kremlin wall. This great American journalist and socialist, founder of the emerging American Communist Party, whose book Ten Days That Shook the World provided one of the most vivid eyewitness accounts of the Bolshevik revolution, had traveled south to Samarkand in the summer of 1920 for a conference of Asian communists. Passing through a market there, he had bought himself a watermelon, bitten into it, and died shortly afterward, one more victim of the great typhus epidemic which ravaged the Russian population throughout that year.

By 1920 he had begun to ask embarrassing questions about the growing bureaucratization in the Party and the government's suppression of all criticism. Alexandra's friend Louise Bryant, who had also traveled from America to Russia as a journalist shortly before the revolution, had met him there and married him. She wanted his body returned to America for burial, but the Soviet government, recognizing the political importance of a state funeral in Moscow for him, persuaded her to agree to this. She was too wracked by grief and tears to speak at this funeral, which was attended by many of his foreign communist friends, including the exiled American anarchists Emma Goldman and Alexander Berkman. Among those who did speak there, "only one person dwelled on the real Jack Reed, and that was Alexandra Kollontai," recalled Emma Goldman:

> "We all call ourselves communists, but are we really? Don't we rather draw life's essence from those who come to us, and when they're no longer of any use to us, let them fall by the wayside, neglected and forgotten? Our communism and our comradeship are dead letters if we don't give ourselves to those who most need us. Let us beware of such communism, for it slays the best in our ranks, and Jack Reed was one of the best." Kollontai's sincere words displeased the high Party members. Bukharin knitted his brows, Reinstein [the elderly American socialist] fidgeted, and others grumbled; but I was glad of what she had said.[9]

As Alexandra spoke Louise Bryant collapsed face down on the damp earth of the open grave. Alexandra, Emma Goldman, and several other mourners managed to rouse her from a dead faint, and took her, sobbing hysterically, back to her hotel. The funeral dispersed. The leaden November skies opened and it poured with rain.

Despite persistent heart trouble, high blood pressure, lingering fever, and the anxieties stirred up by the deaths of Inessa Armand and John Reed, Alexandra returned to work. An armistice with Poland had just ended the civil war, but it could bring little rejoicing. The railway lines were filled with immobilized and rusting stock, the factories were deserted, the mines in the Donets Basin were flooded, people's houses had been burned, bridges had been destroyed, and shops were boarded up. Everyone except the foreign journalists the Bolsheviks wanted so desperately to impress suffered the pangs of hunger. But even foreigners were moved to tears by what they saw. Dora Russell, a young socialist (married to Bertrand Russell) who was later involved in the birth control movement in England, visited the Soviet republic in that year and was unbearably saddened by the factories, with their "silent machinery, the workers drilling themselves in industrial techniques, the pride in invention, all against the background of battle and hunger . . . ' "It's all my own invention," said the White Knight'—this sprang immediately to my mind."[10]

As the Whites receded from the south the agonizing aftermath of war increased Russia's misery and chaos. Bandits roamed at large. Groups of specially appointed party workers were dispatched to the provinces to seize grain—and detachments of Red soldiers would just as regularly follow them as angry peasants refused to forfeit their grain supplies in exchange for worthless pieces of paper money. Throughout the summer and autumn of 1920 the Red Army suppressed one peasant rebellion after another. In the cities workers living close to starvation and subjected to the further violence of labor conscription were in an angry and rebellious mood. Increasing numbers of them rallied to the Workers' Opposition, convinced that the wretchedness of their lives was caused, in reality and in law, by an uncaring and bureaucratic party. Emma Goldman asked a group of workers how the government was to meet their demands, with food shortages so acute. " 'Food shortages?' the men exclaimed. 'Look at the markets! Do you see any food shortages there? Speculators and the new bourgeoisie, that's what the matter is! One-man management is our new slave-driver; first the bourgeoisie sabotaged us, now they're back in control. But just let them try to boss us, let them try!' "[11]

With the great illegal black market—not to speak of Moscow's open black market on Sukharevka Street—corroding the country's few remaining resources and corrupting peasants, workers, and bureaucrats alike, the Bolsheviks in the last months of 1920 made a frantic leap into wholesale nationalization of all firms still privately owned. "Sowing committees" were sent out to the villages to control by decree the sowing and harvesting on 20,000,000 individual peasants' holdings, peasants were rewarded for increased yields, and the government authorized physical attacks on the *kulaks* (the rich peasants)—a category which nobody in Russia then or subsequently was able to define. (Lenin merely stated that party workers on the spot would be able to recognize a *kulak* immediately without any trouble: a man who had bought a horse for forty-five pounds of grain, for instance, must be a *kulak*).[12] All these measures indicate the desperation of Bolshevik thinking at that time, a desperation which leaped at quick solutions and short-term responses, and against all odds regarded the continuation of war policies as providing a short-cut to communism. It was in this spirit, in November 1920, that a law legalizing abortion was passed. Alexandra, who rejoined the Zhenotdel as its new director in that month, had only played a minor part in drawing up this law, but she, like most party leaders, regarded this as a liberating and long-overdue measure.

During the civil war too many women had been resorting to dangerous illegal abortions for the problem to be ignored any longer. Half of these women had suffered serious subsequent infections, an estimated four percent of them had died, and the operation was still justifiably regarded as highly dangerous. For although the Commissar of Health, Semashko, had effectively raised standards of hygiene in Russia and had encouraged the Red Army to do battle against the dirt and disease endemic in the war-torn countryside, most medical services were provided by volunteers whose qualifications were minimal. Just as available contraception was too inadequate for any birth-control program to be realistic, so the dangers of abortion in a country where one doctor served an average of 5000 people were considerable. It was partly for this reason that Lenin described the law passed that November as an "inevitable evil," and not to be regarded as any conscious attempt to change family policy. As early as 1913 he had emphasized that "freedom from medical propaganda is one thing, the social theory of neo-malthusianism is quite another," accepting abortion as a necessary health measure, but dissociating himself from the reactionary Malthusian implications of the powerful pro-abortion lobby that developed at that time among doctors and criminologists.[13]

Russia was still too poor and lacking in material and educational resources for contraception to be made available to the great masses of the people. Moreover, added to the old fears which Lenin had expressed before the First World War—that bourgeois governments might try to prevent the socially "inferior" classes from breeding—was now a new fear: Russia had lost some 11,500,000 of its citizens to famine, epidemic, and war, and many in the government were expressing their alarm that if the birth rate continued to fall, the country would soon be seriously underpopulated. Most Bolsheviks therefore, although anxious to abolish the old legislation which had outlawed abortion and the hypocrisy which had banned information on contraception, were guided in their attitude toward abortion, as toward most of their other pieces of remedial social legislation, by the desire to remove its causes: to make both motherhood and work genuinely possible for all women, so that they were no longer forced by the terrible strain of their double work-load to risk their lives in dangerous operations or abandon their children to the streets.

However, poverty and other economic priorities prevented the new government from going deeply enough into the sort of measures required if this ambitious ultimate aim was to be realized, and these served as the excuse which allowed many merely to ignore the problem. Economic backwardness, combined with a long-standing resistance to the "social engineering" ideology of the early European birth-controllers, blinded the Bolsheviks to the truth which now seems to us so self-evident: that an essential component of woman's liberation is her control over her fertility. The law was described as a "transitional health measure, demanded by the surviving moral standards of the past and the difficult economic conditions of the present." Alexandra too seems to have regarded it in this way, although she did at least have a clear picture in her mind of how communism, with its state-supported nurseries, would encourage parents to share the responsibility for other people's children, and so gradually make abortion one more painful option women could put behind them. Now that Russia had recognized free abortions in state hospitals as women's "elementary democratic right"—the first country in the world to do so—she believed that the Party must initiate widespread public discussion of the new sexual morality. In the sexual effervescence of the post-revolutionary years thousands of men and women—many of them mere teenagers, many of them previously married—were eagerly embarking on "free liaisons." Free of the Church and free often of economic dependence too, these liaisons were all too often destroyed by the age-old problems of jealousy, male arrogance, and irresponsibility. People must now be encouraged to define themselves and their needs in the new Soviet society. Otherwise the revolution would collapse.

Alexandra was clearly speaking for her own needs. In July 1920 Dybenko had commanded the Second Cavalry Division on the southern front in the Caucasus, where he had successfully routed Denikin's forces. He returned to Moscow in the autumn (just as Alexandra was returning to the world again after her long illness) and, encouraged by her to continue the military studies they had embarked on together earlier that year, enrolled as a student in a preparatory course at Moscow's Military Academy. The housing situation was desperate, and Dybenko clearly had no desire to live in Moscow's Hotel Metropole, where most Red Army soldiers and sailors lived in unparalleled squalor, without heat or light and with only the most rudimentary cooking and washing facilities. He moved into Alexandra's modest room at the Hotel Nationale, and whatever tensions there already were between them can not have been eased by this new life of theirs, in which they were in such extremely close daily contact with each other. There were evidently domestic problems too. For beside the fact that Dybenko preferred a life in the saddle, on the move, and sleeping under the stars to a dull civilian existence in a hotel, he was also used, as an army commander, to much better food than the standard gruel and two-ounce daily bread rations, which hardly bothered Alexandra at all. It is highly likely also that there were far more serious emotional conflicts between them; to judge from the highly autobiographical fiction which Alexandra wrote later, Dybenko distressed her greatly by sleeping with at least one young woman (possibly even her secretary) who came to visit.[14]

But this shared life did have its compensations, and Alexandra was never utterly despondent so long as she had work which absorbed her. Misha managed to visit more frequently now from Petrograd, and the hotel room was always available to anyone else, including her secretaries and several women from the Zhenotdel, who might need it. These crowded conditions in which she and her extended family lived together made life cheerful, although frequently exasperating. "We're very crowded here," she wrote in her diary in November:

> At first we were allocated only one room, but we eventually managed to fight for another. There are five of us, Pavel, me, my secretaries Maria Petrovna and Ekaterina Vasilevna, and either Mishulya visiting from Petrograd or a typist clattering away for hours on end. I have no space to myself, but these are unimportant details which we're literally barely conscious of. The Zhenotdel, its success and work, overshadows everything else . . .[15]

This work involved Alexandra and her co-director, the veteran Bolshevik and worker Vera Golubeva, in numerous trips to the Orgburo, which supervised the staffing of all party organizations and thus controlled the posting of Zhenotdel workers and decided the priorities of their work. There they discovered to their horror that they were expected to sit through lengthy meetings at which women's issues were placed at the bottom of the agenda. When they protested, they were merely asked to wait outside until the discussion came round to the women. Almost more serious than this, however, was the generally unpleasant attitude toward women which prevailed among the Orgburo members. "They jokingly refer to us as *centrobaba* and *babkom*," Alexandra complained in her diary. The insulting word for woman, *baba*, banned from the Russian language at the First All-Russian Women's Congress in 1918, was still widely used by many men and was guaranteed to infuriate every self-respecting woman. As Kondordia Samoilova, an organizer of that congress, wrote in 1920, most men in the Party still regard women's work as "beneath their dignity," and were little concerned about the prejudice which dogged every campaign. The women's organizations became increasingly isolated in their struggle to promote enlightenment in the midst of economic collapse, so that before Alexandra could think of pushing for a campaign to deal with the desperate problems which forced so many women into prostitution, she had to plead her case at some length at the Commissariats of Justice and Social Welfare.[16]

In March 1917 one of the Provisional Government's first reforms had been to abolish the grim "yellow tickets" by which the tsars had sanctioned the prostitution rampant in every poor street, public bar, and dancehall. Apart from this, nothing had been done to help these wretched women, who became objects of such deep disgust that after March 1917 "indignant citizens formed local committees and raids on brothels took place. The women were arrested and thrown into labor camps—and still prostitution continued."[17] This continued throughout the summer and autumn of 1917, when John Reed observed "prostitutes in jewels and expensive furs, walking up and down, and crowding the cafés," and Praskovya Kudelli watched in horror as "women and girls, hardly more than children, carried on with painted faces, half-drunk eyes, and cigarettes dangling from their hands."[18] It was one of the most extraordinary features of the October Revolution—and a fact marked by countless foreign observers—that as the propertied classes were forced to flee the country and withdraw from public life, the prostitutes vanished too, virtually overnight, from the streets. Hotels, cafés, bathhouses, dancehalls, and other trysting places were nationalized and many prostitutes were conscripted into labor service; it was only as the civil war drew to a close that women, often victims of the new "free marriages," abandoned by husbands or lovers and unable to support their children, took to the streets to solicit for their survival. The new marriage law had failed to ensure that men provide their spouses with alimony; many were too poor to do so, many of them moved on to other towns to serve in the army or the factories and formed new ties, and the majority had no desire to change their old irresponsible ways.

One of the first things Alexandra did on joining the Women's Department in November 1920 was to revive the dormant commission which she herself had formed at the end of 1919 to fight prostitution. Although street prostitution was still relatively insignificant in its proportions, she foresaw the time when economic crisis might prompt even larger numbers of women to see it as the only option open to them. Her main aim, outlined in an article for *Communist Woman* and elaborated in a book entitled *Prostitution and Ways of Fighting It* which came out the following year, was to tackle the constraints which forced a woman into a long- or short-term relationship with a man for financial reasons.[19] The Zhenotdel commission, in collaboration with the government, stipulated that all women found prostituting themselves on the streets would be taken along to the Commissariat of Labor, where they would be encouraged to attend courses of study, helped to get jobs, or sent to recuperate at sanatoria. Only if a woman was repeatedly found guilty of prostitution would she be sentenced to a term of hard labor. "There is no special culpability attached to prostitution," said Alexandra to Louise Bryant, who (though still in distraught mourning for her husband John Reed) worked with her on the commission. "They are in no way to be segregated from any other kind of labor deserter. This is a revolutionary and important step we have taken, worthy of the first workers' republic in the world."[20]

Helped by Louise Bryant, Alexandra organized a series of meetings to help women of the streets to find work and medical attention. Just as important as these practical measures, in her opinion, was the need to help these women to gain some self-esteem, so that they might realize not only that prostitution was a form of labor desertion which damaged everyone in society but, more importantly, that it undermined the solidarity women must feel for each other if they were to improve their lives. Many of her experiences on this commission (and possibly some rather more painful personal experiences with Dybenko) were revealed in a short story she wrote in 1923, "Sisters." In this story she depicted with a touching honesty the friendship which developed between a woman demoralized by her profligate bread-winning husband and the prostitute whom he has brought back to the house. As they learned to trust and respect each other, the two women realized that the life of the prostitute was little worse than the caged life of an economically dependent wife. Leaving her husband and her home, the narrator of the story struck out for a life of independence; an independence which despite its terrifying uncertainties was nevertheless infinitely more genuine and hopeful than her former passive and depressing life.[21]

The new morality would arise from the new economy, wrote Alexandra in *Prostitution and Ways of Fighting It.* But there could be no "new economy," created as it must be by men and women working together as equals, if men did not cease to regard women as their inferiors and if women did not struggle to change their own feelings of inferiority.

Work with prostitutes combined naturally with all the other tasks of the Zhenotdel. With the help of Vera Lebedeva, who had been responsible for the mothers-and-children department of her commissariat (which department was now part of the Commissariat of Health), Alexandra arranged and led talks, discussions, lecture courses and popular poster exhibitions on childcare. Dora Russell, who had visited Russia to see for herself the great Bolshevik experiment, was taken by her to one exhibition, where she saw posters explaining the proper care of a child and displaying mothers and children of every nationality (black and white) in an iconlike depiction of infant mortality rates. Alexandra told her, "The care of children and the matter of child labor are not immediately being considered by the men comrades." (Russell observed that "she had stressed the importance of ending child labor, but there were many who felt this would have to wait until better times.")[22]

Alexandra encouraged local Zhenotdel delegates to send peasant women to Moscow. There they were made welcome, given food and accommodation, told how to care for their babies and prevent disease, and instructed in Russian political affairs. "A woman who has gone to Moscow from some remote village is more or less of a personality when she returns, and you may be sure that her journey is a great event for the whole village," Alexandra told Louise Bryant. "She always goes back well equipped with literature and educational posters, and she naturally stimulates an interest among everyone in her community in matters of politics and hygiene—and especially among the women."[23]

There seemed no end to what she did in the winter of 1920. "Sometimes I am so exhausted that I fall asleep the moment I get home and sit on the sofa; but after ten or fifteen minutes I'll be at work again."[24] At the end of December she attended the Eighth All-Russian Congress of Soviets at the small lecture theater of the old Polytechnic building in Moscow and was once more elected to the Executive Committee. The delegates must commit themselves, she insisted, to drawing women into the unions and government departments and ensuring that local soviets encouraged women to organize nurseries and all the other things needed to reduce housework. "If they take my wife away from me, then I can't work!" one man in the audience shouted to her. Nobody was taking his wife away, she assured him. Women were already working outside the home, but they now had three jobs to tackle: that of factory worker, wife, and mother.[25] The resolution was passed in what she described with considerable pride as a "major victory," but after all most men in the Party were only too quick to recognize the liberating principles of doing away with housework, and Lenin had written most eloquently on the subject:

> Notwithstanding all the liberating laws that have been passed, woman continues to be a domestic slave, because petty housework crushes, strangles, stultifies, and degrades her, chains her to the kitchen and the nursery, and wastes her labor on barbarously unproductive, petty, nerve-wracking . . . drudgery. The real emancipation of women, real communism, will begin only when a mass struggle (led by the proletariat in power) is started against this petty domestic economy . . . Do we devote sufficient attention to this question which, theoretically, is indisputable for every communist? Of course not . . .[26]

These admirable sentiments removed women's liberation to a rather more distant future than Alexandra was prepared to accept, however, for she was convinced that it was women who must take up the struggle to create a new culture of everyday life, and that it was in the very process of this struggle that they would begin to realize some equality in their lives. In an article in *Communist Woman* in November 1920 outlining the Zhenotdel's tasks and at a national Zhenotdel conference shortly after the Eighth Soviet Congress in December she accepted the assumption that the organization of men and women workers was indivisible but not the widespread view that the Zhenotdel should simply spread the Party's message among women; on the contrary it should stand as the representative of women's interests within the Party and the government. The principles which defined these interests were fundamental to the whole work of building the state, and it was inconceivable that women should be expected to contribute to this process if still burdened by the ignorance that chained them to their kitchens.[27]

Alexandra took Dora Russell to this Zhenotdel conference (which was held in the Bolshoi Theater) and it made a deep impression on her:

> Only three years had the Revolution been in progress, yet here was a packed hall of peasant women to ventilate their problems. Their reception of Kollontai amounted almost to worship. She did, in fact, look marvelous. She was a woman of taste and elegance, yet new clothes and style were the last things that could then be considered; there were no materials except perhaps the traditional coarse Russian linen. It was of this, in its natural fawn color, that Kollontai's dress was made. But, from the high collar to the sweep of her skirt at her feet, it fitted perfectly to her figure. Her wavy dark hair was short, and, as she spoke, she held out her arms, lifted her chin and shook her short curls. She was an unforgettable, graceful, inspired leader of women. One after the other the women came to the platform to speak, with their young and eager, or old and gnarled faces, kerchiefs on their heads. And they spoke with the direct and simple warmth that I have now come to know in assemblies of

women the world over, when, stirred by some common purpose, they open their mouths for the first time ever in public.[28]

With the end of the war the Zehnotdel was now ready to shift its priorities from mobilization to the subtler, more optimistic work of consciousness-raising. Alexandra knew how facile and foolish it was to believe, as so many Party leaders apparently did, that once people's work relations were changed under communism, a new equality and freedom between men and women would automatically come into being. She believed on the contrary that now that couples were no longer being forced apart by war, many women would experience even more painfully than before the conflicts between passion and independence, their seemingly irreconcilable needs to create better and more equal relationships with men and yet subordinate their personal feelings to work and political activity. For the vast majority of women in Russia the end of the war spelled a retreat to their old subservience and exploitation both at home and at work. As she told Emma Goldman, whom she invited to work with her, most women were "ignorant of the simplest principles of life, physical and otherwise, ignorant of their own functions as mothers and citizens"; the Zhenotdel still had neither the resources nor the party support to reach the women who were so cruelly oppressed by the strict sexual codes of the Muslim, Buddhist, Christian, and Jewish religions in the Central Asian regions, the Caucasus, and the Volga.[29]

There was a deeper conflict, however, which underlay Alexandra's work for the Women's Department throughout the autumn and winter of 1920 as her name began to be linked with the Workers' Opposition. She too bitterly resented the highly paid bourgeois "specialists" who in ever larger numbers were assuming control in the unions, soviets, and government. They were widely regarded as an insult to the workers' state, symptomatic of the way the party center overrode every democratic principle in selecting local union committees which, as almost all union members felt with increasing bitterness, were incapable of representing them. For Alexandra to have endorsed these criticisms would inevitably have meant jeopardizing her work at the Women's Department, yet it was precisely there, in her battle to win respect and recognition from the Orgburo and the commissariats, that she began to feel the true strength of these criticisms. All the hopes inspired by the revolution and repressed through three long years of war came pouring out that winter as the relationship among the masses, their unions, and their party leaders was subjected to searching scrutiny. Conflicts among the Central Trade

Union Council, the Supreme Economic Council, and the Commissariat of Labor had intensified, and the Workers' Opposition began to assume an openly factional character, no longer merely appealing to the Party on the basis of its past promises and program for workers' control but calling explicitly for economic power to pass to the unions.

Throughout that winter in a series of impassioned debates among unions, soviets, and Party, increasing numbers of workers rallied to the Workers' Opposition; Alexandra still hesitated to join and thus risk her work at the Zhenotdel. It was not until February 1921, when the imminent Tenth Party Congress offered the Workers' Opposition the possibility of presenting its platform, that she committed herself to this group and interpreted its demands to an overwhelmingly hostile central committee.

At the Ninth Congress in March 1920 numerous delegates had complained that the ideals of the revolution were being swamped by paperwork and by the burgeoning subcommittees of the Supreme Economic Council. But apart from Shlyapnikov and Lutovinov, few of those delegates had backed their complaints with any specific proposals, and the central committee's response had been to set up a control commission, empowered to investigate the political background, morality, and efficiency of party members. The unions' important role, it was stated, was to "replace the capitalist cartels as the basic organizers of industry." But since neither union leaders nor members had any defined relationship with the state and the Supreme Economic Council, it was far from clear how they were to fulfil this function. In September 1920 the unions' authority was still further undermined.

As Alexandra and every agitator knew, sabotage was gradually bringing the entire railway system to a halt. To howls of protest from the unions Trotsky retaliated by setting up a highly centralized transport committee, "Tsektran," which granted itself extraordinary military powers over workers on both the railways and waterways. Coolly dismissing the antagonism this move provoked, Trotsky insisted that the roots of the dissatisfaction with Tsektran's extraordinary powers lay with hidebound union leaders who needed "shaking up." Displaying a terrifying indifference to the understandable fears of the workers, he pointed out that since Soviet Russia was a workers' state, they had nothing to fear from the unions' incorporation into that state. What was needed was a "regime in which each worker feels like a soldier of labor who cannot freely dispose of himself; if he is ordered to transfer jobs, he must carry out that order, and if he does not, he is a deserter who must be punished. And who will execute this? Why the unions of course . . . That is the militarization of the working class . . ."[30]

Although a great many party leaders were prepared to admit the temporary necessity of Tsektran, few went as far as to support the extreme statements with which Trotsky announced its formation; the enemies of Tsektran on the other hand (and there were many of them) were by no means necessarily the friends of the Workers' Opposition. Lenin argued that Soviet Russia was nothing like the "workers' state" which Trotsky so abstractly proposed, but one distorted by the bureaucracy (in ways he elaborated in some detail), dominated by the peasantry, and endangered by the "conceit and militarism" of its War Commissar, Trotsky. Supported by a minority on the central committee who saw the widespread hostility to Tsektran as outweighing its usefulness, Lenin called for its abolition. Bukharin then proposed in a resolution which consolingly incorporated both the general hostility to Trotsky and the vision of better things to come that the unions could only be governmentalized when the state was unionized and when both unions and state disappeared in the "communistically organized society."

All these differences were as mere squabbles, however, compared to the growing fear that the Workers' Opposition—the "greatest danger to our continued existence," as Lenin described it—was threatening to split the Party. It already had the support of the entire metal-workers' union and of many workers in the Moscow area, where it commanded about a quarter of party members' votes. Large numbers of workers in southeast Russia too, particularly in the Donets Basin, the Kuban, and Samara, were driven by the excessively militaristic zeal of the local parties' political departments to support the criticisms of the Workers' Opposition, as did a majority of the Ukrainian party members.

It was at the Eighth Soviet Congress in December 1920 (when Alexandra pressed the claims of the Women's Department) that these conflicts received their first public airing. The day after the congress ended, hundreds of union and party members met together in the magnificent Bolshoi Theater; the unions at last had the chance to state their case, and the Workers' Opposition was officially recognized as a major force within the Party. Out of the great number of opinions expressed, many of which for tactical reasons blurred into each other to the point of being almost indistinguishable, three main groups emerged: that of Lenin, that of Trotsky and Bukharin (they joined forces one month after this meeting), and that of the Workers' Opposition. Throughout the months leading up to the Tenth Party Congress in March 1921 these groups were to battle for the people's allegiance. In December 1920, as Shlyapnikov put forth the views of the Workers' Opposition, Alexandra joined Medvedev, Lutovinov, and various other prestigious and popular leaders of the metal-workers' union in popularizing them.

At this important joint meeting of union and party members in December 1920 Shlyapnikov announced that the Party, inundated with bourgeois specialists, technicians, and other non-proletarian elements, had over the past two years narrowed the scope of the unions to the point that their hostility to the Party was undisguised. The only possible way to resolve this and get industry on its feet was for industrial management to be transferred to the unions. At factory level, control would be with the factory committees; control over higher-level economic decisions would lie with the unions, which would ratify every economic appointment— not a single person was to be appointed to any administrative/economic post without their agreement. Separate unions would elect managers for the various branches of the economy at regular national congresses; local trade-union conferences would elect local managers. The culmination of this bold program, which envisaged transforming industrial organization from below, was the demand for an All-Russian Producers' Congress, to be convened so that the central management of the entire economy could be elected. Given this structure, the various industrial departments would inevitably act with greater coordination and unity of purpose; more impor-tantly the structure would create "a real possibility for the working masses to influence and initiate the organization and development of our econ-omy." No less radical was the proposal for a new egalitarian wage policy, with money being progressively replaced by rewards in kind.

Diametrically opposing the Workers' Opposition was Trotsky's re-stated faith in the "transformation of the trade unions into production unions" as the "greatest task of our epoch"; bourgeois administrators in the unions should be able to take over management jobs without being supervised by commissars. Bukharin, attempting to integrate some of the Workers' Opposition proposals into the main party program, insisted again that "workers' democracy in production" would only come about with the disappearance of both unions and state under full communism.

Rounding on this surrender to "syndicalism" and on Trotsky's demagoguery, Lenin focused his main attack on the Workers' Opposition. The unions could not possibly play any independent part either in initiat-ing or in carrying out economic policies. As the "link" between Party and masses, these "reservoirs of state power" must rather regard themselves as "schools of communism," which were to educate their members in political and administrative matters along the lines laid down by the Party. The organized working class still needed the protection of the unions; Trotsky was wrong to think the unions could be turned into instruments of the state. The unions' complaints (partly justified, to be sure) needed attention, but they were wrong in calling for radically different government. "*We* must use these [union] organizations for the defense of the workers from their state, and for the defense of our state from the workers," he said, in one of his most illuminatingly confused statements about the transitional Soviet society (formally constituted in December 1922 as the Union of Soviet Socialist Republics), with all its bureaucratic abuses and inequalities. The Workers' Opposition had fallen into the same trap as Trotsky in basing their very different conclusions on the assumption that Russia was a "workers' state." In the classless state of the future an All-Russian Producers' Congress would no doubt be most desirable; at the moment, when the defeated counter-revolution was still fighting to regain power, it was folly even to mention such a thing.

As for the Workers' Opposition's idealistic wage policy, this must be countered by a policy determined by the Central Trade Union Council and designed to increase productivity. There had been enough "chatter about principles" in Smolny; what was needed now was fewer pompous phrases and more plain everyday work. Persuasion was to be preferred to constraint. "We shall extend democracy in the workers' organizations but not make a fetish of it."[31]

There was little agreement among central-committee members on the precise degree to which this should be realized and unions allowed to participate in government; their unanimity lay in their hostility to the Workers' Opposition, a hostility surely intensified by the suspicion that the Workers' Opposition might in many ways be right. For even though many felt that these proposals could have waited for the promised economy of abundance, when they might have been more acceptable, the opposition had by revealing the stark misery of the workers' lives raised all too painfully the unacceptable question of whether conditions in Russia in 1917 had really been such as to allow the Bolshevik revolution to fulfil its promises.

The program of the Workers' Opposition was certainly somewhat muddled, as Lenin was of course the first to point out. But few party leaders could disagree with the central point of its analysis: that in economically backward Russia, in which vast numbers of workers had been killed by the war and in which the majority of the population were peasants, the Party, which reflected the social composition of the country as a whole, could no longer be said to represent the working class. Alexandra believed, just as she had believed when she first became a revolutionary in the 1890's, that the workers must be the agents of their own liberation. Because the Party's class composition had changed since the revolution to the point that it could no longer represent the workers' needs, it must authorize the unions to do so. Just as it had been necessary to create, in the Zhenotdel, an organization which would help women to assess their evolving needs in the new society, it was only the unions which could now encourage workers to assert their independence and creativity.

Over the next three months, against a steady crescendo of acrimonious and often personally hostile arguments, the three groups, and numerous smaller groups representing various other positions on the union question, prepared themselves for the Tenth Party Congress. In *Pravda* Zinoviev, Trotsky, Bukharin, and Lenin hurled such bitter criticisms at each other that Lenin and Zinoviev launched an "official" campaign to limit opposition speakers' time at the congress; they were to be allowed to speak only in the name of officially sanctioned "platforms," and thus every speech was made into an issue of affirmation or denial of confidence in Lenin. Against a background of appalling hunger, intense frost, and violence, while strikes continued at the past year's rate of forty a month, "platforms" and personal antagonisms proliferated. Official rations— down to 800 grams of bread a day for metal workers, 600 for other shock workers (those working in the mines and in various key industries), and 200–400 for most people—were irregularly distributed and rarely fulfilled; starving workers began to organize foraging committees to storm the villages; savage and desperate, they attacked any peasant they suspected of hoarding bread. Armed detachments sent out to suppress them acted with equal brutality. This bitterness was reflected in the polemics which daily filled the pages of *Pravda* with diametrically opposing views on every aspect of Soviet society and its economic management. Bukharin and Trotsky joined forces and published their views in January, as did Lenin and his "platform of ten"; and on January 25, 1921 the *Theses of the Workers' Opposition* appeared, signed by Shlyapnikov.

Although these *Theses* were not signed by Alexandra, the lively amplification they gave to the views expressed at the Moscow congress suggest her guiding hand. This time the argument was rather more emotional. The transition from war to the construction of the new state should be accompanied by more democratic work conditions; what the Party had done instead was to reduce the unions' power and repudiate all the experience which had led the workers to make such superhuman sacrifices for the revolution. If in October 1917 the masses' involvement in the work process had been the measure of the success of the revolution, the only guarantee of the future success of that revolution must be the masses' continued participation in all aspects of the economy. The unions had enough skilled workers for them to extend their administrative responsibilities; if the bourgeois technical "specialists" were removed from the Supreme Economic Council and deprived of the administrative power they enjoyed in the factories, workers would no longer be drained by the demoralizing struggle to resist them, and productivity would inevitably rise. The unions would soon be "mature" enough to bring all their members together into an All-Russian Congress of Producers, in which workers would be able to draw on their own experiences and needs to decide how the economy could best be managed, and thus initiate genuine "self-management." Until that time the Central Trade Union Council could administer the economy. The rationing system could be replaced at once by free communal housing which would improve the workers' lives immeasurably. All the primary tasks of the economy could be fulfilled, but only if the Party encouraged the workers, who had made the October revolution, to express their needs and desires spontaneously.[32]

In their strongly worded conclusion the *Theses* came close to accusing the Party of betraying its members. There was no mention of how this program was to be financed or how workers' administration of the economy was to be integrated with the Party's administration of the country —in fact there was no mention at all of the Party's role. Socialism, and eventually communism, it was assumed, would be achieved only when its agents were properly organized to express their needs, for socialism was a question of social relations, not industrial technique or machinery. The class struggle continued, the *Theses* implied, but now it was not the bourgeoisie but the Party, sixty percent of whose members were of bourgeois origin, which distrusted and opposed the masses and grimly clung to power.

Alexandra's lingering unexpressed distrust of the theories on which Lenin had built the vanguard party turned to hope that this party, now that the revolution had been made, could turn into a genuinely proletarian organization; the implied hope, inspired by Rosa Luxemburg and the Dutch revolutionary theorist Anton Pannekoek, was that the Party would eventually dissolve itself into the masses. What Alexandra did not adequately recognize was that the Bolsheviks' claim to represent the masses' consciousness was by now too firmly rooted to be shaken by mere exhortations for more workers' control in the unions.

Three days after the *Theses* appeared in *Pravda*, the same paper carried an article written by Alexandra, "It's Time to Analyze Matters," in which she accused the Party of betraying the proletariat by insisting on a slow transition to socialism. "If we had argued with the same prudence and caution in 1917 as we do now, our Party would never have led us onto that straight but rocky path which has shortened the road to communism; instead it would have carried us along that more tested road through the swamps and forest wildernesses of history."[33] Throughout February 1921, as Trotsky and Zinoviev toured the country in agit-trains propagandizing their opposing views on the union debate which they were to present to the Tenth Congress, Alexandra began to assume responsibility, along with Shlyapnikov, Lutovinov, and Medvedev, for popularizing the Workers' Opposition platform. Without any centralized leadership or any intention of presenting itself as an alternative to the government, and without any figures available to indicate its precise membership, it was nevertheless beginning to speak for the vast majority of dissident workers, as Alexandra discovered at the numerous meetings she addressed during that month. Although Dybenko did not formally join the Workers' Opposition (probably fearing, like so many others, that it threatened to split the Party), it is most likely that his sympathies were with them. Alexandra was particularly well received by the young soldiers and sailors to whom she spoke; a young man who had enrolled at Moscow's Military Academy, where Dybenko was a much-admired student, described how Alexandra's marriage to Dybenko predisposed large numbers of the students there to welcome her. At one meeting in the Military Academy 250 of the 300 people in the audience voted for the Workers' Opposition.[34] It was some time during February that Alexandra began to draft the pamphlet on the Workers' Opposition that she was going to present to the party congress.

It was in February too that she was invited by some young party cadres at Sverdlov University, generally regarded as a hotbed of radicalism, to give a series of lectures on women in the economy. She had many friends there, and her popularity ensured that her lectures, which she continued until July, were well attended and passionately discussed. For one young Zhenotdel worker named Serafima Lyubimova, "Alexandra Mikhailovna was a lofty example of what a revolutionary should be like, and we all tried to be like her."[35]

In the spring of 1921, as Alexandra worked on her document for the Workers' Opposition, there was far more eloquent evidence of the starving workers' distress in Moscow, and particularly in Petrograd, than any number of documents and resolutions could possibly suggest. Petrograd workers were on half rations; deprived of fuel, they would creep out at dusk, dragging sledges over the frost-hard streets to scavenge with the last drop of their strength for firewood and scraps of food. Armed guards stood by the woodpile outside the Astoria Hotel, which housed leading party members in relative splendor, and strikes and demonstrations, broken up by Red soldiers, were by the end of the month turning into demonstrations against the army itself. On February 24 a state of siege was declared in the city. Food supplies were rushed in. Concessions were rapidly made to allow a certain amount of foraging. Large numbers of strikers were arrested and foragers, as before, were shot.

It was four days after this, on February 28, that the sailors garrisoned at Kronstadt, the island fortress in the Gulf of Finland, issued in the name of their soviet a program which amounted to a demand for a "third revolution." Pamphlets outlining this program were distributed in the working-class districts of Petrograd, where they found such an immediate response that the following day 1200 workers and sailors gathered on the main Kronstadt square to demonstrate their support. The soviets must be reelected by secret ballot, proclaimed the sailors; freedom of speech for all political parties must be restored; artisans and unions must be granted their freedom; there must be an amnesty for all revolutionary political prisoners and an end to official propaganda, requisitioning, and the shooting of foragers. The official propaganda they attacked then swung into action. The Kronstadt mutiny was described by the government as a White conspiracy, led by a fictitious "General Kozlovsky" and engineered by the Mensheviks and Socialist Revolutionaries. But the sailors had won the support of too many people in Petrograd for the government's version of events to be credited there. On March 2 the Kronstadt sailors formed a provisional revolutionary committee led by one Petrichenko and various other proletarian ratings, and the demonstrations in the city turned into a general strike.

In the fifteen days of its existence, from March 2–17, the revolutionary committee managed to put out a daily paper which penetrated the smokescreen of official evasions and outright lies about the mutiny. Soldiers sent to disperse the strike in the city were turned back. "At Vasilev Island," wrote the French-born left Bolshevik Victor Serge in his inspiring *Memoirs of a Revolutionary*, "I saw a crowd, composed overwhelmingly of women, standing in the snow-white street, obstructing and slowly pushing back the cadets from the military school who had been sent to clear the approaches to the factories. It was a quiet, sad-looking crowd; they told the soldiers of their misery, called them brothers and pleaded for their help. The cadets took bread from their pockets and shared it out . . ."36

Countless Red soldiers, demoralized by the drastic reorganization measures Trotsky had introduced into the army, were losing their old fighting spirit, and this kind of "fraternization" with the rebellious towns-people was almost as common as desertion. The navy, however, as was revealed at a fleet congress in February 1921, resisted Trotsky's rigid methods even more openly, despite the attempts of Raskolnikov, com-mander of the Baltic fleet and Trotsky's faithful follower, to apply them. Although the Kronstadt sailors of 1921 were not the same men who four years before had been the most passionate and class-conscious defenders of the revolution, they were all sailors of long service among whom the revolutionary traditions had strong roots. A quarter of them left the Party in March 1921, in one of the most telling reflections of the Party's crisis. On March 6, when Trotsky announced that if the sailors did not surrender the government would re-assert control over the garrison and smash them by force of arms, nobody felt this crisis more acutely than the Red Army soldiers and sailors mobilized for this bloody confrontation with the Kron-stadt rebels.

It was the government's intention not only to smash the rebels physically but to destroy the morale of the countless people who supported their demands and disbelieved the official version of the Kronstadt events as a "White-engineered" revolt. The heroes and idealists who had led the army in 1917 and had so inspired their successors at Kronstadt were the very people whom Trotsky appointed to confront the rebels; Dybenko was put at the head of the prestigious Podvoisky regiment which was to lead the attack. An interview with him in the popular Petrograd daily *Red Paper* gave just a hint of the anguish he felt as he accepted this responsibil-ity, and of the almost schizophrenic attitude with which so many Bol-sheviks balanced their loyalty to the Party against their sympathy for their Kronstadt comrades. He described how all military units participating in the attack had to be reorganized; how during the first days of these military preparations overwhelming numbers of Red Army soldiers an-nounced that they did not wish to fight their "little brothers"; how most of his soldiers still regarded the Kronstadt sailors as those most devoted to the revolution, and themselves shared the same grievances that had caused the sailors to revolt—hunger, inadequate clothing, and miserable housing.37

Baffled and torn, like most party members, Dybenko realized the Kronstadt program to be just but felt that the consequences of the sailors' rage and despair were too great to be allowed to pass unchecked. With the working class decimated by war, with workers representing only forty-one percent of party membership (as opposed to fifty-nine percent in 1918), and with production slashed to less than one seventh of its 1913 level, the Bolsheviks faced an isolation and possible defeat too terrible to contemplate; this uprising by their formerly most inspired supporters must therefore be accepted as a betrayal, and suppressed.

16

Workers' Opposition

When the sailors' program finally filtered through to Moscow past the barrier of official propaganda, the similarity of their grievances to those addressed by the Workers' Opposition was immediately evident. It was also evident, long before the Tenth Congress started on March 8, that the Workers' Opposition was as powerless against the authority of the center as was the sailors' garrison against the massed forces of the Red Army. Alexandra's pamphlet on the Workers' Opposition was, she complained, prevented by the central committee from reaching anything like the number of people who wanted to read it, and she herself had to pay the cost of printing it. Against the claim by Trotsky's secretary that some 250,000 copies were distributed was her own more likely account to Angelica Balabanova that she had had it printed in secret and managed to circulate only 1500 copies, and those with much difficulty.[1] It quickly became a forbidden document, which today is better known in the West than in the Soviet Union.

Firmly based in the unions, the Workers' Opposition had considerably greater support than all previous oppositions, including that of the Kronstadt sailors. But unlike the sailors' program, and despite all previous experience, Alexandra's document aimed its appeal not at the workers in whose name it was written, not even at the Party and congress as a whole, but at the party leadership, the least understood element in every leftist's thinking. "Ilich will ponder, he will listen to us," she wrote, in an appeal to Lenin's earlier more radical self, the Lenin of *State and Revolution* and the *April Theses*. "Then he will turn the party rudder toward the opposition. Ilich will be with us yet."[2]

"There can be no self-activity without freedom of thought and opinion," said the pamphlet. "We give no freedom to class activity, we have ceased to rely on the masses, hence we have bureaucracy with us. That is why the Workers' Opposition considers that bureaucracy is our enemy, our scourge and the greatest danger to the future of the Communist Party itself." There could be no talk of changing class relations, insisted the Workers' Opposition, until workers were given the power to control the economy; it was for this power that they had fought to overthrow the Tsar, and it was in this superhuman struggle to realize all their most precious hopes that they had identified with their party and brought it to power. Now that so many of the active workers of 1917 had been wiped out by war and famine, however, the surviving workers in the Party had lost contact with their class roots to the point that they could no longer be truly said to represent their class. The link between the workers and the Party had then been further weakened in the three and a half years following the revolution, in which it could be seen that the Party was actually encouraging the workers' retreat from active political life. One-man management, representing the "individualist conceptions of the bourgeois class," was a method of organizing production which was totally detached from the aspirations of the collective, but which nevertheless now found its "reflection in every sphere of human endeavor":

> The higher up the ladder of soviet and party hierarchy we go, the fewer oppositionists we find, yet the deeper we penetrate into the masses, the more response we find to our program. If the masses depart from the "upper" elements, if there appears to be a crack between the government and the "lower" elements, that means there is something wrong with the "upper" . . . The Workers' Opposition sprang from the depths of the industrial proletariat of Soviet Russia, an outgrowth not only of the unbearable living and working conditions of seven million industrial workers, but also of the vacillations, inconsistencies, and downright deviations of our soviet policy from the earlier class-consistent principles of the communist program.

In trying to steer a middle course between the various classes competing for power, the pamphlet continued, the Party ended up by digressing from its class line along a dangerously regressive path. Enough! the workers were saying. This adaptation smacks of opportunism!

One visit to the inconvenient, filthy, overcrowded mansions which had formerly housed the bourgeoisie in such comfort, and which now housed the workers in such extreme squalor and discomfort, was enough to make one think that there had been no revolution at all. Yet were the "specialists" housed in hovels? Were they subjected to the dampness, foul air, and poisonous gases in the factories which undermined the workers' health and spirits? The Workers' Opposition included all these problems of improving workers' lives in its general economic policy for the rapid forced march to communism which, said the pamphlet, the workers were now demanding. It was because they saw what a low priority the Party assigned to their housing and working conditions that workers had despaired of the government and turned to the unions. And even though the unions were being drained of energy as the Party absorbed their best members and further weakened their links with the masses, the Workers' Opposition would remain as the most vital expression of working-class energy, for its role was precisely to raise all these perturbing questions, and appeal to the Party to "lend an ear to the healthy voice of the wide working masses."

Never before had the Party been so rich in ideas on the unions, the pamphlet declared—the opportunities before it were boundless. But if workers were to find new methods of work and a new stimulus to increase production (their most important task as they approached communism), they must have the freedom to experiment, to develop new creative capacities and discover new forms of production. Lenin had described the unions as the "schools" of communism—but workers gained their political education from *every* aspect of their lives; the unions, as the organizations most capable of expressing their evolving needs and aspirations, could actually be the *creators* of communism too. It would of course be naïve to consider dismissing the "specialists," but it would be equally foolish to imagine that workers would respond to the labor incentives these "specialists" wanted to introduce. The workers must rather assert their control over such potentially valuable administrative centers as the Supreme Economic Council, and use their services (as the capitalists had used the services of similar economic bodies) to make their labor easier. The rising capitalist class had found the incentive to labor and had founded capitalism without the help of "specialist" representatives of the obsolete feudal economy. So too for those who followed them: "Production and its organization—this is the essence of communism."

The Workers' Opposition, the pamphlet continued, deplored the numerous petty restrictions the Party imposed on its members. Every group and organization—even a society to protect birds—had to be "incorporated" into the state machine; its initiative was then deadened by formal decisions handed down by the central organizations of the Party, the government, and the various committees attached to the Supreme

Economic Council, which represented the views of one individual, or at most those of an extremely narrow collective. The miracle of enthusiasm now needed to hoist Russia out of its war-weary lethargy could only be expected from workers, who had most to gain from a revitalized proletarian party and the purging of the bourgeoisie from its ranks.

Quoting from the figures of the Commissariat of Supplies, which showed that some twenty percent of its employees were bourgeois "specialists," fifty percent "tradesmen and salesmen," seventeen percent workers, and thirteen percent peasants, Alexandra's pamphlet went on to insist that this preponderance in all the commissariats of people fundamentally hostile to communism was "breeding an atmosphere altogether repugnant to the working class . . . These servile, well-paid hired lackeys of capital, who acquire more importance with every day that passes, bring decay into our Soviet institutions with their resentment of all revolutionary activities and their predilections for the immutable customs of the past." All non-proletarian elements like these should be immediately expelled from the Party, her pamphlet concluded; non-workers and those who had joined since 1919 should acquire "workers' status" by doing a three-month period of manual labor, and people should be elected, not appointed, to the Party.

On March 8, 1921, two days after Trotsky had delivered his ultimatum to the Kronstadt sailors, the Tenth Party Congress met in the Kremlin. A shared and bitter sadness overshadowed all the acrimony of the past months as delegates met gloomily to celebrate the end of War Communism and the beginning of the new economic policies of peacetime. Lenin spoke for everyone when he remarked sadly, "We have failed to convince the broad masses." "Comrades," he said as the congress opened, "we have lived through a remarkable year. We have allowed ourselves the luxury of discussions and disputes within our party. I don't know how you will assess it all now. Has this luxury in your view been fully consistent with our material and moral forces?" By the end of the congress sadness had turned to hysteria, the "luxury" was condemned as a "disease," and the "Ilich" appealed to by the Workers' Opposition had become the "chief petty bureaucrat" of an "unproletarian government." A week after Lenin's opening remarks he was saying, "I must stress now that it is a great deal better to discuss with rifles than with the theses of this opposition. We need no opposition, comrades, now is not the time! Put yourself either on this side or on that—but with a rifle, and not with the opposition!"[3]

Two months earlier Lenin had recognized party members' right to form separate groups and canvass for votes (even though Zinoviev had rigged these votes to secure a majority for Lenin). By the end of the congress that right had been withdrawn. Midway through the proceedings 200 delegates, including such left Bolsheviks as Dybenko and the passionate democratic centralist, Andrey Bubnov, left the Kremlin for Kronstadt, to the sound of thunderous applause. There they fought the rebels on the ice of the Finnish Gulf outside the Kronstadt fortress, and thus they demonstrated their faith in the Party. Subsequent discussions were periodically interrupted by glowing reports of the gory progress of their battle with the sailors, and the remainder of the delegates mobilized to fight the Workers' Opposition, the submerged iceberg of discontent within the Party, of which Kronstadt was the most visible tip.

On the first day of the congress Alexandra spoke only to translate the speech of Jacques Sadoul, who was one of the French delegates. But her Workers' Opposition pamphlet had already made a considerable impact. In the interval between sessions Angelica Balabanova saw her sitting in the lobby with Sadoul, trying to persuade him to support the Opposition. "At that moment Lenin entered the lobby at a brisk pace. He looked very tense, and did not stop to return greetings. Walking up to Alexandra Kollontai's interlocutor, he said to him angrily: 'What, are you still speaking to this individual?' He walked into the assembly hall and immediately became engrossed in the reading of the pamphlet, entirely oblivious to his surroundings, even to greetings and words addressed to him directly. As he read on, his face darkened more and more . . ."[4] The next few days would see the most bitter battle of ideas ever witnessed at a party congress, with Shlyapnikov, Medvedev, Lutovinov, Alexandra, and another workers' oppositionist named Milonov ranged in open opposition to Lenin, Trotsky, and the majority.

In her diary Alexandra noted the gathering tension which greeted the distribution of her pamphlet:

> The Workers' Opposition is standing as a separate group. I hurriedly distribute my pamphlet. The atmosphere is tense and strained—the Kronstadt uprising was just a few days before, and the congress is burdened by these events. Now my pamphlet is in Lenin's hands; he leafs through it irritably, shaking his head in disapproval. Then the storm burst. For three quarters of an hour Lenin fulminated against the Workers' Opposition and my pamphlet . . .[5]

In this speech, an emotional one even for Lenin, a quite exceptional amount of name-calling was substituted for criticism, and this set the tone for all the personal innuendo and sarcasm to which his supporters subsequently resorted in attacking the Workers' Opposition. Claiming not to have read the pamphlet beyond its call for all power to pass to the producers (the workers)—at which point, he said, he was too choked by disgust to continue—Lenin then went on to prove that he was in fact thoroughly acquainted with its contents. He lambasted the Opposition as petty bourgeois, syndicalists, a menace to the revolution, "caused in part by the entry into the party ranks of elements which have still not completely adopted the communist worldview," and reminded delegates of the dangers of such "deviation" (his first recorded use of the word) in times of external threat.[6]

On the second day of the congress Alexandra spoke to defend the Workers' Opposition, denouncing the party bureaucracy as the source of the cleavage between the government and the masses. The party leaders had only the foggiest understanding of the workers' grievances; they should reestablish contact with the rest of the population by engaging in regular three-month stints of manual work, purging the party of all the non-proletarian elements who distrusted the masses, and taking the positive steps outlined in her pamphlet to encourage workers' self-management. Lenin then accused the Workers' Opposition, fairly legitimately, of failing to specify how the party leaders were both to prevent these divisions between themselves and the masses and to create new links between the workers and the peasants: "I contend that there's a connection between the ideas and slogans of the petty-bourgeois counter-revolution and the slogans of this opposition, which although it doubtless has its honest and misguided supporters, is nevertheless inspired by disrupters who choose to add to the chaos of the Kronstadt rebellion, . . . People writing pamphlets like these should be exposed and eliminated." He then rounded on his old friend Shlyapnikov, for "continuously harping on about his 'authentically proletarian character,'" and exclaimed, in a descent to innuendo rare for him, "Well, thank God we all know that comrades Shlyapnikov and Kollontai are class-united and class-conscious." "No," he concluded, "the Workers' Opposition is either for the Party or against it, and if it continues as it is doing it must be expelled for its demagogic call to dismantle the entire apparatus."

The discussions over the next four days—ostensibly about the unions but more fundamentally about the function and unity of the party—raged with equal passion, for they had to be settled before the economic policies of the new period could be tackled. Between March 9 and March 13 Bukharin, Trotsky, and several other central-committee members all weighed in against the Workers' Opposition; the general hysteria of their attacks was well indicated by Bukharin's exceptionally petty and malicious remarks. Ridiculing the proposal in Alexandra's pamphlet that all party members should spend three months of every year engaged in manual labor, he conjured up the picture of the dignified diplomat Chicherin, with only three months to attend to his duties abroad, after three months in a factory, three months in the army, and three months in a sanatorium recovering. He then, without any evident relevance to the discussion, began to read an extract from Alexandra's recent article, "The Cross of Motherhood," in which she discussed, in a somewhat muddled fashion, a play she had seen in Germany in 1914. The three protagonists in this play were the Virgin Mary, the mother superior of a convent, and a young nun, and its message was that in bearing a child, a woman was often forced to sacrifice it to the world. Bukharin was mercilessly sarcastic in tearing this article to pieces. Alexandra had referred to the way in which in this play the Madonna was represented as the "highest essence of maternity." Such statements were nothing but "disgusting, sentimental Catholic banalities."

Bukharin raised much laughter at her expense, laughter that bordered on the hysterical. Angelica Balabanova noted the restraint with which Alexandra answered him and compared her calmness to the frenzy of Bukharin and Lenin. On March 13 Alexandra spoke to demand why, if the Party had relied on the masses throughout the war and in the heroic defense of Petrograd, they could not be relied on now in peacetime. Why, she demanded, had Bukharin described this aspiration as "petty bourgeois," when he himself had expressed alarm over the way the Party was beginning to grant concessions to private ownership and the landed peasantry? Personal attacks did not strengthen his case—"Jupiter, you are angry, and that means you are wrong!" The Workers' Opposition had come up with a specific program to tackle ills whose existence he had all but admitted, she said—going on to assert the popularity of this program among the masses (to jeers of "Yes and at Kronstadt too!"). "The workers know there's something wrong," she continued undaunted, "but instead of running to Vladimir Ilich's office for a chat, as so many of our more timid comrades did, we proposed a series of practical measures for cleansing our ranks and reviving our mutual relations with the people."[7]

But for Lenin, the oppositionists had to be driven to the wall before any of the urgent questions of the new economy could be discussed. "All these reflections about freedom of speech and criticism which abound in the speeches of the Workers' Opposition constitute nine-tenths of the content of those speeches, the rest of which make no sense at all." For him it was the ending of the war emergency measures and the restarting, at all costs, of the stagnant economy which had to take priority over all discussion. The political measures devised to crush the opposition were not so dissimilar from the military measures adopted by the government both to crush the Kronstadt rebellion and to replace the requisitioning of grain from the peasants (which had continued with such catastrophic results throughout the war) with a grain tax. This tax, which meant an end to the government's control over the grain supply and the introduction of a virtually free trade in grain, was one of the first and most important features of the New Economic Policy (the NEP). And yet this policy, of such momentous significance, was only discussed very briefly on the penultimate day of the congress, and of the 330 pages of the official report of the congress a mere twenty are devoted to it.

Before these new policies could even be discussed, Lenin conferred with the Workers' Oppositionists and on March 15 ordered Shlyapnikov and Kutuzov to withdraw their resignation from the central committee. He then went on to present his proposals for the New Economic Policy. The economic and political alliance between the proletariat and the peasants, threatened during the civil war and by the unavoidable requisitioning of grain, was to be safeguarded now by granting the peasants relatively free use of the land and its products. The NEP's main purpose was to "increase at all costs the quantity of output," to expand large-scale industry, and thus to provide the economic basis for the dictatorship of the proletariat. Although the "commanding heights" of the economy were to remain under state control, private enterprise was to be selectively authorized, and the power already granted to economic and technical "specialists" was to be considerably increased.

Few Bolsheviks could have foreseen in 1917 that they would by 1921 be reluctantly forced to accept the need in Russia for this strange new mixed economy, in which agriculture would be overwhelmingly in private hands, private trade would be legalized, numerous small-scale manufacturing companies would come into being, and the new managers who ran them, the "Nepmen" and "specialists," would flourish at the expense of the workers. Few Bolsheviks foretold so clearly the ills which would beset the new economy as those in the Workers' Opposition.

On March 16, the final day of this traumatic congress, two highly contentious resolutions were passed in an attempt to close party ranks. Described by Trotsky as temporary, they were denounced only by the Workers' Oppositionists, who feared, only too presciently, the crippling effects they would have on the Party's future work and the enormously increased disciplinary powers they granted to a small group of leaders. The first, "On Party Unity," empowered the central committee to "abolish all factionalism" and, in a secret clause agreed to by most only with great reluctance, authorized it to expel anyone judged by a two-thirds majority to be in breach of party discipline. The second, "On the Syndicalism and Deviation in Our Party," was aimed specifically at the Workers' Opposition. This opposition, claimed the resolution, was clearly the product of petty-bourgeois trade-union influences; its platform, potentially disastrous in a time of famine and demobilization, threatened to reduce the Bolsheviks to complete impotence. The spreading of its ideas was "incompatible with membership in the Communist Party," which must not shrink from expulsions at this critical time. Only the Party could unite the working class against such deviations; the oppositionists must "submit to party discipline," abandon any idea they might have of resigning from the Party, and continue in a less factional manner to apply their impeccably high moral standards to clearing the Party of unprincipled bourgeois careerists.

Only Shlyapnikov and Medvedev spoke out against the first resolution and its hated secret clause as an intolerably savage weapon plainly being wielded against them. Shlyapnikov's bitter tirade expressed all Alexandra's fury at this banning of "factions." "I haven't seen or heard anything more slanderous or demagogic than this resolution in all my life, in twenty years' Party membership," he raged, warning that if it was passed, the oppositionists would resign all their positions in the Party and take their case to the court of the international communist proletariat. He was referring to the executive committee of the Comintern, which, like the Comintern itself, was very much a creation of the Bolsheviks. Four of its seven members were Russians, and the other three loyal Bolshevik supporters, and they had little authority to assess the justice of the case Shlyapnikov was now threatening to bring before them.

The Party's pledge to end the "extreme organizational centralism" of the war years slipped almost unnoticed past the two resolutions which contradicted it so blatantly. Its only concession to the oppositionists was to urge the control commission, which had been established at the Ninth Party Congress the previous March, to investigate each member of the Party even more thoroughly, with a view to purging its ranks of persons guilty of the "uncommunist" crimes of drunkenness, debauchery, corruption, robbery, and careerism; a year later, in 1922, a quarter of the Party's members were expelled for failing to convince the control commission of their socialist probity.

Shlyapnikov had not lightly threatened to take the oppositionists' complaints to the Comintern, but for the three months following the Party congress, until the Comintern held its Third Congress in June 1921, the Workers' Opposition had to accept that having addressed its appeal to the Party leaders, it was now in no position to appeal to those same leaders for its survival. Its members were extremely sensitive, however, to all the ways in which the economic and political balance began to shift after the Tenth Congress to the course toward what was to be known as the New Economic Policy, or NEP. The private sector, the petty bourgeoisie, and the "specialists" began now to assume a central importance in an economic policy regarded by Lenin as a necessary tactical retreat from the principles of the revolution, and bitterly criticized by many leftists as a contradiction of all previous policies. When the proposal to introduce a grain tax was passed at the Tenth Party Congress, the Oppositionists felt that this first step toward a market economy had been clearly foreseen by the hiring of "specialists." The Oppositionists' weakness, increasingly evident over the months that followed this congress, was in their inability to provide any alternatives to the NEP. It was not until the summer of 1921 that they began to expand their old criticisms of the Party into an explicit attack on the NEP and reiterate the long-buried faith that only an international proletarian revolution could set the economy of the Soviet republic to rights, encircled as it was by enemies and ravaged by war.

Since Klara Zetkin was ill, Alexandra, her deputy on the women's Comintern bureau, assumed with a number of other Zhenotdel workers most of the work for the Second Communist Women's Congress, which was to precede the Third Comintern Congress in June. Her hope now was that the international perspectives of this congress would embrace both the proposals of the Workers' Opposition and the commitment to drawing women into the work of making the world revolution, although it is clear from her silence on women's issues in her Workers' Opposition pamphlet how isolated she felt these issues to be from all the others. Another important reason for this silence, revealed in two articles she wrote a few days after the Tenth Congress, was the extreme reluctance of most male trade unionists to help women struggle for their equal rights at work.

Alexandra's isolation in the Party now seemed likely to cause trouble for Dybenko, even though it was of course inconceivable that it would reflect as painfully on him as his earlier confrontations with authority had disgraced her. The five months in which they had lived together in Moscow in the Hotel Nationale had been uncomfortable for both of them, and Dybenko's part in the brutal suppression of the Kronstadt rebellion can only have cast one more shadow on their troubled relationship. When Dybenko received a series of military postings after this, it began to appear increasingly unlikely that they would ever be able to live together for any length of time again. Immediately after the battle at Kronstadt, in which 4127 people were wounded, 527 killed, and countless numbers drowned or left to die on the ice, Dybenko was appointed commandant of the fortress there. Less than a week later he was hurrying back to the Tambov region, just south of Moscow, to put down a large peasant army which had been organized by a right-wing Socialist Revolutionary named Antonov. By May 1921 he had so thoroughly reinstated himself in the Party's good graces that he was appointed Commander in Chief of the Western Black Sea Coast.

It was probably there, in the spring of 1921, that Alexandra wrote another of her undated letters to him: "There was a time, Pavel, when our intimacy could help you and lighten your path. But now I feel that not only am I no longer any help to you, but that I'm definitely standing in the way of your future development."[8] There were attempts at a reconciliation throughout 1921 and 1922, but they were undoubtedly growing apart. It is possible that Dybenko was disturbed by the renewed warmth of Alexandra's friendship with Shlyapnikov. It is more likely that Dybenko was already involved with the young and relatively apolitical woman whom he was to marry at the end of 1922, and that Alexandra had realized that this affair was far more serious than all the others which had grieved her so much. She probably realized that this woman would be better suited to him than she herself had been in the four years they had spent together.

Alexandra's isolation in the Party threatened also to undermine her work in the Women's Department, just as her isolation as a woman reduced the opportunities of speaking for them in the Workers' Opposition (for the unions' attitudes toward women she found just as hidebound as those of most party members). Women workers represented seventy-five percent of the members in the textile and tobacco-workers' unions, so her silence on the important issues concerning them in the unions was particularly striking. This silence indicated a quite justifiable fear that few union leaders would take the initiative in helping women to overcome the problems of unemployment and redundancy that they inevitably faced as the war came to an end. Her Workers' Opposition pamphlet, which addressed itself to the Party not to the unions, had not been the right context in which to raise these problems.

What she did do in her pamphlet, however, was to attack the squalor of people's domestic lives, and the passion with which she did so probably derived from her own direct experiences of the problems confronting women living at her hotel. The Hotel Nationale, which housed the families of numerous party and union workers, was far from luxurious. It offered no rations except three quarters of a pound of bread every other day, although the hotel provisioning committee did operate a cooperative system, whereby stocks of some luxuries, like pots of jam, would be bought every few weeks. Most people there ate in the large communal dining room, where meals costing 5–7 rubles were served from 2:00 to 7:00 P.M., and the hotel provided the same meals—glasses of tea, plates of soup with slivers of horsemeat, buckwheat porridge, and a slab of margarine—to various canteens around Moscow. But although these food supplies were relatively good, meals were abominably prepared by large numbers of badly paid servant women, who themselves received vastly inferior food and were chivvied and chased around by an array of officials and inspectors who also checked the passes of anyone coming to visit.

It was not surprising that many residents preferred not to eat in the hotel canteen at all but to prepare their own food in the hotel kitchen, where there was always a savage scrabble for a place on the one large stove which served everyone. Emma Goldman, who stayed there, observed how greedily watchful the women were of any extra foodstuffs people might prepare on the stove; she observed too that, despite the fact that these women were often quite crude and brutal in their attitudes toward each other, they had an instinctive sense of justice and readily identified with the servants who worked there, intensely resenting the fact that next door to this kitchen was another, where incomparably better meals were cooked for the more privileged party workers staying in the hotel. Adjoining the communal kitchen was a laundry which also supplied boiling water; people were constantly passing in and out to make tea, chat, and air their grievances. Opposite all these rooms was a long corridor with a window at which people traded their meal coupons for plates of food. Many brought their own plates and took them not to the canteen but to their own rooms, convinced for no very good reason that they would in this way be given larger portions of food.[9] (The walls of the buildings opposite the hotel provided a much brighter picture than these dismal struggles within. Formerly painted a dull ocher color, they had been given over to bold experimental painters, who had covered these street canvases with delightful designs in clear primary colors which blended well with the red kerchiefs and peasant coats of the women and men who passed up and down the busy street.)

In two articles which Alexandra wrote for *Communist Woman* directly after the Tenth Congress in March, she not only voiced the fear that women's needs were being neglected by the unions but made good some of the omissions of her pamphlet with a rather more confident prediction of women's capacity to organize their lives along different and better lines. The best way for the Party to encourage the unions to discover new and more creative methods of work was to improve the lives of women workers; without doing so, and drastically, any talk of increasing productivity was completely meaningless. For the economy to operate profitably now, when prices were so high, there would inevitably have to be an increase in unemployment, in which the new unskilled workers, mostly women and raw peasant recruits, would be the first to lose their jobs.

Women's experience in the economic and social life of the war years uniquely qualified them, she argued, to lead the social reorganization of the country, for they were the ones who had seen what personal horrors the war had wrought—they were the ones who had seen families disrupted, children orphaned. Since finances were not available, they would have to organize their own nurseries, but this was no bad thing, in her opinion. Class-consciousness and self-awareness grew not only out of people's common experiences of exploitation at the workplace, but also out of their shared experiences of association in the community. The recent dramatic changes in living conditions and arrangements, she felt, offered most women the chance of learning how to make fuller lives for themselves and to create a new culture of everyday life. Her optimism was well founded. As Konkordia Samoilova had noted in 1920, one provincial women's congress in that year had organized thirty-eight day nurseries for the children of peasant women, who had "previously feared day nurseries like the plague."[10]

This message Alexandra repeated to the trade unions in a *Pravda* article, shortly after the Fourth Trade Union Congress in May 1921. Why were there so few women attending? And why had the unions not honored the commitment made at the Eighth Congress of Soviets in December 1920 to drawing women into all levels of their economic and political organization? If they were not to fall by the wayside under the NEP, women urgently needed the extra training that would give them equal access to skilled jobs, and the Party must work with the Zhenotdel to fight the prejudice in the unions which excluded women from this training and the jobs to which they were entitled.[11]

Articles such as these may have been widely read by men and women in the cities of Russia, but they spoke to none of the problems which still crippled the women of the eastern Soviet republics and kept them immured and isolated behind their veils. Only now that the war had ended, with the Zhenotdel boasting some 70,000 delegates representing 3,000,-000 women and with large numbers of women joining the Party and becoming soviet delegates, could a start be made on the extremely subtle consciousness-raising work needed to persuade the women of the East to abandon their veils and confront some of the age-old Muslim customs which oppressed them. It was only after a great deal of patient and sympathetic work that the Zhenotdel would be able to induce these women to reveal some of the horrifying details of their veiled existence, for to women who had been sold off by their fathers in marriage at the age of ten and often younger, and beaten and terrorized from then on, the prospect of revealing their faces to the world meant certain death at the hands of their families.

Alexandra decided that what was needed was to persuade some of these women to come to Moscow for a congress, where in a theatrical display of their new-found liberation they would throw off their veils. Her plan was characteristically bold. Most Bolshevik educators had assumed that the best way to reach Muslim women was by persuading Muslim men to grant their wives and daughters more freedom; Alexandra had fewer illusions. For almost all Asian women leaving their homes for a congress could only earn them the hatred and contempt of their families, and lead inevitably to divorce and the loss of their children. The twenty or so Zhenotdel workers who set off in the spring of 1921 for Azerbaijan, Turkestan, Bashkiria, the Crimea, and the Caucasus were not, however, to be swayed by these considerations. With considerable courage and resourcefulness they managed to pick up a few words of the local languages and gradually gain the trust of the women there, so that it was not long before these women were braving the fury of their families and inviting the Western strangers back to their homes.

By the end of March forty-five Muslim women, most of them from Turkestan, had been persuaded to attend a preliminary congress in Moscow to decide how their work should continue. Unveiled, these women gathered in Moscow, and from April 5–7 they discussed with an eager group of Zhenotdel workers the best way to change the Muslim laws which had bound them and which still kept their sisters immobilized under the heavy horsehair garment, the *paranja*, which covered them from head to foot. To tear off this fetishistic symbol of their sexual enslavement was seen as the most eloquent way of demonstrating their liberation. "We were silent slaves . . .", "Our husbands beat us with sticks and whipped us whenever they felt like it . . .", "We've had enough of our stuffy veils!"—one by one the Muslim women began to reveal with increasing boldness some of the horrors of their former imprisoned lives.

It was decided first of all to set up clubs, literacy classes, and nurseries in the Central Asian regions and generally provide an example of the sort of benefits the Soviet government was offering to women. Work was to start in Turkestan, where a fairly large proportion of women were paid servants and handicrafts workers, and it was hoped that some of the first women to benefit from the Zhenotdel's work there would accept an invitation to attend the Third Comintern Congress in Moscow.[12]

Over the next few years women party workers trooped off in large numbers to various Eastern regions, and soon even the remotest mountain area had its Zhenotdel tent. Energetic women organizers like Nadezhda Kolesnikova, an old Bolshevik and skilled agitator, and Olga Chulkova, who had been a populist teacher in the 1890's before joining the Bolsheviks, braved the terrifying hostility of the male population in Turkestan and Abkhasia (where Bolshevik control was by no means secure) and adopted a variety of methods for meeting and communicating with the local women. Olga Chulkova and her team set up their tent in Sukhumi, from which they set off on long treks across the mountains; stopping at the camps and mountain villages of Abkhasia, they showed to the fascinated women there magic-lantern slides, health charts, and even an early Soviet film depicting a heroic Muslim woman who refused to marry the old man to whom she had been sold. In other areas Zhenotdel workers were no less successful. They managed to meet local women in bathhouses or in small workships. Nurseries were set up and women's discussion clubs and social centers were opened, which soon became as popular as the bazaar. The Zhenotdel women's club in Baku, for instance, had thousands of members.

As increasing numbers of Muslim women in Central Asia began to discard their veils the men reacted with predictably ferocious hostility. Women were set upon by men with wild dogs and boiling water as they emerged from the Baku women's club, an eighteen-year-old Uzbek woman was thrown into a well, and one twenty-year-old Muslim woman was hacked to pieces by her father and brothers when she had the audacity to put on a bathing suit. All these crimes were classified by the government, in consultation with the Zhenotdel, as "counter-revolutionary offenses." Despite the perils of their new liberation countless Muslim women joined the Zhenotdel as assistants and translators and were soon appointed to leading administrative posts. Many of them, persuaded to further their studies, left for Moscow to enroll in the university, where they threw themselves into their new lives with enormous enthusaism and soon had no desire to return home.[13]

Throughout the spring and summer of 1921 Alexandra combined this work and all the organizational work involved in preparing for the Comintern women's congress with a continuation of her lectures on women in the economy for the radical young party workers at Sverdlov University. In these lectures (published two years later as *Women's Labor and the Evolution of the Economy*) she described the history of the family under capitalism: how the bourgeois family, an institution which was based on the accumulation of wealth and thus encouraged individuals to compete with each other, had helped to concentrate capital; how the ideal of the bourgeois family had been sanctified by the Church, which operated so very harshly in various ways against women; and how as women entered the workforce the contradictions between this ideal and the realities of people's lives became apparent and the disintegration of the nuclear family slowly gathered momentum.

This was Alexandra's most complete attempt to go beyond most previous analyses of women's oppression as merely equivalent with capitalism. She intended primarily to popularize the idea of women's dual importance to the economy in production (work) and reproduction (giving birth to, and rearing, the next generation), rather than to discuss sexual relations explicitly; her main purpose was to show that increased mechanization would soon make the sexual division of labor a thing of the past. This division, which enslaved women, was reinforced by private property, she said, for private property securely nailed women to the hearth of the isolated family unit, but the actual moment of their enslavement was the moment when productive labor fell to men and secondary labor (housework) fell to women.

We might question her assumption that the struggle against women's social inferiority, encouraged by the workers' republic, would eventually abolish this division. She felt that although "in its search for new forms of the economy and of living which meet the interests of the proletariat, the Soviet Republic has inevitably made a number of mistakes," and although practice lagged far behind intention, the government was nevertheless guided by the right ideas in its attitudes toward childcare and recognized that women should be able to engage in productive work without sacrificing their desire to have children. Women would only fulfil these two needs, however, when the collective spirit had developed to the point that the responsibilities for looking after children were equally shared by everyone. Every sensible bourgeois mother, after all, knew that "social education gives a child something that the most exclusive maternal love cannot give" and shifted at least a part of the care of her children to the nanny, the kindergarten, the school, or the summer camp.

Alexandra did not, even to this educated audience, take the opportunity to call for more contraception and instead looked forward to a time of greater abundance when women no longer would have to resort to abortions. In fact she conjured up a quite frightening vision of a future in which, helped in various ways by the state to combine motherhood with work, women would be able to achieve what amounted to a near-perpetual state of pregnancy. "The instinct of reproduction" could be elevated into the ennobling "instinct of motherhood": to make this genuinely possible was one of the main priorities of the new state, she said. Thus she repeated with the same confusing interchangeability that had marked her earlier writings her ideas of the "state" and of the "collective": her knowledge of what actually existed in Soviet Russia with her feeling for what should be; her sensitivity to people's various sexual needs and her acceptance of the harsh necessity of increasing the population; her assumption that economic progress would assure women of their liberation went hand in hand with an awareness of all the lingering sexual prejudice which threatened on the contrary to drive them back to unproductive housework and isolated motherhood.[14]

"You ask me, children, what I did in the great year of 1921? Well, I fought under the red banner of the Comintern for your happiness."[15] It was with these words that Alexandra announced in *Pravda* the second Comintern women's conference in Moscow, which women from the radical minorities of twenty-one socialist parties attended from June 9–15, 1921. This conference, in the spirit of all Comintern gatherings, was intended to unite all the women on the radical left of the European socialist parties, and to inspire them with the victories of October and the achievements of the Zhenotdel to fight reaction and further the world revolution. But more dramatic than all the resolutions she had drafted, and all the work she had put into bringing thirty women from Europe and Scandinavia to Moscow, was the impact made by a group of women delegates from Azerbaijan and Georgia. Calmly countering the criticism from many party members hostile to the Zhenotdel, that their attendance would be excessively "theatrical," Alexandra merely pointed out, in conversation with Louise Bryant, that all conferences were theater. More than that, these women's courage in confronting all the enmity and violence from their families that would make it impossible for many of them to return to their homes was an inspiration to every woman struggling for her equality in the new society. "That moment when the delegates of the eastern Soviet republics walked in and raised their *chadris* [*their veils*] before the conference was a symbol of our victory in joining the women of the East to communism."[16]

The main Comintern congress, which assembled in the throneroom of the Kremlin on June 22, 1921, was a far more complicated affair, for its main business was to approve the New Economic Policy and condemn the Workers' Opposition. Alexandra had translated her Workers' Opposition pamphlet into French (she had had no time to translate it into German) and had managed to distribute a small number. But Lenin and Trotsky had also circulated their own official reports of the new policies, and her pamphlet was greeted with an almost total lack of response by the fifty foreign delegates (from France, Spain, Germany, Holland, Poland, and Hungary), who were inclined on the whole to see no further than the official party line. Lenin's speech on the NEP was warmly applauded, as was Trotsky's sharp defense of the Party against accusations of violence and disciplinary extremes. Alexandra delivered her report on the Comintern's work among women; a trade-union International was set up at the Russians' initiative; and the delegates met happily at a special session on July 5 to discuss the tactics of the Russian Communist Party, give their blessing to the NEP, and damn the Workers' Opposition.[17] After this session Alexandra became preoccupied with the fear that the Workers' Oppositionists would be arrested. It was not reasonable to fear this, since oppositionists were not yet being subjected to such extreme punishment, but it prompted her to give several copies of her pamphlet for safekeeping to a delegate named Reichenbach, a member of the German Communist Workers' Party (the KAPD), a few of whose members were beginning to voice criticisms of the Bolshevik government which were similar to those of the Workers' Opposition. All the other delegates, even including her old acquaintance Jacques Sadoul, trailed dutifully after Lenin and Trotsky and showed such a wilful blindness to the real conditions in Russia that she felt impelled to speak. Although she still had a boundless faith in the imminence of another, more fruitful phase of the revolution elsewhere in Europe, the problems in Russia were, she felt, of vital importance to all revolutionaries abroad. Their support of the Bolsheviks amounted to nothing if they were not made fully aware of the famine, pestilence, and poverty endured by the Russian people, and the acrimony, the paralysis, and the tendency to annihilate all opposition which were so grievously distorting the Bolshevik Party.

> I stood there in a torment of anxiety. Surely to say nothing would have been cowardice. I went up to Lenin. "Vladimir Ilich, I want to break party discipline and take the floor." "Break party discipline? And you ask my blessing? When people do that, they don't normally ask permission beforehand." "All right, I'll take you at your word, Vladimir Ilich; I won't ask permission, but I'll enter my name on the list of speakers."

Seeing then that she was serious, Lenin attempted to dissuade her from doing so by urging her to look instead at all the achievements of the past year—the electrical stations, the literacy program—which put the Workers' Opposition criticisms in the shade.[18] But she was determined to speak. "People were sitting in a state of sleepy semi-torpor listening to the closing speeches," recalled Marcel Body (a French delegate, who in 1922 was to be Alexandra's secretary), "when Kollontai's name was announced. Everyone rushed back, including Lenin, to hear her deliver the theses of the Workers' Opposition in German. She ended with an appeal for solidarity from foreign communist parties, but she got no applause . . ."[19]

Speaking with great emotion to an unresponsive and uncomprehending audience, few of whom had seen her pamphlet or knew anything about the circumstances of the Tenth Congress, Alexandra began by saying that she represented only a "small minority" but felt that there were duties more compelling than obedience to the Party. Capitalism was dying throughout the world, she continued; in its place workers must start to create new methods of production or "humanity will finally perish." But whereas the rich peasantry stood to gain from the NEP, the new policies granted no comparable concessions to the working class, the class on which the government should be relying.

The NEP, she said, was an insult to the revolutionary class. For it had given capitalism the chance to reassert itself in Russia, and creeping into power, as every Russian worker knew only too well, was a new bourgeois class which had deep spiritual affinities with its brothers in the West. Lenin, in talking of all the mechanical innovations in Soviet industry, had said not one word about educating the workers and encouraging the new Soviet person to develop, and yet it was precisely because the workers had not been consulted in decisions on the new economy that the Party had suffered its recent crisis. It was this crisis that prompted her speech now, she concluded, and made it urgent that the Workers' Opposition be supported as a vital working-class nucleus within the Party which would enable Russia to complete her revolution when the European revolution finally came.[20]

The end of her speech (which she delivered in German, the first language of the Comintern, and then translated in rapid succession into French and Russian) was greeted with a deafening silence. In the row behind her sat Lenin, Trotsky, Zinoviev, Bukharin, Kamenev, Rykov, and Radek; they had been whispering continuously while she was speaking. She finished, and "I went through the hall to the exit. Nobody greeted me and I had known that this would happen, but I found it very painful nonetheless."[21] Even more painful were the savage public rebukes that her speech provoked the following day from Lenin, Trotsky, and Bukharin. It was sheer nonsense to say that capitalism was dying away, retorted Trotsky, when capitalism was manufacturing large quantities of guns with which to destroy the Soviet system, and it was sheer obstinate dogmatism on her part to claim that the Party resorted to any extremes of violence against the workers. Besides this, since the October Revolution had secured the rule of the proletariat in Russia, the government could afford to make some concessions to the peasantry. Bukharin then launched into an attack on her Menshevik past and her muddled, over-emotional views of things. She claimed to speak for the Workers' Opposition, he said, but in fact she spoke only for herself. Lenin recorded his agreement with both of them, and first he and then Trotsky took Alexandra aside afterward, telling her angrily that she had had no right to speak and that no duty was more compelling than that of party discipline.

She began to regret having given her pamphlet to Reichenbach of the KAPD, but there was little she could do about this, for he had left for Germany and had immediately set about having it published there. Unknown to most party members, the pamphlet had also been published in Chicago (sent there presumably by Shlyapnikov, not by Alexandra), and from April to July 1921 it had been serialized in London in Sylvia Pankhurst's paper, *The Workers' Dreadnought*. The pamphlet appeared in the summer of 1921 in Berlin, provoking the party leaders to a fury infinitely greater than that of the SPD leaders nine years before, when *Around Workers' Europe* had brought Alexandra for the first time into such painful confrontation with party authority in Germany. In 1921, as in

1912, one of the most anguishing aspects of this confrontation was the sense of isolation it brought her. Of course Alexandra had an old and trusted friend in Shlyapnikov, and she had allies in various other members of the Workers' Opposition, such as Medvedev and Lutovinov. But Misha, still buried in his books in Petrograd, had taken little interest in the Workers' Opposition, and it seems that she was loath to burden him with her anxieties. As for Dybenko, in his new post as a military commander in the Crimea he was far removed from these party disputes. Now, as before, it was apparently her old friend Zoya Shadurskaya who gave her the support she so badly needed. It is possible that Alexandra wrote to Zoya, who had been working as a journalist outside Moscow for the past two years, asking her to come to Moscow; at any rate by the summer of 1921 Zoya had not only joined her there but had added her signature to the Workers' Opposition platform.

In the two months following the Comintern congress Alexandra shifted her attention from the Workers' Opposition to the problems besetting the Zhenotdel. Increasing numbers of local women's departments were being disbanded by the regional parties, and in the July issue of the party central committee's biweekly newsletter she published a decree forbidding party organizations to take any such arbitrary measures. But her commitment to the Workers' Opposition had irrevocably damaged her reputation, and her personal misfortunes were reflected in the precarious state of the Zhenotdel central organization. Much of Alexandra's attention over the past months had been directed elsewhere, and numerous Zhenotdel workers ceased to trust her after she had espoused the Workers' Opposition. This was partly responsible for the fact that of the forty-two women originally assigned to work in the Zhenotdel center there remained by the end of that year only twenty-three. Many longstanding women organizers had died. Konkordia Samoilova (the "heavy artillery" of the women's movement, as Alexandra once described her) died of typhus in the spring of 1921; of the other women activists in the 1917 group only Klavdia Nikolaeva and Lilina Zinovieva (Zinoviev's wife) were still alive. With the NEP, the Zhenotdel suffered great cutbacks in staff and the amount of money allocated to it.

Alexandra's sense of grievance at the contemptuous manner with which the party leaders had dealt with her went very deep. Moreover it seemed to Shlyapnikov all too probable that the Eleventh Party Congress the following year would dismiss the Workers' Opposition even more harshly if they did not organize in advance some support from abroad. It was most likely Shlyapnikov who now formed the desperate plan of taking his complaints, as he had threatened, to the executive committee of the Comintern. He was joined by twenty others (half of whom had belonged to the Workers' Opposition), but not by Alexandra, who was reluctant to jeopardize all her work in the Party and its Women's Department. The month after she had finished the last of her Sverdlov lectures, in August 1921, and shortly after her pamphlet had appeared in Germany, she was sent off on an agitational assignment to Odessa, where she stayed for the next six months, removed from the possibility of any more embarrassing outbursts. Dybenko joined her there briefly, but by now it was clear to both of them that their relationship had broken down irrevocably. Shortly after she arrived there she wrote "Tsar Hunger and the Red Army," a propaganda article addressed to the soldiers who were organizing the peasants to harvest and distribute their meager crops in the midst of famine and drought.[22] She also embarked on two autobiographical essays and a long article which appeared in *Communist Woman* at the end of that year, "Theses on Communist Morality in the Sphere of Sexual Relations."

Taking up many of the issues raised by her Sverdlov lectures, she anticipated the time when, under full communism, consumption would no longer be organized individually and the external economic functions of the family would disappear. The workers' state must concern itself not with unnaturally prolonging the life of the moribund family unit, she argued, but with all the emerging sexual attitudes and relationships which best served to strengthen the collective. Emphasizing the importance of the legal aspects of women's liberation, she nevertheless saw the marriage law as ready to be superseded by new laws to protect mothers and supervise the welfare of their children. Both mother and father should be able to decide how much of the responsibility for the care of their children they wished to assume. As for the kind of marriage relationship most desirable at that time, she limited herself to two criteria: the health and the size of the population. Since each historical period had created the sexual relationship most appropriate to its needs, so too the workers' state would undoubtedly arrange its relationships to suit its own best interests, having first gone through the long and painful process of confronting the hypocrisy and possessiveness that had made for both the unhealthy restraint and the obsessive promiscuity of the past. Comradeship would fuse the hearts and minds of individual members of the collective, and while new and more appropriate forms of marriage were discovered relations between the sexes would be enriched by an incomparably greater understanding of a whole range of joyful sexual experiences, however long or briefly they might last.[23]

These "theses" and her lectures won Alexandra enormous popularity among young people, for whom she was already an inspiring example of revolutionary courage and generosity, and it is worth noting that despite her low status in the Party at that time these works were published and widely and enthusiastically discussed by a great many people in and out of the Party. But she lived in Odessa in a state of constant anxiety. In August 1921 Shlyapnikov had attacked the NEP at a party cell meeting, and Lenin had been roused at last to demand his expulsion from the Party. So great was the antagonism of many central-committee members for the Workers' Opposition that one old Bolshevik militant named Mikhail Frunze had threatened to argue with Shlyapnikov "with guns." Although a majority of the central committee refused to vote for Shlyapnikov's expulsion, he was severely reprimanded and from then on many oppositionists were threatened by former comrades, had their telephones tapped and their mail intercepted.[24] The control commission intensified its purge of "non-socialists" from the Party. Whether or not Alexandra was thus threatened, she felt increasingly isolated in her desire to open up and extend the debates within the Party and to keep the Zhenotdel alive.

Although she doubtless felt more acutely conscious than ever before of her ambiguous position in the Party, her voice rang out with all its old defiance in an interview with her which appeared in February 1921 in the *Chicago Tribune*. "I badgered the government single-handed on the question of giving women representation in all economic institutions, and I won my point" she was reported as saying in the article "Kollontai Fights for Her Sex: First Woman Commissar Heckles Government Till She Gets Action."[25] This article was cited in January 1922 when the central committee called her back to Moscow and relieved her of the directorship of the Zhenotdel. Her position was no longer tenable, she realized; the KAPD was using her pamphlet in Germany to make its own criticisms of the Soviet government; the IWW had published it in Chicago, with an introduction praising her for exposing the brutality of the Bolshevik dictatorship. As well as making these contacts abroad she was still in touch, the central committee alleged, with dissidents in Russia. The official pretext for her dismissal from the Zhenotdel, however, was her inefficiency as an organizer.

Angry and disillusioned, she was condemned to political inactivity after her return to Moscow. She did, however, find some outlet for her angry energy when she learned that Dybenko had mercilessly crushed a peasant rebellion in the Tambov region, near Moscow; she managed to plead successfully with Lenin and Nadezhda Krupskaya for the release of some twenty peasant women, who had had little to do with the rebellion but who had been imprisoned in intolerable conditions in Moscow. It must have been sadly obvious to her that Lenin's health, burdened by so many years of relentless responsibilities and anxieties, was failing him. Gripped by headaches and tormented by insomnia and nervous tension which he was too strict with himself to admit, he found it quite impossible to relax fully and rest as his doctors were urging him to. Even during the long walks he forced himself to take, his thoughts would return again and again to the political problems which preoccupied him so obsessively, and his illness began to grow progressively worse. It was quite clear that he would be able to play little part in the Eleventh Party Congress, due to start in March 1922.

It was on the eve of this congress, in February, that Alexandra, exasperated by inactivity, at last decided to join her name to the twenty-one other signatories of Shlyapnikov's petition. And having committed herself so far, she agreed to present this petition with him before a hastily convened special commission of the Comintern executive committee. On February 24, 1922, she presented a report to the Comintern executive on the activities of the Zhenotdel over the past six months, apparently hoping in this way to clear herself of the charges of inefficiency that had been made against her. Two days later she and Shlyapnikov presented their petition, known as the Declaration of the Twenty-Two, to the Comintern and demanded a hearing. There can have been little doubt in her mind that by doing so she was condemning herself to ostracism and censure. Charged at the Eleventh Congress, totally unjustly, with initiating this hopeless venture and broadcasting to communists abroad the failings of the workers' state, her removal from party work seemed assured.

The Declaration of the Twenty-Two, listed twelve specific criticisms already advanced by the Workers' Opposition, and added six charges concerning the harassment to which opposition groups had been subjected. Pointing to the fact that sixty percent of Bolshevik Party members were non-proletarian, it emphasized the paradox whereby "any attempt to draw the workers to the state is called 'anarcho-syndicalism,' and its advocates are subjected to persecution and disgrace." A highly embarrassed commission of seven people (including Klara Zetkin, the British communist McManus, and the Bulgarian Kolarov) gathered in the Kremlin on February 28, 1922, to pass judgment on this bewildering document and its proponents. It must have been especially painful for Alexandra to have to confront her old friend and teacher Klara Zetkin, and to know that however well-disposed the foreign communists who gathered in the Kremlin might be, the outcome of the hearing was never in any doubt. "They show you foreigners formal parades and spectacles, but that's only for show," said Shlyapnikov. "In reality there are mighty strike movements, and the workers are breaking with the present government, for this wave of rebellion, you see, is very serious indeed." "And when the workers strike," added Alexandra, "the Red Army troops are used as strikebreakers." The four foreigners sat in silence as Trotsky, Zinoviev, Stalin, and Stalin's ally, the old Bolshevik Rudzutak, struggled with the undignified task of refuting all such charges. They gave the foreigners copies of the Tenth Congress resolution banning factions and accused the protesters of violating them. The Bolshevik leaders, they insisted, were dealing creatively with problems that were fully recognized; the Workers' Opposition was to be condemned for endangering party unity.[26] The Comintern executive duly condemned them.

The following week the Twenty-Two had to answer for their outrageous document in far less uncertain terms at the Eleventh Party Congress. Lenin had, as predicted, been prevented from playing any part in this affair by a series of illnesses which were undermining his strength and gradually removing him from political work. It was Felix Dzerzhinsky, who had been entrusted in December 1917 with the thankless task of organizing and running the famous political police (the Extraordinary All-Russian Commission for the Struggle Against Counter-Revolution, or "Cheka") who now had to take on, with Trotsky and Stalin, the equally thankless task of recommending punishments for the group. Since the Workers' Opposition was still rallying supporters among the party rank and file and threatened to bring a considerable number of supporters (including many from Nizhny Novgorod) to the party congress, all local parties were ordered to condemn the workers' oppositionists and if necessary expel them. Shlyapnikov and Medvedev lost their seats on the Trade Union Council, and together with them Alexandra was summoned before the control commission to explain why they had taken their appeal to the Comintern. Harsh measures, it was implied, would be taken against them at the congress. They were to be punished for a variety of offenses, all of them equally serious: the Workers' Opposition had printed leaflets and appeared at meetings to put their line across after they had been specifically prohibited from doing so, Alexandra's speech at the Comintern congress amounted to calling for a break with the Party and was "widely used by all those presses hostile to us," Medvedev and Shlyapnikov had received agitational letters from abroad, and all had met to draft a petition that was patently factional. Long before their petition had been rejected, Alexandra, Shlyapnikov, and Medvedev had realized that their expulsion from the Party would be proposed; they therefore defended themselves by passionately appealing to past hopes and resolutions, and by angrily attacking the idea that they had been involved in any sinister factional conspiracies.

When the Eleventh Congress opened in the Kremlin on March 28, 1922, large numbers of delegates arrived in an angry mood, determined to reduce the power of the control commission, which had been so drastically purging the Party over the past year. But they were preempted by the ailing Lenin, who appeared to make an opening speech in which he furiously attacked the Workers' Opposition. The NEP was a retreat from the revolution to be sure, he said, but in any retreat discipline was doubly necessary, and the Workers' Opposition had flagrantly broken discipline. When an army retreated, he continued, machine-guns stood by, and when the orderly retreat became disorderly, they gave the order to fire. This was why he urged that Shlyapnikov, Medvedev, Kollontai, and all the other unrepentant oppositionists should now be expelled from the Party. That evening a leading member of the control commission named Sholtz announced that he had completed his investigation of the Workers' Opposition and was fully convinced that its members were guilty of factionalism. Medvedev, Shlyapnikov, and Kollontai ("who are the organizers of this business") were clearly guilty of this newly defined crime, which they had compounded by organizing support in conspiratorial meetings. Alexandra was signled out for the most criticism; her Menshevik past was cited, and it was pointed out that by allowing her pamphlet to be published abroad, she had given encouragement to people all over the world who were hostile to the Bolsheviks.[27]

Since Alexandra was attacked in greater detail than the others, both publicly and privately (particularly by Trotsky), and since she was charged with being the "leader" of the Twenty-Two, she was the first to answer the charges against them when she spoke on March 29. There had unfortunately been all too few secret meetings, she retorted. What the Party seemed unable to understand was that, Workers' Opposition or no, a party split was inevitable unless its line was changed. "The basic content of our appeal says, 'The Party is split off from the masses. This split exists—that is our misfortune, that is our pain . . .' When you go to a factory where there are 900 workers and where, during a meeting on some party resolution, 22 of them vote, 4 abstain, and the rest simply don't vote at all, this shows inertia, this demonstrates the split, that dark side of life in our Party against which we must fight. And another thing demonstrates that split: is it not typical that here, at this congress, we hear not one word in the political report of what the working class should actually *do?*" Shlyapnikov followed her with an equally impassioned speech, which was all the more devastatingly eloquent for omitting all reference to "bourgeois specialists" and thus concentrating all his attack on the Party itself. He stressed that her pamphlet had only been circulated abroad because it had brought its supporters harassment and ostracism at home. Their "declaration" had emerged out of a very few hours of "secret" meetings and could not possibly be interpreted as a "factional plot," since "our desire is to see the Party united, that Party which we all created with our own hands, along with thousands of workers, in the underground and during the revolution. We cannot so easily leave this Party or desire a split."

Alexandra, although stating how flattered she was to be accused of "leading" the Twenty-Two, categorically denied it, "in view of the fact that I consider our other twenty-one comrades, people like Kopylov, Mitin, and Tolokantsev, to be so class-conscious and such good comrades . . . that I could in no way lead them. Rather, I myself have learned a great deal from associating with them." She then dealt with the specific charges against her. Accused of circulating her pamphlet abroad, she pointed out, perhaps rather naïvely, that she had asked the German Communist Workers' Party to withhold it from publication and that she could not be held responsible for their refusal to do so. The charges had also mentioned her Menshevik associations before 1915; as a member of the Zimmerwald left she could hardly believe that her prerevolutionary credentials were any less reputable than anyone else's. As for the "ridiculous" charge that they had spread their complaints "too widely," on the contrary, they had only had time to prepare such a small number of translations of her pamphlet into French that there had not even been enough to go round the Comintern congress last year. And they had turned to the Comintern precisely because "we saw there was something wrong with our Party":

> I say to you now that in our Party a sick, sad process is going on at the moment. What will be left of it if it is deprived of its red corpuscles, the working class? It will stand flabby, lymphatic, inert, and uncreative. It was our fear of this process that drove us to address our appeal to the Comintern. Comrades, turn the attention of our leaders, who won't listen to our words of warning, to this process. Perhaps our voices will

force the leaders to consider what is happening, turn their attention to the mass exit from our workers' Party, to the fact that all activity in the Party is decreasing, to the fact that the working class no longer feels at home in our Party.

It was the duty of every party member, she concluded, to address the proper party section with their criticisms and complaints, to expose errors and demand their correction. "We stand by our resolutions at the Tenth Party Congress on workers' democracy and the freedom of inner-party criticism, and we want them put into practice. We want the principal leading role of the working class in our Party to be firmly established and recognized, not just on paper but in reality. In the creativity of the working class lies our salvation!" These words were followed by an equally cutting speech from Shlyapnikov, who declared that the Party was as demoralized as it had been in the worst years of the tsarist reaction, and that the NEP was a flagrantly anti-working-class policy.[28]

Their sincerity brought them loud applause from a number of delegates. A majority of them voted against the Workers' Opposition, and two recent members of the group were expelled. Shlyapnikov, Medvedev, and Kollontai, old Bolsheviks who still had considerable standing, were saved from expulsion—"in open defiance of Lenin's demand to expel them," wrote Trotsky.[29]

Nineteen twenty-two, wrote Alexandra, was a bleak and unfruitful year for her. "My 'theses,' my sexual and moral views, were bitterly fought by many party comrades of both sexes, as were still other differences of opinion in the Party regarding guiding political principles. Personal and family cares were added thereto, and thus months in 1922 went by without any fruitful work." As she remarked ironically to the Italian communist writer Ignazio Silone, who was in Moscow at the time: "If you happen to read in the papers that Lenin has had me arrested for stealing silver spoons from the Kremlin, that simply means I'm not entirely in agreement with him about some little matter of agricultural or industrial policy." "Kollontai had acquired her sense of irony in the West," Silone commented, "and she only used it with people from the West. But even then, in these feverish years of building the new regime, how difficult it was for us to reach any understanding with Russians on the simplest, and for us the most important, questions."[30]

Shortly after the Eleventh Party Congress, in March 1922 Alexandra once more left Moscow for Odessa. Leaving behind her all thought of any major political work, she resigned herself to the prospect of making her living as a writer, and possibly taking up some obscure post in the Party. Dybenko visited her there briefly, and once again their time together was filled with the tension and bitterness of the separation they knew was inevitable. It was during these difficult months in Odessa that Alexandra wrote some of her most inspired articles on the new morality, and started work on a novel and several short stories—her first attempt at fiction since Korolenko's rejection of the short story she wrote in 1895. Although Alexandra stopped working with the Zhenotdel after February 1922, she continued to receive enormous support from a great many delegates there. Earlier that year Angelica Balabanova had been approached by various central-committee members who asked her to replace Alexandra as its director. She had refused, disliking the manner in which the offer was made and pointing out that she had neither Alexandra's talents for organization nor the enthusiasm for defending women's activities. Alexandra's old underground friend Elena Stasova, with whom she had gradually lost contact, was also approached as a reliable candidate for the post, but she had never shown any interest in women's work.

The woman eventually chosen to replace Alexandra at the beginning of 1922 was Sofya Smidovich, a revolutionary since the 1890's and leader of the Moscow Zhenotdel since 1919. Her status in the Party was not high, and it was expected that she would set the tone for the new, more modest ambitions, of the Zhenotdel. No longer would the women's departments struggle to gain the full representation of women's interests in the Party; they would work instead now to ensure merely that women received adequate maternity protection and were not fired unjustly. As she assumed her new position she spoke out sharply against the new sexual freedom, those who wrote about it, and the very many women in Russia for whom Alexandra Kollontai was still a profoundly inspiring and exceptional figure. And so it was that Alexandra's progressive and pioneering ideas on people's infinite capacity for love began gradually to be regarded as guilty by association with all her connected aspirations for a society in which the working class, not the Party and its organizations, would decide how best and most efficiently they could work.

If she failed herself to make the positive connection between these two strands in her thinking, her more conservative critics were not slow to do so—negatively—as the response to an article of hers in the spring of 1922 demonstrated very clearly. The first of her three "Letters to Communist Youth," which appeared in the magazine for young Bolsheviks *Young Guard*, followed quite consistently on her "theses" and her Sverdlov lectures and was probably prompted by the many personal and sexual problems raised at these lectures by her young and enthusiastic audience. But the editors of *Young Guard* had seen fit to decorate the title-page with a series of rhetorical question-marks and to accompany the article with a brief note dissociating themselves from the views expressed. An indication of the repressive standpoint from which all her writings on sex so rapidly came to be viewed was the torrent of abusive letters provoked by this inoffensive article, which *Young Guard* published in subsequent issues. This alarming response had been systematically encouraged by the editors, who had published alongside her article a piece by the notoriously reactionary psychologist Professor Zalkind, whose hymn to sexual abstinence rang out with all the force of his authority and orthodoxy.

Yet Alexandra herself received letters from many young people who were moved by what she had written, and for whom she would remain for many years a much truer voice of the young revolution's hopes. In these articles she was addressing young people who were approaching maturity in a period when the emotions of tenderness, numbed by war and starved by famine, had for so long been replaced by the brief, brute instinct of reproduction that they had gone underground.

Society in the past, she said, based as it was upon competitiveness and the accumulation of private property, had prostituted love by making of it a commodity and confounding it with the desire to possess one's sexual partner. This she had observed in her earliest writings on sex as far back as 1911. That self-centered all-confounding love of the romantic myth could not grow, for it looked inward to the holy citadel of marriage, which became a cover for storms of jealousy and possessiveness, and gave men sanction to exploit, incarcerate, stupefy, and deceive women. The revolutions of 1905 and 1917 in Russia had released people's great reservoirs of natural energy, energy which both killed and caressed. Young people had rebelled against the old hypocritical assumption that erotic love required virtues so rare, and required people to be so perfectly matched, that it could only be sanctioned by marriage. Many people had embarked in those years on a series of casual sexual relationships in which women inevitably suffered (and which Alexandra was to describe, in a subsequent article, as no better than an excrescence of bourgeois morality). Yet it was precisely in these crude, soulless affairs that men and women learned painfully to see each other as separate identities, to be trusted, not owned and deceived.

The ideals of the revolution said that love for one person increased every faculty of thought and feeling and that to exalt one person was to exalt every other social relationship. Love, she felt, was always ennobling. The generosity of one person could educate a colder and cruder companion to love; and even if the other person did not respond and moved on, one would be left the greater, and one's love would dwell in the rest of society. The revolution had released people from the mystical spiritual astronomy of romanticism and allowed them to feel a warmer sympathy and truer sensitivity to each other.

Then the civil war had separated people. Absence, the great falsifier, left them in a tangle of pain and untruth. People embarked on brief, precarious love affairs, were hurt, and lied to cover their confusion. In the civil-war years sexual relationships were all too often the same casually ruthless exercises in power that they had been before—but with the important difference that women, as well as men, were learning to initiate and end relationships. There was no time for words of love, only for brief kisses snatched before parting. The bloody road out of the horrors of the past was the only road open to people, and it hardened them. But it also strengthened them emotionally. The revolution and civil war educated people to a more comradely kind of love, and erotic passion was replaced by the more sociable virtues of friendship. Men and women worked and fought together, tended each other when they were sick, and held the pall when their comrades died.

Now that the war was over, love, compassion, and sensitivity to others' needs were returning, along with all the delicacy and nobility of erotic love. And in the chaos of poverty, famine, and social disruption left behind by the war, love was one of the solidest experiences that people could know. People now realized that when a man and woman stood for each other as for the whole of humanity, this kind of generous and universal love could be as filled with peace and poetry as nature itself. Love in its present form, Alexandra wrote (in one of the later "Letters"), was so complex, so far removed from its original impulse—the biological instinct of reproduction—and indeed so often in direct opposition to this, that it was perhaps better to ask ourselves what we are, rather than what love is.

In an age of increasing psychological complexity, love—tender eroticism, comradely love, maternal love, love for the collective and the Party, and the conflicting love for two people of the opposite sex—often appeared in very confusing forms to people whose capacities for love had for so long been denied. There were no Ten Commandments for love; one could only assess a person's conduct as correct if it was in harmony with the interests of the group. But in the new society, she insisted, people should bravely recognize these conflicts, not suppress them. For in doing so they would recognize that it was through the many and various aspects of love that people wove the threads which would make for them a whole web of social relationships, a society of their own creation and a home, in which they were no longer lonely spectators and travelers.

In love—the community with what we experience outside ourselves —people could see the other person not as an object to be owned but as one who stood for the whole of society. This was why, Alexandra wrote, however great two people's love for each other might be, "the ties binding them to the collective will always take precedence, will be firmer, more complex and more organized."[31]

This "Letter," like all her other writings on the transformation of sexual relationships, the possibility of a new erotic sensibility, the conflicts between the needs of the individual and those of the collective and between sexual passion and revolutionary commitment, is of extraordinary inspirational and historic value for women today, as it was to women in Russia in the 1920's. Yet she wrote it at a time when her prestige in the Party was at its lowest ebb, when, at the age of fifty, her "great love" for Dybenko was collapsing, and when her own hopes for the future were nerve-rackingly uncertain. Much of the same optimism, many of the same insights and conflicts (which she had largely suppressed in years of political writing), were expressed with an awkward tentativeness and moving honesty in the fictional trilogy which was published the following year, *Love of Worker Bees.*

Not long after Alexandra had left Moscow, Lenin had had a stroke which paralyzed him and removed him from active life. Stalin was acting party secretary that summer, and it was to him that Alexandra wrote, asking for a modest party post somewhere in Russia. She had little hope that her request would be answered and was prey to anxieties about the punishment with which the Workers' Opposition had been threatened. For the central committee, however—which, with Lenin mortally ill, was more preoccupied with its internal affairs than with any suitable punishment or coercion they might be able to dream up—it seemed far more urgent to clear all the awkward oppositionists out of the country. It is unlikely that her letter to Stalin was the "frank and touching letter of repentance" described by her 1947 biographer, and far more likely that Stalin was keen to make use of Alexandra's experience abroad. At any rate, shortly after sending her letter, and much to her surprise, she received a cable from him with orders to return to Moscow, where the Commissariat of Foreign Affairs would assign her a diplomatic post.

Although she had not formally broken with the Workers' Opposition, she discovered when she returned to Moscow that the central committee's hostility to her factional activities was now far outweighed by their reluctance to subject their fragile Soviet diplomacy to ridicule by appointing a woman ambassador; this was one break with traditional diplomacy which even the Bolsheviks (who had nonchalantly broken with every rule of traditional diplomacy at the Brest-Litovsk peace negotiations with the Germans in 1918) were reluctant to contemplate. But her old friend Georgy Chicherin (one of the Bolsheviks' most distinguished diplomats), who ran the Commissariat of Foreign Affairs with Maxim Litvinov, had recommended her so highly for her knowledge of foreign languages, her experience abroad, her good manners, and her acquaintance with the rules of etiquette, that the Bolshevik central committee was hardly able to refuse her a diplomatic post. Other countries were not so ready to break with protocol, however. Canada, for example, rejected her at once, and it was only in September 1922 that Norway agreed to accept her as a member of the small Russian trade delegation there, which the Soviet republic hoped to extend into a full diplomatic embassy.

Alexandra spent much of her time in Moscow between June and October 1922 in the modest top-floor room of the Foreign Commissariat where her gentle, cultured, and quixotic friend Chicherin led his solitary bachelor life, in very much the same squalor as he had lived when she first met him in Europe in 1908. He still had the same messianic faith in the value of work, and ate, slept, and breathed diplomacy. But although he instructed Alexandra in the protocol and the goals of Soviet diplomacy, it is unlikely that his chaotic style of living and working was one which appealed to Alexandra. He tended to work from ten in the evening until ten in the morning, and slept during the day; his desk was always in the most scandalous state of confusion; he was habitually unpunctual, had a deep loathing for the telephone, was constantly mislaying important telegrams, and, as before, had a great aversion to replacing his tattered old clothes with an outfit more appropriate to his rank. Although he supported no particular party line, few could fail to be impressed by his candor and simplicity—few, that is, except Litvinov, who shared the running of the commissariat with him. There was no love lost between the two, and they had little in common, personally or politically. Litvinov was as fleshy and jocose as Chicherin was ascetic and sensitive, and he supported rapprochement with the West whereas Chicherin regarded Germany as the pivot of Soviet foreign policy and Asia as its special concern: Chicherin was isolationist and anti-Western. Litvinov, however, was the more popular of the two with the central-committee members, especially Stalin, and in 1930 Chicherin was ousted and Litvinov ran the commissariat alone.

In these months in Moscow, although Alexandra was no longer working for the Zhenotdel, she evidently still had many friends there. Vera Golubeva, who had been Zhenotdel co-director with her, was still a close friend, as was Klavdia Nikolaeva, with whom she had worked since 1907. She was in touch, too, with the many young people she had met at the Sverdlov University, who had been so moved by her articles on the new morality, and she continued the optimistic tone of these articles in a little book she wrote at that time entitled *Soon: In 48 Years' Time.* In this she portrayed a communal house in Soviet Russia in the year 1970. It is filled with innocent childlike people who have known neither capitalist injustice nor the Soviet secret police.[32]

She also published the "Second Letter to Young Workers" in the journal *Young Guard.* She had been criticized for writing in her first letter that no "rules" for moral conduct could be laid down. She reiterated this now, and she took to their necessarily harsh conclusion her earlier statements about the individual's obligation to subordinate his or her personal desires to those of the collective. There was much of her own sad experience in the words which concluded this letter: "If a member of the collective does not obey and support the orders of the collective, its morality, its social rules, the collective will not tolerate that person in its midst. Expulsion from the collective has always been and remains the harshest and most terrible of punishments for a person. . . ."[33] These thoughts were consistent with her earliest writings on morality, although her use of the word "collective" had now changed from meaning the working class to meaning both the Party and the nation. She had recognized since she first joined the Bolsheviks that the Party had the right to demand obedience from its members; she was now expressing her willingness to obey.

While in Moscow in the summer and autumn of 1922 she saw her old and dearest friend Zoya, who promised to visit her abroad—as did Misha, too, who at the age of twenty-eight had just finished his studies at Petrograd's Technological Institute and was now working there as an engineer. Their love and support must have compensated considerably for the increasing hostility which was now being directed toward her by Sofya Smidovich and the new Zhenotdel leaders, as well as by those in the Party who had so viciously attacked the ideals of the Workers' Opposition. The Eleventh Party Congress had spelled the end of this idealistic group, and their inspiring but sadly unrealistic program. Shlyapnikov, Medvedev, and Lutovinov, demoralized but not yet broken, tentatively tried over the next few years to revive the Workers' Opposition, but the terror which they had so presciently foretold was soon to be directed against them, as against thousands of other Russians convicted of "crimes" far less serious.

On October 9, 1922, Misha, Zoya, and a number of her other friends accompanied Alexandra to Helsinki. They said their tearful farewells as she boarded the ship which was to take her across the Gulf of Bothnia to Sweden. A few days later she arrived by train in Oslo, the Kristiania of her exile years before the revolution. She had little more idea about what her diplomatic duties would entail than the scraps of information she had gleaned from Chicherin, and little idea, indeed, that any diplomatic work would be expected of her at all. "I truly thought," she said later, "that this appointment was a pure formality, and that I'd find time in Norway for my writing."[34]

17

Exiled in Diplomats' Europe

By October 1922 faith in the Bolsheviks' humanistic revolution of love was withering with the last leaves of autumn. To the idealists and romantics who had helped to make that revolution, it was inconceivable that life existed outside the Party, yet none of them could have drawn the terrible conclusion that it was precisely the authoritarian nature of this Party that was making life impossible in Russia. None of them could yet have admitted the diabolical proportions of the bureaucratic counter-revolution. For although they saw the power of the bureaucracy to crush them, they did not see that this crushing machine already existed within the Party too. Perhaps it was because the Workers' Oppositionists were the first to sense this that Alexandra was so speedily sent abroad.

Over the next fourteen years oppositionists would struggle at all costs to stay in the Party and call it theirs—desperately claiming that it was proletarian and socialist, even though it was sick, corrupt, and murderous. Torn and morally confused, tortured by the sense that their own circumstances were somehow isolated and exceptional, haunted by guilt over their "non-proletarian" origins and their non-Bolshevik pasts, many of them who were threatened with expulsion would feel over these years that they had no choice but to start again with a new conciliatory relationship with the Party, accepting official versions of the truth, and rallying the Russian people against the internal and external enemies of the revolution. For Alexandra, expulsion meant political death. As the number of Party members who killed themselves in those years indicates, exile might have driven her to suicide. As it was, her removal from Russia made it impossible for her to intervene when, five years later, the crisis predicted by the Workers' Opposition came, and the left oppositionists were expelled from the Party.

Alexandra's own survival—for the next thirty years she lived a life of resignation and tireless hard work and gradually put many of her former ideals behind her—was exceptional in such cruel times, when the ranks of all her old Bolshevik comrades were so savagely thinned by Stalin's purges. But this survival was ensured only after the most ferocious attack on her sexual theories had made them so totally unacceptable that even now few people in the Soviet Union know of them. Even before she left Russia, as her autobiography tells us, her books, articles, and published letters were being "bitterly fought by many party members of both sexes."[1] In 1921 her eloquent defense of people's unlimited powers of love was being described by one party member as contributing to the "poisonous miasma of capitalism which continues to infect the social atmosphere." In 1922 Bukharin was writing off her "purely physical" attitude to sex as mere "vulgar materialism." The year after her banishment she had become the target of an increasingly vocal group of "sex-conservationists" who saw sexual energy as a function of class energy, to be harnessed to the revolution, not frittered away for pleasure. By 1937 the sociologist Volfson was finding it necessary to revile the "coarse, animal anti-Marxist views" of Kollontai and others in order to exalt the virtues of monogamous marriage.[2]

Alexandra had seen how buried sexual energies, released by the revolution and striving to transcend the old morality, had clashed again and again with an ever-present sexual conservatism which drew its strength from prerevolutionary ideology. Doubtless many young people had abused her enlightened assumption that "free love" was progressive and revolutionary, and had exalted in her name new forms of sexual exploitation; as Trotsky said in 1923, "Communist theory has outstripped our actual everyday life by ten years, and in some respects by a century."[3] By the time she left Russia, sexual conservatives were mobilizing to attack not only the sexual "excesses" she was considered to have condoned but her ideas, personality, and "bourgeois" origins too.

This attack, like the physical liquidation of thousands of idealists who suffered far worse punishments than hers, was justified by the need to find culprits for a state of affairs in Russia which was becoming increasingly insupportable. By 1922 a third of the women in the workforce had lost their jobs for no economic, social, or political reason other than sexual prejudice, and for those who did manage to keep their jobs in the first years of the NEP the old exploitation not only continued but sprang up unhindered in the new, smaller private enterprises now dominated by the profit motive. Seven million waifs roaming the streets in savage armed gangs and about 122,500 divorces in 1922 alone provided eloquent evidence of the marital instability of those years, and of the preconditions for prostitution established by the NEP. Crowds of women who had been abandoned by their husbands and could not find work filled the towns; in Petrograd there were estimated to be 32,000 prostitutes, quite as many as there had been before the revolution. Drug-taking and gambling flourished among the "red businessmen" (the "Nepmen" who managed the new private enterprises); the housing shortage remained acute, and for exploited and exploiters alike venereal disease reached the proportions of an epidemic, against which Soviet medical services had neither the propaganda nor the medicine they needed.

Alexandra's sexual theories and the libertarian views she expressed as a member of the Workers' Opposition were particularly embarrassing to the central committee, however, because her standing was so high both among people in Russia and in the Comintern, and among those she had known abroad before the revolution. Since she was a woman fighting on two fronts, with neither aspirations to leadership nor a power base within the Party, it was doubtless assumed that it would be easy to remove her from political life in Russia. Stalin's personal views on women were despicable, and he was in no sense a liberationist, but he had a peculiarly old-fashioned resistance to subjecting them to harsh punishment. The very qualities that made her so popular and so hard to punish now made her a valuable candidate for Soviet diplomacy. The short-term response to this troublesome woman was clearly to get her out of Russia, to ensure that her ideas were discredited and her Party work forgotten, and to keep her in ignorance of what was happening in Russia by a prolonged enforced absence.

In 1922, only two years before Lenin's death, the Soviet Union was already under Stalin's rule while most people in the country did not even know his name. Yet as early as 1919 he had been more deeply immersed than anyone in the personal politics of the Party. It was at the Eighth Party Congress in 1919 that the Politburo and the Orgburo had been set up (the first to take urgent political decisions which were then reported back to the central committee, the second to conduct all the Party's organizational work). One Politburo member was to serve on the Orgburo, and it was the mediocre Stalin who was considered the most suitable candidate for this post as bureaucratic liaison officer. In 1922 the Politburo was still making all major policy decisions, and the Orgburo was in complete control of all staff appointments.

At the Eleventh Congress in March 1922 Stalin had responded with glee to the leftists' demand that the central committee be expanded and collectivized, and had insisted that the work of this committee, which was top-heavy with organizations, must be coordinated by a new office, the General Secretariat, headed by him. Theoretically subordinate to the central committee, its work confined to preparing the agenda for meetings, seeing to documentation, and transmitting decisions from the leaders to lower functionaries and cadres—Stalin's General Secretariat was soon all too obviously beyond any party control. Alexandra had been subjected to especially harsh censure at the Eleventh Congress for considering "dissent inevitable if the Party does not take the path of the views expressed by comrades Kollontai, Medvedev, and Shlyapnikov."[4] Dissent was indeed inevitable. Shortly after the congress, top Party leaders were expressing alarm at Stalin's vastly increased powers.

His staffing of local party organizations ensured that full-time workers in the party, the unions, the army, and the government followed a quasi-military discipline which he enforced by frequent transfers. Few could now deny the Workers' Opposition's insights into the widening gulf between full-time and part-time party workers, and its denunciation of all the material advantages that accrued to party functionaries. By 1922 party organizations throughout Russia had been realigned into a military chain of command, and only among the members of the Politburo did long friendship make for any semblance of collective spirit. At the end of that year Trotsky was complaining bitterly of the power of local party secretaries, now simply agents of the General Secretary, independent of local organizations. But by then he himself was figuring prominently in the vast files and dossiers which the Orgburo was compiling; by the time he was expelled from the Party in 1927 and the first purges began, 400,000 party members, 1300 factory managers, and 20,000 officials had all incurred the suspicion of the General Secretary and had had their lives filed away for future purges. As Stalin consolidated this nationwide network of control, whereby he could order people at a moment's notice to change jobs and residence, or move from party work in the capital to remote diplomatic posts and semi-exile, party members were frequently bewildered as to whether such a sudden transfer was meant as an honor or a disgrace, and whether or not, if they had displeased Stalin personally or politically at some time in their lives, this might be held against them.

Even those quite close to Stalin could hardly claim to know him. All anyone knew was that his intellectual powers were limited and that his political behavior was dictated by the moods, needs, and pressures of the vast machine he had created. He knew how to justify each new repressive act in the light of previous party statutes, and he availed himself particularly of those contentious resolutions banning factions that had been passed at the Tenth Congress. He was taciturn, preferring to listen to others talk and rarely revealing himself. Since Lenin's illness most people feared the lack of any leader of comparable brilliance to succeed him, and Stalin was regarded as the very personification of mediocrity, someone who would simply keep the Party going on the lines established by Lenin; initially few questioned his claim to be less intolerant than others, the "guardian of Lenin's doctrine," the follower of the "middle road." It was because the "middle road" was not possible in a time of revolution that he was forced repeatedly to leap to this side and that, classifying more and more activities as unpardonable.

Marxists, unlike the nineteenth-century liberals who preceded them, had always emphasized that there were historical instances when force was inevitable—citing in particular the French Revolution and the American Civil War. But the use of force, they stressed, was to have narrow limits. Indeed it was on the assumption that the fortunes of any revolution were shaped by the economic and social processes creating it that Alexandra had joined the Bolshevik Party in 1915. Force, as Marx said, was the midwife of every society pregnant with the new, helping the baby into the world when its time had come; after that her job was done. As Isaac Deutscher has said in his biography of Stalin, "Force was the mother of Stalin's society"[5]—all else was hypocrisy. For idealists like Alexandra the old myths of party unity still had the power to inspire and transform the old society. For Stalin they represented an anesthetic for the terrible transitional period until industrialization and education had done their work in engineering people's souls.

Alexandra had more than one reason to dislike Stalin. On her return to Russia in March 1917 she had been dismayed by his compromising policy of support for the Provisional Government; his lewd comments on her relationship with Dybenko had also revealed a deep contempt for women. She was to sense the full force of this contempt as director of the Zhenotdel. It was at the Eleventh Congress that one of her former colleagues pointed out that the Zhenotdel did not have full rights within the Party and that when the Orgburo invited the heads of central-committee departments to its meetings, the Zhenotdel was invariably excluded.

When the Orgburo did deign to meet the Zhenotdel directors, they were told to wait in the hall and were only called in when the subject under discussion concerned women. Alexandra's successor, Sofya Smidovich, irately pointed out that for all the Party's talk of the "usefulness" of the women's departments, it gave them precious little support: if they were truly "useful" they should be supported; if not, they should be dissolved, for better that than have them "drag out the miserable existence they are now leading in the provinces."[6]

Their existence was miserable indeed, for in 1922 the government had withdrawn money to pay women apprentices in the government, soviet, and party departments, and the Zhenotdel staff had been reduced from forty to twenty-one, with only five paid organizers at the provincial level. As Alexandra knew from bitter experience, the union leaders constantly tried to prevent the Zhenotdel from having any influence on their activities; it was only through the intervention of the Party that women organizers were represented at all in the unions. In the first year of the NEP, doubts about the Zhenotdel's usefulness multiplied, women felt unsupported and unsure of themselves, and local women's departments continued to be arbitrarily and often violently disbanded despite numerous central-committee circulars deploring this. After the Tenth Congress in March 1921 the Party urged that there should be more coordination between the Zhenotdel and the agitprop departments, which effectively meant the subordination of the former to the latter and the increased isolation of the Zhenotdel from the party center.

In the textile town of Ivanovo, near Moscow, where a good sixty percent of the workforce were women, the Party refused to allow the Zhenotdel to hold delegate elections, and various party organizations in the Moscow region even called for the Zhenotdel to be liquidated. "Many people state that there are dangers that the new economic conditions are not only destroying the possibilities for work among women, but also will strengthen the enslavement of working women . . . ," said one organizer at a national Zhenotdel meeting in November 1921. There was a general decline in women's attendance at party congresses too. At the Ninth and Tenth Congresses in 1920 and 1921 something like five percent of the delegates were women; at the Eleventh Congress, despite the fact that in the summer of 1922 seventeen-and-a-half percent of party members were women, they were only two percent of the delegates.

Without experience, resources, or support from the Party's male majority it became increasingly difficult for the Zhenotdel to enforce equal pay for equal work. The gigantic nationwide network of party organizations needed to socialize household labor seemed far beyond the powers of the Party as a whole, let alone of the 40,000 women in the Russian Communist Party in 1922. Moreover many women felt that assigning the tasks of their own emancipation to them left the sexual division of labor intact, and that they should not be solely responsible for deciding how best to cope with housework, child-rearing, and social welfare. If Alexandra failed to connect her sexual theories with the other strands in her political thinking, her disjointedness was that of the Zhenotdel itself, which—however progressive its campaigns against illiteracy, its work with Muslim women, and its aspirations for transforming women's everyday lives—always served the interests of the Party. Again and again women's interests and those of the Party conflicted; and, again and again women's interests were subordinated to the Party from which they drew their strength.[7]

The Soviet republic's first trade delegate in Oslo was Yakov Suritz, an ex-Menshevik of genuinely liberal sympathies whom Alexandra had probably met before the war in Stockholm, where he was a member of the Russian colony. He was greatly surprised to receive a telegram from Moscow announcing that he was to be joined by Alexandra; although it was not clear what her duties would be, it was obvious to him that this was no ordinary appointment. "The party central committee was sending her to us in order to get rid of an embarrassing personality, who for various reasons they had to treat tactfully," wrote Suritz's (and later Alexandra's) private secretary, Marcel Body.*[8]

On her arrival in Oslo, Alexandra attended a brief diplomatic reception at 34 Drammenswein, the comfortable three-story house occupied by the Soviet trade delegation. She then retired to the same small red Tourist Hotel in the beautiful mountainous resort of Holmenkollen, which had so delighted her seven years earlier. There she immersed herself in writing her novella and two short stories, and adjusted to her new life. *Love of Worker Bees* came out in Russia the following year in a small edition as part of the series *Revolution in Feelings and Morality,* and was followed by her second fictional trilogy, *Woman at the Threshold: Some Psychological Studies.*[9]

Writing these, her first published works of fiction, with a candid and

---

*Body (a French-born Bolshevik) wrote his memoirs of Alexandra immediately after her death in 1952. In these he emerges as a somewhat unstable and self-centered man, greatly prone to overemphasize his own influence on Alexandra's activities; but they are useful nonetheless.

moving simplicity which she hoped would make her insights accessible to working women who might not otherwise read novels, Alexandra described the changes in women's sexual feelings, their confusions and their new strength, throughout the years of the revolution and the early period of the NEP. In fiction she could examine more openly than in political writings the connection between the economic pressures of female unemployment, dwindling nurseries, and mounting prostitution which were driving women back into the confines of monogamous marriage and solitary housework, and the more insidious psychological pressures which were so deeply rooted in the NEP. Through her three main women protagonists in *Love of Worker Bees*—Vasilisa Malygina (the central character in the novella of that name), Olga Sergeevna (the narrator of "Three Generations") and the narrator of "Sisters"—she explored the ways in which women were struggling to understand these pressures and offering each other solidarity and sympathy in the process.

All of them meet their lovers in the sexually effervescent days of the October revolution. Their feelings of confidence and strength are released, and they happily anticipate loving and living with their lovers as long as shared political work keeps them together. But feelings so long denied are not so easily understood. Olga Sergeevna, a middle-aged underground worker, embarks spontaneously on a liaison with a younger comrade, but she has for too long separated the question of her own liberation from the theoretical liberation of women which is written into her Party's program for the socialist future, and she is deeply shocked to discover that her daughter Zhenya has not only been sleeping with her (Olga's) lover but with several other men too, claiming that her enjoyment of sex in no way interferes with her party work. Alexandra's critics would later try to prove that Zhenya's attitudes were those of her creator, but in fact she is clearly as bewildered by this guiltless promiscuity as is Olga Sergeevna. Alexandra quite obviously loves the political idealism which Zhenya, with her early experiences during the civil war of collective living and sexual equality, promises to bring to her party work in the 1920's, but she concludes her story by questioning whether this youthful promiscuity really represents the sexual revolution she has envisaged, or whether in the chaos of war and revolution young people might simply not yet have had the chance to learn how to form deep and lasting relationships.

In Vasilisa Malygina's joyful and obsessive relationship with her husband, Volodya, many of Alexandra's own tormented feelings for Dybenko emerge. Indeed it was while she was writing this trilogy that Alexandra managed finally to exorcise her fears of a final separation. She wrote urging him to remarry. Dybenko visited her in Oslo in January 1923, and when he returned to Moscow a few days later, they had both agreed amicably that their affair was over. "Imagine," Alexandra wrote to Zoya and her sister, Vera Yureneva, after he had left, "nobody here can even guess what I'm feeling. I'm working flat out, and I've put all my sufferings aside to put all I have into the buying of herrings and sealskins and the selling of wheat . . . I feel better this way, it had to happen . . ."[10]

Constantly separated from Volodya by party assignments in different parts of Russia, Vasilisa Malygina, like Alexandra, suffers unendurable sexual loneliness and finally decides to abandon her party work to join him in South Russia as his wife. She soon discovers that, as manager of one of the new enterprises created by the NEP, Volodya is enjoying all the material privileges of his position and expects her to live on his terms, in his house, wearing the clothes he buys for her, and dutifully supporting him in his disagreements with the Party. Surrounded by Volodya's servants and repulsive "Nepman" friends, paralyzed by political inactivity and the slowly dawning suspicion of Volodya's unfaithfulness, Vasilisa struggles against illness and depression to understand the ways in which Volodya is exploiting her and to find a new independent life for herself outside the home he has created for her, with all its lies and luxuries. When she does eventually leave him, it is to embark on a more honest and optimistic life of hard-working independence.

The narrator of "Sisters" also meets her husband at the height of the October days, but by 1921 the two have drifted apart as the NEP turns the man who was once her comrade into a demoralized, drunken, profligate "Nepman." She loses her job, her child's nursery is closed, and her husband starts to bring prostitutes home. Imprisoned within her home and with no life outside it, she feels powerless until she finally manages to talk to her husband's prostitute while he sleeps drunkenly in the next room. Discovering then how similar her life is to that of the woman forced onto the streets, she derives the courage to leave him. Her economic dependence on him and her fear of his love-making could hardly be more demoralizing than the more open prostitution of her sister in suffering. Despite its terrible and bewildering costs her liberation, like Vasilisa's, is genuine and hopeful.

The most engaging work in her collection of short stories entitled *Woman at the Threshold* was "A Great Love," which went into a second edition in September 1927. It dealt with some of the complex and conflicting demands of sexual passion and revolutionary dedication, and drew its inspiration from three passionate intellectuals and revolutionaries—Lenin, Nadezhda Krupskaya, and Inessa Armand—in whom she had seen these conflicts embodied in her years in exile and just before the revolution. A few of Lenin's letters to Inessa Armand were published in 1939, six years after Nadezhda Krupskaya's death, and more were included in the fifth edition of Lenin's complete works in 1965. By then it was quite obvious that Alexandra's novel was a *roman à clef,* but her writings had been so successfully submerged that this was of little interest to anyone in Russia. (In America the novel was translated in 1929 by Lily Lore, who was married to the man who had invited Alexandra to America in 1915.)

Even when the novel appeared in Russia in a small edition of 15,000 copies, Alexandra had been too widely discredited for it to cause very much comment—which is a pity, because it was written with a great deal of conviction and with the same, almost raw honesty which informed *Love of Worker Bees.* Alexandra believed that women writing fiction should try to keep as close as they could to the reality they perceived in their lives; for (as she wrote in a footnote to her 1913 essay, "The New Woman"): "The less harsh reality is romanticized, [and] the more contemporary woman's psychology is fully and truthfully presented, with all her migraines, her struggles, her problems, her contradictions, her complexity, and her aspirations, the richer the material for the spiritual image of the new woman that we will be able to study."[11]

Alexandra had first observed the relationship among Lenin, Nadezhda Krupskaya, and Inessa Armand when she was in Paris in 1909. "All of this happened long, long ago," opens the story (which is narrated by Natasha, a clear reflection of Inessa), "long before humanity knew anything of the horrors of war, and when the gigantic upheavals of the revolution were still waiting in the dim and distant future." The two other main characters, Anyuta and Zhenya, bear a striking resemblance to Nadezhda and Lenin, although it is unlikely that many people in Russia would have recognized Lenin from this description of him in exile, with his money troubles, his illnesses and the ruthless way in which he subordinated emotions to intellect. In describing how Anyuta's interests are not only subordinated to Zhenya's all-consuming passion for work but how she is actually insulted by their comrades, Alexandra casts an unfriendly eye at the cruel ways in which Stalin's supporters often dealt with Nadezhda Krupskaya. She quotes, for instance, the words of Yaroslavsky (that formidable critic of Alexandra's ideas and a leading light of the control commission), that Nadezhda Krupskaya was "stealing Lenin's precious time" shortly before his last illness.

Zhenya and Anyuta meet the talented and idealistic Natasha in exile, shortly after she has left her husband. She moves in with them, works with them politically, and shares their lives. Through Natasha's experiences the growing love she and Zhenya feel for each other is described. Gradually, through the intense new self-awareness which this "great love" brings to her, Natasha begins to sense that Zhenya does not understand her need for independent work, but rather assumes that she, like Anyuta, is his creature. She feels imprisoned by him. "It was possible that in the future some common work might throw them together again," the story concludes, as Natasha bravely leaves Zhenya to make a more independent life for herself. "But the great love which had made her heart beat all those years had fled for good, and nothing, no tenderness, no prayer, not even understanding, could reawaken it."

The anonymous heroine of the story "Thirty-Two Pages," also in this collection, faces similar conflicts between independent work as a research scientist and her need to be with her husband who is employed in a small provincial town, far from her own place of work. She walks down a foggy street one night examining her feelings, knowing that she will "go ahead all her life, toward her goal—her scientific work . . ."

> Going, as now, through the fog, but knowing there's a light ahead . . . What does she care if it's difficult, if her feet stick in the slush of the roadway, that the hem of her skirt whips across her legs, that her package of books and shopping weighs her down? Isn't it always difficult to be alone? In return she would have her freedom, she would belong again to her beloved work, and there would be no more misunderstanding or resentment when he fails to listen to her soul and to value her work. Living and *not* suffering? Living and *not* loving someone again to despair? Well, why not? He might not understand that. But when they were together and she had to reassure herself again and again that he still loved her, her work—so imaginative and well organized—simply stood still. For all those months. Oh, what it was like to be jerked away by that searing thought that tormented her conscience: that in five months she had only written 32 pages.[12]

While she was writing this book in Holmenkollen, Alexandra began to establish contact with some of the Norwegian radicals with whom she had been friendly seven years before—there was Egede Nissen, the elderly bohemian and intellectual, leader of the left Norwegian socialists, and his wife, with whom Alexandra had organized International Women's Day meetings in Norway in 1915; she also met again the leader of the Norwegian transport union, Anderson, and the young radical Tore Nerman. It was through old friends like these that she hoped eventually to persuade the liberal Norwegian government to extend diplomatic recognition to the Soviet Union. Shortly before she left Moscow, Chicherin had warned her that she was not to take one step that might be interpreted as interference in Norwegian politics, and she was anxious to confine her first diplomatic activities to these informal contacts. A number of articles appeared in the Norwegian press shortly after her arrival in which various of her acquaintances urged that the survival of Soviet Russia was in the interests of Norwegian trade.

Marcel Body visited her daily at Holmenkollen to keep her informed of the Soviet delegation's activities in Oslo, and it was not long after she had arrived that Body began to receive regular visits from the administrative secretary of the Comintern, Kobetsky, who wanted to make sure that Alexandra was not making trouble. Kobetsky told Body later that on his return to Moscow, Zinoviev (president of the Comintern) had asked him to comment on Alexandra's behavior. Kobetsky, who was not one to pass malicious judgments, amazed Zinoviev by his objectivity. "Watch out," he was told, "you've never met a woman like her before!"[13]

On December 8, 1922, Alexandra left Oslo for The Hague, where a peace congress had been called by the Trade Union International. The Soviet government had decided that Alexandra, with her knowledge of numerous foreign languages, was the best person to represent them at this gathering of moderate socialists, whom she might be able to persuade in informal discussions to support the Bolsheviks' fourteen-point peace program. Among the delegates she met there, from Germany, France, England, Italy, and Sweden, were various Mensheviks and Socialist Revolutionaries. "It was as if the dead had risen from their graves," she said. "Their proposals for peace seemed as dead and lifeless as all their old proposals for reform and compromise had seemed before."[14] She read out the Soviet government's proposals for their role in maintaining peace; it called for a united workers' front to make war on all bourgeois governments, for the destruction of the Versailles Treaty, and for the publication of all secret treaties. The proposals were rejected, but when she read a statement on the Bolsheviks' commitment to women's equality she was warmly applauded, and someone in the audience shouted, "You yourself, Madame Kollontai, are an example of those principles!"[15]

Shortly after she returned to Oslo, she learned that Suritz was soon to be transferred to Turkey and that she was to replace him as head of the trade delegation. Suritz introduced her to the prime minister and to the foreign minister, Esmark, with whom she was soon on friendly terms

—but not before she had broken diplomatic protocol and incurred a formal rebuke from him in her first attempt to inform herself on Norwegian affairs. She had written round to all the various ministries asking for information, only to be told that protocol demanded that she make all her enquiries through the Foreign Ministry. Undaunted, she protested to the government that the new Oslo telephone directory (which appeared in February 1923) had listed the non-existent tsarist Russian embassy and placed the Soviet delegation in the trades and firms section; a correction slip was inserted at her insistence.

Few people in Oslo had heard of Alexandra when she first arrived there. Yet in May 1923, when Suritz left for Ankara (shortly afterward to become Soviet ambassador in Paris) and Alexandra succeeded him, she was immediately greeted by a deluge of insults in the conservative Norwegian and émigré Russian press. For quite a few weeks Oslo was buzzing with rumors about this bloodthirsty, coarse, cruel, amoral Bolshevik woman who dressed like a man, drank vodka, smoked day and night, and knew not the most elementary human decency. In Russia, it was said, she was responsible for thousands of murders and had called for the nationalization of women and the factory-farming of children. Since none of the numerous journalists who met her that spring could fail to be impressed by her charm and sincerity, her pleasant appearance, and her knowledge of eleven languages, the first crude wave of rumors was replaced by the allegation that she was a "bad communist" whom the Bolsheviks wanted to recall from Norway since she sprawled in a luxurious Oslo flat, draped in furs and dripping with diamonds stolen from the Tsar, and made constant trips to Paris to replenish her splendid wardrobe. One French paper managed to combine aspects of both types of rumor, representing Kollontai as some sort of decadent terrorist, whose feathered hat was red with the blood of innocent victims. American industrialists opposed to child-labor reforms claimed that the American feminist movement was part of an international feminist conspiracy masterminded (sic) by Kollontai. The conservative Norwegian papers announced that she was smuggling Bolshevik spies into Norway by arranging marriages with Norwegian citizens.

The Oslo hotel to which she moved from Holmenkollen was called the Ritz, but it was quite unostentatious, and her two small attic rooms there, which she loved for their light and height, were very modest. As for her dress, she rarely wore anything but a black or blue suit, and never wore any jewelry except a chain for her glasses which had belonged to her mother. Alexandra kept to much the same daily routine during all her years as a diplomat—waking early, doing her exercises to some old records of military music which she had brought from Russia, taking a shower, drinking some coffee, and settling straight into her work. She managed to cajole her small staff at the delegation into working a ten-hour day but often stayed behind at the Drammenswein building long after they had left. In the spring of 1923 she met daily with representatives of Norway's main fishing businesses, who urged her to arrange for them to sell their herrings in the Soviet Union. When eventually she received an official order from Norway's Department of Foreign Trade to open negotiations for an exchange of Norwegian herrings and Russian wheat, she embarked on a long round of meetings with traders and government officials.

After a particularly long meeting with a group of fish exporters, an agreement was prepared and everything was settled except the price; Alexandra drove a hard bargain. "I have the agreement here before me on the table," she told them. "It's ready to be signed, every point has been precisely spelled out, and there remains only this wretched fifty öre per barrel which divides us. Meanwhile, this transaction is the first step toward establishing a multimillion-kroner trade exchange between Norway and Russia. Surely, gentlemen, you won't ruin not only this transaction but all prospects for a Russian market in the years ahead?" After several more hours of discussion they agreed on a compromise, with the Norwegians reducing their price by twenty-five öre and the Russians increasing theirs by twenty-five. "And if I've acted arbitrarily, I'll pay for it out of my salary for the rest of my life," she said.[16] Protesting like the gentlemen they were, the traders at last agreed to her original proposal. When she returned home, she found one white rose waiting for her. In Moscow the deal was celebrated less romantically, and one satirical paper published a snide cartoon of her sitting under an umbrella selling wheat and buying up vast quantities of herrings.

Another agreement over which she labored many hours concerned Russia's official sanctioning of Norwegian fishermen and trappers in Soviet waters. Working on this late into the night, long after the other Russians had left the building, she toiled on into the weekend, when the whole population of Oslo had left for Holmenkollen to watch a skiing competition. During most weekends she too tended to rush off to the nearby mountains with her friends, to practice her inept attempts on skis in the late snows of spring. "The Norwegians die laughing when they see my skiing failures . . . I can cope all right when I'm on flat ground or going uphill, but when I go downhill I start gasping for breath, my arms and legs get tangled up, and I flop down into the snow. It's much safer just to take off my skis and put them on my shoulders."[17] She much preferred to spend her free time in taking long mountain walks, and most Saturdays she would put on her strong shoes, pack a rucksack, and join her Norwegian friends and Russian colleagues for a scramble up the mountain paths outside Oslo. Climbing up grim bare rocks far above the town, they would cross stark ravines, and stop at some cool lake or stream where they would make a campfire and eat their supper before arriving at a mountain shelter. They would spend the nights there on a straw mattress before beginning the climb down, and Alexandra would return to work, her head refreshed and her legs aching.

Her work in Oslo was not confined to trade agreements. After she had finished her fictional trilogies, several articles by her appeared in the Russian press. On April 13, *Pravda* carried her article "The Work of the Women's Departments in the New Conditions," in which she argued—more pragmatically than before but without any inconsistency with her previous writings on the subject—that since the government evidently did not have the financial resources to establish nurseries and canteens, new societies might be formed to draw women, in and out of the Party, into the work of setting up children's homes. "If only comrades would cease to consider it necessary to jump heavily on anyone who says anything at all new," she concluded sadly, "would cool their polemical ardor somewhat, and stop building every 'molehill' into a 'principled difference' or 'deviation' . . ."[18] This "polemical ardor" which she so lamented had taken the form of a renewed attack by party leaders on the "feminist deviations" detected among thousands of Russian women.

Since the end of 1922 a number of non-party women's papers had been appearing in the cities of Russia; they had enjoyed such wide popularity that in January 1923 *Rabotnitsa* was revived to combat their influence. Shortly after this Vera Golubeva proposed the scheme which prompted the ideas contained in Alexandra's article: since the Party showed such little interest in the women's departments, Golubeva suggested that men and women outside the Party could form themselves into special societies to tackle the problems of women's liberation; as a first step they could establish model experiments in communal living. Few of the Zhenotdel leaders greeted Golubeva's suggestion with any enthusiasm; most of them considered that their first task was political consciousness-raising; "model experiments" and all other such idealistic notions could wait. At the Twelfth Party Congress in April 1923 the Zhenotdel officially condemned her proposal as a "feminist deviation" and called for more party control over the women's departments. This deplorable resolution was passed despite Sofya Smidovich's complaint that the congress was attended by the lowest number of women delegates ever (one percent) and that "bourgeois chauvinism" (i.e., male chauvinism) was indeed very firmly rooted in many party members. A month later *Pravda* published an article repudiating the ideas of both Golubeva and Kollontai. There were "feminist tendencies" in the Soviet Union, it said; working women could all too easily be seduced away from the class struggle if they were encouraged to form societies to improve their living conditions.

Two other articles by Alexandra which appeared in Russia early in 1923 in *Young Guard* provided yet more ammunition with which to attack her "feminist tendencies." As her thoughts turned increasingly to the ways in which literature reflected and shaped consciousness she made the subject of her third "Letter to Young Communists" an analysis of the poems of Anna Akhmatova. In "The Dragon and the White Bird" she took issue with many communists who considered Akhmatova's work decadent and outmoded. Anna Akhmatova did not have to be a communist, she argued, for her poems to be moving and worthy of serious thought; in her love poems she had described with a powerful and prescient clarity that conflict between the old morality and the new which tore at every communist's heart. The "new morality" was understood only by a tiny intellectual minority of men and women in Russia; most people still considered that "Eve came from Adam's rib" and were utterly nonplused by the prospect of combining sexual relationships with comradeship. Akhmatova's poems, then, touched on two themes of great importance which needed to be illuminated and discussed before they could be resolved—men's incapacity to recognize women's individuality, and women's difficulties in combining creative independence with the need for love. These themes were eloquently expressed by her images of the "white bird" (woman's growing consciousness of her own personality) and the "dragon" (man's tendency to depersonalize women). Here then was a clue as to how men might be reeducated not to kill the "white bird" —a task infinitely more difficult and more fulfilling for women, Alexandra suggested, than renouncing men altogether.[19]

In her next article, "Make Way for Winged Eros," Alexandra reflected that now that the civil war was over, people were able to read not only *Pravda* but poems and novels too, and go to the theater; at the same time they were no longer forced into short, stressful sexual relationships but could explore the more poetic aspects of erotic love. This was not to say that the revolutionary battle was over, for the civil war was now entering into a more complex ideological phase; nor was a preoccupation with sexual matters a sign of decadence, as some comrades insisted, for it was essential for the collective to define now what forms sexual relationships should take in the new proletarian culture. After a brief discussion of the ways in which love had been expressed in the clan and the tribe, in feudal and in bourgeois societies, she concluded that sexual relationships were never purely biological but had always been regarded as a social factor of the greatest importance, whose legal forms reflected the needs of each type of society. The love of sympathy and understanding—this must be the ideal to which a proletarian society should aspire. This "multifaceted love," which she had mentioned before, was claimed by some Russians to be synonymous with promiscuity, but it was nothing of the sort—it was intended to suggest a proper respect for different types of love relationships among different sorts of people. Since Russia was still in the painful throes of transition, personal love must still be subordinated to love and duty to the collective, but she had no doubt that proletarian ideology would, like all previous ideologies, set its own definitions of love:

> Respect for the right of the other's personality will increase and a mutual sensitivity will be learned; men and women will strive to express their love not only in kisses and embraces but in joint creativity and activity. The task of proletarian ideology is not to drive Eros from social life but to rearm him according to the new social formation, and to educate sexual relationships in the spirit of the great new psychological force of comradely solidarity.[20]

The three articles Alexandra wrote in Oslo and her stories, which appeared that summer, gave the signal for the most virulent attack on her ideas. It was headed by one of her former young colleagues at the Zhenotdel and an editor of *Communist Woman*, Paulina Vinogradskaya. In a lengthy article entitled "Questions of Sex, Morality, and Everyday Life" (which appeared in the June 1923 issue of the literary review *Red Virgin Soil*) Vinogradskaya declared that Kollontai's unwholesome concern with sexual matters was anti-Marxist. It was, she added, particularly "petty-bourgeois intellectuals" like Kollontai—writing in Norway where "the bourgeoisie was comfortably installed on the back of the proletariat"— who displayed this obsession with purely social problems; her curiosity about the communist future was absolutely typical of those bourgeois liberals who flirted with socialism. But then, "Comrade Kollontai was always wont to swim in a sea of hackneyed and banal phrases diluted merely with a sickly sweet sentimentality and adorned with rhetorical curl-papers."

Especially dangerous, to Vinogradskaya's way of thinking, was Kollontai's observation that living and acting like a communist meant thinking and feeling like a communist, for which there could be neither mechanical rules nor party instructions, but which could only be realized by a thorough grasp of communist ideology and of the atmosphere and living conditions of the working class. "We don't see why party instructions cannot help us in this, as in other matters, to live like communists," said Vinogradskaya, reminding the reader of Kollontai's own cavalier attitude toward party discipline. Problems of love did not deserve one tenth of her attention, moreover. Much more important were the tasks of education and the family, of which, Vinogradskaya claimed quite unfairly, Kollontai had mentioned not one word to all those young communists among whom she had such a following. She had grossly misjudged the political situation and the consequences of her ideas, for now was not the time for "romance" and "emotions"; now was the time to draw breath for the coming political battle. Russia was too poor, salaries were too low, more than half the population was illiterate and ill-housed, students were ill-fed, and there were at least 500,000 orphans—the time was simply not ripe for Kollontai's personal views on the morality of the future.

To write, as she did, that communist society should be based on the potential for loving, rather than on productive work relations, was "going too far, even for a Socialist Revolutionary"; she was annexing Marxism to Tolstoy, St. Joan, and Kropotkin. Her "multifaceted love" clearly meant multiple cohabitation; it *might* be possible in the future for one man to live with several women, and for one woman to live with several men, but in the present conditions of poverty and female unemployment, it was children, not love, that must be central to sexual relationships. Only one completely cut off from the masses and enjoying a comfortable life could talk so blithely about the "cult of love." To be sure in the upper ranks of the Party there were some people who lived happily with several sexual partners, and this, Vinogradskaya supposed, must be considered "progressive." But this could not but rob them of the time and energy which was due to the Party and could certainly not be recommended for the present.

The Zhenotdel should not be spending its energies in trying to abolish the family but in rooting out the power of religion, the customs of the past, and the problems of abandoned children, abortion, and prostitution. Kollontai, said Vinogradskaya, was clearly not a Marxist, since for her the "sexual struggle" took precedence over the class struggle; any Marxist knew that "women's true liberty depended on ending the yoke of capital, not on an all-out war against men." What, then, many people might be asking, did Kollontai have to teach women workers? One could but wonder how she had come for so long to be considered a leader not only of the Russian communist women's movement but also of the international women's movement. The answer was simple: she had gained her influence before the revolution, before women's class-consciousness had been awakened, when they were attracted to anyone who spoke to them of their needs and hopes.[21]

According to Marcel Body, articles now began to appear regularly on the third page of *Pravda*, signed "A.K." and dealing with the ideas of the family and free love in the Young Communists' organization, the Komsomol, in terms which parodied Alexandra's writings with such ludicrous crudity that she was soon receiving a voluminous stream of mail from people in Russia who demanded how she could defend such uncommunist ethics. Before Vinogradskaya's article appeared, however, even such progressive and humane women as Trotsky's wife, Natalya Sedova, and Nadezhda Krupskaya were voicing criticisms of Alexandra's work. Sedova, in an interview in *The New York Times* early in 1923, declared that Kollontai was nothing but a "feminist," and Krupskaya had started to express the opinion that Kollontai's work should not appear in party publications. Few people in Russia understood her writings on the complete psychological emancipation of women. At best her fiction was regarded as nothing more serious than idealistic ramblings; at worst, many feared, the criticisms of the NEP which she made in this fiction suggested that she was about to return to the Workers' Opposition.

Vinogradskaya's article may well have prompted a hostile response to Alexandra, as it was clearly intended to, and the article itself was a defamatory parody of her ideas, but there is no evidence in any of the issues of *Pravda* for that year of any such articles by Alexandra Kollontai. We must therefore regard with some caution Body's claim that Alexandra wrote repeatedly to Stalin asking him to clear up the confusion, and that when the articles continued to appear, she decided to leave for Moscow to complain to him in person.[22]

There were other less pressing diplomatic reasons for Alexandra's thirteen-day visit to Moscow in the summer of 1923. One issue over which she had labored many hours was the problem of Soviet territorial rights to the Arctic archipelago of Spitzbergen. Until 1920 Spitzbergen had been a no-man's-land whose coal and fishing rights had been shared by Sweden, Norway, and Russia. Then, at a conference of various capitalist countries in Paris in that year, Norwegian sovereignty over the islands had been established, and the other participants had agreed to share the use and profits of Spitzbergen's resources. For Russia this meant the loss of an important source of coal to her northern ports. After reading up as much as she possibly could on the subject and talking to Norwegian explorers and oceanographers like Fridtjof Nansen and Roald Amundsen, Alexandra decided she would have to return to Moscow to receive instructions as to how she might ask Norway to intercede between the Soviet Union and the other countries for a reconsideration of her territorial claims.

Doubtless she was also anxious to discover whether Vinogradskaya's ideas really represented the feelings of the Zhenotdel and the Party. She probably also hoped that the symposium on cultural problems which Trotsky had organized for party workers that summer would reveal some rather more thoughtful responses to the problems of everyday life in the Soviet Union. The articles which Trotsky wrote in *Pravda* that June (later reprinted in book form as *Problems of Life*) reflected the concerns of many party leaders: "We lack sufficient civilization to pass straight on to socialism, though we have the political requisites . . . for us, the social and political overturn have proved to be the precursor of the cultural overturn, that cultural revolution in the face of which we now nevertheless stand." These preoccupations were to haunt the ailing Lenin until his death.

Trotsky's ideas—his concern that the Party should turn its attention to raising the level of culture in Russia, his observations on the stresses to which men and women were subjected in their family lives, and his insistence that the Party should examine the customs of people's everyday lives more closely[23]—were warmly welcomed by most women in the Party, but in the July issue of *Red Virgin Soil* the acerbic Paulina Vinogradskaya launched into another of her characteristic attacks. It was evident to everyone in Russia, she retorted, that the Soviet Union retained nine tenths of the evils perpetrated by the past. Challenging Trotsky's emphasis that the Party should inform itself on living conditions in the country, she argued that women could make some immediate progress toward their emancipation if the Party would provide real leadership. She pointed out that the most ignorant and backward women greeted the destruction of the individual household more readily than did the wives of highly placed party leaders, since it was precisely these ignorant women who felt they had least to gain from the family; she cited disapprovingly the large numbers of women who were having abortions merely in order to escape the slavery of the kitchen and the family.[24]

Traveling back to Russia with Body by boat and train, Alexandra felt as though she were "on wings."[25] Far outweighing all the anxieties she anticipated in Moscow was the exciting prospect of seeing Misha, who had just got married. With only two weeks in Moscow to see Misha, his wife (most probably a former student with him in Petrograd), and her friends, as well as to make the rounds of the Commissariats of Foreign Trade and Foreign Affairs, she had hardly a moment to herself. Her evenings were fully taken care of; the moment she arrived, she was summoned to appear before the inquisitorial control commission and was questioned closely on her relations with the defunct Workers' Opposition. She did receive a delegation from this group at the International Hotel for party workers where she was staying, but sensing their powerlessness and demoralization, she sadly declined to reply when one of them asked her to represent them abroad. Yet day after day she was greeted with a striking lack of openness by commissariat officials, and every evening she continued to be subjected to the control commission's prolonged and insufferable investigation of her past political activities.

If she refused support to the Workers' Opposition, it was because by the end of 1922 this group had been overtaken by two new clandestine groupings. The Workers' Truth, which claimed to be non-political, aspired only to educate workers and encourage them to strike and protest. The more militant anonymous members of the ultra-leftist Workers' Group, however, were calling on all former members of the Workers' Opposition, the democratic centralists, and all honest party members to remove Zinoviev, Kamenev, and Stalin from the central committee, and were reiterating many of the complaints against the bourgeois "specialists" which the Workers' Opposition had first elaborated in 1919. Lutovinov, a longtime leader of the metal-workers union, was one of the Workers' Oppositionists who supported this group and urged the Party to reexamine the wage question. "As long as these oppositions exist, there must be some reason for them," he said. "If they are anonymous, then that is because there is no chance to criticize openly and people are branded as 'Mensheviks' for doing so."[26] He was sent to Berlin for a "cure," and the Workers' Group was rounded up by the secret police and arrested in June, shortly before Alexandra arrived.

It was the Twelfth Party Congress in March 1923 that saw the surreptitious start of the long campaign against Trotsky and his "Menshevik past," and against all those who longed to end Stalin's monopoly of the central committee. A deeper reason for this campaign, however, was the need for scapegoats for a new economic crisis—the "scissors crisis," in which agricultural prices fell and industrial prices rose. As industry was increasingly concentrated in the most efficient factories, unemployment in the cities rocketed and wages were cut; throughout the summer, workers began to strike and demonstrate. Members of the Workers' Truth who encouraged these strikes were picked out and arrested by the secret police, and as this group gradually disintegrated more critics of oppression began to speak up, only to be answered by more oppression. Wages were eventually increased, the peasants were conciliated, and the "scissors" were temporarily closed; but the problem was to be endemic throughout the 1920's.

By the late summer of 1923 the left was in disarray, and Alexandra may well have agreed with Shlyapnikov that the workers' groups were powerless and that Trotsky's opposition was concerned only with dismantling the party's bureaucracy and did not give a fig for the workers.[27] Nonetheless, not only did she continue to be summoned daily to the Kremlin to explain herself to the control commission, but (according to Body's questionable claim, at least) the crude articles signed "A.K." continued to appear in *Pravda*. She decided to apply for a personal interview with Stalin.

Alexandra and Body were subjected to a long wait in the central-committee offices in the Kremlin. Eventually Stalin's two subordinates on the General Secretariat, Molotov and Kuibyshev, appeared and greeted them "with that solid assurance conferred on them by the fact that they already held some of the immense power Stalin had concentrated in his hands."[28] The door to Stalin's office was opened by Unschlicht, president of the military tribunal, and Alexandra was admitted into the presence of the General Secretary. He greeted her warmly, she told Body afterwards, and peering closely into her face, asked after her health and diplomatic work, and begged her to tell him if she needed any help. To this she replied angrily that she was sick of being summoned before the control commission to be interrogated about an activity she had long since abandoned. "What, are they making your life miserable?" he apparently replied, squeezing her hand and promising to "enquire" into all allegations against her.

From then on the summonses to the control commission stopped as abruptly as did the articles in *Pravda*, more official invitations to the various commissariats came her way, and she was able to return to Oslo somewhat reassured. She had also been greatly reassured to find Misha well and working happily in his new job in Moscow as an engineer, apparently unaffected by his mother's disagreements with the Party. She liked his wife, and it must have been a comfort for her to know that Misha was now living a more settled life.

There was still cause for grave anxiety, however. Even though Stalin realized that her prestige and popularity in Russia and abroad were very considerable, Alexandra Kollontai remained an enigma to him. And even when a member of the Workers' Opposition was summoned to the control commission after her departure and assured him that she had made no commitment to them, Stalin began increasingly to fear the influence of the old Bolsheviks. ("People schooled in underground methods and therefore incapable of positive thinking," was how he later described them.) "Old Bolsheviks" and "former Mensheviks"—the distinction between them was very slight in Stalin's paranoid mind. Alexandra, like all the former left oppositionists who had joined the Bolsheviks in the political realignments of the 1914–17 period, was being made to feel increasingly vulnerable and tainted by her "Menshevik past." It was not until 1936 that the full sadistic weight of Stalin's repression fell on the "Trotsky–Bukharin gang," and thousands were arrested, imprisoned, and shot.

18

Years of Uncertainty

When Alexandra returned to Oslo she discovered, as she was to do after every subsequent departure, that the conservative press was insinuating that she had been recalled. Undaunted, she resumed her work for Norway's legal recognition of the Soviet Union. That autumn and winter she spent much of her time in the old Western Hanseatic port of Bergen, helping to establish a joint Soviet-Norwegian shipping company which would build Soviet ships and transport Norwegian wood to various countries in Europe. Leaving Bergen after one particularly hectic round of negotiations, she leaped out of the train as it approached a high mountain pass near the perpetual snowline. After staying the night in a clean little mountain shelter where she could gaze in peace at the clear sky, the thick snow, the steel-blue mounain lakes and glaciers, she returned to Oslo. Shortly afterward the first cargo ship was completed, and she was back in Bergen to launch it and to celebrate her second trade deal with Norway. In November she took up the issue of Russia's rights to Spitzbergen and handed the Norwegian Foreign Ministry a note in which she suggested that this might be the prelude to normalizing relations between the two countries. At the end of December 1923 she was invited to the Foreign Ministry in Oslo and affably informed that she was to start negotiations with the government for the full diplomatic recognition of the Soviet Union.[1]

From Alexandra's departure from Moscow until the following January leftists in the Soviet Union united to launch the most serious attack on the government since 1918. In October 1923 the anonymous signatories of the "Declaration of the Forty-Six" declared that the regime was killing all initiative, that it was the hypertrophe in the Party which caused these illegal groupings within it, and that there must be a "new course" toward increased workers' democracy; the Party must be cleared of those who were openly terrorizing the people. Throughout November and December a new group of left oppositionists, led by Trotsky, began to emerge. Though admitting the validity of much of what the Workers' Opposition had said, they failed to appeal to old oppositionists like Shlyapnikov, who not only distrusted Trotsky's authoritarian temperament but considered that he and his supporters had no real base among the workers. Moreover this opposition had no program to back its idealism; its chief aim was to show that the Party had no real program, only a pack of lies; they themselves often merely repeated the resolutions passed at the various party congresses, insisting that they would apply them better and that they were the true defenders of party unity.

In November 1923 Stalin wrote his first article for *Communist Woman*, stating that the Zhenotdel's aim must be to "draw into the construction of our Soviet life the millions of peasant women." As he consolidated his leadership over the next two years by proclaiming the alliance between peasants and industrial workers this became the official objective of the women's departments. The numbers of women peasants recruited to the Zhenotdel did increase markedly. At the end of 1923 thirty percent of delegates were workers and forty percent were peasants; by July 1925 sixty-three percent were peasants and only eighteen percent were workers. But at a time when fewer and fewer efforts were being made to emancipate either working or peasant women, these figures revealed little more than Stalin's early policy of conciliating the peasants. Few village women were involved in the work of building up the new agricultural cooperatives.[2]

By the end of 1923 Stalin was quite openly using the power of transfer against all those who opposed him. When the Thirteenth Party Congress opened on January 16, 1924, it was obvious to all that it had been stagemanaged by Stalin from beginning to end. None of the views of the oppositionists were heard, no decisions were discussed, and Stalin declared that the recent wave of factionalism had nothing to do with the bureaucracy, or with any other real issue, and everything to do with the essentially "unproletarian" nature of his enemies. As the proceedings were about to open Nadezhda Krupskaya circulated among the central committee members Lenin's "testament," which he had written the previous year and in which he demanded that Stalin be removed from power. Yet at this congress, which Lenin was by now too ill to attend, such was the grief felt by those who loved him and knew he was dying, and such was the hysterical fear of Stalin, that Zinoviev could calmly announce that Lenin's fears had been proved groundless over the past years. Stalin was unanimously supported by a show of hands.

Trotsky was then made to recant his oppositionist views, but he did so in such a way as to make his recantation meaningless. The debates were as dull as were *Pravda*'s reports of them, and every successive congress was marked by the same lifelessness. All the delegates, haunted by fears of Lenin's death, felt paralyzed by insecurity. For all of them who rallied so fervently at that time to the call for party unity, this unity became the supreme political virtue; it accorded perfectly with Stalin's dull new exegetic science of "Marxism-Leninism," which split hairs, chopped logic, and avoided at all costs any new consideration of problems which did not fit with those which had been elaborated by the leaders of the October revolution. Many sincere leftists, romantically predisposed to worship the proletariat, began to exalt the idea that the Party was acting with one mind and one will, and that political division could only be a symptom of class division. And so they too began to fall prey to Stalin's tendency to secure a majority by appealing for unity, bending past resolutions and arguments so as to fit the new conditions. The women's movement, less affected by party dogmatism, retained its comparative freedom to debate for the next couple of years, but by 1929 the party leaders realized that they had underestimated the innovative powers of the Zhenotdel, and it was suppressed.

On January 21, 1924, shortly after the Thirteenth Congress ended, Alexandra heard that Lenin had died. "In the delegation we are all going around stunned, stricken and sobbing," she wrote. "It's so ghastly, so painful, as if the whole world has been devastated by the loss. Poor Nadezhda Konstantinovna . . ."[3] She spoke at a great funeral meeting held in Oslo's largest hall and, battling against her own tears, spoke to the sound of sobs. Even the newspapers lamented Lenin's death and the loss of a great and humanitarian statesman. But there were suggestions too that with the death of its leader the "communist experiment" would prove to be bankrupt; it was this that unfroze Alexandra's will and forced her back to work.

By the end of January the governments in Rome, London, Oslo, and Stockholm were considering legal recognition of the Soviet Union, and Alexandra was anxious that Norway should be the first to do so. Visiting the foreign minister, Esmark, she pointed out to him all the economic benefits that would accrue to Norway if she were the first to recognize the Soviet government. She presented him with a forty-eight-hour ultimatum.

But the day after her visit was a Sunday, and the Norwegian parliament —the Riksdag (now called the Storting)—rarely sat on Monday. By Tuesday it was already too late, for England, shortly followed by Italy, had already established diplomatic relations with the Bolsheviks. It was not until February 15 that diplomatic relations between Norway and the Soviet Union were finally opened. The following day Alexandra visited the new foreign minister, Michelet, as the Soviet Union's official ambassador to Norway. On March 10 she received instructions from Moscow to establish a Soviet embassy in Oslo.

When, on September 6, 1924, she presented her credentials to the Norwegian king, she was no longer being pursued by the gossip and rumors that had made her life so difficult when she first arrived. Rarely now did she meet the extreme misogyny that had at first greeted her, and references to her sex were rare and moderate. Michelet, for example, once attempted to deflect her from pursuing some contentious point by referring to her new dress. "On the contrary, it's the one I always wear when I visit you," she retorted. "Nevertheless, it's quite charming," he replied, in a gallant effort to avoid more serious matters. There were many occasions of petty, tedious irritation, but now it was as a Bolshevik rather than as a woman that she felt most people's hostility was directed against her.[4]

She moved from her hotel into the embassy building on Drammenswein, living with forty other Russian officials and their families, among whom she was extremely popular. She helped to eliminate the scourge of paperwork and officialdom, much as she had done as a commissar, and all members of the embassy staff and various Norwegian chauffeurs and cooks ate together in their little Russian "island." "We live permanently on guard here," she wrote to a friend. "It's as if we're on a floating island in the midst of a surging sea. There's no storm or tempest visible on the horizon, but still the surge continues . . ."[5] In light of the prevailing hostility to Russia which she experienced in Oslo she urged her staff to work ten or twelve hours a day preparing a new trade agreement between the two countries whereby foodstuffs and industrial goods were to be exchanged. By the end of 1924 she had been laid low by the strain of overwork and anxiety, and heart trouble confined her to her bed until early the next year.

Three months after Lenin's death Stalin was already codifying "Leninism" in a series of lectures at the Sverdlov University, where Alexandra's own lectures had enjoyed such popularity three years before. The "Lenin enrollment" brought 200,000 new members into the Party, while forty percent of the old party members were subjected to interrogation by the Control Commission. The purges and the monstrous campaign against Trotsky had started. Alexandra can have known few of the details of this gathering wave of terror in the Soviet Union, for it was one of the more extraordinary aspects of Stalin's regime that this vast country was so hermetically sealed by police control that few outside Russia in the coming years knew anything of the power struggle and the terror which accompanied it. If she had known of the outrageous inhumanity, cynicism, and mania to which her Party and its police departments were sinking, she might well have not believed it. Such was the enormous moral capital of the revolution that Russia's 160,000,000 people complied with unbelievable resolution and energy with the programs, plans, and purges which Stalin foisted upon them.

After Lenin's death Shlyapnikov and Medvedev returned to some of the arguments of the Workers' Opposition and in late January 1924 they drew up the "Baku Letter"—a programatic statement on workers' control. The letter was hastily suppressed, and Shlyapnikov was dispatched to the Paris trade delegation, where he started writing his invaluable memoirs of 1917. As for Yuri Lutovinov, another comrade from the Workers' Opposition, Stalin's dictatorship left him bereft of hope and friends, and he shot himself in Berlin. Many more killed themselves after Lenin's death, anticipating only too presciently the terror that was to follow. Two years later suicide among people under thirty had reached epidemic proportions, with as many as thirty people killing themselves every day in the newly renamed Leningrad. By the end of 1924 Trotsky had lost all control of his War Commissariat. But even after January 1925, when he resigned from his post as president of the Military Revolutionary Council, he was saying little. To Alexandra the battle must have seemed to be one between the two leaders, for neither of whom she could feel much sympathy: she had suffered too much in the past at the hands of both of them.

Her feelings for Trotsky were mixed, she told Body. As a writer, orator, and political organizer he was incomparable, she felt, but "he's made himself too many enemies as Commissar of War; he's too rigorous, not human enough. Those whom he wanted to shoot for minor crimes, and who only owe their survival to appeals to Lenin or Stalin, won't quickly forgive him," she said, in a clear reference to Dybenko's past troubles. As for Stalin, she continued, he realized that Trotsky had many admirers but few friends within the Party. Stalin corresponded to the average—not to say mediocre—militant and used this to his advantage; he had the ability to talk simply to any worker, militiaman, or soldier. Of

Bukharin, on the other hand, she had a very high opinion, despite her past political disagreements with him. Zinoviev she loathed as much as she had loathed him in March 1917 for his fatuous vanity. As for Vyacheslav Molotov, she was amazed at the prominence to which he had risen in the Commissariat of Foreign Affairs; she realized that he was capable only of carrying out Stalin's orders. Only Alexei Rykov, who succeeded Lenin as the president of the Council of People's Commissars, filled her with any confidence: "He is solid, sensible, not ambitious, and stable," she told Body.[6]

But few in the Bolshevik government felt such confidence in Alexandra. At the beginning of 1925 an officer of the control commission visited her in Oslo, clearly hoping to be able to draw up a damaging report on her to present to Moscow. "I didn't see our flag flying over the embassy," he complained to Marcel Body. "And have you checked the walls for microphones?" Body explained that the flag was only flown on holidays and protested that in a peaceful country there could be no grounds for suspecting espionage. Alexandra was then questioned. Why, the officer wanted to know, had neither she nor Body been sending reports back to Moscow on each other's activities? "But I've only good to say of Marcel Yakovlevich; we're working for the same things and collaborate closely on everything," she retorted. "Maybe, but nevertheless this solidarity is strange," said the officer. "So you'd like us to knife each other?" "Why not? Divide and rule . . ." (Body's imagination may have got the better of him in reporting this exchange, but in essence it was probably accurate). When the officer proceeded to interrogate the Norwegian doorman, Alexandra came to the end of her patience and pointed out that his behavior violated the laws of common decency. He returned to Moscow clearly dissatisfied with their poor security arrangements and generally insubordinate behavior, and Alexandra was so outraged by his intrusion that she wrote an angry complaint to the secretary of the control commission. The answer was not long in coming.

When the control commission wrote back announcing that Body was being recalled to Moscow, Alexandra felt tempted to return then and there to thwart this intrigue before it went any further; she was only dissuaded from doing so by Body, who felt it was only symptomatic of far worse intrigues to come. Nevertheless, ill, fatigued, and feeling that she had come to the end of her useful work in Oslo, she wrote that summer to Litvinov asking to be relieved of her post: "I intend to go to Moscow to ask the chief of administration and the Commissariat of Foreign Affairs to relieve me of my work in Norway, for I am morally and physically exhausted and have had enough of the perpetual 'uniform' which the work demands."[7] She also longed to see Misha and his wife, as well as Zoya and her old friends in Moscow.

There were other pressing reasons for her return to Moscow in June 1925. That summer the government had thrown open to public debate its proposals for a new marriage law. The passion with which the most searching questions about marriage and the family were aired between 1925 and the passing of the law in 1926 amazed many party members, who regarded this as an essentially "non-political" matter. Long ago it had been decided to encourage the masses to participate in drawing up this legislation, since it would affect them so deeply. To Alexandra the fact that this new law was not simply issued by decree must have indicated an encouraging concern with fulfilling that promise. The thousands of articles, discussions, and meetings on the subject (there were 6000 meetings between 1925 and 1926 in the villages to discuss the new law and countless similar meetings in the towns) showed that the issues of men's and women's obligations to each other and to their children did not follow any set party lines but indicated rather a conflict between peasants and city-dwellers, old and young, men and women. By the time the year was up one woman delegate called Gnilova was reporting at a party meeting that the crucial question of alimony had turned into "nothing but a campaign of ill-will against women."[8] It was on the question of alimony that Alexandra made her contribution to the debate (at packed meetings between June and October 1925, and in numerous articles).

The Bolsheviks' first marriage law in 1918 had been an indication of their desire to liberate women by making marriage a question of simple registration, and by granting them the right to free divorce and to alimony. But few had felt that there was anything very communistic about making men legally responsible for women's economic well-being and potentially responsible for their children. "The existing legislation on the family . . . was created by the methods of bourgeois law," a member of the supreme court frankly stated:

> This legislation has not and cannot have anything communist in it, as some comrades are trying to prove . . . The state puts it thus: if two people propose to get married, these two must first undertake to help each other, and second, if they intend to have children, they must undertake to keep these children, feed, rear, and educate them. In a communist society this care is undertaken by society itself, without making its individual members bear these responsibilities. But during the period of transition we are forced to follow the example of bourgeois countries . . .[9]

Since for a variety of reasons large numbers of couples did not bother to register their marriages, the number of unregistered marriages soon greatly exceeded those registered. By 1925 countless women in such unregistered unions faced a perilous future if they were unemployed and abandoned by their bread-winning husbands. The struggle against the Church was now seen to be of secondary importance to the need to protect the "weaker" party. Therefore when the government proposed to make all marriages legal, whether registered or not, so that all spouses should be committed to supporting each other "during unemployment," they clearly intended to make women (well over seventy percent of the unemployed in most cities) the financial responsibilities of their husbands.

However, as it soon emerged from numerous meetings and in voluminous correspondence in the press, men in the cities greatly feared the consequences of a law which they could not avoid by simply not registering their marriages. Especially feared was the proposal made by a delegation of women workers that property should be shared in divorce cases, for many men had profited from the 1918 law, which had not stipulated that property should be shared in marriage since this might have been an incentive to marriages of economic calculation. For the peasants the question of recognizing unregistered marriages was even more threatening, for not only did such marriages represent to them the "loose living" of the city, but the demands for alimony represented a real danger to the peasant household, the *dvor*. The 1922 land code had established that the property of the *dvor* was to be the common property of every man, woman, and child within it. It was now for progressives in the Party to point out that women could only be equal members of this household as long as they were registered wives; they certainly could not take from the *dvor* what was legally theirs if they were divorced. There had been too many cases of "seasonal wives," married during harvesttime and thrown out in the autumn with a sack of potatoes, for this to be ignored any longer.

Men's fears were expressed chiefly in terms of women's "avoiding work" or conceiving children merely in order to claim maintenance payment, and the whole vexed issue was further complicated by a general puzzlement as to how to define a *de facto* marriage, how to exclude from the benefits of alimony women who entered into merely "casual relationships" with men, and how to determine properly the mutual obligations of married couples whose work forced them apart for long periods. Moreover many people feared that to recognize *de facto* marriages was tantamount to recognizing the church marriages which were still so popular in the villages. The government proposed to define marriage simply as two people living together in a joint household and the announcement of this to a third party. The law was not intended, as many in the West imagined, to cause the family to wither away, but on the contrary, to strengthen the bonds of marriage by making men legally and economically responsible for women.

The only voice raised against the proposed new law's unsocialist attitude toward women and the demeaning economic basis for marriage which it threatened to create was that of Alexandra Kollontai. Since the withering away of the family was not immediately foreseeable, she argued that even under the conditions of the NEP it was still possible to retain a socialist perspective and instill collectivism—she cited Marx's assertion that it was in social and economic transition that communal forms of living were born. Again and again, in numerous meetings in Moscow and in several articles, she insisted that men should not be expected to be economically responsible for women and that the whole notion of alimony demeaned both the donor and the recipient. The sad fact of the matter, in fact, which few could deny, was that it was only the "Nepman" with money in his pocket who could afford to pay alimony; the richer peasant would only be able to do so by selling a cow or waiting for the piglets to be born. Yet strangely enough Alexandra's attack on the whole regressive system of alimony was not even supported by those most vocal leftists who urged the rapid collectivization of the peasantry and would swear on every other issue that private property led to social backwardness.

Alexandra insisted that if men and women were to be regarded as equal partners, who would stay together as long as love lasted, then the law's categories of "registered" and "unregistered" wives (which were equivalent anyway), and of "casual lovers," were both unnecessary and humiliating. The latter category appeared to refer in a particularly insulting fashion to the young peasant girl, generally living in the city in conditions of terrible congestion and poverty. But to classify women in any way was a gross violation of privacy; it was all part of that pernicious and deep-seated tendency to regard women merely as sexual categories. "Registered" wives should not be expected to demean themselves in court to beg for money; as for single mothers and abandoned wives since the courts could not possibly enforce payment from men who did not have money, this was clearly not the way to help them. Any woman, Alexandra argued, should be eligible for state support if she had served her society and given it children.

She recognized that for the time being the NEP would create a great deal of unemployment and hardship for women, but unlike many of her former Zhenotdel colleagues, who felt that women could no longer effectively fight for their rights, she argued that there were still the resources available to replace the individual household. Her bold plan was to abolish the whole alimony system, inspired as it was by the assumption that the woman was the "weaker partner," and set up in its place a general insurance fund, to which the entire adult population would make graduated contributions, starting at two rubles a year. With 120,000,000 rubles annually at their disposal the government could begin to augment the pitifully small number of day nurseries (545 throughout the whole of Russia in 1925), provide support for single mothers, and open homes for mothers and children who had no accommodations.[10]

Alexandra's second plan for safeguarding the rights of women, which was more long-term and less immediately practicable, was that couples embarking on relationships should draw up their own marriage contracts in which they could define their responsibilities toward one another. This sort of contract would be particularly useful, she felt, in helping couples to see how much time women still spent on housework. (Economists estimated at that time that women spent something like ten percent more of their time working). Women should understand that "their housework also counts for something, and is recognized to be just as important as the work done in the factories and plants. For as long as we have the consumer cell in the form of the working family we must understand that the woman's labor in this cell must be taken into account and valued. This would lead to a real equality among the members of the cell, not only in words but in deeds."[11]

Both her proposals needed to be widely discussed by the Party if they were to be made effective and acceptable; the second in particular, she realized quite well, could only be made to work if it was used by the Party and the Zhenotdel as the basis for a campaign to teach peasant women their rights. Many young people responded warmly to her plans, and one student wrote to *Komsomolskaya Pravda* (the Young Communists' paper) suggesting that the general fund could be augmented by an additional tax on wine, theater tickets, and various other amusements. But few government or party leaders took them up on this, and the Zhenotdel director, Sofya Smidovich, immediately rejected them as unworkable. Many others in the Party, although approving the first plan in principle, felt that it would be unfair to burden the peasants with more taxes. But large numbers of them took the more simple conservative view that alimony discouraged "immorality"; and they criticized Alexandra's inconsistency in offering the "fantasy" of complete liberation from family responsibilities while proposing a marriage contract generally regarded as "petty bourgeois."

Few in fact, apart from Trotsky, deigned even to discuss her ideas, and even he felt that taxes were all very well for industrial purposes but not for social experiments, for which the time was not ripe. He argued that social consciousness came first and that the state could only build new social institutions with the masses' cooperation. Underlying his arguments, however, was the old-fashioned assumption that every assistance possible should be given to "the weaker sex," and it was for this reason that he supported the new law Alexandra argued that on the contrary the new social consciousness Trotsky spoke of could only be instilled by the gradual introduction of progressive new social measures and that women should be liberated from the debilitating "protection" of alimony offered by the law.

Her articles for the cultural review *Screen*, for *Komsomolskaya Pravda*, and the legal journal *Workers' Court* were published early in 1926, after she had returned to Oslo, and provoked a response even more hostile than the attack against her three years before. It was Sofya Smidovich—speaking, it seemed, a completely different language from her predecessor at the Zhenotdel—who took it upon herself to direct the "great mass of our proletarian youth" toward the proper sexual attitudes and expose for them the "half-baked notions of Comrade Kollontai." Prompted perhaps by the photograph of Alexandra's handsome and challenging face—the face of a fifty-four-year-old woman who was still young —which appeared on the front page of *Screen*, Smidovich referred witheringly to Kollontai's elegant dress and language as clear evidence of her outdated views and her bourgeois-intellectual past. She lamented the fact that so many women were being urged by irresponsible men to have indiscriminate sexual relationships and to conform to the punishing standards of the "new woman." The Zhenotdel should now be helping women to protect themselves against the "African passions" which Smidovich claimed had been released by Kollontai's writings and which could not but encourage promiscuity and marital instability.[12]

The March issue of *Young Guard* published an article by one Emelyan Lavrov entitled "Young People and the Sexual Question (Some of the Consequences of Comrade Kollontai's Latest Revelations)." In bourgeois countries, he thundered, young people might flit from flower to flower enjoying the "love of worker bees." In the Soviet Union chastity was to be regarded as a more seemly sexual norm—he himself had spent eight years in prison and prolonged abstinence had done him no harm. Kollontai's ideas had now outlived their usefulness and must be condemned, especially her demand that the government should take responsibility for children. This could only incite every young person and raw adolescent to think that they could enjoy life to the limit and satisfy their sexual appetites in the manner apparently condoned in Kollontai's novel. Her "ultra-leftist" rejection of the family could only be regarded as petty-bourgeois decadence, which must inevitably lead to great physical weakness. The family could not possibly be abolished in a society which had not yet even built socialism and eighty percent of whose population were peasants. The bases of the family existed, comparable to the bases of the state. In the transitional society the family must have both collective and individual functions; as long as society could not provide for children the family must do so. Ideas which in any way weakened this obligation could not be tolerated. Kollontai's plan for an insurance fund clearly sprang from such ideas, since to her oversimplified way of thinking the only alternative to the bourgeois family was "free love." The Party must now oppose these bankrupt ideas of hers as fiercely as it had previously opposed all outmoded and religious attitudes toward the family. Although she did not openly condone it, her writings were nevertheless the chief cause of young people's rampant promiscuity in Russia.[13]

Curiously enough it was at the height of the 1925 marriage debate that Lenin's much-quoted words to Klara Zetkin on sexual behavior in the Civil War years were published, five years after the discussion allegedly took place. His main preoccupation then was with the "glass of water theory"—"the theory," he told Klara Zetkin, "that in a communist society the satisfaction of sexual desires, of love, will be as simple and unimportant as drinking a glass of water."

> This glass of water theory has made our young people mad, quite mad. It has proved fatal to many young boys and girls. Its adherents maintain that it is Marxist. But I think it is completely un-Marxist. Of course, thirst must be satisfied. But will the normal person in normal circumstances lie down in the gutter and drink out of a puddle, or out of a glass with a rim greasy from many lips?
>
> Drinking water is of course an individual affair, but in love two lives are concerned and a third new life arises. It is that which gives rise to a duty towards the community.

As for promiscuity and those who condoned it, "there is no place for it in the Party . . . promiscuity in sexual matters is bourgeois, it is a sign of degeneration . . . [and it] wastes the health and strength of the young."[14]

This "famous theory," as Lenin called it, was probably nothing more than a commonly misquoted vulgarization of Bebel's analogy between sexual appetites and the healthy satisfaction of hunger and thirst. And as it happens, Alexandra could have taken issue with none of Lenin's arguments in this discussion with Klara Zetkin (almost his only lengthy pronouncement on sexual matters). Her own tendency was rather to welcome all relationships based on genuine affection and shared creative work, and if she did not defend herself against attack, it was because they were so wildly defamatory. When the next attack on her ideas, following those of Smidovich and Lavrov, was launched in May 1926 by Yaroslavsky, the solid Stalinist on the control commission, it was clearly symptomatic of the Party's increasing fear of any innovative ideas, and an indication that arguments could now be advanced only by those claiming to be the "guardians of Lenin's doctrine," that Yaroslavsky should invoke Lenin's 1920 statement as his only model for the new morality. Proletarian morality, Lenin had said, should serve the working class in its struggle. This, Yaroslavsky hastened to add, meant accepting the authority of the Party, the vanguard of that class. Kollontai's ideas encouraged people to "fritter away precious nervous and sexual energy," which should instead be directed toward the gigantic intellectual tasks facing the Russian people. She did not seem to realize that liberating women was an extremely slow business, and in the meantime, although he was not necessarily going to advocate asceticism, he regarded abstinence as no bad thing. People must take the consequences for their sexual activities, and by revising the marriage law the state would be encouraging people to consecrate their valuable energy to the tasks of production.[15]

It had been clear since the end of 1925—when Trotsky and his leftist supporters were joined by Zinoviev, Kamenev, and others who for a variety of reasons opposed Stalin's grip on the Party—that Stalin's attacks on his enemies were not in any way concerned with accuracy, let alone subtlety. Few in the Zhenotdel joined any of the opposition groups. However Klavdia Nikolaeva, virtually the only woman to support Zinoviev's opposition in Leningrad, complained bitterly to the Party of its official housing policy, pointing out that in the new flats being built there were no central kitchens and each family unit was completely self-contained. Alexandra, isolated by exile from the opposition and linked to it only by a few friends like Klavdia Nikolaeva and Shlyapnikov (who joined it briefly), was on numerous occasions blamed for a mounting atmosphere of sexual brutality and a wave of sexual attacks which swept the towns and villages.

During 1925 and 1926 there was a virtual epidemic of gang rapes, and a few of the more cynical students declared themselves for the withering away of all morals. When fifteen youths raped a girl on a scabby patch of wasteland in Leningrad, the control commission was already so overburdened with nasty "morals cases" that it was decided to give the defendants a show trial. Making free use of such subjective terms as "petty-bourgeois debauchery" and "sexual chaos," which had little meaning for Alexandra, the control commission sentenced five of the youths to death. Victor Serge, a brilliant and humane left oppositionist, saw the causes for such cases in the fact that "sexuality, so long repressed, first by revolutionary asceticism and then by poverty and famine [was] beginning to recover its drive in a society cut off from any spiritual nourishment." But even he did not think to question whether the Party might not have found a rather too suspiciously convenient scapegoat for these cases. "Books like those of Alexandra Kollontai propagated an oversimplified theory of free love," he wrote in his autobiography. (Can he have read her books?) "An infantile variety of materialism reduced 'sexual need' to its strictly animal connotation. 'You make love just as you drink a glass of water, to relieve yourself.' "16

Yet despite all the attacks on Alexandra, her ideas on the new woman and the withering away of the family continued to inspire too many people for them to be eradicated completely. It was only ten years later that they were officially regarded as heretical.

The 1925 marriage debate was the last occasion on which any issue of public importance was openly discussed, and it was virtually the last occasion on which Alexandra was able to express herself openly on the women's movement in Russia. Her request to be relieved of her diplomatic post was not granted, and at the end of 1925, shortly before the Fourteenth Party Congress in December, she returned to Oslo. At this congress Zinoviev's opposition, joined now by Nadezhda Krupskaya, was defeated. It was probably a desperate and confused hope that party unity might now be a possibility, and a desire to establish her own credentials as an old Bolshevik, that prompted Alexandra to send to the central committee all the letters that Lenin had written to her during the war. She can hardly have been unaware, however, of the glee with which Stalin would greet the letter in which Lenin referred to Trotsky as a "hesitant element."

Something of the anxiety she must have been feeling as she returned to work in Oslo—anxiety for Misha's safety, for her friends, and for the ominous developments within her Party—was detected by the German communist Ruth Fischer, who met her in Berlin, en route from Moscow. Fischer found her "depressed and unwilling to continue the 'hopeless struggle.' "[17] The American feminist Katherine Anthony, who visited her at the embassy shortly after she returned to Oslo, confirmed the impression:

> As you enter her office a pair of large grey eyes, thoughtful to the point of sadness, is raised to greet you, but a quick smile assures you that their owner is in no need of sympathy. You present your business . . . and at once you feel in contact with an overflowing energy . . . Presently the telephone rings and Her Excellency interrupts her conversation with you in whatever language that may happen to have been conducted (she speaks eleven), to converse in fluent Norwegian [*she had first started to learn Norwegian in 1915, and by now her command of the language was perfect*]. There's something electric and modern about her, impossible to define, something swift and electric and in keeping with our modern age.[18]

Politically unaligned and savagely attacked, Alexandra continued to be popular both in the Soviet Union and abroad. This was an embarrassment to the Soviet government, which was clearly confused as to the best way of eradicating her influence in Russia. The decision to pack her off in the autumn of 1926 to head the Soviet trade delegation in Mexico could only have been regarded as a punishment, scarcely less extreme than the diplomatic and administrative "posts" in Bashkiria, Kazakhstan, Turkestan, and the Arctic regions which were offered to oppositionists the following year. For Mexico City, 7347 feet above sea level, was dangerously high for one with such a weak heart and such high blood pressure as Alexandra's; the sudden removal to Mexico's dry hot altitude from the cold lowland humidity of northern Scandinavia and Russia could not but make her very ill. This ghastly surreptitious exercise was to be repeated on numerous party members who could not, for various reasons, be disposed of more openly. (In 1936, for instance, when Gorky was becoming an embarrassment to the Party, his tubercular condition was greatly aggravated when he was sent off to the Crimea and encouraged to stand around bonfires; he was then recalled at short notice to a freezing Russian winter, and he died soon afterward of pneumonia.)

On April 16, 1926, *Pravda* announced that she was returning to Moscow, before resuming her new post: "Yesterday the Soviet Ambassador to Norway, Comrade Kollontai, left Oslo accompanied by a large crowd of people from the diplomatic corps and the Foreign Ministry."[19] She was seen off on the train by sad Norwegian and Russian friends and various trade-union delegations; the Norwegian prime minister sent a large bunch of flowers. As she moved into the sumptuous hotel reserved for high party workers on the banks of the Moscow River the Party was preparing for mass expulsions and the removal, at all costs, of Trotsky. For that spring, after Zinoviev's supporters had been expelled from the Party, a united opposition to Stalin began to form around Zinoviev, Trotsky, Kamenev, and Nadezhda Krupskaya.

The breadth and bitterness of these top party leaders' complaints against the cruel and authoritarian measures being adopted by the Party (formulated in a 100-page program) were already striking panic into the hearts of all Stalin's supporters. Leveling their attack on the anti-socialist forces unleashed by the NEP, the 2,000,000 unemployed, the low wages, the conversion of the unions into organs of the state, the fact that it was forbidden to strike and that six percent of the peasants were rich at the expense of thirty to forty percent who were poor—they aimed to get some 30,000 signatures for their program in order to present it to the Fifteenth Party Congress the following December.

Also staying in Alexandra's hotel, with his family, was Maxim Litvinov of the Foreign Commissariat, with whom she had a few veiled conversations about the recent developments in Russia. She was able to talk more openly with Georgy Chicherin, who still shared with Litvinov the leadership of this commissariat, but he was scarcely involved in the party faction fighting. The only people to whom she could fully open her heart were her old friend Zoya and Misha and his wife (who was apparently working—possibly, like Misha, as an engineer). These three were frequent visitors to her hotel room. Shortly after she arrived in Moscow, however, she received another visitor, a young woman whom Trotsky sent round to urge her to sign the oppositionists' program. This illegal opposition did hold a series of meetings during the spring and summer of 1926, at which it attracted a few supporters, but it was no secret that numerically it was tiny, with only a few thousand followers in Moscow, and an insignificant number in the rest of the country. Alexandra declined to join. Kristian Rakovsky, a left Bolshevik whom she very much admired, rebuked her for doing so, but in the fear and fever of that stuffy summer, when the confrontation with Trotsky was reaching the most hysterical levels of abuse and so many of his supporters were already being sent off to Siberia, Alexandra found it hard to believe that the equally ferocious hostility to Stalin could ever succeed in replacing him with anyone better. As it was, the oppositionists' program, for which they managed to get only 6000 signatures, proved to be mere child's play when they were finally driven to the wall the following year.

Alexandra preferred to take up the cause of people more neglected and less supported. She had had some faith in the idealistic head of the secret police, Dzerzhinsky. After his death in 1926 it was his successor, Menzhinsky, whom she begged to intervene in the case of a young unmarried pregnant woman who had visited her; this woman had been expelled from her sleazy room by a "popular tribunal," and was now threatening to jump in the river. Alexandra made numerous visits to the Zhenotdel, too, urging it to defend the woman's rights, and eventually this poor victim got her room back.[20]

By September, after she had dutifully read as much as she could about Mexican politics and history, Alexandra was preparing to leave Moscow, physically and emotionally exhausted. It was then that the "Baku Letter," written by Shlyapnikov and Medvedev two years before, was suddenly unearthed. Shlyapnikov had briefly joined the united opposition; Alexandra had already disgraced herself in the debate of the past year. Now all the old buried fury at the Workers' Opposition came pouring out again as the writers of the "Baku Letter" were denounced by the government as the "right-wing danger in our Party." More dangerous even than the Trotskyists was the alliance they had contemplated with the "international financial plutocracy." Merely for advancing Lenin's view that foreign concessions should be encouraged as a means of building up heavy industry, the old Workers' Oppositionists, disorientated and demoralized, now became victims, more easily identifiable than the "Trotskyists," of a savage attack.

By the time Alexandra had left Moscow, few oppositionists could take any more of this hysteria. Trotsky, Zinoviev, Kamenev, and Pyatakov all tried to make some sort of peace with the Party and struggled to remain within it. Nadezhda Krupskaya withdrew from the opposition in terror at what was happening in Lenin's name. And Shlyapnikov and Medvedev, oppositionists to the end, finally agreed to sign a capitulation and renounce the "Baku Letter," Alexandra was assumed to have proved her own renunciation of the Workers' Opposition. She would be well out of the way in Mexico, where it was clearly Stalin's intention to condemn her to a life of loneliness and ill health.

As it was, she was ill before she set off and was dreading the thought of another separation from Misha and her friends. She decided to make her way to Mexico via Berlin to get treatment from the heart specialists there whom she had consulted before. At the Russian-Polish border her trunks were lost, and she was told to carry on without them. Eight days later they were returned to her in Berlin, but the secret police had not attempted to conceal the traces of a thorough search of all her belongings.[21] Her path to Mexico was fraught with further difficulties, for her application to the American embassy in Berlin for a transit visa across the United States was rejected on the explicit orders of the American Secretary of State, Kellogg. "Madame Kollontai is one of the most prominent members of the Russian Communist Party," Kellogg wired the Berlin embassy, "as well as being a delegate to the Comintern."[22] Many Americans were puzzled by this decision and considered that it was intended as a slight to Mexico rather than to Russia. Why, people asked in a series of letters to the American press, if hundreds of Russians were allowed in to buy cotton and tractors, was this one woman refused entry?

Alexandra had instead to cross to Mexico via the Caribbean, and early on the morning of November 21, 1926, she left the French port of St.-Nazaire on the *Lafayette*. After a wearying week at sea the ship docked in Havana, where all the other passengers were allowed to disembark. "The Cubans are such vassals of the United States that they wouldn't even allow me, a woman traveling alone, onto their shores," she wrote to Litvinov.[23] Various organizations friendly to the Soviet Union had organized a demonstration to welcome her to Cuba, but they had to send her letters of support instead. The other passengers returned from shore bringing her flowers, presents, and messages of sympathy, and the *Lafayette* set off for Mexico.

As they steamed into the Mexican port of Veracruz Alexandra glimpsed a large crowd of Mexicans on shore, women in their embroidered shirtlike dresses, men waving their sombreros, and a Negro waving a red handkerchief, all of them gathered to give her a cheerful welcome. But she was already feeling so exhausted by the long sea voyage that she had to refuse to address the crowd, and was taken off by the Mexican foreign minister to the station. From Veracruz there was a suffocating, dusty twelve-hour train ride to Mexico City, where she was welcomed at the station by a crowd of people and a forest of red banners: *"Long Live Comrade Kollontai!"* they read, and *"Long Live the Soviet Union!"* But once again she felt unable to linger, for she was already breathless and gasping. She was taken to a hotel, and she went to bed. Later that night she awoke, her heart palpitating wildly, her breath labored; she called for the doctor and could only hope that he was right when he assured her that, given time, her organism would adjust to the altitude. It never did, and soon after she arrived she was writing to a friend, "You can not imagine how dry it is here and how hard it is to breathe—even breathing is such a labor here."[24]

Debilitated by Mexico's climate, Alexandra felt little confidence in her ability to follow the complex course Mexican politics had taken over the ten years since its bourgeois revolution in 1916, in which progressive businessmen and members of the urban middle class had broken the stranglehold of the old feudal economy (whereby 11,000 plantation owners had sixty percent of the land, and eighty-eight percent of the population were landless peons) and expropriated the American-owned oil properties. Before 1916 Mexico was a country in which the standard of living of the wage-earning population was much lower than that of other Latin American countries like Argentina and Uruguay; fifty-two percent of the population lived in miserable huts, and the infant mortality rate passed the figure of 300 for every 1000 live births. Large masses of the Mexican people had been unaffected by the revolution, which took the country but one step out of a colonial feudal pattern of development toward an economy of a semi-capitalist type.

Its new constitution, which granted the Mexican middle classes full rights to their land and its wealth, was bitterly opposed by the United States, which had enjoyed a monopoly over its satellite's valuable oil supplies. The Mexican Communist Party, founded shortly after the revolution and led by the American communist Bertram Wolfe, was also attacked by America, and this ensured that in 1925 Wolfe was expelled from Mexico. The Communist Party had an almost equally fierce opponent in the active socialist trade union organization, the Confederación Regional de Obreros Mexicanos (CROM). Alexandra's predecessor in Mexico, S. Pestkovsky, had supported both the Mexican Communist Party and its contacts in America, and had been asked to leave shortly before Alexandra arrived for doing so. Clearly she was going to have almost no political leeway at all.

The new Mexican president, Plutarcho Calles, had come to power with a program calling for national independence, agricultural reforms, a limitation of the powers of the Church, and a fuller development of Mexico's indigenous industry. But time and again these reforms were deferred for fear of damaging relations with the United States, relations which had taken a pronounced turn for the worse in 1924 when Mexico, first of all Latin American countries, extended diplomatic recognition to the Soviet Union. Alexandra arrived just as Mexico's conflict with America over her oil interests was reaching a crisis, and America was quick to point to her diplomatic appointment as an indication that Mexico was about to adopt "Bolshevik policies."

The sun beat down from a blazing sky when, on December 24, 1926, Alexandra presented her credentials to President Calles. Cameras whirled and reporters jostled as she delivered a speech in French in which she praised the achievements of the Mexican revolution and the courage of the people who had fought to make it. A long round of diplomatic engagements followed, and she managed to make a number of Mexican friends—intellectuals in whom she was delighted to discover a love for the music of Prokofiev and the poetry of Mayakovsky. She was introduced to Diego Rivera, for whose paintings she developed a lifelong passion. Not long after she arrived, she held showings in the embassy building of two new Soviet films, *Abrek Zauer* and *Death Bay*. The first of these was an Oriental adventure film, which was evidently very popular in Russia and abroad. The second, made by the young director Abram Room in the summer of 1926, with subtitles by Victor Shklovsky, a Russian poet of great elegance, was enormously popular. It traced the adventures of a group of Bolsheviks in exposing a tsarist police provocateur who had wiped out a group of Bolshevik sailors before the revolution. It was a melodrama, with the villain portrayed as a grotesque savage and the heroes embodying the highest revolutionary virtues, but it had a psychological authenticity about it, and Alexandra had no trouble in selling both films to the government. She did not confine herself to these activities, however, and soon started negotiations so that the Soviet Union might buy Mexican lead.

It was in January 1927, shortly after she had opened these negotiations, that the American Secretary of State started up a systematic campaign against Soviet diplomacy. His article, "On the Aims and Policies of the Bolsheviks in Mexico and Latin America" claimed that Russia was plotting to export revolution, and was widely circulated in the press and embassies throughout the West. The article struck such panic into the heart of the government officials and businessmen with whom Alexandra was negotiating that at the end of January she felt impelled to visit the President to protest that her purpose in Mexico was to establish trade and cultural relations, not to sow the seeds of revolution.

But her own precarious health was making all her work increasingly difficult. "I'm really just a Leningrad bog-dweller," she wrote to a friend. "I get so weary when there's no moisture. I long for water . . ."[25] After suffering a frightening heart attack, she was advised by her doctor to move out to Cuernavaca, situated on a broad plateau in the Sierra Madre, and there, despite her anxieties about abandoning her work, she breathed more easily. "Here the air is motionless, the sky flat, unshadowed, glassy, as if we are under a huge bell-glass. Even the beautiful bright flowers on the winding paths are motionless," she wrote in her diary.[26] But she had barely had time to catch her breath and appreciate the beauty of the old monastery in which she was staying (which still retained the traces of the Spanish conquest) before she was summoned back to Mexico City for an interview with the foreign minister. She knew in advance what it would be about.

Various Soviet trade unions had been sending financial donations and messages of support to an illegal strike of railway workers in Mexico. Alexandra was asked for her assurance that these donations would stop. The only answer she could give, however, was that workers' solidarity in struggle lay outside the sphere of her diplomatic responsibilities. The strike continued, the streets of Mexico City were filled with demonstrators, and the Soviet films which she had promoted and which continued to draw large audiences were now denounced by the government as Bolshevik propaganda. When the manager of the cinema showing *Death Bay* was arrested, Alexandra was quick to protest and he was soon released. But this mounting campaign against the Soviet Union lent yet more heat to Mexico's conflict with the United States over her oil interests. The press started up a personal campaign against Alexandra, and open American intervention against the Mexican government was anxiously anticipated.[27]

Alexandra was forced once more to leave the capital, but even the pleasant hotel in Cuernavaca where she had stayed before was no longer so eager to welcome her, for even here the menace of an invasion or an American-engineered counter-revolution was in the air. As she was sitting in a restaurant there one afternoon she was approached by an affable-looking man who, after introducing himself as the Governor of Morelos and declaring how delighted he was to meet her, invited her to be his guest the following day for a tour of the town hall. Next day she waited for him for several hours and was just putting the excursion out of her mind when his flustered secretary arrived; after kissing her hand, he apologized for the governor's absence—he had been arrested and a column of troops had occupied the town. Whether they were there to represent the government or to arrest the government was not clear, but he urged her to leave at once.

As she hurried back to her hotel she heard gunshots. She only just managed to get a seat on a tiny overcrowded open bus which was filled with men grimly holding revolvers out of the sides to shoot at bandits. She took her place among her silent, ferocious-looking traveling-companions, and they lurched off into the hills toward Mexico City. With every corner they turned, and every new likely looking ambush-point they passed, Alexandra wondered weakly what ransom might be demanded from her. Then at last they negotiated a particularly sharp bend, the bus jolted sickeningly, and Mexico City came into sight. The men put away their revolvers and began to smoke, and she joined them in a deep sigh of relief.

Alexandra would not be able to breathe deeply again until she left Mexico for good, but it was not until May 1927 that she wrote to the Commissariat of Foreign Affairs begging, for health reasons, to be relieved of her post.

By June 1927, when the Commissariat of Foreign Affairs announced that Alexandra was being granted a temporary release from her post in Mexico, her pleasure at the prospect of leaving was tremendous. She would miss the sapphire seas and the palm-trees, but she knew quite well that at the age of fifty-five she could not expect to live much longer if she stayed on in Mexico. She was determined that her "temporary" release should be permanent. There were numerous dinners and parties in her honor before she was seen off, on June 23, by delegations of trade unionists and several friends. She boarded the steamer, bearing with her a coconut, a great Mexican carpet, and a painting by Diego Rivera. The moment the boat steamed into the English Channel, with its fog, damp, and rain, she began to feel healthier. "I'm already home," she wrote to Tatiana Schepkina, her old friend in Leningrad, "although I suppose I really don't have a home."[28]

19

The Last Years – The Purges

Never any home but in the Party. When Alexandra returned to Moscow that June in the tenth anniversary year of the revolution, she found the leaders of the Party contorted by paroxysms of hostility to the oppositionists, who were now openly declaring that all talk of party unity was a sham, a façade for its mistakes. Just before she returned, the Soviet trade mission in London had been raided; there were sudden fears of war, the oppositionists were branded as "defeatists," and this lent weight to Stalin's insistence that they should be expelled en masse.

The battle of Marxist and Leninist quotes with which Stalin tried to justify this had begun. Taking Lenin's statement that the "complete victory of socialism in Russia is impossible without the active cooperation of some advanced countries, among which we cannot include Russia," Stalin pointed out that "complete victory" was not at all the same thing as simple "victory"; and so, by declaring that Trotsky's talk of "permanent revolution" and the leftists' hopes for an international revolution was all nonsense, he was able to proclaim his own complacent philosophy of "socialism in one country." Trotsky and the united opposition were now insisting that on the contrary any victory of socialism in Russia was out of the question unless the proletarian movement was gradually extended throughout the world. The only alternative future for the Bolshevik revolution remained the "Thermidorian reaction," with the bureaucracy usurping the power of the Party, the Party usurping the people, and one individual usurping the Party.

With the Party so fiercely attacked, it now became increasingly urgent to silence the opposition before the time came for the huge nationwide demonstrations with which the anniversary of the revolution

457

was to be celebrated in November, and before the Fifteenth Party Congress which was to follow. Many prominent oppositionists were still being dealt with circumspectly and cleared out of the country rather than arrested. Trotsky, whose prestige and moral authority were still enormous, was a more difficult case and could not so easily be removed, but the veteran left oppositionist Krestinsky was packed off to head the Soviet embassy in Berlin; Kristian Rakovsky was sent to London and then to France, where he joined Pyatakov and two other left oppositionists, Preobrazhensky and Krasikov; Antonov-Ovseenko, who had led the Bolsheviks' assault on the Winter Palace, was sent to Czechoslovakia. In October 1927 Alexandra received orders to resume her post in Oslo (her successor there had not been popular); her presence in Russia during the emotional anniversary celebrations would clearly have been an intolerable reminder of past ideals.

She had not, however, joined the oppositionists—far from it. The words of a *Pravda* article of hers which appeared on November 1, 1927, disguised what must have been an acute terror at the chaos which threatened Russia, ruled as it was by a disunited Party whose members were now trooping off to exile and prison by the hundred. Writing of the selection of delegates to the Fifteenth Congress, she put all her hopes now in the unanimous votes *against* the opposition. This sign of increased party unity, she wrote, was "definitely an outcome of the mental and spiritual growth of the rank and file, a growth in the direction of collective thinking." The "collectivist system of work" had triumphed over "individual initiative," which showed that the "masses' fundamental need was for discipline to be observed." As against the "petty bourgeois interpretation of democracy . . . dormant in the opposition," she declared the commitment to a united party, that "collective work produces an utterly new idea of the meaning of discipline . . . as merging one's own will with that of the collective body . . ."

The masses were too busy building the new life to listen to the opposition, she continued. Their work was concentrated in numerous collectives: in soviets, unions, commissions, and committees. Nowhere in the world did the collective way of working take precedence over the individual as in Russia. Often, to be sure, these collective organizations held up work and made it difficult for people to take any initiative, but this was another question. What was important was that from these collective beginnings a new approach to the life of the masses was emerging, a completely new ideology. She concluded her article with an oblique attack on those party leaders who had formerly attacked the Workers'

Opposition, and who were now attacking Stalin in very much the same way: "If the opposition finds defects in the Party . . . who, if not the famous members of that opposition, established them in the first place? The masses' memory is not so short. It seems from what the oppositionists say as though the policies of the Party and the structure of the apparatus became corrupt only at the moment when those oppositionists broke with the Party . . ."[1]

On November 7, a week after this article appeared and Alexandra had left Moscow, the oppositionists' counter-demonstration in Moscow was barely noticed amid the vast official demonstrations which filled the streets and squares. Trotsky was assailed with gross insults and flying objects at a meeting he tried to address. A few days later Trotsky and Zinoviev were expelled from the central committee and Adolf Joffe, a consistent leftist and one of Alexandra's old friends from her days as an exile in Berlin, committed suicide. Zinoviev threw himself on the mercy of the central committee, begging to be readmitted, and Kamenev recanted his oppositionist views to avoid expulsion.

The Fifteenth Congress opened in December with Stalin's words, to be repeated monotonously at every successive congress—"The Party is making uninterrupted progress in all fields." The oppositionists were expelled en masse from the Party as a "Menshevik or Socialist Revolutionary deviation," and only Zinoviev and Kamenev were saved. "The iron curtain of history was about to fall on you, but you got out of the way just in time," Bukharin remarked to them with a deathly jocularity. Many people, less pliable and cowardly than these two, repeatedly affirmed their loyalty to the Party at this congress, but the central committee had already begun its work of removing the more prominent of the expelled oppositionists to central Siberia.

Rakovsky was sent off to a "post" in Astrakhan, where his poor health could not be expected to withstand the climate for long. Evgeny Preobrazhensky, an old left Bolshevik, former central-committee member, and renowned economist, was dispatched to a similar "post" in the Urals. Ivar Smilga, a youthful and energetic former central-committee member who had been one of Lenin's most devoted supporters, was sent off to central Siberia. Karl Radek left for northern Siberia, Muralov for the Tara forests, and four other friends of Trotsky's—Serebryakov, Smirnov, Sapronov, and Sosnovsky—were all sent off to equally remote parts to occupy equally non-existent "posts." When Trotsky was offered his post in Alma Ata, he refused all such "friendly negotiations," organized a last heroic resistance to his deportation, and had eventually to be carried off bodily from his flat to the train. Hundreds of deportations followed. With an unbelievable and tragic optimism born of boundless courage, countless revolutionaries cheerfully set off for the wastelands of Russia, there to work for the "salvation of the revolution."

"About myself personally, I can only say I have not acclimatized . . ."[2] Alexandra wrote to Litvinov from Oslo in December 1927. She also wrote to Trotsky and Natalya Sedova expressing her sympathy with them after their deportation. But as fear and self-censorship entered the consciousness of every Russian who wanted to stay alive, Alexandra's remarks were to become increasingly guarded; censorship and self-censorship ensure that we have very little evidence at our disposal with which to interpret her feelings in those ghastly years. Shlyapnikov was for the moment safely writing the third volume of his vast and invaluable memoirs of 1917; the previous October he and Medvedev had written to the Politburo and the central committee condemning "any organized expression of opinions contradicting party decisions." Dybenko, who had moved up through a succession of high military posts and was now Commander of the Central Asian Armies, was widely known to be a personal enemy of Trotsky's. His great courage in past battles had assured his popularity; it was not until ten years later that the purge of the army would begin.

By the end of 1927 Alexandra can have had no doubt that the left opposition, which she had so idealistically joined in 1918, was now dead, deprived of its leaders and of any mass support. The executions eight years later would finally bring to a close the whole tragic history of that opposition. There were, it was true, a few oppositionists still at liberty who wanted to set up an illegal organization in Russia whereby they might gradually gain the strength to plan their future rehabilitation in the Party. There were a few others, too, who had no faith in such illegal methods and wanted to defend their views more openly. But few could think that either method was likely to succeed.

Isolated and out of touch with the mood of people in Russia as her visits to Moscow became increasingly infrequent, Alexandra perhaps did not realize how many revolutionaries felt quite as isolated and confused as she; Misha, in his letters to her from Moscow, apparently reflected an almost total lack of interest in the power struggle in Russia, and since this detachment augured well for his safety, it must have been a considerable relief to her. From Alma Ata, Trotsky repeated that the Party must still be supported at all costs; many former oppositionists rallied to that call when the anniversary celebrations in November 1927 were followed by the encouraging announcement of a seven-hour day with no reduction in pay and the abolition of taxes for the poor peasants. In 1928, when the acute famine and grain crisis prompted Stalin's first five-year plan and a sudden swing toward the leftists' program for a rapid collectivization of the peasants, some 5000 former oppositionists sank their differences with the Party. "We have ten years," said Stalin, "in which to catch up with the West." The alternative was to be forcibly submerged as an agricultural colony of capitalism. However cruelly and idiotically Stalin's plan was applied, few leftists could deny that it expressed the essence of their own program.

The leftists had said, Tax the rich peasants—Stalin said, Liquidate them. They had said, Limit and reform the NEP—Stalin said, Abolish it. They had called for rapid industrialization—Stalin proceeded to carry this out on a vast scale: there was incalculable suffering and ruthless exploitation of people's labor. As Victor Serge commented, many sincere revolutionaries preferred to capitulate and build factories than "defend lofty principles in the enforced indolence of captivity."[3] Over the next eight years local party cadres were sent into the villages with orders to collectivize all peasant property, down to chickens, rabbits, and hoes, in an effort to achieve at lightning speed one-hundred-percent collectivization; thousands of peasants burned their crops and killed their livestock rather than agree to be collectivized; something like 5,000,000 peasant families disappeared into exile for refusing to give up their land and animals, and countless more were shot for "concealment of stocks." Those eight years hardened many revolutionaries' resolve and limited their options.

So it was that countless idealists became convinced that scapegoats could be found for a system that was unworkable. The transport system was in chaos—technicians were arrested. Mining was in crisis—"saboteurs" were shot without trial. An "industrial party" was charged with plotting a counter-revolution with the backing of Poland and England— five people were shot. A "peasant party" (a group of professors who opposed all-out collectivization) was arrested—its "members" were shot. In the face of the agonies suffered by Russia's 160,000,000 people, all opposition came to seem increasingly sterile; the vital importance of rebuilding the economy, at whatever frightful cost, seemed to put more and more ideological differences into the shadows.

As people in Russia became increasingly confused and hopeless, never knowing whom to trust and whom to blame, the terror struck deep into Alexandra too, who was saved from despair only by her boundless capacity for work, her ability to make friends, and the diaries in which she confided many of the fears which could not be expressed abroad. Throughout her years of diplomatic exile these diaries were kept under strong lock and key in her desk, and since her death they have been kept under the far more impenetrable lock of the Soviet archives.*

"Here it's a foggy wet autumn," she wrote to Litvinov after she arrived in Oslo at the end of 1927. "I can't remember when people behaved with such suspicion toward us. I assure you, it's not much easier here than it was in Mexico. However, we'll see. In Mexico I never took my eyes off our 'neighbor'. Here it's perfidious Albion [England] we have to keep our eyes on . . ."4 (She was referring to the raid of the Soviet trade mission in London that summer.) In her first months there she was preoccupied by the irritating business of furnishing the old tsarist building on Uranienborgvein, into which the Soviet embassy had just moved. "If I had a wife she'd relieve me of these tedious chores," she complained ironically in her diary. "That's the inconvenience of being a woman ambassador—you have no wife or housekeeper, and so carry a double burden; as it is, I'm both ambassador and wife."5

There were numerous meetings to attend at which she promoted trade and cultural relations between the two countries. In March 1928, for example, she was particularly pleased to be asked to address a meeting called to commemorate the anniversary of Ibsen's death; she talked with genuine enthusiasm of the way in which women of her generation had been inspired by Nora, the heroine of A Doll's House, who had left her husband to find her freedom and the right to be treated as an equal of men.

Winter was the "diplomatic season," when Alexandra had to give dinner parties and be sociable. Misha and his wife came to stay for a few weeks with her that summer, and Zoya, who visited her in Oslo in the winter of 1928, enjoyed the warm sociability of her friend's parties around a candle-lit table, which reminded her of a Rembrandt painting. But might Alexandra not be sick, she wondered, of this tinsely, showcase existence? Yes, she eventually confessed, it was indeed all very boring: "So many times I've longed to disconnect the telephone, sit at my writing table, and write about everything I've done."6

It is a pity she did not. Ilya Ehrenburg, the Soviet writer who conveyed with such passion the atmosphere in Russia and in exile before and after the revolution, visited Alexandra in Oslo early in 1929 and found

---

*Various passages from these diaries have been released and are contained in her official Soviet biography, as well as in the articles of G. D. Petrov, quoted in Chapters 7 to 10.

her eager to discuss the possibilities of new Russian art forms. The Soviet literature she had seen so far impressed her very little. Art demanded revolutionary new forms, she insisted, and she talked with great admiration of the young painters whose work she had seen in Mexico and Norway, and of her favorite artist, Van Gogh.

Ehrenburg had first seen and admired Alexandra in Paris in 1909, when as a very young and raw revolutionary he had heard her speak at the Russian exiles' meeting-place on the Avenue de Choisy. Her words then —that people could only be happy when universal human happiness was attained—had been close to his heart. Meeting her for the first time in person twenty years later, he found her still handsome, and still, at the age of fifty-seven, youthful. They went for a walk in the hills outside Oslo, and "I barely managed to keep up with her as she scrambled up the steep rocks. There was a wonderful youthfulness about her manner of arguing and her dreams for the future—for this was in 1929, when it was still possible to argue and dream." Walking through the town with her, he was amazed by the number of people who ran up to her on the street to greet her; when they went into a café, the musicians immediately recognized her and began to play Russian songs in her honor. Politicians too, he discovered, spoke of her with great respect, while artists and poets often awaited with some anxiety her opinion on the latest exhibition or book.[7]

At the end of 1929 Alexandra learned that the Soviet ambassador to Sweden was dying and that she was to replace him in Stockholm. She returned to Moscow to discover that in this "historic" year of Stalin's fiftieth birthday the city was being swamped by posters and statues glorifying the leader's kindly features. Every town and village in Russia was similarly adorned, and the press was filled with nauseating birthday tributes. She saw Misha and his wife, of course, and Zoya, as well as a few other close friends but, as she told Marcel Body, who met her shortly after she arrived in Stockholm early in 1930, "I don't recognise anyone in Moscow now, apart from a dozen or so comrades. What can you do? How can you oppose the apparatus? How can you fight, or defend yourself against injury? For my part, I've put my principles into a corner of my conscience and carry out as well as I can the policies dictated to me."[8] She may already have been regretting the article she had written in 1927 on the virtues of party unity, which was reprinted in 1927 in the French communist paper L'Humanité. (Body claims that this article was dictated to her word for word by her party superiors.) Since then she had written nothing but two memoir articles, about Lenin and about the women who had fought for the October revolution. There were other, particularly deep reasons for her feelings of sadness and defeat, for at the end of 1929 the Zhenotdel was virtually dissolved.

Stalin's Secretariat, which had by then amassed under its control all the party organizations dealing with agitprop, staffing, the press, accounting, statistics, the villages, and women's work, was in the midst of being reorganized in the autumn of 1929. Many of its former functions were absorbed by those of the agitprop section, which was now split into two departments—one for agitation and mass campaigns, and one for culture and propaganda. The party's departments on women's work and village organization were to be abolished and incorporated into the agitprop's department for agitation and mass campaigns. The Zhenotdel had done important work, it was announced, but now its work was done, for the Party as a whole could now assume all the work of liberating women, and there already existed a strong body of liberated women in the Party who could ensure that it fulfilled its promises.

More deep-seated fears of the Zhenotdel emerged, however, at the Sixteenth Party Congress, which took place in June 1930, after Alexandra had left for Sweden. Women, announced Stalin's loyal supporter Kaganovich, were the backbone of the resistance to collectivization; they needed more political education and not so much talk about improving their lives. The Party that required such superhuman sacrifices from the people in the interests of its five-year plan, obviously could not but consider the Zhenotdel, however loyal, as a very great embarrassment. Created for the official purpose of drawing Russia's women into the process of their emancipation, the Zhenotdel's real purpose had always been to enforce and make real the Bolsheviks' paper reforms for women in and out of the Party. As the five-year plan began to mobilize men and women in massive numbers into the labor force, the Zhenotdel, with its questioning attitudes toward the Party's authority, was now dismissed as an anachronism. Praskovya Kudelli, an old Bolshevik of some standing, made a final plea at this congress for the Party not to forget all those working women who had contributed so much to the economy and who still enjoyed none of the benefits promised to them in their homes; for women, she stressed, especially those struggling to combine work and home life with political activities, suffered from an impossible conflict of interests in these three separate spheres of their lives. Her words were lost in the wind.[9]

When Alexandra arrived in Stockholm and settled into the Soviet embassy in Karlevagen, she had few illusions about the extreme difficulty of improving Soviet-Swedish relations, for Sweden had just proposed to the other Scandinavian countries the establishment of a northern Baltic anti-Soviet pact. At first, few people dared to attend the receptions at the Soviet embassy which Alexandra—who based all her diplomatic work on the principle that "the diplomat who does not give her country new friends is not a diplomat"—devoted so much of her energy to organizing. It was not long after her arrival, however, that when she asked twenty people to dinner, fifty would come; and it was soon understood that she kept open house in the evenings for anybody who shared Russia's hatred of the fascism that was beginning to poison Europe. The Swedish papers began to follow her every move, noting the people she talked to at official receptions, and if possible the substance of her conversations there. There were soon few in Stockholm who did not know her as witty and often ironic in discussion, and generous and unselfish with her close friends and their families.

Her old friend Hjalmar Branting, leader of the Swedish Socialist Party, had died in 1926, but his son and daughter, George, a journalist, and Sonya, a lawyer, were two of her dearest friends in Sweden, and she frequently visited them in their fourth-floor flat in the bright street of Nortullagaten, near Stockholm University. This street lay at the foot of a hill on which stood the tower of Stockholm's old observatory, a reminder of Hjalmar Branting's passion for astronomy; he had spent many nights there, or on his own roof, gazing at the stars.

Ada Nilson, a feminist and doctor of liberal, rather than socialist, sympathies, became a close friend of Alexandra's at this time, as did another Swedish woman, a writer named Elen Michaelson, who was a disciple of the feminist Ellen Key and whom Alexandra helped compile a book about women in the Russian revolution. Naima Wifstrand and Karl Gerhardt, two of Sweden's finest actors, were also frequent visitors to the Karlevagen embassy. Alexandra entertained in a large and comfortable ground-floor room, adorned with Mexican paintings and carpets and a large oil portrait of her sister Jenny, whom she much resembled. Meals were simple but always punctual and hot, and although Alexandra herself did not smoke, cigarettes were always passed round afterward.[10]

She loved Stockholm, as she had loved it forty-two years before when she had first visited it with her mother at the age of sixteen. She loved its stark granite buildings, its tree-lined streets, its parks, its white nights, the pale blue waters of the surrounding lakes, and the distant outlines of the forests and fjords outside the city. In appearance this major center of northern capitalism had much in common with Leningrad. Shortly after arriving in Stockholm, she went through the tiresome procedure of presenting her credentials to Sweden's prim King Gustav, and it was only after this that a small announcement appeared in the newspapers to declare that her official and permanent banishment from Sweden in 1915 had been revoked.

Over the next two years her life of ceaseless work was relieved only in the summer, when Misha and his wife would visit her for a few weeks and they would take a short holiday in a tourist resort near Stockholm. Her diplomatic work focused on negotiating for the Soviet Union a long-term credit arrangement with Sweden, and by 1933 such was the trust she managed to inspire among Swedish government officials and industrialists that she arranged for some gold reserves, concealed by Kerensky in various Swedish banks, to be returned to Russia. In that year she was awarded the Order of Lenin for her contribution to women's work in Russia. Hypocrisy could hardly go further. There can have been little rejoicing for her in that year in which, three years after Shlyapnikov had been forced to make a public confession of his "political errors," he was expelled from the Party as a "degenerate." Medvedev too was expelled. But there were many other old comrades and friends from whom she now heard nothing; they could only be presumed dead.

In 1931, when Stalin announced himself as official "father of the Russian people," he proposed that capital punishment was the proper punishment for oppositionists. He already had his own personal police force within the secret police, and his proposal was rejected in horror by more humanitarian colleagues like Bukharin and Zinoviev, but even they were being ostracized now as increasing numbers of central-committee members began to be described as "rightists," "Mensheviks," or "Trotskyists." Stalin eventually managed to get his proposal accepted five years later. In 1931 he had to content himself with a law that made families accountable for their relatives' political activities. This law struck panic into everyone's heart and made Alexandra long for the all-too-brief visits of Misha and his wife to Sweden, and dread their return to Russia.

They came to see her, however, for no longer than a few weeks in every year, and her contacts with Russians became increasingly scarce. No Russian who did visit her there could fail to be impressed by the genuinely collective way she worked with the embassy staff, the warm, cheerful atmosphere around the dinner table at which everyone gathered to eat (cooks, chauffers, porters, and officials), and the sensitivity with which Alexandra helped and encouraged her colleagues and their families. All knew of the support she had given to the Russian cook at the embassy, Anna Petrovna, who had had a great desire to have a baby without getting married. (When her baby was born, Anna Petrovna named him Misha, and Alexandra became a sort of second mother to him.) One Russian professor who visited Stockholm for a conference of historians recalled the countless small ways in which she managed to make him feel welcome there, and many others had occasion to describe with affection and admiration her unpretentious and uncomplaining style of living and working.

It was not until May 1934 that she managed to extend her contacts with the Soviet Union. In that month she set up a Swedish-Russian cultural society, and over the following years she was able to entertain at the embassy a number of writers, artists, and musicians, among whom her more prominent guests were David Oistrakh, the writers Ehrenburg, Sholokhov, Korneichuk, and Ginzburg, and one old Bolshevik who, until his death in 1934, managed to keep out of the Soviet power struggle—Lunacharsky.

In March of that year she managed to conclude a hundred-million-kroner loan with which the Soviet Union was to buy Swedish industrial goods. She later had to urge Russia to cancel its application for this loan, which was widely attacked by conservatives in the Swedish government as "adventurism"; but she went on to represent the Soviet Union in arranging a tripartite agreement whereby its export of timber would be brought into line with that of Finland and Sweden. In that year too she invited a number of reporters, industrialists, and government officials to greet the arrival of a hydroplane from Leningrad. Steeling herself for her first plane flight, she returned for a two-week visit to Moscow with the Swedish foreign minister, Rickard Sandler.

Steeling herself in Moscow against the terrifying hysteria which had followed the assassination in January 1934 of Stalin's colleague Kirov, Alexandra can have had no doubt that this was to be the signal for a new mass of trials and purges. The arrest of hundreds of party members for their "moral responsibility" for Kirov's death was the start of the black purges of the next twelve years. Of the 1966 delegates to the Seventeenth Congress—the "congress of victors"—shortly before Kirov's assassination, 1108 were to be purged, as were 98 of the 139 central-committee members.

Apart from an obituary article for Nadezhda Krupskaya, who died in 1933, and an article for *Rabotnitsa* in 1937 describing women's activities in 1917, Alexandra wrote nothing more for the Soviet press until 1945.[11] As the value placed on human life in Russia dwindled, bewilderment and fear for herself and for Misha forced Alexandra to conceal her grief and defend her country against those in Stockholm who attacked it for the wrong reasons. The glee with which many in the West greeted the first show trials must have made this grief particularly unbearable.

When the USSR was elected to the League of Nations in 1934 and Alexandra was made a member of the Soviet delegation, she may have derived some hope that this organization might have a liberalizing effect on Soviet domestic policy. The League of Nations had been formed in 1920 in Geneva by five of the principal world powers—Britain, France, Italy, Japan, and the United States (Germany joined in 1926 and resigned in 1933)—with the aim of achieving permanent world peace through negotiation. Its vague brief was to deal with any matter which appeared to threaten peace, to enforce a strict recognition of the borders established after the First World War, and if aggression against these was threatened, to advise on the necessary measures to be taken. By 1931, however, the rise of fascism in Germany was already making the League appear increasingly powerless and unstable, prone when in doubt to sprout yet more commissions and sub-commissions. It may be hard for us to realize now what extraordinarily high hopes many Europeans of all persuasions placed in the League of Nations. Alexandra joined commissions on the opium traffic and nutrition, as well as on the legal rights of women, and from 1934 to 1939 she traveled several times a year to Geneva, where she soon had a circle of close women friends. There was the staunch Swedish feminist, Kerstin Hesselgren; two English women, Miss Holsworth and Mrs. Corbett-Ashby, a member of the International Alliance for Suffrage and Equal Citizenship; a French feminist called Mme Malaterre-Seller; and, from America, Grace Abbott, Mary Anderson, and Freda Miller.

In January 1935 Kamenev and Zinoviev were the first Bolshevik leaders to be arrested; the purge of the old Bolsheviks had begun. Shlyapnikov was arrested and imprisoned in that year too. As Alexandra traveled back and forth between Oslo and Geneva, drowning her anxieties in endless committee work on the legal rights of women, there must have hovered about her grief for Shlyapnikov the haunting realization that with his imprisonment the heroism of the revolution for which she had fought was being buried alive.

Her friends became even more precious to her. When Republican Spain's new ambassador, Isabel Palencia, arrived in Stockholm, she found a huge bunch of flowers awaiting her in her room and a note from Alexandra in which she apologized for not welcoming her in person since she had had to leave town.[12] Isabel soon became her closest friend in Stockholm, the only person she could expect to understand something of the loyalties that tore her apart—and the anguish, which she could find no words to express. One bitter March day in 1936 she telephoned Isabel and begged her to go for a drive with her. Isabel found her ill and sad, her face pale and swollen from crying. Sitting silently with her friend as they drove past the frozen fir trees which lined the snow-covered road near the city, Alexandra seemed to sink further into her silent depression, fighting tears and clasping Isabel's hand. She talked a little, of the friends whose imprisonment she had just heard of—apparently her doctor in Moscow had also been arrested. Yet months of anxious torment had not brought her any closer to understanding the depths of savagery to which her Party had descended. "Life confronts us with so many things which are hard to understand," was all she could say to Isabel.[13]

In June 1936 Gorky died of drink, despair, and induced illness. Shortly afterward the death sentence was introduced for political "crimes." In July, following Franco's attack on the Spanish Republic, Alexandra suffered a heart attack and went to recuperate in a sanatorium near Göteborg. "Our romantic epoch is finished," she lamented to Marcel Body, who met her there. "Once we were able to take some initiative, push for a new order. Now we can only take orders . . . The new man has no critical sense or analytical faculties. There's no comradeship any more among my Party colleagues and our activities are compartmentalized." It would be unrealistic to imagine, she added, that Russia could go from absolutism to liberty in a few decades—perhaps one just had to be resigned to the dictatorship of a Stalin. Perhaps this was inevitable, for blood flowed now, but innocent blood had flowed under Lenin too. Perhaps Russia, without discipline, culture, or the experience of liberty, was not historically ready for democracy. Perhaps Stalin would manage to keep Russia out of the world war which Franco's attack was now making an ominous and imminent possibility.[14]

In August 1936 the first show trial opened in Moscow. Kamenev and Zinoviev were charged with forming a terrorist group allied to the Gestapo and sentenced, like "mad dogs," to be shot. Their trial was followed by the arrest, torture, and murder of countless other less well-known Bolsheviks, of whose fate few in Russia or abroad had any knowledge. But the terror was to make headlines again in January 1937, when Radek, Pyatakov, and the "anti-Soviet Trotskyist center" were subjected to the second great show trial. Despite their last desperate attempts to save their families by paying homage to "our great Stalin" and approving the execution of Zinoviev and Kamenev, they were all convicted of sabotage and espionage. Pyatakov was sentenced to death, and Radek was sent to prison, where he was murdered shortly afterward. Shlyapnikov was among the hundreds of old Bolsheviks tortured and murdered in more obscure circumstances in that year. Alexandra had most probably assumed him to be already dead. Her own survival and Misha's freedom from harassment —and his apparently total lack of political involvement—must have seemed little short of miraculous to her. Its cost to her was depression, insomnia, and palpitations, the gradual collapse of all her old beliefs and a haunting feeling of guilt and increasing powerlessness.

When Germany and Italy sent troops against the Spanish Republic at the end of 1936 and Franco's massive system of concentration camps shattered all hopes of democracy in Spain, Alexandra could submerge her own feelings of despair by surrounding Isabel and her family with love and support. They would all listen to the radio together, waiting eagerly for news; they would sit around singing Spanish folk melodies or the songs of de Falla and Albéniz, and they gave parties. Isabel organized Christmas celebrations at the Spanish embassy, to which Alexandra and her colleagues were all invited, and the Russians treated their Spanish friends to a traditional Russian New Year's party. It was the support that Alexandra and Isabel derived from each other in those dark days that made their lives bearable.

Isabel had a daughter, Marissa, whose husband was fighting in Spain. After Marissa had her first child in Stockholm's maternity hospital, not a day passed when Alexandra did not visit them after supper with gifts of food or a Russian toy for the baby, Jan, and she often stayed to cuddle the baby, or play pick-a-sticks with Marissa. She urged the staff at the Soviet embassy to donate a proportion of their salaries regularly to supporting the women and children in Republican Spain.[15] Every day, Isabel recalled in her 1947 biography of Alexandra, her friend would visit or send a note to the embassy urging them to keep their spirits up. And even when illness or work forced her to leave Stockholm, the little notes would continue to arrive, often accompanied by presents and packets of food.

There were Alexandra's Swedish friends too, among whom she discovered the warmth that enabled her to survive these years emotionally: the Brantings, and Sonya's young son, Jakov; her secretary, Ema Lorentsson; the daughter of the Swedish playwright, August Strindberg, and her Russian husband; and the eminent woman surgeon, Professor Nanna Schwartz. Lena Wickman, daughter of the publisher of one of Sweden's most prestigious newspapers, is now living in London, and remembers how as a child she made immediate friends with Alexandra, who became a sort of "favorite aunt" for her. Her father, she recalls, was never too busy at the office and always ate at home if he knew that Alexandra would be visiting.[16] Alexandra feared constantly for Misha and his wife of course, but it seems that both of them were as safe from danger as it was possible to be in Moscow in those ghastly times. "My children are well and happy in their country," she wrote to Isabel, "and that is such a great comfort to me."[17]

At the end of 1936 the Soviet embassy moved to a new two-story house in Villagaten, in which Alexandra had a small flat on the first floor. Now, together with a number of her friends, she began to organize a series of fund-raising concerts and parties to aid the Spanish Republican fighters. In Geneva too she joined a small number of Soviet and Scandinavian representatives at the League of Nations who pledged support for Republican Spain.

But 1936 and the two years which followed must have been the blackest in her life. In 1937 the purge of the Red Army began, and she was tormented with anxieties for Dybenko, anxieties every bit as painful as those she had suffered for him in 1918. From June 1937 trials began in which three marshals, every officer who had commanded a military district, two out of every four fleet commanders, and anything from a third to half of Russia's 75,000 officers were to be arrested and shot. The first to be sentenced in a highly secret trial in June was Marshal Tukhachevsky, a figure of unquestionable honesty, great dignity, and international repute. The fact that Dybenko, now commander of the Leningrad Military District, was one of the nine judges who sat to condemn Tukhachevsky to death for treason made the whole terrible case infinitely harder for Alexandra to bear when news of it emerged. Perhaps it was her connections with Dybenko that explained the instructions she received to leave for Moscow at the end of that year. According to Marcel Body, she did not expect to return.[18] She was the only surviving oppositionist and the only member of the first Bolshevik government (apart from Stalin) who was still alive. In Moscow, terrified for her life, she wrote an article abjectly attacking Zinoviev and Kamenev for opposing the armed uprising in October 1917. The article may have ensured her reprieve, but she was still in disfavor with Moscow when she returned to Stockholm, for as ambassador she was always too apt, according to the government, to soften its line when she felt this would better serve some long-term purpose or hasten diplomatic agreement.

By early 1938 Dybenko himself had been demoted and was tried for treason at an in camera trial which Stalin himself attended. Promised a post in the Urals if he confessed, he did so, and was sent off to take over the lumber industries of the Urals forests. He was shot as he got off the train. After 1956 General Dybenko was rehabilitated, along with all the other generals massacred by Stalin. For Alexandra his murder seemed to spell the end of all hope. She mourned his death only to the solitary trusted confidant she had made of her diaries—and this we only know from the confession of the secret-police agent who in 1943 rifled those diaries for such revelations.

At the end of that year Ezhov became head of the secret police, and the "Ezhov days" (the Ezhovshchina) were launched with a devastating purge of all Stalin's former colleagues. The third show trial opened in March 1938, with Bukharin, Rykov, and several others standing in the dock to defend themselves against charges of plotting to kill Lenin in 1918 and working with Trotsky and the Gestapo to restore capitalism in the Soviet Union. It was perhaps the monstrous nature of these charges that led to Rykov's partial rehabilitation in 1956 and the discussions now underway in the Soviet Union which make Bukharin's rehabilitation seem imminent.

Early in 1938, when Ilya Ehrenburg was passing through Stockholm on his way from Moscow to the fighting in Spain, he found Alexandra saddened and much aged, she now looked her sixty-six years and was clearly not well. Isabel was there, talking enthusiastically about the Republican fighters in Spain, and Alexandra was encouraged by her words to remark, "I well believe it; everything is not lost yet." It was only when Isabel had left that she felt able to talk a little more openly of Russia. "How are things there?" she asked, adding immediately, "Don't tell me —I know." As he left she wished him strength, "You'll need twice as much now, not only because you're going to Barcelona, but because you've just come from Moscow."[19]

She expressed rather freer views about events in Russia in a letter in 1938 to Zoya. The bloody horrors there were an inevitable part of the revolution, just as the persecution of heretics had been an inevitable accompaniment of the Renaissance, and they would end:

> Now I value and understand that epoch the Renaissance—a time when thought progressed and people searched for something new—quite differently. What persecution of thought there was! And what a will to defend one's beliefs! It has so much in common with our epoch. . . . Those who made discoveries about the universe then were considered more heretical than those who tried to reform social relations later on.
>   What we are experiencing now is the battle of moribund capitalism with the creators of new social relations and economics. . . . Then the

transition from one stage to another was accompanied by wars, political
intrigues, terror—everything. Well, time passes, and in the squares where
Jan Hus and Giordano Bruno were burned long ago, their monuments
now stand![20]

Alexandra may well have returned from Moscow at the end of 1937 in
some disfavor with the government. But after March 1938 and Germany's
flagrant annexation of Austria, Russia's fears of Nazi aggression overshadowed her comparatively minor fears about the party loyalty of one of her
most renowned diplomats. Finland, an independent state standing at the
gates of Leningrad, now represented an intolerable threat to Russian
security; although as a member of the League of Nations Finland leaned
towards the neutrality of its Scandinavian neighbors, her strategic importance to both Germany and Russia was too great for this neutrality to be
realistic. Alexandra had little choice but to work with the Soviet government in the secret overtures made to Finland in the spring of 1938 to
persuade her to revise some of her borders, particularly those in the north.
The Karelian Isthmus, between Lake Ladoga and the White Sea (and
near the Kuusa estate where Alexandra had spent her happiest times as
a child) was now providing Germany with easy access to Soviet territory.

The negotiations lingered on with the Finnish government, which
intransigently declared its right to neutrality and only came into the open
the following year. Hitler's agreement to help his fellow dictator in Spain,
with soldiers and 500,000,000 marks (an enormous sum at that time), was
made in equal secrecy. His more blatant seizure of Austria in 1938 was
preceded by a barrage of propaganda which was to become typical. He
issued an ultimatum to the Austrian chancellor that an Austrian Nazi
must be made Minister of the Interior, with control of police and security,
and that another was to be appointed Minister of War. Then, without
waiting for a response, he marched in, throwing all leading Austrians who
might resist into concentration camps. The pattern was next repeated in
Czechoslovakia, whose northeastern region, the Sudetenland, contained
German-speaking inhabitants. Hitler charged that these "former German
citizens" (which they were not) were being cruelly abused by the Czechs,
and one atrocity story after another about the savagery of the Slavs was
concocted.

By now the Allies, France and Britain, though very slow to react,
were becoming seriously alarmed at Hitler's seizures of territory, each of
which was followed by the assurance that it would be the last and that
henceforth he wanted nothing but peace. The Allies finally warned him

that he was forcing them into preparing for war. But their fear of Germany was quite equal to their distrust of Russia, a distrust which Stalin heartily reciprocated; Hitler's confidence grew. Czechoslovakia's independence was guaranteed by France and Russia, but Russia could not make good this guarantee and come to the aid of the Czechs unless she got the consent of Poland and Rumania to send troops across their territory, which it was certain they would not give. Russia did not have to act unless France did, and France, having built in what was called the Maginot Line the most elaborate frontier fortifications in history, was determined to hide behind them and await events. Britain had allowed her army to dwindle to the point that she was unable to offer Czechoslovakia any effective aid.

When the British prime minister, Neville Chamberlain, became the spokesmen for the Allies in the summer of 1938 in dealing with Hitler, he was clearly quite incapable of grasping the Führer's fantastic determination to conquer Europe, and ultimately the world. Chamberlain flew three times in as many weeks that summer to Germany, where he was subjected to hysterical monologues in which Hitler insisted that Czechoslovakia was a threat to world peace. By then German rearmament had so far outstripped the military strength of France and Britain that they were eventually forced to accept the catastrophic Munich settlement, which rendered Czechoslovakia powerless against Hitler.

That summer, as the Swedish government and many of Alexandra's friends left town for their holidays, Alexandra sat in Stockholm in a torment of anxiety; Europe seemed to be waiting paralyzed merely for the next message from Hitler's headquarters in Berchtesgaden, or London. "If England really is as weak as from all appearances it seems to be, if her military strength is at such a low ebb that she can be trampled on to this extent, Hitler won't be long in striking," she predicted to Isabel.[21]

Fascist elements began to organize within the German colony in Stockholm, and the Swedish pro-Nazi "Northern Society" began publishing its appeals to the Swedish army to "go east" and attack Russia. As German engineers began to make increasingly frequent and unconcealed visits to the Åland Islands, then under Finnish control, to sound their waters, Alexandra and various other Soviet officials intensified their pressure on Finland to cede this area around the Finnish Gulf to Russia. But they were forestalled. Sweden and Finland, insisting that a Soviet naval base in this area would violate their neutrality, arranged joint fortification of the Åland Islands.

Alexandra's diplomatic anxieties were, however, for a while subordinated to more personal griefs and worries, for in that year Zoya died. With her death Alexandra lost her best and closest friend—the friend who had first told her the meaning of that exciting word *constitution* when they had first met as little girls of seven in Sofia; the friend who had helped her through her first conflicts with Vladimir; the friend who had told her the painful truth about her first literary efforts and had refused to flatter her; the friend who had never failed to cheer her when she visited her in exile before and after the revolution; the friend with whom she had lived in the early days of that great revolution, and who had supported her throughout all her conflicts with the Party in the Workers' Opposition.

Her gloom lifted when she heard that Misha's wife had just had their first child, whom they named Vladimir. In the spring of 1939 they all came to visit. She could forget some of her anxieties in playing with little Volodya, but there were anxieties now for Misha too; apparently he had inherited her weak heart, and as soon as he arrived he was confined to bed with myocarditis. Caring for her grandson, her daughter-in-law, and her sick son (she was, as Isabel said, prone still to see the child in her grown-up son) took its toll on her own weak heart. The anguishing realization of Republican Spain's imminent collapse also played its part in inducing another heart attack. It was as she prepared to leave Stockholm for a sanatorium in nearby Saltsjöbaden that she wrote to Isabel, just a few days before the end of the Spanish Civil War:

My very dear friend,

I have sometimes felt as though life had robbed me of the gift of tears, but this morning, when reading of the heroism of the Spanish people . . . I have not been able to stop weeping. And my thoughts turned to you in admiration and friendship. A friend who knows you well, as I do, feels just by looking at you that one can feel Spain, its courage, its suffering, and its marvellous endurance.

My dear, I am sending you two little baskets of strawberries, one for Marissinka and the other for you alone. Also a little coffee of a brand I like. Tonight I am going to Saltsjöbaden to stay until Sunday, but on Monday I shall see you.

Yours in friendship and love,
Alexandra[22]

In the summer of 1939 the Spanish Republic was defeated, and Franco set up his fascist government in Madrid. Isabel had to leave Stockholm, and at Alexandra's recommendation she went into exile in Mexico. "My very dear Isabel," Alexandra wrote to her there, "I think of you constantly. The reaction has set in now, and I am afraid for your health. It makes me so unhappy to be separated from you in these days when you need me, but, Isabel dear, I was at the end of my strength, with a wretched heart attack and a 230 blood pressure . . ."[23]

A conference of the powers opposed to Hitler met in Moscow that summer, but little came of it, for when Chamberlain asked Russia to guarantee the frontiers of Poland and Rumania he offered no *quid pro quo* from the West. It was then that Stalin began to make his own overtures to Hitler, even though the Führer, as long ago as 1936, had announced his intention of annexing not only the Ukraine but Siberia too. To placate Nazi anti-Semitism, Stalin dismissed his Jewish foreign commissar, Litvinov, and replaced him with Molotov. In his speeches he began abruptly to omit all his former vituperations of the Nazi menace. After several months of negotiation the German foreign minister, Ribbentrop, saw Stalin, and on August 23, 1939 the notorious Hitler-Stalin pact was signed, thus making not only possible but inevitable the outbreak of war. Ostensibly the pact merely said that each country would remain neutral if the other was involved in war, but in fact there was a secret clause which divided up immense territories in Eastern Europe, and gave to Russia three independent countries, Finland, Estonia, and Latvia, the Rumanian provinces of Bessarabia, and all the Polish territory between the Russian border and Warsaw. Hitler, who had his sights set in other directions, merely got Lithuania.

Two weeks after this pact was signed, Hitler invaded Poland, and on September 3 Britain and France declared war on Germany. Russia now made public her negotiations with Finland, and in October, when anti-Soviet feeling in Stockholm was at its height, Alexandra was recalled to Moscow to advise the Soviet government on how best to approach Sweden when Russia formulated her "minimal adjustments" in Finland: a naval base at the western end of the Finnish Gulf, a small area of a few dozen kilometers northwest of Leningrad—"in return for which," said Molotov, "we are willing to give them an area twice that size."[24] Finland was also promised a mutual assistance pact similar to those signed by the Soviet Union with the Baltic republics.

The Russian proposals were rejected; Finland announced herself to be committed to the declaration of neutrality which she and the other

Scandinavian countries had signed, and Alexandra returned to Sweden in poor health. In a long letter written in the autumn of 1939 to her Swedish feminist friend Dr. Ada Nilsson, she tentatively recorded some of her feelings about the Hitler-Stalin pact, and tried to defend it. She wrote from the Saltsjöbaden sanatorium, where she was recuperating.

My dear, dear friend Ada,

Yesterday I so wanted to tell you how highly I value our friendship, how grateful I am to you for all you have done for me, how much I prize our spiritual harmony and the way we understand each other when we talk of world affairs and the role of my country.

This morning I greatly enjoyed walking around Saltsjöbaden. I love autumn, when the sky is such a dark blue, the first burning colours of autumn appear and the air is so full of freshness and energy. I suddenly had a feeling which I know so well from the time when I was a child: life is beautiful. Autumn, I have always felt, is full of promise; the beautiful days will come again. I'm never so happy in springtime. Spring is too restless for me and makes me melancholy. But autumn—what exactly does it promise? Well, the hope that I shall be able to achieve some small thing this winter, and help to make some peace in this world which is so fraught and warring. The best one can say is that there's no stagnation, for that is the worst thing of all.

Dear Ada, didn't you as a child want the world to free itself from all its old "traditions"? Now the world is in the process of totally remaking itself—isn't that what we wanted when we were young? However, there *is* a more intelligent way of solving world problems than simply by seizing arms, and that is by negotiation, which is embodied now by the League of Nations.

I don't know, perhaps there will still be wars—but surely humanity will evolve new methods by which governments can negotiate. And that thought gives me hope. So I'm not pessimistic, you see, and I look into the future with joy and confidence. Do you understand me, dear Ada?

Your loving friend,
Alexandra

P.S. A few days ago I received a letter from some Polish refugees who want to take their revenge on me. "If you value your life, you'd better leave here," these unfortunate people wrote. I just smiled. Do I "value" my life?

I wonder. I enjoy my life, certainly, and love it. But, ah me, if only these people threatening me could hear me say to you how beautiful it would be to die on the barricades; to die for a cause would be such a logical and dignified way of ending my life.[25]

Ada Nilsson was to remain a close friend, but many of her old friends broke all contact with her after the pact. She was forced to entertain the German ambassador, Prince von Wied, whom she had formerly treated with extreme coolness. But her general optimism was sustained in the months that followed, even after the Finns' rejection of the Russians' territorial proposals; her tireless efforts to negotiate a peace in the tragic war that broke out between these two countries shows this. On November 29, 1939, after a skirmish between Finnish and Russian soldiers on the northern Finnish Karelian border, the Soviet Union launched its attack. The four months in which the Finnish army, ill-equipped and massively outnumbered, resisted Russia in one of the coldest winters on record (minus thirty degrees Centigrade most of the time) was later known as the Winter War. As the Finns became transformed in the Western press into white-hooded heroes defending their snow-clad landscape against the "Russian bear," European conservatives and liberals alike were roused to unprecedented hostility against Russia. "We all said she had blood on her hands," said Lena Wickman, recalling the hostility most people in Stockholm felt for Alexandra during that terrible war.[26] The League of Nations, shortly before its death, expelled the Soviet Union for its aggression; but no country, despite endless assurances of support, actually provided Finland with direct military aid. The Finns' meager forces were, however, augmented by a small international brigade of sympathizers, including 8000 Swedes, and it was no secret that Sweden was sending arms and supplies to Finland. Swedish-Soviet relations were strained almost to breaking point.

In January 1940, Alexandra, acting on her own initiative, visited the Swedish foreign minister, Gunther, to warn him that his government was violating its own neutrality and jeopardizing its relations with Russia. In what was widely regarded as a triumph of Alexandra's tactful diplomacy, Swedish policy changed to one of seeking peace. By the middle of February, when Russian troops began penetrating the series of pillboxes in Finland known as the Mannerheim Line, Sweden agreed to help Russia and Finland negotiate peace. It was through Alexandra and with the support of the Swedish government that the Finnish foreign minister, Vaino Tanner, initially made contact with the Soviet government. For three anxious weeks, after days of uninterrupted negotiations and sleepless nights, Alexandra labored with Tanner over the peace treaty they both so passionately wanted.

On March 4 Finland's Marshal Mannerheim told the Finnish government that his army could no longer resist the Russians, and on that day Alexandra and Tanner, the outlines of their treaty completed, met secretly with various representatives of the Finnish government in Saltsjöbaden. On March 12 the treaty was signed. "I've rarely met anyone of such intelligence," said Karl Gerhardt, Alexandra's actor friend in whose house the treaty was signed. "Strong convictions usually preclude broadmindedness and tolerance; Mme Kollontai really has immense tact."[27]

But Finland had yielded about a tenth of her territory to Russia. Neither her part in the war nor Alexandra's part as mediator between Finland and Russia was over.

Only a few weeks after the treaty was signed, the "phony war" in the West ended, and after the British failed to defend Norway, Hitler occupied both Norway and Denmark. On May 10, the day on which Churchill replaced Chamberlain to lead a three-party coalition in Britain, Germany began to attack the West, bombing Belgium and Holland and pouring paratroops and mechanized forces into these countries in a lightning attack which forced Belgium to surrender. By the summer of 1940 Trotsky's assassination in Mexico by the Soviet secret police seemed like just one more bloody episode in a war in which Germany already controlled all ports from Norway to the South of France. That autumn Germany began to claim the right to move troops and materials through Finland, a right which Russia enjoyed and could therefore hardly refuse to her ally. Swedish firms began to give open support to the Finnish and German armies; war materials began passing through Sweden by land and sea; the Wehrmacht's transit depot stood at the Swedish-Finnish border; Swedish-Soviet relations deteriorated, as did German-Soviet relations. In March 1941 the Swedish diplomat Gunnar Hagglof recalled attending one of Alexandra's diplomatic lunch parties. She asked him his opinion of Germany's attitude toward her country, since he had just returned from Berlin. He told her that he expected Hitler to declare war on Russia. "I saw tears in her eyes as she sat for a moment in silence. Then she tapped my hand mildly and said: 'Be quiet, my dear Mr. Hagglof. You have no right to tell me this and I have no right to listen to you.' "[28]

On June 22, 1941, Germany attacked Russia and "Operation Barbarossa" was launched. It was impossible to know in those panic-stricken days of the Nazis' Eastern onslaught exactly how Finland and Russia became entangled for a second time in war with each other, a war which was to continue for the next three years. Border attacks on both sides precipitated a Soviet land-and-sea attack and renewed defensive action by the Finns. The Finns, however, were not formally committed to fighting on the side of Germany until 1944 and insisted throughout the years which preceded that commitment that they were fighting an entirely separate war against Russia. By December 1941 Finland had reoccupied all the territories that had been ceded to Russia, and the thousands of Finns displaced by the Winter War had returned. But once these initial gains had been won, there was little enthusiasm in Finland for the war against Russia, and the Russians' heroic and brilliant defeat of the German invaders found few Finns prepared to support Hitler's drive on Leningrad or his planned assault on Murmansk.[29]

By early 1942, as twenty-six countries committed themselves to fight the Axis powers, the myth of Nazi invincibility was dying; although Finland was imprisoned in the Baltic and economically and militarily dependent on Germany, it was clear that Germany could no longer support her. Alexandra was delegated by the Soviet government to meet secretly with the Finnish leaders and try to arrange some sort of peace settlement, but all her attempts to negotiate foundered, and discussions dragged on spasmodically for the next three years. Yet although German troops were at Gdynia and Königsberg, threatening to cross the Baltic into Finland, it was clear that they were merely waiting to be deployed elsewhere. Hitler failed to provoke Sweden into war with Russia by bombarding Northern Sweden with shells bearing Russian letters, and from then on the Swedes' covert aid to Germany was reduced.

Alexandra was able to promote the increasing sympathy of many in Sweden for Russia by producing a daily bulletin on Russia's war struggle. As many as 10,000 copies of this bulletin were distributed every day to people in all parts of the country, and it was especially popular among the clergy there who were now declaring their solidarity with the clergy in the Norwegian resistance movement. She also organized for donations to be sent from Sweden to Russia to help the war effort and worked with a group of people helping to evacuate Russians from occupied countries. All this work earned her, on her seventieth birthday in 1942, the Red Banner of Labor for her services to the Soviet state, and a promotion, early in 1943, to the rank of Supreme Ambassador.

But the strain was telling on her. By the middle of August 1942, her friend Ada Nilsson was becoming concerned about Alexandra's health, even though Misha and his wife, who had come with little Volodya to stay with her, were urging her to rest. Ada had to leave Stockholm that summer, but before doing so she begged Misha ("Engineer Kollontai") to see that his mother did not work herself to death. "Ah," he said sadly, "but you know yourself that she won't let anyone tell her what to do. Work is the most important thing for her." So she continued working, day in, day out, at her table, sleeping and eating little, until one evening she collapsed with a severe heart attack. It was characteristic of her that before she allowed Misha and Ema Lorentsson to take her to Stockholm's Red Cross Hospital, she insisted on tidying her papers. Ada was called back to town to care for her in the hospital, and was horrified to see her lying unconscious, her face a bluish-black color. She urged Misha and Ema to ask Professor Nanna Schwartz, out of Stockholm at a medical congress at the time, to return, for it seemed that she might be dying. It was lucky that they did, for Professor Schwartz had a supply of a new drug, heparinin, which was being used for such cases; after asking Misha's permission, she had the drug injected, and Alexandra regained consciousness. "You're so good," were the first words she said on coming round. And from then on her faculties returned to her remarkably quickly.[30]

After a few weeks Alexandra discharged herself from the hospital. She recuperated for the next five months in Saltsjöbaden, where she was soon reading and writing with much of her customary energy. But with a body virtually paralyzed and a blood-pressure count of over 200 she tired quickly; she was forbidden to work more than three hours a day. Misha and her friends made the months in Saltsjöbaden pass relatively quickly for her; she emerged at the beginning of 1943, frail and confined to a wheelchair. But neither her illness nor her indefatigable work and the promotion it brought her exempted her from the suspicion of the Soviet government, as one secret-police agent, allotted the unenviable task of investigating her activities, testified in his memoirs. Although his chief motives in engaging in this unpleasant work seem to have been the acquisition of a nice new overcoat and the enjoyment of some decadent Western culture, his account of his visit rings true.

Vladimir Petrov arrived at the Soviet embassy in Stockholm shortly after Misha had left for Russia, in March 1943, ostensibly to work as a clerk. (Many of these posts were occupied by police agents, responsible both for Soviet internal security and foreign espionage.) His real function was to serve as a cipher clerk and to check the security and party loyalty of the ambassador and her staff. He was assured before leaving Moscow that any diplomat promoting close relations with the people in whose country he or she was stationed could only be prompted by a desire to collaborate with enemy intelligence agencies. "The only Soviet citizens who might not appreciate this danger," Petrov reasoned, "were those who had been abroad too long, had been exposed to the corrosion of liberal ideas, and were therefore out of touch with the ideological climate in the Soviet Union."[31] He was not prepared for the favorable impression this "corroding" atmosphere in Stockholm was to make on him. Coming from Moscow, where party leaders like Molotov lived in luxurious villas under armed guard, and where most leading party members could only be glimpsed through the back windows of the fleets of cars in which they were whisked about the city, he was immediately struck by the unpretentiousness of Swedish political life. The foreign minister, Günther, wearing a worker's peaked cap, frequently visited Alexandra on his bicycle, he discovered. (He did so both in deference to her failing health and so as to avoid attracting attention, for many of their meetings were held secretly.)

For Petrov, Alexandra was a figure of great stature, whose name had figured in the official *History of the Communist Party,* and he did not relish at all the task assigned him of ferreting out her diaries, photocopying them, and sending them back to Moscow. She was a white-haired old lady of seventy-one, now usually confined to her wheelchair, but he found her full of energy, humor, and kindness when he and his wife arrived at the embassy. She asked them anxiously about the dangers of their journey from the White Sea port of Archangel and through London, begged them to rest and take care of their health, and urged them to take advantage of Sweden's excellent food supplies and not to squander all their money on new clothes. Everyone in the embassy loved her, the Petrovs discovered, as they joined Alexandra, her devoted Swedish secretary, and all the officials, porters, cooks, and housekeepers who worked there in a cheerful meal around the large dining-room table. Even the Swedish policeman posted outside the building was invited in to eat.

It was precisely the closeness of these friendships, however, that Petrov had been instructed to suspect; once suspicions had been aroused, Petrov observed, the Soviet government was always able to find countless other reasons to justify them. There was certainly no way Alexandra's work could be faulted, however much her manner of working and living might leave to be desired. Whenever she received an assignment from Moscow, he discovered, she would first discuss it with her first secretary. Then she would invite all her friends from the Swedish Foreign Ministry to lunch, at which she would with great sensitivity indirectly raise the questions relevant to her assignment. She would continue these discussions at greater length at informal friendly meetings with her contacts in the Swedish government, encouraging all her staff to broaden their circle of Swedish acquaintances in the process, and generally helping them to assert themselves in their diplomatic activities. Then, gathering every scrap of information she had amassed, she would draw up some of the most comprehensive reports submitted by any Soviet diplomat, and all this by methods quite alien to the elaborately conspiratorial habits of most Soviet officials. "Now where in hell does an old woman get information like that?" Petrov's superior in the Swedish embassy demanded with grudging admiration as he despatched one of Alexandra's competent and voluminous cables back to Moscow.

Petrov had not anticipated that the task of dismissing Alexandra's chauffeur and secretary, and replacing them with official Soviet appointees, would be so distressing. Her chauffeur, Vistrim, wept, and her Norwegian housemaid begged to be allowed to stay, but there was little they or Alexandra could do. She did, however, refuse to be parted from her secretary, Ema Lorentsson, whom she paid from then on out of her own salary. When an official replacement, Elena, arrived from Moscow, Alexandra was never more than guardedly polite and entrusted little important work to her.

It was when she left Stockholm for a weekend with Ema at the Saltsjöbaden sanatorium, some time in the spring of 1943, leaving her unpopular hectoring deputy, Semënov, in charge that Petrov steeled himself for some criminal work. With the help of Elena and a police agent called Vasilev, who worked as the embassy night-watchman and operated a secret transmitter from his flat on the top floor, Petrov found the locked desk in which Alexandra kept her diaries (it had been stressed that she should know nothing of this delicate operation). Vasilev, who was something of a technical expert, made a clean job of breaking open the lock. None of them, however, had anticipated that her writings would be so voluminous; it took them three days and nights, working flat-out, to photocopy and send back to Moscow all her buried thoughts. Moscow was apparently pleased with their work. But although Petrov discovered from these diaries copious expressions of grief at Dybenko's murder, he found little else in them that could possibly be regarded as incriminating. Maybe he was simply not politically sophisticated enough to decipher her thoughts.

Whatever the Soviet government found there to incriminate Alexandra, it must have been clear that, ill as she was, she was much too popular abroad and much too valuable a diplomat to be recalled.[32] It was at about this time that Finnish government representatives approached Alexandra and asked her to suggest to Moscow that moves toward a peace treaty might at last be made. The negotiations dragged on through the next year and relied far too heavily on her for her to abandon her post. Early in 1943 Alexandra decided to take a personal initiative in the matter. She invited a prominent Swedish banker named Marcus Wallenberg to see her. Warning him that if the war continued, he stood to lose the capital he had invested in Finland, she suggested that it would be in his interests to urge the Finnish president, Ryti, to break with Hitler. Unofficially then, as a guest of Wallenberg, Alexandra embarked on secret talks with the Finnish diplomat Paasikivi in Wallenberg's sumptuous Grand Hotel.

In June 1943 a new crisis interrupted these talks. Russia's assault on the Karelian Isthmus in northern Finland broke through the Finnish defenses. Ribbentrop rushed in person to Helsinki, and President Ryti agreed "not to make peace with the Soviet Union except in agreement with the German Reich."[33] The Americans withdrew their diplomats from Helsinki, Ryti was ousted by a government unanimously opposed to his alliance with Hitler, and by the end of August Alexandra was wiring Moscow to request that a delegation of Finns be received there so that an armistice might be negotiated. Peace terms were presented in a Russian ultimatum dated September 2, a ceasefire was arranged for two days after that, and by September 19 an armistice had finally been signed, in what was widely regarded as a great personal triumph for Alexandra's diplomacy.

But as German troops were evacuated from Finland and interned the endless anxieties of a war which for three years Alexandra had struggled so tirelessly to mediate had sapped her strength. After months of sleepless nights and constant palpitations she longed only to rest. One bad stroke was followed by a thrombosis which paralyzed her left side and was further complicated by pneumonia. For several months she was very close to death. Misha hurried to Sweden to be with her. Ema Lorentsson nursed her devotedly, and she was encouraged to live by her many Swedish friends who visited her. Gradually her strength returned, and after six months in the Saltsjöbaden sanatorium she was able to sit up, read, and talk. Her left leg and arm and the side of her face were paralyzed, and she could not move from her wheelchair, but her spirits lifted when she heard, in January 1944, that the Nazi siege of Leningrad had ended. With every month that followed there were new Russian successes. As the warmth of spring returned she went back to work at the embassy and was soon writing to a friend: "I've just paid with a paralyzed arm and leg for all that time I spent preparing the negotiations. I just stayed on working in the battlefield until the Finnish delegation left for Moscow, when I finally took to my bed with exhaustion and pneumonia."[34]

For the next year she continued working at the embassy, but she tired quickly now, and much of her work had to be delegated to her deputy, the unpopular Semënov. In March 1945 she was recalled to Moscow, and a Soviet diplomat called Chernyshev flew out to Stockholm to replace her. A large party was held for her in Stockholm's Grand Hotel, and her friend Sonya Branting recalled that, despite exhaustion and ill-ness, not once did Alexandra refer to her own problems. She talked only of the heroic resistance of the Russian people against the Nazis. "She glowed with happiness," said Sonya. "What a brave, brave person she was."[35]

The morning after this party, at dawn, she arrived at Stockholm airport where a Russian military plane was waiting to take her, Ema Lorentsson, two nurses, and her doctor friend, Professor Nanna Schwartz, back to Moscow. It was thirty degrees below zero when they arrived back in Moscow, and there was nobody to meet them at the icy airport. They eventually managed to find a car which drove them into the town, and on the way they met the men who had set out to greet them at the airport; their car had driven into a snowdrift and they were standing at the side of the road, waving their caps jubilantly.

In Moscow a small, comfortable two-room flat was waiting for Alex-andra on Bolshaya Kaluzhskaya Street. She and Ema Lorentsson made a pleasant home for themselves, decorating the flat with the bright carpets and paintings which Alexandra had brought back from Mexico, and installing there a cat whom they named Alexander. Alexandra began to unravel some of the memories contained in the diaries she had carried back with her. The scraps of paper and exercise books in which she had written her private thoughts over the past thirty years (mostly in pencil) had to be put in order, and so eagerly did she embark on the work of dictating their contents to Ema that she could not possibly contemplate dying. "One must write," she believed, "not only for oneself but for others, for all those faraway unknown women who will live later. Let them see that we were not heroes or heroines at all, just that we believed passionately and ardently. We believed in our goals and we pursued them; sometimes we were strong, and sometimes we were very weak."[36]

At the age of seventy-three her work routine hardly differed from the demanding routine she had set herself through all the years of her working life. From ten o'clock to three she would work with Ema; after that she had her work cut out for her as adviser to the Commissariat of Foreign Affairs, for there were hundreds of letters to be written and documents to be commented on. Shortly after she left Sweden, her Swedish and Norwegian friends proposed her as a candidate for the Nobel Peace Prize; they were more sorry than she was when another candidate was accepted instead.

She had more time to devote to her family now. Misha, his wife, and six-year-old Volodya, were constant visitors. When Alexandra's official Soviet biography was reissued in Moscow in 1970, Volodya was a writer and professor of economics, but in 1945 he was still signing himself in letters to her as "your devoted grandson Volodya, the stamp-collector" (her voluminous mail from abroad provided him with endless new samples). She also had time to spend with her old friends. Among the many people who visited her were Litvinov and the writers Ignatiev, Tarle, Ehrenburg, and Konchalovsky. There were others, too, with whom she had lost touch over the years after the revolution and with whom she now re-established contact: Ivan Maisky, whom she had first met before the revolution in London, and who was now a prominent diplomat; Vera Lebedeva, who had worked with her in the Commissariat of Social Welfare in the Department for Mothers and Children; and Elena Stasova, her first friend in the underground revolutionary movement, whom Alexandra had found so daunting when she was known as "Comrade Absolute." Elena's tendencies toward authoritarianism and her hostility to the women's movement after the revolution had led her to a rather unquestioning acceptance of Stalin's government, and this had cooled their friendship—yet it was a joy to be reunited. "Yes, friend of my youth and friend of my old age," Elena wrote to Alexandra, "how good it is to think that you and I can calmly look ahead and rejoice in our country's achievements, knowing that our drop of effort too went into its success. I embrace you, my dear, good friend."[37]

Soon after she returned to Moscow, she was invited to address a meeting in the Writers' Club. Rarely had the audience been so tense and hushed as when this old Bolshevik was wheeled onto the stage and prepared to talk about her experiences working with Lenin. She was so moved and confused that she felt unable to speak, and had to have her speech read for her.

Anna Itkina, her Soviet biographer, last saw her in the autumn of 1946 and found her sad-eyed and ill, tormented by high blood pressure and frequent heart attacks. But her voice was still strong and her eyes still flashed, and when a woman telephoned to ask if she could increase her bread rations, she went about it with all the enthusiasm and good sense which were so familiar from the days when they had first worked together in the spring of 1917.

Although Stalin was now entering into the final, most demented stage of his paranoia and was known to be preparing the purge to end all purges of all his former associates, it is unlikely that Alexandra suffered from the harassment and surveillance that made so many party members' lives such hell. The policy was obviously to let her live out the rest of her days as a feeble and inconspicuous pensioner. In September 1945, however, her services to the Soviet Union during the Second World War were recognized and she was awarded her second Red Banner of Labor. Ema helped her to prepare for this tiring occasion, and there was a short article in *Pravda* commemorating the event, accompanied by a photograph of her in an elegant black velvet dress. "Dear Ema," she wrote in her diary, "she helps me to forget I'm an invalid, and so other people do not notice it either, as I sit in my chair, my hair brushed, in my velvet dress—black with white lace—wearing only a little powder (for one must look natural when one's an old woman)."[38]

She preferred quieter activities. "There's a balcony outside my window near my writing table, and there I've trained the little tomtits and sparrows to come. The trust with which they sit on the net bag which I've filled with butter or fat is so touching . . . Look, another tomtit has come, and I love its dark blue head and its trust . . ."[39]

Inactivity begat anxiety—"I worry about the future of my son, and about Ema, to whom I'm so very grateful for everything . . ."—but it also prompted her to jot down some reflections on her past:

> The various different periods of my life have differed so much from one another that it's really as though I had lived not just one life but many lives. It hasn't been an easy life, it hasn't been a bed of roses by any means . . . But it's had everything—achievements, enormously hard work, recognition, popularity amongst the masses, persecution, hatred, prisons, failures, and lack of understanding of my basic ideas on the women's question and the right approach to sexual matters; many painful ruptures with my comrades, arguments with them, but also long years of close friendly work in the Party . . .[40]

In the summer she left Moscow for a country resthome for party workers and their families, and there the writer Savva Dangulov visited her in 1948. Her wheelchair had been pushed under the trees by a group of young men and women who sat round her eagerly talking. "The capacity to relate to other people and to develop those relationships—that's the chief quality needed in diplomacy," she observed when one young person inquired about the guiding principles of her work abroad.[41]

Sonya Branting stayed with her in the winter of that year in her flat and found in Alexandra the same warmth and generosity she had experienced when they were close friends in Stockholm. "To be a friend means to find the language of the heart," Alexandra remarked to Sonya as she returned to Sweden. She had plenty of work to do, she assured her, for she had in her diaries enough material to fill ten 300-page books. "Dear Nikolai Dmitrevich," she wrote to the writer Teleshov in January 1950, "it's not at all surprising that you're feeling worse. At our age any sharp change of atmosphere or temperature immediately reflects on our nerves and organism. I'm not at my best this year, but I very much hope that with the warmth my strength will return. In Sweden they consider that old age only starts at ninety, and Bernard Shaw when *he* was ninety begged people not to congratulate him. 'I'm only almost old!' he said."[42]

Her strength did return that spring, and the following spring, but her cramped invalid existence was becoming more and more irksome:

> It's strange how when I was in Sweden I bore all that heavy work, undertook the negotiations with the Finns, fought to keep Sweden out of the war, and forgot that I was an invalid. But a few years after my arm and leg were paralyzed I'm feeling all the weight and responsibility of my work. How did I endure it in Sweden when I was so ill! Now I'm constantly annoyed by my invalid state, my complete dependence on other people's help.[43]

Friends and books and the loving care of Ema kept her spirits up, however, and in February 1952 she was writing to Zoya's sister, Vera Yureneva: "I'm sitting up in my chair dictating letters. Yesterday I had no pain in my chest, so I'm up for a couple of hours. My heart is in a serious way but as I haven't nearly finished my work on this planet I have no intention of flying off into the interplanetary expanse as a small atom ... I'm in a good mood. . . ."[44] After all, there was International Women's Day to be celebrated on March 8.

It was on March 8, 1952, shortly before her eightieth birthday, that Alexandra was stricken by excruciating pains in her heart. At 4:20 the following morning she died. She was buried in a simple ceremony at Novodevichii Monastery, where a white marble plaque now bears the simple words: *"Alexandra Mikhailovna Kollontai. 1872–1952. Revolutionary, Tribune, Diplomat."* Her friends in the West eagerly scanned the

THE LAST YEARS—THE PURGES | 489

Russian papers for news of her death, anticipating an article to amplify those few words on her grave and to honor the thirty years she had devoted to the revolution. But there was nothing, not even the smallest official obituary, in those days when any *apparatchik* was guaranteed the most florid of eulogies. There was, however, a short and affectionate tribute to her in the pages of *Izvestia*, signed by a small group of her friends and associates.

"Her body may be at Novodevichii but her immaterial being belongs to her friends in the West," wrote Marcel Body soon after her death.[45] It seems now that Alexandra Kollontai's admirers here may be able to make proper amends for that and so many other slights.

One of the fortunes of her life was the immense strength which allowed her to survive such slights. Shortly before her death she was reading history avidly and, in doing so, rereading the story of her own life. "I'm now absorbing the living pages of history," she wrote to a friend:[46]

> The world never stagnates, it's always stirring, new forms of life are always appearing. And I love to look back now at the path trodden by humanity, or run forward to the wonderful beautiful future which humanity will inhabit, spreading its wings and saying "Happiness! Happiness for everyone!"

NOTES

Russian and other foreign books will be referred to on the first occasion in Russian (with English translation), and thenceforth in English with asterisk. Exceptions to this rule are those works referred to extremely frequently (Itkina, Body, etc.), which will simply be followed by op. cit.

Chapter One TOO MUCH FAMILY HAPPINESS

1. An affectionate diminutive of Alexandra.
2. Anna Itkina, *Revolyutsioner, tribun, diplomat; ocherk zhizni Alexandry Mikhailovnoi Kollontai (Revolutionary, Tribune, Diplomat: A Brief Life of Alexandra Mikhailovna Kollontai)*, 2nd edn, Moscow 1970, p. 5.
3. Five rubles was about $1.06.
4. A. M. Kollontai, *Den första etappen (First Steps)*, Stockholm 1945, p. 140.
5. Kollontai, *Autobiography of a Sexually Emancipated Woman*, ed. Iring Fetscher, trans. Salvator Attanasio, London 1972, p. 9. This was first published in Munich in 1926 as *Ziel und Wert meines Lebens (The Aims and Worth of My Life)*; there is no Russian translation.
6. Ibid.
7. Kollontai, *And Dreams Come True*, in *Iz moei zhizni i raboty (From My Life and Work)*, ed. I. M. Dazhina, M. M. Mukhamedzhanov, et al., Moscow 1974, p. 28. This chapter was first published in English in 1939–1940, then republished in Russian translation in this selection of her autobiographical writings.
8. Kollontai, "Iz vospominanii" ("From My Memories"), in the journal *Oktyabr (October)*, Moscow 1945, no. 9, p. 68.
9. Kollontai, *And Dreams Come True*, p. 49.
10. Ibid., p. 53.
11. Kollontai, *Autobiography of a Sexually Emancipated Woman*, p. 10.
12. Kollontai, *First Steps,* * pp. 83–4.
13. Kollontai, *And Dreams Come True*, p. 54.
14. Ibid., p. 46.
15. Kollontai, *First Steps,* * p. 209.
16. Kollontai, "Iz zapisnykh knizhek poslednikh let: 1946–1951" ("From the Notebooks of the Last Years: 1946–1951"), in Dazhina et al. (eds), *From My Life and Work,* * p. 370. First partially published in the Soviet newspaper *Komsomolskaya Pravda*, Moscow, on June 29, 1972.
17. Kollontai, *First Steps,* * pp. 216–19.
18. Ibid., pp. 218–20.
19. Kollontai, *Autobiography of a Sexually Emancipated Woman*, p. 9.

Chapter Two SMALL DEEDS

1. Kollontai, *Autobiography of a Sexually Emancipated Woman*, p. 11.
2. Kollontai, *And Dreams Come True*, pp. 69–70.
3. August Bebel, *Woman Under Socialism*, trans. D. De Leon, New York 1971, p. 156.
4. Kollontai's article, "Velikii borets za prava i svobodu zhenschiny; pamyati Avgusta Bebelya" ("A Great Fighter for the Rights and Freedom of Women; Memories of August Bebel"), first appeared in *Pravda* on February 17, 1913, was reproduced as the introduction to the 1918 Russian edition of *Woman Under Socialism*, and is contained in *A. M. Kollontai: Izbrannye stati i rechi (A. M. Kollontai: Selected Articles and Speeches)*, ed. I. M. Dazhina, M. M. Mukhamedzhanov, et al., Moscow 1972, pp. 113–125.
5. Kollontai, *And Dreams Come True*, p. 72.
6. E. Stasova, *Stranitsy zhizni i borby (Pages of Life and Struggle)*, Moscow 1960. See also *Vospominania (Memories)*, an amplified version of the above, ed. V. N. Stepanov, Moscow 1969.
7. Kollontai, *First Steps,* * p. 257.
8. Kollontai, *And Dreams Come True*, p. 73.
9. Kollontai, "Osnovy vospitania po vzglyadam Dobrolyubova" ("Dobrolyubov's Educational Principles"), in *Obrazovanie (Education)*, St. Petersburg 1898, nos 9–11.
10. See Rose Glikman, "The Russian Factory Woman, 1880–1914," in *Women in Russia*, ed. Dorothy Atkinson, Alexander Dallin, and Gail Warshofsky Lapidus, Brighton 1978, pp. 63–83.
11. V. I. Lenin, "Chto takie 'druzya naroda'?" ("What are the 'Friends of the People'?"), in *Polnoe sobranie sochinenii (Collected Works)*, 5th edn, Moscow/Leningrad 1966.
12. That is, the Union of Struggle for the Emancipation of the Working Class.
13. I. I. Yanzhul, *Ocherki i issledovania (Sketches and Investigations)*, Moscow 1884, p. 381.
14. Kollontai, *And Dreams Come True*, p. 79.
15. Ibid., p. 80.
16. For this translation see Alfred Meyer, "Marxism and the Women's Movement," in Atkinson et al. (eds), *Women in Russia*, p. 16.
17. Kollontai, *And Dreams Come True*, p. 87.
18. Kollontai, *K istorii dvizhenia rabotnits v Rossii (Toward a History of the Working Women's Movement in Russia)*, Kharkov 1920. Parts of this have been translated by Alix Holt in *Alexandra Kollontai: Selected Writings*, London 1977. Here, Holt, p. 40.
19. Werner Thönnessen, *The Emancipation of Women: The Rise and Decline of the Women's Movement in German Social Democracy 1863–1933*, London 1976, p. 57.
20. Richard Stites, *The Women's Liberation Movement in Russia: Feminism, Nihilism and Bolshevism 1860–1930*, Princeton 1978, pp. 191–3.
21. Peter Gay, *The Dilemma of Democratic Socialism: Eduard Bernstein's Challenge to Marx*, New York 1952.
22. Kollontai, *And Dreams Come True*, pp. 91–2.

Chapter Three POPULISTS AND MARXISTS

1. Kollontai, *Autobiography of a Sexually Emancipated Woman*, pp. 12–13.
2. Itkina, op. cit., p. 26.
3. Kollontai, "Avtobiograficheskii ocherk" ("Autobiographical Essay"), in the journal *Proletarskaya Revolyutsia (Proletarian Revolution)*, Moscow 1921, no. 3, p. 262.
4. See Evelyn Anderson, *Hammer or Anvil*, London 1945, pp. 1–23, for a useful summary of SPD history.
5. Thönnesson, op. cit., p. 46.
6. Engels, *Origins of the Family, Private Property and the State*, New York 1972, p. 159.
7. Ibid., p. 152.
8. See Eli Zaretsky, *Capitalism, The Family and Personal Life*, London 1976, pp. 90–96, and Rosalind Delmar, "Looking again at Engels' Origins of the Family," in *The Rights and Wrongs of Women*, ed. Juliet Mitchell and Ann Oakley, London 1976, for a useful discussion of Engels and the contemporary women's movement.
9. Rosa Luxemburg, *Social Reform or Revolution*, Colombo, Sri Lanka 1973.
10. Eduard Bernstein, *Evolutionary Socialism: A Criticism and an Affirmation*, London 1909.
11. Kollontai, "Sotsializm v Finlyandii" ("Socialism in Finland"), in the journal *Zarya (Dawn)*, St. Petersburg 1902, no. 4.
12. V. I. Lenin, "Sotsial shovinisty i internatsionalisty" ("Social Chauvinists and Internationalists"), in *Complete Works*, vol. 31, pp. 466–7.
13. Kollontai, *Autobiographical Essay*,* p. 263.
14. Ibid., p. 264.
15. Kollontai, "Die Arbeiterfrage in Finnland" ("The Workers' Question in Finland"), in the journal *Soziale Praxis*, Berlin 1900, no. 9.
16. V. Karelina, "Rabotnitsa v Gaponovskikh obschestvakh" ("The Working Woman in the Gapon Organizations"), in P. F. Kudelli (ed.), *Rabotnitsa v 1905 g. v S-Peterburge (The Working Woman in 1905 in St. Petersburg)*, Leningrad 1926, p. 14.
17. Itkina, op. cit., pp. 35–6.
18. Kollontai, "Novaya zhenschina" ("The New Woman"), an article she wrote in 1913. The English translation is contained in *Autobiography of a Sexually Emancipated Woman*, pp. 51–103.
19. Kollontai, "Industry and Trade in the Grand Duchy of Finland," in the journal *Nauchnoe Obozrenie (Scientific Review)*, St. Petersburg 1901, no. 7.
20. G. Plekhanov and P. Axelrod, *Perepiska (Correspondence)*, Moscow 1925, vol. II, p. 168.

Chapter Four WHAT IS TO BE DONE?

1. Kollontai, *Autobiographical Essay*,* p. 266.
2. Kollontai, "Plotovischiki v Finlyandii" ("Raftsmen in Finland"), in the journal *Russkoe Bogatsvo (Russian Wealth)*, St. Petersburg 1902, no. 9.
3. Kollontai, *First Steps*,* p. 110.
4. Kollontai, *Zhizn finlyandskikh rabochikh (Life of the Finnish Workers)*, St. Petersburg 1903.

5. Kollontai, *Iz moei zhizni i raboty (From My Life and Work)*, Odessa 1921. This book was reprinted fully in *Deyateli SSSR i Oktyabrskoi revolyutsii (Activists of the USSR and of the October Revolution)*, a special supplement to the *Entsiklopedicheskii slovar russkogo bibliograficheskogo instituta Granata (Encyclopaedia of the Granat Russian Bibliographical Institute)*, 7th edn, Moscow 1927–29, p. 199. *From My Life and Work* is also reproduced (with some abridgements) in Dazhina's book, already quoted, which confusingly bears the same title. It is Dazhina's edition that has been mostly used here.
6. Lenin, *Complete Works,** vol. 47, p. 6.
7. A. Ryazanova, *Zhenskii trud (Women's Labor)*, Moscow 1924, p. 34.
8. Kollontai, *Towards a History of the Working Women's Movement*, Holt 1977, p. 42.
9. Kollontai, *Polozhenie zhenschiny v evolyutsii khozyaistva (The Position of Women in the Evolution of the Economy)*, Moscow 1922, p. 126.
10. From Ekaterina Breshkovskaya's biography, *Little Grandmother of the Revolution*, ed. Alice Stone Blackwell, Boston 1930, pp. 177 and 120.
11. Kollontai, *Towards a History of the Working Women's Movement*, Holt 1977, p. 46.
12. Kollontai, *From My Life and Work,** Dazhina, p. 98.
13. V. Karelina, op. cit., p. 14.
14. Kollontai, *From My Life and Work,** Dazhina, p. 101.
15. Ibid., p. 99.
16. Ibid., pp. 99–100.
17. Kollontai, *Towards a History of the Working Women's Movement*, Holt 1977, p. 43.
18. V. Karelina, op. cit., p. 14.
19. Kollontai, *Towards a History of the Working Women's Movement*, Holt 1977, p. 43.
20. Ibid., p. 49.
21. Ibid., p. 44.
22. Kollontai, *Autobiographical Essay,** p. 268.
23. Kollontai, *Towards a History of the Working Women's Movement*, Holt 1977, pp. 44–5.
24. N. Krupskaya, quoted in L. D. Trotsky, *Stalin: An Appraisal*, London 1961, vol. 1, p. 101.
25. L. D. Trotsky, *Nasha revolyutsia (Our Revolution)*, Moscow/Leningrad 1926.
26. L. D. Trotsky, *The History of the Russian Revolution*, trans. Max Eastman, New York 1932, p. 216.

Chapter Five AFTER BLOODY SUNDAY

1. Proceedings of the Third Congress of the Russian Social Democratic Party, quoted by Solomon Schwartz, a Menshevik activist of the time, in *The Russian Revolution of 1905*, Chicago 1967, p. 133.
2. Kollontai, *Autobiographical Essay,** p. 269.
3. Ibid.
4. Kollontai, *Towards a History of the Working Women's Movement*, Holt 1977, p. 44.
5. A good account of the various parties' attitudes toward the suffrage issue is in Stites, op. cit., p. 204.
6. Kollontai, *Towards a History of the Working Women's Movement*, Holt 1977, p. 45.

7. Kollontai, "Problema nravstvennosti s positivnoi tochki zrenia" ("The Problem of Morality from the Positive Point of View"), in the journal *Obrazovanie (Education)*, St. Petersburg, September 1905.

8. Kollontai, "Etika i sotsial-demokratiya (po povodu state g. Pokrovskogo v No. 4 *Polyarnoi Zvezdy)*" ("Ethics and Social Democracy: On Mr Pokrovsky's Article in Number 4 of *Pole Star*"), *Obrazovanie (Education)*, St. Petersburg, February 1906. These articles are also quoted at some length in E. I. Breslav, "A. M. Kollontai—Propagandist leninskikh idei v mezhdunarodnom rabochem dvizhenii" ("A. M. Kollontai, Propagandist of Lenin's Ideas in the International Workers' Movement"), in *Vestnik Leningradskogo universiteta (Leningrad University Chronicle)*, 1967, no. 14. This is one of a series of booklets on various party propagandists.

9. Kollontai, *From My Life and Work,** Dazhina, p. 103.

10. See Stites, op. cit., p. 205.

11. Kollontai, *Towards a History of the Working Women's Movement,* Holt 1977, p. 50.

12. Kollontai, "Rol feministok i proletariarok v zhenskom osvobozhditelnom dvizhenii" ("The Role of Feminists and Proletarian Women in the Women's Liberation Movement"), in the paper *Severo-Zapadny Golos (Northwestern Voice)*, St. Petersburg 1906, no. 1.

13. Kollontai, *From My Life and Work,** Dazhina, p. 103.

14. Kollontai, "Chto takie sotsial-demokraty i chego oni khotyat?" ("Who Are the Social Democrats and What Do They Want?"), in *Rabochii ezhegodnik (Workers' Annual)*, St. Petersburg 1906.

15. Kollontai, *Autobiographical Essay,** p. 272.

16. Kollontai, *From My Life and Work,** Dazhina, p. 104.

17. E. Fortunato, "Nash drug" ("Our Friend"), in the journal *Neva*, Leningrad 1959, no. 3, pp. 111–21.

18. See Rose Glikman, "The Russian Factory Woman 1880–1914" in *Women in Russia*, op. cit., p. 80.

19. Stites, op. cit., p. 207.

Chapter Six HECKLING THE FEMINISTS

1. Thönnesson, op. cit., p. 64.

2. Pamphlet cited in Peter Nettl, *Rosa Luxemburg,* 2nd edn, Oxford University Press, Oxford 1969, p. 227.

3. Also quoted in Nettl, p. 250.

4. Kollontai, *Autobiographical Essay,** p. 282.

5. Thönnesson, op. cit., p. 66.

6. Kollontai, *Mezhdunarodny den rabotnits (International Women's Day)*, a pamphlet she wrote in Moscow in 1920. English translation by Alix Holt, London 1972.

7. Kollontai, "Itogi Manngeimskogo kongressa" ("Results of the Mannheim Congress"), in the Menshevik journal *Sovremenny Mir (Contemporary World)*, St. Petersburg, November 1906.

8. Kollontai, *Towards a History of the Working Women's Movement,* Holt 1977, p. 54.

9. Appeared in the journal of the St. Petersburg textile union, *Fabrichny Stanok (Factory Loom)*, 1908, nos 1–2.

10. Report of the Stuttgart congress in *Mezhdunarodnye sotsialisticheskie soveschania*

rabotnits 1907–1910 (International Socialist Conferences of Working Women 1907–1910), a book published in Moscow in 1918 and reprinted in abridged form in A. M. Kollontai: Selected Articles and Speeches,* Dazhina, p. 91.

11. Kollontai, Autobiographical Essay,* p. 282.
12. Ibid.
13. Trotsky, My Life, London 1970, p. 211.
14. Kollontai, International Socialist Conferences of Working Women 1907–1910,* p. 91.
15. Ibid., p. 83.
16. Kollontai, Sotsialnye osnovy zhenskogo voprosa (The Social Basis of the Women's Question), St. Petersburg 1908. From the selective translation by Alix Holt in Alexandra Kollontai: Selected Writings, p. 58.
17. Ibid., p. 63.
18. Tatiana Schepkina Kupernik's unpublished memoirs are quoted in Itkina, op. cit.
19. A report of this speech is contained in the feminist journal, Soyuz Zhenschin (Women's Union), St. Petersburg, March 1908.
20. Reports of this congress are contained in Olga Volkenstein, "Itogi pervogo vserossisskogo zhenskogo sezda" ("Results of the First All-Russian Women's Congress"), in the journal Russkaya Mysl (Russian Thought), St. Petersburg 1909, no. 2; and A. Ermansky, "Vserossisskii zhenskii sezd" ("All-Russian Women's Congress"), in Sovremenny Mir (Contemporary World), St. Petersburg, January 1909. Linda Edmondson's article, "Russian Feminists and the First All-Russian Congress of Women" (in the journal Russian History/Histoire Russe), University of Pittsburgh 1976, vol. 3, part 2, pp. 123–40, is an excellent survey of the work of the congress.

Chapter Seven EXILED IN WORKERS' EUROPE

1. Kollontai, Autobiographical Essay,* p. 280.
2. Stites, op. cit., pp. 186–87.
3. Itkina, op. cit., p. 56.
4. G. D. Petrov, "A. M. Kollontai nakanune i v gody pervoi mirovoi voiny, 1908–1916" ("A. M. Kollontai in the years before and during the First World War 1908–1916"), in the journal Novaya i Noveishaya Istoria (Recent and Most Recent History), Moscow 1969, no. 1, p. 68.
5. Itkina, op. cit., p. 56.
6. Kollontai, Autobiographical Essay,* p. 281.
7. Alin, Lenin à Paris (Lenin in Paris), Paris 1962, p. 54.
8. Kollontai also referred to her colleague Maslov in her Autobiographical Essay of 1921. Gustav Johansson, in his Swedish biography of Kollontai, Revolutionens ambassador: Alexandra Kollontay's liv och gärning, åren 1872–1917 (The Ambassador of the Revolution: Alexandra Kollontai's Life and Work from 1872–1917), Stockholm 1945, gives details of the affair without naming the man, and in later interviews with Kaare Hauge, he and Kollontai's secretary, Ema Lorentsson, confirmed that the man was Maslov. See Kaare Hauge, Alexandra Mikhailovna Kollontai: The Scandinavian Period, 1922–1945, Ph.D thesis, University of Minnesota 1971.
9. Kollontai, Autobiography of a Sexually Emancipated Woman, p. 7.

10. Angus McClaren, *Birth Control in Nineteenth-Century England,* London 1978, contains many useful comparisons with Germany.
11. C. E. Schorske, *German Social Democracy 1905–1917,* University of California Press, Berkeley 1965, p. 41.
12. Kollontai, *Autobiography of a Sexually Emancipated Woman,* p. 18.
13. Itkina, op. cit., p. 56.
14. Kollontai, *Po rabochei evrope (Around Workers' Europe),* St. Petersburg 1912, p. 10.
15. Ibid., p. 14.
16. Ibid., pp. 51–2.
17. Ibid., p. 77.
18. Ibid., p. 87–8.
19. Sheila Rowbotham, *Hidden From History,* London 1974, pp. 72–3 and 94–5.
20. Kollontai, *Around Workers' Europe,* * pp. 153–4.
21. Ibid., p. 116.
22. Quoted by Ruth Hall in her *Marie Stopes: A Biography,* London 1978, p. 102.
23. Kollontai, *Around Workers' Europe,* * p. 164.
24. Kollontai, "Zadachi konferentsii po borbe protiv prostitutsii" ("Tasks of the Conference Called to Struggle Against Prostitution"), in the journal *Sotsial Demokrat (Social Democrat),* St. Petersburg 1910, no. 14.

Chapter Eight THE COLLAPSE OF INTERNATIONALISM

1. Kollontai, *Autobiography of a Sexually Emancipated Woman,* p. 22.
2. Kollontai, *Around Workers' Europe,* * p. 265.
3. Kollontai, "Itogi vtoroi mezhdunarodnoi zhenskoi sotsialisticheskoi konferentsii" ("Results of the Second International Socialist Women's Conference"), in the journal *Nasha Zarya (Our Dawn),* St. Petersburg, September 1910.
4. Kollontai, *Around Workers' Europe,* * p. 287.
5. Itkina, op. cit., p. 63.
6. Kollontai, *Autobiography of a Sexually Emancipated Woman,* p. 22.
7. Kollontai, *Around Workers' Europe,* * p. 290.
8. Ibid., p. 269.
9. G. D. Petrov, op. cit., p. 72.
10. Kollontai, "Sudba chelovechestva i vopros narodonaselenia" ("The Fate of Humanity and the Population Question"), in the journal *Zhizn (Life),* Paris, September 1910.
11. Kollontai, *Around Workers' Europe,* * p. 216.
12. Kollontai, *International Women's Day,* trans. Holt, p. 9.
13. Kollontai, *Novaya Moral i rabochii klass (The New Morality and the Working Class),* Moscow 1918. (Includes these two articles and another she wrote in 1913.)
14. Ibid., pp. 40–41.
15. Kollontai, "Dvizhenie menazherok (khozyaek) vo Frantsii" ("The Housewives' Movement in France"), in the journal *Nasha Zarya (Our Dawn),* St. Petersburg 1911, nos 9–10.

16. Itkina, op. cit., p. 74.
17. Kollontai, *Autobiographical Essay,* * p. 284.
18. G. D. Petrov, op. cit., p. 74.
19. Kollontai, "Iz zhizni tekstilshits v Belgii" ("The Life of Women Textile-Workers in Belgium"), in the journal *Fabrichnaya Zhizn (Factory Life)*, St. Petersburg, February 1912.
20. C. E. Schorske, *German Social Democracy 1905–1917*, op. cit., p. 246.
21. Reports of this speech in the conservative Swedish press are quoted in Ema Lorentsson's article "A. M. Kollontai v Shvetsii" ("A. M. Kollontai in Sweden"), in the journal *Novaya i Noveishaya Istoria (Recent and Most Recent History)*, Moscow 1966, no. 1, pp. 106–11.
22. G. D. Petrov, op. cit., pp. 74–5.
23. Kollontai, *Around Workers' Europe.* *
24. Itkina, op. cit., p. 74.
25. Ibid., p. 79.
26. Kollontai, "Okhranenie materinstva" ("The Defense of Maternity"), in the journal *Nasha Zarya (Our Dawn)*, St. Petersburg 1913, no. 9.
27. Kollontai, *Autobiographical Essay,* * p. 287.
28. Ivan Maisky, *Journey Into the Past*, London 1962, p. 30 and pp. 88–96.
29. Kollontai, "Novaya Zhenschina" ("The New Woman"), in the journal *Sovremenny Mir (Contemporary World)*, St. Petersburg 1913, no. 9. Republished in Kollontai, *The New Morality and the Working Class,* * and contained in English translation in Kollontai, *Autobiography of a Sexually Emancipated Woman*, pp. 51–103.
30. Kollontai, *International Women's Day*, trans. Holt, p. 10.
31. Kollontai, *From My Life and Work,* * Dazhina, p. 123.
32. G. D. Petrov, op. cit., p. 76.
33. Kollontai, *Autobiographical Essay,* * pp. 289–90.
34. Two articles for *Die Gleichheit* on International Women's Day in Russia; "Types and Forms of Maternity Insurance," for the journal *Novaya Zhizn (New Life)*, Petrograd; "Tasks of the Working Women's Leaflet," in *Listok Rabotnitsy (Working Women's Leaflet)*, no. 1, Paris, May 25, 1914; "The International Women's Conference," for *Nasha Rabochaya Gazeta (Our Workers' Paper)*, Petrograd, May 30, 1914; "The International Tasks of Women's Day," in *Severnaya Rabochaya Gazeta (Northern Workers' Paper)*, Petrograd, May 1914. All these quoted from Holt 1977, pp. 324–5.
35. Petrov, op. cit., p. 77.
36. Kollontai, "Otryvki iz dnevnika 1914 goda" ("Excerpts from a Diary for 1914"). First published in the journal *Zvezda (Star)*, Petrograd in 1924 (no. 4), then published separately in 1925. Abridged version in Dazhina 1974, p. 142.
37. Ibid.

Chapter Nine WAR ON WAR!

1. Kollontai, "Excerpts from a Diary for 1914," Dazhina 1974, pp. 143–4.
2. Ibid., p. 143.
3. Ibid.

4. Rosa Luxemburg's observations in Nettl's biography, op. cit., p. 389.
5. Radek's autobiography in *Encyclopaedia of the Granat Russian Bibliographical Institute,* * p. 154.
6. Kollontai, "Excerpts from a Diary for 1914," Dazhina 1974, p. 145
7. Ibid., p. 147.
8. Ibid., p. 149.
9. Ibid., p. 152.
10. Ibid., pp. 154–5.
11. Ibid., pp. 157–8.
12. Ibid.
13. Ibid., pp. 161–2.
14. Ibid., p. 167.
15. Ibid.
16. Ibid., p. 172.
17. Lenin, "September Theses," in *Complete Works,* * vol. 26, pp. 1–7.
18. Lenin, *Complete Works,* * vol. 49, p. 20.
19. Ibid., p. 39.
20. Kollontai, "Golos Lenina" ("The Voice of Lenin"), was first published in 1963 in the journal *Oktyabr (October)*. These memories of Lenin, which date back to Kollontai's early involvement with the Bolsheviks during 1905, are reprinted with a few abbreviations in Dazhina 1974. Here, p. 171.
21. Itkina, op. cit., p. 184.
22. Trotsky, op. cit., p. 172.
23. G. D. Petrov, "A. M. Kollontai v gody pervoi mirovoi voiny" ("A. M. Kollontai during the First World War"), in the journal *Istoria SSSR'a (History of the USSR)*, Moscow/Leningrad 1968, no. 3, pp. 87–8.
24. Lenin, *Complete Works,* * vol. 49, pp. 39 and 43.
25. Itkina, op. cit., pp. 185–6.
26. G. D. Petrov, "A. M. Kollontai during the First World War,"* p. 89.
27. Kollontai, "The Copenhagen Conference," in the journal *Nashe Slovo (Our Word)*, Paris, January 29 and February 2, 1915; "What Is to Be Done? A Reply to Socialists," *Nashe Slovo*, February 19; "The Women's Socialist International and the War," *Nashe Slovo*, March 7. All cited in Holt 1977, bibliography, p. 325.
28. Kollontai. Part of her diary for this period is included in Dazhina 1974, p. 174.
29. Itkina, op. cit., p. 95.
30. G. D. Petrov, "A. M. Kollontai During the First World War,"* p. 88.
31. Ibid., p. 89.
32. Angelica Balabanova, *My Life As a Rebel*, London 1938, pp. 150–1.
33. Kollontai, *Rabotnitsa za god revolyutsii (The Working Woman in the Year of the Revolution)*, Moscow 1918, p. 28.
34. Kollontai, excerpt from her diary for this period, in Dazhina 1974, p. 174.
35. Lenin, *Complete Works,* * vol. 49, pp. 49–76.
36. Kollontai, *Komu Nuzhna Voina? (Who Needs War?)*, Bern 1916 (2nd edn, Petrograd 1917).
37. Kollontai, "From a Norwegian Diary," Dazhina 1974, p. 176.

38. Ibid., p. 180.
39. Ibid., p. 181.
40. Michael Futrell, *Northern Underground*, London 1963, p. 106.
41. Lenin, *Complete Works*,* vol. 49, pp. 117–18.
42. Kollontai, in Dazhina 1974, p. 186.
43. Ibid.
44. Ibid., p. 187.

Chapter Ten AGITATING FOR REVOLUTION

1. Trotsky, *My Life*, pp. 284–5.
2. Kollontai, in Dazhina 1974, p. 190.
3. Lenin, *Complete Works*,* vol. 49, pp. 138–9.
4. Kollontai, in Dazhina 1974, p. 195.
5. Excerpts from Kollontai's American Diaries were first published in the journal *Istoricheskkii Arkhiv (Historical Archive)*, Moscow 1962, no. 1. They appeared again, together with excerpts from the diary of her second (1916–17) trip, in the journal *Inostrannaya Literatura (Foreign Literature)*, Moscow 1970, nos 1–2. An abridged version of these is in Dazhina 1974. Here, p. 199.
6. G. D. Petrov, "A. M. Kollontai during the First World War,"* p. 90.
7. Trotsky, *My Life*, pp. 282–3.
8. G. D. Petrov, "A. M. Kollontai during the First World War,"* (in a personal conversation with Nakoryakov), p. 95.
9. Kollontai, "American Diary," in Dazhina 1974, p. 199.
10. Kollontai, in Dazhina 1974, p. 201.
11. Ibid., p. 200.
12. Lenin, *Complete Works*,* vol. 49, p. 163.
13. Kollontai, in Dazhina 1974, pp. 202–3.
14. Ibid., p. 209.
15. Ibid., pp. 210–11.
16. Itkina, op. cit., p. 111.
17. Kollontai, in Dazhina 1974, p. 211.
18. Ibid., p. 216.
19. Ibid.
20. Lenin, *Complete Works*,* vol. 49, pp. 199–200.
21. Excerpt from Kollontai's diary quoted in G. D. Petrov, "A. M. Kollontai during the First World War,"* p. 96.
22. Itkina, op. cit., p. 117.
23. Ibid., p. 123.
24. Kollontai, in Dazhina 1974, p. 228.
25. G. D. Petrov, "A. M. Kollontai during the First World War,"* p. 96.
26. Quoted in G. D. Petrov, "Meridian Lines of Friendship,"* pp. 164–5.
27. Kollontai, in Dazhina 1974, p. 218.
28. Trotsky, *The History of the Russian Revolution*, pp. 126–7.

29. Lenin, *Complete Works,** vol. 49, pp. 399–400 and 401–3.

30. Kollontai, "Skoree v Rossiu!" ("Back to Russia!"), written in 1936–37, edited in 1943 as part of a projected book about the February revolution, and partly published in 1967, after her death, in the journal *Sovetskie Arkhivy (Soviet Archives)*, no. 2. Here, Dazhina 1974, pp. 240–2.

31. Kollontai, "V tyurme Kerenskogo" ("In Kerensky's Prison")—she is writing about her return from a later perspective—was first published in the Moscow journal *Katorga i Ssylka (Hard Labor and Exile)*, no. 7, in 1927. It was republished as a brochure the following year. Reproduced from the latter in Dazhina 1974, pp. 276ff.

32. Itkina, op. cit., p. 130.

33. Itkina, op. cit., p. 130.

Chapter Eleven MILITANT SPRING

1. G. Comte, *La Révolution russe par ses témoins (The Russian Revolution by Its Witnesses)*, Paris 1963, p. 111.

2. Quoted by Marcel Liebmann in his clear and invaluable book, to which I owe much, *The Russian Revolution. The Origins, Phases and Meaning of the Bolshevik Victory* (translated from the French by Arthur Pomerans), London 1970, p. 114.

3. Kollontai, *Autobiography of a Sexually Emancipated Woman*, p. 29.

4. Kollontai's reminiscences of this event are in her memoirs "Kak my rabotaly v semnadstatom godu" ("How We Worked in 1917") and "Delegatkoi na soveschanie levogo Tsimmervalda" ("A Delegate to the Left Zimmerwald Conference"), which are reprinted from the archival manuscripts in Dazhina 1974, pp. 249ff.

5. Kollontai, "Tvorcheskoe v rabote tov. Samoilovoi" ("The Creative Work of Comrade Samoilova"), in *Revolyutsionnaya deyatelnost Konkordii Nikolaevnoi Samoilovoi: Sbornik vospominanii (The Revolutionary Activity of Konkordia Nikolaevna Samoilova. A Collection of Memoirs)*, published by Tsentralny Komitet RKP(b); Kommissia po istorii oktyabrskoi revolyutsii. i RKP(b) (Central Committee of the Russian Communist Party [Bolsheviks]; Commission on the History of the October Revolution and the Russian Communist Party [Bolsheviks]), pp. 8–9.

6. Kollontai, in Dazhina 1974, pp. 244–7.

7. Kollontai, "Nash pamyatnik bortsam za svobodu" ("Our Memorial to the Freedom Fighters"), in *Pravda*, March 6, 1917. Reprinted in Dazhina et al. (eds), *A. M. Kollontai: Selected Articles and Speeches,** pp. 205–7.

8. Minutes of the whole Bolshevik conference from Trotsky (who was not there—how he got his information is a mystery), in *Stalin's School of Falsification*, New York 1937, pp. 231–301. Also from A. Shlyapnikov, *1917'y God (The Year 1917)*, Moscow 1923–27, in which, in three huge and immensely valuable volumes, he writes his own eyewitness account of the revolution; here vol. III, pp. 203–311.

9. Itkina, op. cit., pp. 137–8.

10. Kollontai's account of Lenin's arrival, Dazhina 1974, pp. 251ff. Another extremely vivid description (one among very many) is in N. Sukhanov, *The Russian Revolution (1917)*, London 1955.

11. Kollontai, in Dazhina 1974, p. 252.

12. Lenin, "Aprelskie Tezisy" ("April Theses"), *Complete Works,** vol. 31, pp. 99–100.

13. Kollontai, in Dazhina 1974, p. 254.

14. Ibid., p. 257.

15. Kollontai, "Kuda vedet 'revolyutsionnoe oboronchestvo'?" ("Where Does 'Revolutionary Defensism' Lead?"), in *Pravda*, April 5, 1917. Reprinted in Dazhina et al. (eds), *A. M. Kollontai: Selected Articles and Speeches,** pp. 208–210.
16. Kollontai, *Around Workers' Europe,** p. 22.
17. Pitirim Sorokin, *Leaves From a Russian Diary*, Boston 1950, p. 59.
18. Kollontai, in Dazhina 1974, p. 260.
19. Kollontai, "A Serious Gap," Holt 1977, pp. 125–7. (First published in *Pravda*, 5 May 1917.)
20. The point is well made in Carole Eubanks Hayden's article, "The Zhenotdel and the Bolshevik Party," in *Russian History/Histoire Russe*, University of Pittsburgh 1976, vol. 3, part 2, pp. 150–73.
21. Kollontai's article on the demonstration, "Demonstratsia Soldatok" ("Demonstration of *Soldatki*"), appeared in *Pravda* on April 12, 1917.
22. N. Selivanova, *Russia's Women*, New York 1923, p. 198.
23. The articles appeared, respectively, in *Pravda*, March 12 and 11; *Rabochaya Gazeta (Workers' Paper)*, March 8, 10, and 15; *Izvestia (News)*, March 26 and 28.
24. Kollontai, "Lenin i rabotnitsy v 1917' om godu" ("Lenin and Working Women in 1917"), in *Rabotnitsa*, Petrograd 1947, no. 1. Published in *Vsegda s vami (Always With You)*, a selection of *Rabotnitsa* articles edited by A. Artiukhina et al., Moscow/Leningrad 1964, pp. 84–7.
25. Kollontai, "In the Front Line of Fire," Holt 1977, pp. 123–5 (article originally in *Pravda*, May 7 and 9.

Chapter Twelve PEACE, BREAD, LAND, AND JUSTICE

1. Quoted in Itkina, op. cit., pp. 85–91. Kollontai's brief record is in Dazhina 1974, pp. 264–5.
2. Kollontai, *Love of Worker Bees*, trans. C. Porter, London 1977, p. 207.
3. Kollontai, "Nashi Zadachi" ("Our Tasks"), in *Rabotnitsa*, Petrograd 1917, no. 1. Article reprinted in Dazhina et al. (eds), *A. M. Kollontai: Selected Articles and Speeches,** pp. 211–13.
4. Kollontai, in Dazhina 1974, p. 267.
5. Ibid., p. 262.
6. Kollontai, *Autobiographical Essay,** p. 280.
7. Kollontai, in Dazhina 1974, p. 276.
8. Kollontai's account of her arrest and imprisonment is contained in her memoir article, "In Kerensky's Prison," op. cit., Dazhina 1974, pp. 276–305.
9. Kollontai, Dazhina 1974, p. 295.
10. Ibid., p. 300.
11. See *Makers of the Russian Revolution: Biographies of Bolshevik Leaders* (edited by Georges Haupt and Jean-Jacques Marie), London 1974, for extremely useful brief accounts of the temperaments and backgrounds of all these Bolsheviks.
12. Kollontai's *Rabotnitsa* article is quoted in N. D. Karpetskaya's book, *Rabotnitsy i Velikii Oktyabr (Working Women and Great October)*, Leningrad 1974, p. 90.

13. Itkina, op. cit., p. 158.

14. Lenin, *Gosudarstvo i revolyutsia (State and Revolution)*, in *Complete Works,** vol. 33, pp. 1–120.

15. Kollontai's memoir of this is in "Na istoricheskom zasedanii" ("At the Historic Meeting"), Dazhina 1974, p. 312. Dazhina has here added various of Kollontai's autobiographical memoirs printed after October 1937 to Kollontai's contribution to *Ob Iliche: Vospominania pitertsev (About Ilich* [Lenin]: *Memories of Petersburgers)*, Leningrad 1970.

16. Sukhanov, op. cit.

17. Kollontai, "The First Conference of Working Women," in *Rabochii Put (Workers' Path*—one of the names *Pravda* temporarily adopted in that period for fear of being closed down). Cited in Holt 1977, bibliography, p. 326.

18. From Kollontai's private manuscripts, published for the first time in Dazhina 1974, p. 316, as "Smolny—Kipyaschii kotel" ("Smolny, a Seething Cauldron").

19. Ibid., p. 314.

20. John Reed, *Ten Days That Shook the World*, London 1966, p. 133.

21. Kollontai, Dazhina 1974, p. 318.

Chapter Thirteen COOKS AND COMMISSARS

1. Kollontai, "Pervoe posobie iz sotsobesa" ("First Grant from the Social Welfare Commissariat"), an article first published in the Moscow journal *Krasnaya Niva (Red Cornfield)* in 1927. Here Dazhina 1974, p. 321.

2. One article, "The First Conference of Working Women" (October 26), is cited in Holt 1977, bibliography, p. 326.

3. To give some idea of the value of 500 rubles: bread was 1 to 2 rubles a pound, sugar 12 rubles a pound, apples and pears (when in season) 1 ruble each, a chocolate bar 10 rubles.

4. Trotsky, *Stalin: An Appraisal*, op. cit., vol. 2, pp. 13–14.

5. Itkina, op. cit., p. 174.

6. Kollontai, "First Grant from the Social Welfare Commissariat," op. cit., p. 323.

7. Ibid., pp. 322–3.

8. Ibid., p. 323.

9. Kollontai, "Pervye Dni Narkomsobesa" ("First Days of the Social Welfare Commissariat"), an article first published in *Izvestia*, November 6–7, 1945. Here Dazhina 1974, pp. 324–8.

10. Louise Bryant, *Six Red Months in Russia*, London 1919, p. 123.

11. Ibid., p. 125.

12. Kollontai, "Kto spas Sotsobes?" ("Who Saved the Social Welfare Commissariat?"), an article written in 1929 but not published. In Dazhina 1974, p. 330.

13. The congress is described by A. A. Arbuzova in her article "Vmeste s partie" ("Along With the Party"), in *Zhenschiny goroda Lenina (Women of Lenin's Town)*, ed. A. Gilyarova, Moscow 1963, pp. 113–21; and, in the same book, "V obschem stroyu" ("In One Organization"), by R. Kovnator.

14. J. Sadoul, *Notes sur la révolution bolchévique (Notes on the Bolshevik Revolution)*, Paris 1971, p. 96.
15. Kollontai, *Autobiography of a Sexually Emancipated Woman*, p. 43.
16. Itkina, op. cit., p. 175.
17. Oyarzabal de Palencia, *Alexandra Kollontay*, London 1947, pp. 163–4.
18. Höglund's memories of this trip are contained in an article he wrote for the Swedish paper *Morgon-Tidningen*, April 18, 1954. See also Albert Rhys Williams's observations in *Lenin, The Man and His Work*, New York 1919, pp. 58–9.
19. Kollontai, "V Smolnom" ("In the Smolny"), an article first published in 1947 in the Petrograd journal *Krasnoarmeets (Red Soldier)*, no. 2. Here, Dazhina 1974, pp. 345–6.
20. *On the Protection of Maternity (Decision of the People's Commissariat of Social Welfare)*, Holt 1977, pp. 140–1.
21. *On the Protection of Mothers and Children (Decision of the People's Commissariat of Social Welfare)*, *Izvestia*, November 19, 1918.
22. Kollontai, "Pervye shagi po okhrane materinstva" ("First Steps in Maternity Protection"), reprinted from a manuscript of 1927, in Dazhina 1974, p. 338.
23. Itkina, op. cit., pp. 175–6.
24. Kollontai, "Po 'bozheskim delam' u monakhov" ("Doing 'God's Business' With the Monks"). First published in 1927 in the Moscow journal *Smena (Change)*, no. 20; republished in the Rostov-on-Don journal *Don*, 1966, no. 4, as "Po sotsialnym delam u monakhov" ("Doing Social Work With the Monks"); reproduced from the former article in Dazhina 1974, pp. 331–2.
25. Ibid., pp. 332–5.
26. Lenin, *Complete Works,* * vol. 32, p. 179.
27. Kollontai, "Dvorets materinstva gorit" ("The Palace of Motherhood Burns Down"), Dazhina 1974, pp. 340–4. First published in 1945 as "Pervye dni Narkomsobesa" ("First Days of the Social Welfare Commissariat"); see above, no. 9.
28. Sadoul, op. cit., p. 181.
29. Oyazarbal de Palencia, op. cit., p. 171.
30. Ibid., p. 173.
31. *Sedmoi ekstrenny sezd RKP(b). Mart 1918. Stenografischeskii otchet (Seventh Extraordinary Congress of the Russian Communist Party [Bolsheviks], March 1918, Stenographic Report)*, Moscow 1962, pp. 88–9.
32. Morgan Phillips Price, *My Reminiscences of the Russian Revolution*, London 1921, p. 247.
33. Kollontai, *Autobiography of a Sexually Emancipated Woman*, p. 40.
34. Angelica Balabanova, *My Life as a Rebel*, p. 277; and *Impressions of Lenin*, trans. Isotta Cesari, Ann Arbor 1964, p. 98.

Chapter Fourteen CIVIL WAR

1. E. H. Carr, *The Bolshevik Revolution*, London 1977, vol. II, pp. 158–84. I. Deutscher, *Soviet Trade Unions*, London 1950. R. V. Daniels, *The Conscience of the Revolution*, Cambridge, Mass., 1960, pp. 119–36. *Pervy vserossiisskii sezd profesionalnykh soyuzov 7–14 Yanvarya 1918 g (First All-Russian Congress of Trade Unions, January 7–14, 1918*, stenographic report), Moscow 1918.

2. In his own autobiography in *Encyclopaedia of the Granat Russian Bibliographical Institute.** Translation in Haupt and Marie, *Makers of the Russian Revolution,* trans. Bellos, London 1974, p. 123.

3. Quoted by Joel Carmichael in *Trotsky. An Appreciation of His Life,* London 1975, p. 235.

4. Itkina, op. cit., p. 179.

5. For an account of women's activities in the civil war, see Stites, op. cit., pp. 317–22.

6. Kollontai, *Autobiography of a Sexually Emancipated Woman,* p. 40.

7. Ibid.

8. K. Samoilova, *Organizatsionnye zadachi otdelov rabotnits (Organizational Tasks of the Women Workers' Departments),* Moscow 1920, p. 15.

9. Kollontai, "Gorod pervykh 'buntarei' " ("Town of the First 'Rebels' "), Dazhina 1974, pp. 349–52 (*Pravda,* October 3, 1918).

10. V. Golubeva, "Vserossiiskii sezd rabotnits i krestyanok" ("All-Russian Congress of Women Workers and Peasants"), in *Kommunistka* (Communist Woman), Moscow 1923, no. 1.

11. Itkina, op. cit., p. 191.

12. Ibid., p. 193.

13. Kollontai, "V. I. Lenin i pervy sezd rabotnits" ("V. I. Lenin and the First Congress of Women Workers"), first published in the collection *O Vladimire Iliche Lenine: Vospominania 1920–1922 (About Vladimir Ilich Lenin: Memories of 1920–1922),* Moscow 1963. Here, Dazhina 1974, p. 354.

14. Kollontai, "Kak my sozvali pervy vserossisskii sezd rabotnits i krestyanok" ("How We Called the First All-Russian Congress of Working and Peasant Women"), in *Kommunistka (Communist Woman),* Moscow, November 1923.

15. Kollontai, *Semya i kommunisticheskoe gosudarstvo (The Family and the Communist State),* Moscow 1919.

16. V. Golubeva, "All-Russian Congress of Working and Peasant Women."* V. Moirova, "Pyat let raboty sredi rabotnits i krestyanok" ("Five Years' Work Among Working and Peasant Women"), in *Kommunistka,* November 1923.

17. Kollontai's diary for January 1919 was prepared for publication by her in the 1940's but published for the first time in Dazhina 1974, pp. 356–7.

18. Ibid., p. 357.

19. Extracts from these articles in E. I. Breslav, *A. M. Kollontai; Propagandist of Lenin's Ideas in the International Workers' Movement.**

20. Kollontai, *Novaya moral i rabochii klass (The New Morality and the Working Class),* Moscow 1918.

21. Kollontai, 1919 Diary, Dazhina 1974, pp. 357–8. And Itkina, op. cit., p. 180.

22. Kollontai, "Karl Libknekht a Roza Luksemburg—bortsy, geroi, i mucheniki" ("Karl Liebknecht and Rosa Luxemburg—Fighters, Heroes, and Martyrs"), *Pravda,* January–February 1919. See Dazhina et al. (eds.), *A. M. Kollontai: Selected Articles and Speeches,** pp. 260–4.

23. Marguerite Harrison, *Marooned in Moscow,* London 1921, p. 78.

24. Emma Goldman, *Living My Life,* New York 1931, vol. 2, p. 757.

25. Kollontai, "Kogo poteryali rabotnitsy?" ("Whom Have Working Women Lost?"), in *Kommunar,* April 2, 1919. See also Dazhina et al. (eds), *A. M. Kollontai: Selected Articles and Speeches,** pp. 266–8.

26. Itkina, op. cit., p. 208.
27. *Vosmoi sezd RKP(b). Protokoly (Eighth Congress of the Russian Communist Party [Bolsheviks], Minutes),* Moscow 1959, pp. 296–300.
28. Articles cited in Holt 1977, bibliography.
29. Itkina, op. cit., p. 183.
30. Ibid., pp. 185–6.
31. Ibid., p. 187.
32. Ibid., p. 188.
33. Ibid., p. 190.
34. Galina Serebryakova, *O Drugikh i o sebe (About Others and About Myself),* Moscow 1968, (chapter on Kollontai) pp. 74–81.
35. Itkina, op. cit., p. 201.
36. Ibid., p. 195.
37. Ibid., p. 193.

Chapter Fifteen THE CRISIS OF THE REVOLUTION

1. *Etapy ekonomicheskoi politiki SSSR (Stages of USSR Foreign Policy),* ed. P. Vaisberg, Moscow 1934, p. 101.
2. "Devyaty sezd RKP(b). Mart-Aprel 1920. Protokoly" *(Ninth Congress of the Russian Communist Party [Bolsheviks]. March–April 1920. Minutes),* Moscow 1960. Lutovinov, op. cit., pp. 239–42. Martynova, op. cit., pp. 334–6.
3. Itkina, op. cit., p. 92.
4. Itkina, op. cit., p. 93.
5. This speculation about her life with Dybenko is based on the novel she wrote in 1923, *Vasilisa Malygina* (see *Love of Worker Bees,* op. cit.), which is very largely autobiographical.
6. Kollontai, "Trudovaya povinnost i okhranenie zhenskogo truda" ("Labor Conscription and the Protection of Women's Labor"), *Kommunistka (Communist Woman),* 1920, nos 1–2.
7. *Devyataya konferentsia russkoi kommunisticheskoi partii (Bolshevikov). Protokoly. (Ninth Conference of the Russian Communist Party [Bolsheviks]. Minutes),* Moscow 1972, p. 188.
8. Marcel Body, "Alexandra Kollontai. Mémoires," in the journal *Preuves,* Paris, April 1952, p. 17. A short biographical sketch of Inessa Armand is contained in Pavel Podlyaschuk, *Tovarishch Inessa: Dokumentalnaya povest (Comrade Inessa: A Documentary Narrative),* 2nd edn, Moscow 1965. Also see a collection of obituary articles, *Pamyati Inessy Armanda (Memories of Inessa Armand),* ed. N. Krupskaya, Moscow 1926.
9. Emma Goldman, *My Disillusionment in Russia,* London 1925, p. 169.
10. Dora Russell, *The Tamarisk Tree,* London 1975, p. 89.
11. Emma Goldman, op. cit., pp. 53–4.
12. Alec Nove, *An Economic History of the USSR,* London 1975, p. 76.
13. Vera Bilshai (ed.), *K. Marx, F. Engels, V. I. Lenin o zhenskom voprose (K. Marx, F. Engels, V. I. Lenin on the Woman Question),* Moscow 1971, pp. 77–9.

14. Speculation based on Kollontai's novel, *Vasilisa Malygina,* op. cit.
15. Itkina, op. cit., p. 202.
16. Ibid., p. 203. See also Konkordia Samoilova, *Organizatsionnye zadachi otdelov rabotnits (Organizational Tasks of the Working Women's Departments),* Moscow 1920, pp. 3–6, 12–28.
17. Louise Bryant, *Mirrors of Moscow,* New York 1923, p. 124.
18. John Reed, *Ten Days That Shook the World,* p. 49. Praskovya Kudelli in the journal *Rabotnitsa,* October 18, 1917.
19. Kollontai, *Prostitutsia i mery borby s nei (Prostitution and Ways of Fighting It),* Moscow 1921.
20. Louise Bryant, *Mirrors of Moscow,* pp. 126–7.
21. Kollontai, "Sëstry" ("Sisters"), in *Love of Worker Bees,* op. cit.
22. Dora Russell, *The Tamarisk Tree,* p. 94.
23. Louise Bryant, *Mirrors of Moscow,* p. 121.
24. Itkina, op. cit., p. 203.
25. *RSFSR. Vserossisskii sezd sovetov. Stenografischeskii otchet (RSFSR. All-Russian Congress of Soviets. Stenographic Report),* Moscow 1918, pp. 205–6.
26. Lenin, *Women and Society* (from his speech at the November 1918 First All-Russian Women's Congress), New York 1938, pp. 11–13.
27. Kollontai, "Zadachi otdelov po rabote sredi zhenschin" ("Tasks of the Departments for Work Among Women"), in *Kommunistka (Communist Woman),* November 1920. Reprinted in Dazhina et al. (eds), *A. M. Kollontai: Selected Articles and Speeches,* pp. 310–15.
28. Dora Russell, *The Tamarisk Tree,* pp. 94–5.
29. Emma Goldman, *Living My Life,* vol. 2, p. 757.
30. Isaac Deutscher, *Soviet Trade Unions,* pp. 36–51.
31. *Vosmoi Vserossisskii Sezd Sovetov. Stenografischeskii otchet (Eighth All-Russian Congress of Soviets. Stenographic Report),* Moscow 1921. Summary of the various positions adopted at the joint meeting afterward, from Isaac Deutscher, *Soviet Trade Unions,* pp. 42–52, and from an appendix to the official report of the Tenth Congress: *Desyaty sezd RKP(b). Stenografischeskii otchet. 8–16 Mart 1921 (Tenth Congress of the Russian Communist Party [Bolsheviks]. Stenographic Report. March 8–16, 1921),* Moscow 1921 (for Workers' Opposition's views, see pp. 360–4).
32. *Zadachi profsoyuzov. Tezisy rabochei oppozitsii. K desyatomy sezdu partii (The Tasks of the Trade Unions. Theses of the Workers' Opposition. For the Tenth Party Congress),* Moscow 1921.
33. Barmin, *Memoirs of a Soviet Diplomat,* London 1938, pp. 116–17.
34. Kollontai, "Pora proanalizirovat" ("It's Time to Analyze Matters"), *Pravda,* January 28, 1921, p. 1.
35. Itkina, op. cit., p. 176.
36. Victor Serge, *Memoirs of a Revolutionary,* trans. Peter Sedgwick, London 1963, p. 126.
37. *Krasnaya Gazeta (Red Paper),* February 1921.

Chapter Sixteen WORKERS' OPPOSITION

1. Raya Dunaevskaya, *Marxism and Freedom,* New York 1964, p. 202; Angelica Balabanova, *Impressions of Lenin,* p. 97.

2. *Rabochaya Oppozitsia (The Workers' Opposition),* unpublished in Russia except for the copies circulated in March 1921, was translated into English in 1921 (in Sylvia Pankhurst's *Workers' Dreadnought,* London), and in 1962 by *Solidarity,* London: producing a new edition with a new introduction by Fabio Petri in 1979. Also contained in Holt 1977. The *Solidarity* edition has been used here.

3. E. H. Carr, *The Bolshevik Revolution,* vol. 1, pp. 205–6.

4. Balabanova, *Impressions of Lenin,* p. 97.

5. Itkina, op. cit., p. 213.

6. *Tenth Congress Proceedings,** pp. 60–5.

7. Ibid.: for Shlyapnikov, see pp. 39, 196, 211 and 287; for Kollontai, pp. 53, 163; for Bukharin, pp. 176–82.

8. Itkina, op. cit., p. 193.

9. Emma Goldman, *Living My Life,* vol. 2, pp. 753–5.

10. Kollontai, "Proizvodstvo i byt" ("Production and Everyday Life"), *Kommunistka (Communist Woman),* Moscow 1921, nos 10–11. Konkordia Samoilova, *Organizational Tasks of the Working Women's Departments,** pp. 18–22.

11. Kollontai, "Profsoyuzy i rabotnitsy" ("Trade Unions and Working Women"), *Pravda,* May 22, 1921. Reprinted in Dazhina et al. (eds), *A. M. Kollontai: Selected Articles and Speeches,** pp. 316–22.

12. Kollontai's article in *Pravda,* April 10, 1921, on the Zhenotdel's work among women of the East, was entitled "Soveschanie kommunistok-organisatorov zhenschin Vostoka" ("Conference of Communist Women Organizers of the East"). See Dazhina et al. (eds), *A. M. Kollontai: Selected Articles and Speeches,** pp. 316–19.

13. See Stites, op. cit., pp. 339–40. Also Rudolf Schlesinger, *The Family in the USSR,* London 1949, pp. 196–8. Fanina Halle, *Women of the Soviet East,* New York 1923. Gregory Massell, *The Surrogate Proletariat,* Princeton 1974. Hanna Ilberg, *Klara Tsetkin,* Moscow 1958, pp. 184–5. Louise Bryant, *Mirrors of Moscow,* p. 121.

14. Kollontai's Sverdlov lectures were published, in book form, partly in 1921 as *Polozhenie zhenschiny v svyazi s evolyutsiei khozyaistva (Women's Position in the Evolution of the Economy),* and partly in 1923, also in Moscow, as *Trud zhenschin v evolyutsii khozyaistva (Women's Labor in the Evolution of the Economy).*

15. Kollontai, "Vtoraya mezhdunarodnaya konferentsia kommunistok" ("Second International Conference of Communist Women"), *Pravda,* June 15, 1921. Reprinted in Dazhina et al. (eds), *A. M. Kollontai: Selected Articles and Speeches,** pp. 341–5.

16. Louise Bryant, *Mirrors of Moscow,* pp. 121–2.

17. See Victor Serge's account of the congress, *Memoirs of a Revolutionary,* pp. 137–44.

18. Itkina, op. cit., p. 214.

19. Marcel Body, op. cit., p. 12.

20. Mark Zorkii, *Rabochaya oppozitsia. Materialy i dokumenty 1920–1926 (The Workers' Opposition. Material and Documents 1920–1926),* Moscow 1926, pp. 90–4.

21. Itkina, op. cit., p. 214.

22. Kollontai, "Tsar-Golod i Krasnaya Armia" ("Tsar Hunger and the Red Army"), in

the journal *Voin Revolyutsii (Soldier of the Revolution),* * August 1921. Reprinted in Dazhina et al. (eds), *A. M. Kollontai: Selected Articles and Speeches,* * pp. 345–9. Also published in Odessa in 1921 (see above, Ch. 4, n. 5) was *Iz moei zhizni i raboty (From My Life and Work),* from which I have quoted; and "Avtobiograpficheskii ocherk" ("Autobiographical Essay") in the journal *Proletarskaya Revolyutsia (Proletarian Revolution),* no. 3, 1921, from which I have quoted widely.

23. Kollontai, "Tezisy po kommunisticheskoi morali v sfere brachnykh otnoshenii" ("Theses on Communist Morality in the Sphere of Sexual Relations") *Kommunistka (Communist Woman),* 1921, nos. 12–13.

24. Zorkii, op. cit., pp. 59–61.

25. Article was printed in *The New York Times,* November 21, 1921.

26. Zorkii, op. cit., p. 62.

27. *KPSS. Odinadstaty sezd RKP(B). Mart-Aprel 1922. Stenograf‌icheskii otchet (CPSU. Eleventh Congress of the Russian Communist Party (Bolsheviks). March–April 1922. Stenographic Report),* Moscow 1961, pp. 166–79.

28. Ibid.: for Kollontai's speeches, see pp. 196–210; for Shlyapnikov's, pp. 186–9.

29. Trotsky, *Stalin. An Appraisal,* p. 357.

30. Kollontai, *Autobiography of a Sexually Emancipated Woman,* p. 44.

31. *The God That Failed,* ed. Richard Crossman, New York 1964, p. 90.

32. Kollontai, "Skoro. Cherez 48 let" ("Soon: In 48 Years' Time"), was published in 1922 in the Russian town of Omsk. See Holt 1977, pp. 232–6.

33. The first letter to working youth was in *Molodaya Gvardia (Young Guard),* April to May 1922. Kollontai's second letter was entitled "Moral kak orudie klassovogo gospodstva i klassovoi borby" ("Morality as a Weapon of Class Rule and Class Struggle"), in *Molodaya Gvardia* from September to October 1922.

34. Kollontai, *Autobiography of a Sexually Emancipated Woman,* p. 44.

Chapter Seventeen EXILED IN DIPLOMATS' EUROPE

1. Kollontai, *Autobiography of a Sexually Emancipated Woman,* p. 43.

2. S. Volfson, *Sotsiologia braka i semi (Sociology of Marriage and the Family),* Minsk 1929, pp. 442–50.

3. Trotsky, *Problems of Life,* Colombo, Ceylon 1924, p. 15.

4. *Eleventh Congress of the Russian Communist Party,* * pp. 421–2.

5. I. Deutscher, *Stalin. A Political Biography,* London 1949, pp. 343–4.

6. *Eleventh Congress of the Russian Communist Party,* * pp. 456–8.

7. See Carol Eubanks Hayden's article, "The 'Zhenotdel' and the Bolshevik Party," op. cit., for excellent concise summary of the rise and fall of the Zhenotdel.

8. Marcel Body, *Alexandra Kollontai. Memoirs,* * p. 13.

9. Kollontai, *Lyubov pchel trudovykh (Love of Worker Bees),* Petrograd 1923. First translated (partially) into English in 1932 as *Free Love.* Translated under original title by C. Porter, London 1977.

10. Itkina, op. cit., p. 194.

11. Kollontai, "The New Woman," in *Autobiography of a Sexually Emancipated Woman,* p. 73.

12. Kollontai, *Zhenschina na Perelome (Woman at the Threshold)*, published under her maiden name, A. Domontovich, Moscow/Petrograd 1923.
13. Body, op. cit., p. 13.
14. Itkina, op. cit., p. 220.
15. Ibid., p. 221.
16. Ibid., p. 224.
17. Ibid., p. 225.
18. Holt 1977, p. 215.
19. Kollontai, "O drakone i 'beloi ptitse' " ("About The Dragon and the 'White Bird' "), *Molodaya Gvardia (Young Guard)*, Moscow 1923, no. 2.
20. Kollontai, "Dorogu Krylatomu Erosu!" ("Make Way for Winged Eros!"), *Young Guard*, Moscow 1923, no. 3.
21. P. Vinogradskaya, "Voprosy morali, pola, byta, i tovarishch Kollontai" ("Questions of Sex, Morality, Everyday Life, and Comrade Kollontai"), *Krasnaya Nov (Red Virgin Soil)*, Moscow, June 1923.
22. Body, op. cit., p. 14.
23. Trotsky, *Problems of Life*, pp. 5–13.
24. Vinogradskaya's article in *Pravda*, July 26, 1923.
25. Itkina, op. cit., p. 228.
26. R. V. Daniels, *Conscience of the Revolution*, op. cit., p. 204.
27. Ibid., p. 228.
28. Body, op. cit., p. 14.

Chapter Eighteen YEARS OF UNCERTAINTY

1. Itkina, op. cit., pp. 225–7.
2. Stalin, "K pyatoi godovschine pervogo sezda rabotnits i krestyanok" ("The Fifth Anniversary of the First Congress of Working and Peasant Women"), *Kommunistka*, November 1923.
3. Itkina, op. cit., p. 228.
4. Ibid., p. 222; see also Palencia, op. cit., pp. 177–80.
5. Itkina, op. cit., p. 233.
6. Body, op. cit., pp. 15 and 16.
7. Itkina, op. cit., p. 234.
8. See Beatrice Brodsky Farnsworth, "Bolshevik Alternatives and the Soviet Family: the 1926 Marriage Law Debate," in *Women in Russia*, ed. D. Atkinson et al., op. cit., pp. 139–65. Gnilova speaking in November 1926 at the Third Session of the Central Executive Committee, quoted in R. Schlesinger (ed.), *The Family in the USSR: Documents and Readings*, London 1949, p. 140.
9. The speaker, P. A. Krasikov, quoted in Schlesinger, op. cit., pp. 133–4.
10. Kollontai's ideas are contained in the articles "Brak, zhenschiny i alimenty" ("Marriage, Women, and Alimony"), in the journal *Ekran (Screen)*, November 6, 1926; "Obschii gorshok ili lichnye alimenty" ("A Common Pot or Private Alimony"), in *Brak i Semya. Sbornik statei i materialov po semeinomy pravu (Marriage and the Family. A Collection of Articles and Material on the Family Law)*, Moscow 1926; "O novom prave po seme i brake" ("About the New Law on the Family and

Marriage"), in *Natisk (Onslaught)*, Moscow, March 8, 1926; and "Brak i byt" ("Marriage and Everyday Life"), in *Rabochii Sud (Workers' Court)*, Moscow 1926, No. 5.

11. Kollontai, "Brak i byt" ("Marriage and Everyday Life").

12. S. Smidovich, "O lyubvi" ("About Love"), in I. Razin (ed.), *Komsomolsii byt (Komsomol Life)*, Moscow/Leningrad 1927. The book also contains articles by the sexual conservative and psychologist, Aaron Zalkind: "Ethics, Everyday Life, and Young People," and "Answer to a Questionnaire."

13. E. Lavrov, "Polovoi vopros i molodezh. O nekotorykh itogakh i novykh otkroveniakh Tovarischa Kollontai" ("The Sexual Question and Young People. Some of the Consequences of Comrade Kollontai's Latest Revelations"), *Molodaya Gvardia (Young Guard)*, March 1926.

14. Lenin to Zetkin in *Reminiscences of Lenin*, New York 1934, p. 48.

15. E. Yaroslavsky, "Moral i byt proletariata v perekhodny period" ("Morality and Everyday Life of the Proletariat in the Transitional Period"), in *Young Guard*, May 1926.

16. Victor Serge, *Memoirs of a Revolutionary*, p. 205.

17. Ruth Fischer, *Stalin and German Communism*, Cambridge, Mass., 1948, pp. 159–60n.

18. Katherine Anthony, article in *North American Review*, New York 1930.

19. Itkina, op. cit., p. 234.

20. Body, op. cit., pp. 21–2.

21. Ibid., p. 22.

22. Ibid., p. 235.

23. Ibid., p. 238.

24. Ibid., p. 240.

25. Ibid.

26. Ibid., p. 242.

27. Ibid.

28. Itkina, op. cit., p. 236.

Chapter Nineteen THE LAST YEARS—THE PURGES

1. Kollontai, "Oppozitisia i partiinaya massa" ("The Opposition and the Party Rank and File"), *Pravda*, October 30, 1927.

2. Itkina, op. cit., p. 247.

3. Victor Serge, *Memoirs of a Revolutionary*, p. 252.

4. Itkina, op. cit., p. 247.

5. Ibid.

6. Ibid., p. 255.

7. Ilya Ehrenburg, *People and Life*, vol. 5, London 1964, pp. 87–9.

8. Body, op. cit., p. 23.

9. *Shestnadstaty sezd vserossisskoi kommunisticheskoi partii. Protokoly (Sixteenth Congress of the All-Russian Communist Party. Minutes)*, Moscow 1930, pp. 341–2.

10. Savva Dangulov, *Dvenadstat dorog na Egle (Twelve Roads to Egle)*, Moscow 1970, pp. 308–15. A curious and rather whimsical book, but valuable for the interviews the

author had with people who knew Kollontai in Stockholm and for the letters to which he had access.

11. Kollontai, "Women Fighters in the Days of Great October," in *Zhenskii Zhurnal* (*Women's Paper*), Moscow 1927, no. 11; "In Memory of V. F. Kommissarzhevskaya," in *Krasnaya Nov* (Red Virgin Soil), 1930, no. 2; "Shock Worker of the Revolution" (about Krupskaya), in *Pravda*, April 22–23, 1933; "Women in 1917," in *Rabotnitsa*, 1937, no. 31. For all these, see Holt 1977, bibliography.

12. Palencia, pp. 202–3.

13. Ibid., p. 239.

14. Body, op. cit., pp. 23–4.

15. Palencia, op. cit., p. 204.

16. Lena Wickman in conversation with the author in 1976.

17. Palencia, op. cit., p. 276.

18. Body, op. cit., p. 24.

19. Ehrenburg, op. cit., p. 89.

20. G. D. Petrov. "Meridian Lines of Friendship,"* pp. 165–6.

21. Palencia, op. cit., p. 246.

22. Ibid., p. 267.

23. Ibid., p. 268.

24. W. R. Mead, *Finland*, London 1968, p. 169.

25. Dangulov, op. cit., pp. 333–5.

26. In conversation with the author in London in 1976.

27. Ehrenburg, op. cit., p. 88.

28. Gunnar Hagglof, *Diplomat*, London 1971, p. 162.

29. Mead, op. cit., pp. 172–6.

30. Dangulov, op. cit., pp. 340–1.

31. V. and E. Petrov, *Empire of Fear*, London 1956, p. 191.

32. Ibid., pp. 192–3.

33. Mead, op. cit., p. 175.

34. Itkina, op. cit., p. 278.

35. Dangulov, op. cit., p. 306.

36. Kollontai, "Iz zapisnikh knizhek poslednikh let, 1946–51" ("From the Notebooks of the Last Years, 1946–51"), in Dazhina 1974, p. 367.

37. Itkina, op. cit., p. 283.

38. Kollontai, "From the Notebooks of the Last Years,"* p. 368.

39. Ibid., p. 368.

40. Ibid., p. 367.

41. Dangulov, op. cit., p. 289.

42. Ibid., p. 300, and Itkina, op. cit., p. 285.

43. Kollontai, "From the Notebooks of the Last Years,"* p. 368.

44. Itkina, op. cit., p. 285.

45. Body, op. cit., p. 12.

46. Itkina, op. cit., p. 286.

PERIODICALS REFERRED TO IN THE TEXT

RUSSIAN

GOLOS SOTSIAL DEMOKRATA (The Social Democratic Voice) Paper of the Mensheviks in exile, Geneva-Paris, February 1908 to December 1911, 26 issues.

ISKRA (Spark) The first underground Marxist paper in Russia, December 1900. Published in Leipzig, Munich, London, Geneva. Became Menshevik after the Bolshevik-Menshevik split, issue 52, October 19, 1903.

IZVESTIA (News) Political daily paper first issued by the Petrograd Soviet on February 28, 1917. Title varied frequently to avoid police suppression.

KOMMUNISTKA (Communist Woman) Official paper of the Zhenotdel, published in Moscow monthly, from September 1919 to October 1929.

KRASNAYA GAZETA (Red Paper) Paper of the Petrograd Soviet, January 1918 to 1939.

KRASNAYA NOV (Red Virgin Soil) Literary, artistic, and scientific review, Moscow, June 1921 to August 1942 (from 1934, organ of the Union of Soviet Writers).

LUCH (The Ray) Legal Menshevik daily paper, St. Petersburg, September 1912 to August 1913. Then, under Dan and Martynov, St. Petersburg, August 1913 to August 1919. Replaced in July 1913 by *Novaya Rabochaya Gazeta (New Workers' Paper)*.

MOLODAYA GVARDIA (Young Guard) Popular monthly review of literature, art, and politics, aimed at young Bolsheviks, Moscow, 1922–1941.

NACHALO (The Beginning) (1) Legal Marxist paper, St. Petersburg 1899. (2) Continuation of *Nashe Slovo* (see below), September 30, 1916, to March 24, 1917, 147 issues.

NASHE SLOVO (Our Word) Internationalist Social Democrats' paper, Paris, January 29, 1915, to September 15, 1916.

NAUCHNOE OBOZRENIE (Scientific Review) St. Petersburg, 1894–1903 (weekly to 1897, then monthly).

NOVAYA EPOKHA (New Epoch) Continuation of *Nachalo* (published in St. Petersburg), Paris, to May 3, 1917.

NOVAYA ZHIZN (New Life) (1) First legal Bolshevik daily, St. Petersburg, October 27 to December 3, 1905, 28 issues. (2) Internationalist Menshevik daily, Petrograd, April 1917 to June 1918.

NOVY MIR (New World) Chief publication of Internationalist Social Democrats; New York, 1911–1916 (weekly).

OBRAZOVANIE (Education) St. Petersburg, 1892–1909 (monthly). From 1905–7 expressed 'legal Marxist' views.

PRAVDA (Truth) (1) Daily paper published by the central committee of the Bolshevik Party, St. Petersburg, April 22, to July 5, 1913. (2) From that time until September 1917,

514 | ALEXANDRA KOLLONTAI

adopted about twelve different names (*Proletarian Pravda, Workers' Pravda*, etc.), to avoid police suppression. (3) Still official Soviet government paper.

PROLETARSKAYA REVOLYUTSIA (Proletarian Revolution) Historical review published by the Marx-Engels Institute, Moscow, 1921–41, 132 issues.

PROLETARY (Proletarian) (1) Central organ of the Russian Social Democratic Party, published in Geneva, May 14 to November 12, 1905, 26 issues. (2) Underground Bolshevik paper founded after Fourth ("Unity") Congress of the Russian Social Democratic Party in Stockholm in 1906. Published thereafter by Moscow and St. Petersburg committees of RSDP, in Finland, Geneva, Paris, August 21, 1906 to November 28, 1909, 50 issues. (3) One of the names adopted, from August 13–24, 1917, by *Pravda.*

RABOCHAYA GAZETA (Workers' Paper) Underground Bolshevik paper, published in Paris, October 30, 1910, to July 30, 1912.

RABOCHEE DELO (Workers' Cause) (1) Underground journal of the Union of Struggle for the Emancipation of the Working Class, St. Petersburg, 1895. (2) Review published by Social Democrats in exile, Geneva, April 1899 to February 1902, 12 issues. (3) Trade union weekly, Moscow, from May 1, 1909.

RABOTNITSA (Working Woman) Bolshevik women's paper, Petrograd. (1) Monthly: February 23 (Women's Day), 1914 to June 1914 (5 issues). (2) Weekly: May 10, 1917, to January 1918.

RUSSKOE BOGATSVO (Russian Wealth) Populist literary and scientific monthly, liberal from the 1890's, St. Petersburg, 1876 to 1918.

SEVERNY VESTNIK (Northern Messenger) Monthly political and scientific review, St. Petersburg, 1885–8.

SOTSIAL DEMOKRAT (Social Democrat) (1) Literary and political review of Plekhanov's Liberation of Labor group, Geneva, 1890–93, 4 brochures. (2) Underground publication of the Russian Social Democratic Party central committee, St. Petersburg, September 17 to November 18, 1906, 7 issues. (3) Underground central organ of the RSDP, St. Petersburg, Paris, Geneva, February 1908 to January 1917 (from 1910, Bolshevik). (4) Daily published by the Moscow Region Bolshevik organization, March 1917 to March 1918, 246 issues.

SOVREMENNY MIR (Contemporary World) Literary and political review, St. Petersburg 1911–15.

VOLNA (Wave) Legal Bolshevik daily aimed at sailors, St. Petersburg, April 26 to May 1907, 5 issues. Then February 1917 onward.

VOPROSY STRAKHOVANIA (Questions of Insurance) Legal Bolshevik weekly, Petrograd, October 1913 to March 1918.

VPERYOD (Forward) (1) Underground Bolshevik weekly, Geneva, December 22, 1904, to May 5, 1905, 18 issues (succeeded by *Proletary*). (2) Legal Bolshevik daily, St. Petersburg, May 26 to June 14, 1906, 17 issues (succeeded by *Ekho*). (3) Collection of articles by the left-wing Bolshevik *"Vperyod"* group, Paris, 1910–11, 3 issues; organ of this group, Geneva, August 25, 1915, to February 1, 1917, 6 issues. (4) Menshevik paper, Moscow, March 1917 to May 1918. (5) Organ of Petrograd internationalist Social Democrats, June 15 to September 15, 1917.

ZARYA (Dawn) Scientific and political Marxist review, Stuttgart, 1901–2, 4 issues. Published by editors of *Iskra.*

GERMAN

DIE GLEICHHEIT (Equality)   Women's paper of the SPD, Stuttgart, 1891–1922.

LEIPZIGER VOLKSZEITUNG (Leipzig People's Paper)   Organ of the left wing of the SPD, Leipzig, daily from 1894 to 1933.

NEUE ZEIT (New Times)   Theoretical review of the SPD, Stuttgart, 1883–1923.

SOZIALISTISCHE MONATSHEFTE (Socialist Monthly)   Revisionists' journal, Berlin, 1896–1923.

VORWÄRTS (Forward)   Central organ of the German Social Democratic movement, Berlin, 1876–1933.

BIBLIOGRAPHY OF ALEXANDRA KOLLONTAI'S WRITINGS

This bibliography is from *Alexandra Kollontai: Selected Writings,* translated and edited by Alix Holt (Allison and Busby, 1977).

BOOKS AND PAMPHLETS

1903 *Zhizn' finlyandskikh rabochikh* (The life of Finnish workers), St. Petersburg.

1905 *K voprosu o klassovoi bor'be* (On the question of the class struggle), confiscated manuscript.

1906 *Finlyandiya i sotsialism* (Finland and socialism), St. Petersburg.

1909 *Sotsial'nye osnovy zhenskogo voprosa* (The social basis of the woman question), St. Petersburg.

1911 *Zapiski agitatora* (The notes of an agitator).

1912 *Po rabochei Evrope* (Around workers' Europe), St. Petersburg.

1914 *Rabotnitsa-mat'* (Working woman and mother), St. Petersburg. *Otryvki iz dnevnika* (Excerpts from a diary), Leningrad (pub. 1924).

1915 *Zheny rabochikh, ob'edinyaites'!* (Workers' wives, unite!), USA (leaflet).

1916 *Obshchestvo i materinstvo* (Society and Maternity), St. Petersburg. *Komu nuzhna voina?* (Who needs the war?), Berne.

1917 *Rabotnitsy i uchreditel'noye sobraniye* (Working women and the Constituent Assembly).

1918 *Rabotnitsa za god revolyutsii* (The working woman in the year since the revolution), Moscow. *Novaya moral' i rabochii klass* (The new morality and the working class), Moscow. *Mezhdunarodnoye sotsialisticheskiye soveshchaniya rabotnits* (The international socialist conference of working women), Moscow.

1919 *Kar boryutsya rabotnitsy za svoi prava* (Women workers struggle for their rights), Moscow. English translation by Celia Britton, Bristol, 1971. *Sem'ya i kommunisticheskoye gosudarstvo* (The family and the communist state), Moscow and Petrograd. *Rabotnitsa, krest'yanka i krasnyi front* (The working woman, the peasant woman, and the Red Front), Moscow. *Bud' stoikom boitsom* (Be a firm fighter). *Ne bud' dezertirom* (Don't be a deserter), Kiev.

1920 *K istorii dvizheniya rabotnits Rossii* (Toward a history of the working women's movement in Russia), Khar'kov. *Mezhdunarodnyi den' rabotnits* (International women's day), Moscow. English translation by Alix Holt, London, 1972. *Kak i dlya chego sozvan byl l vserossiiskii s'ezd rabotnits* (How and why the First All-Russian Congress of Working Women was called), Khar'kov.

1921   *Polozheniye zhenshchiny v svyazi s evolyutsiei khozyaistva* (The position of women in the evolution of the economy). *Rabotnitsa i krest'yanka v Sovetskoi Rossii* (The working woman and the peasant woman in Soviet Russia), Petrograd. *Prostitutsiya i mery bor'by s nei* (Prostitution and ways of fighting it), Moscow. *Iz moei zhizni i raboty* (From my life and work), Odessa. *Rabochaya oppozitsiya* (The workers' opposition). Unpublished in Russian. Translated into English, London, 1921 and 1962.

1922   *Skoro—ili cherez 48 let* (Soon—In 48 years' time), Omsk.

1923   *Lyubov' pchel trudovykh* (Love of worker bees), Petrograd. Translated into English as *Free Love*, London, 1932. New translation by Cathy Porter under original title, London, 1977. *Zhenshchina na perelome: psikhologicheskiye etudy* (Women on the threshold of change: psychological studies), Moscow and Petrograd. Published under Kollontai's maiden name, Domontovich. *Trud zhenshchin v evolyutsii khozyaistva* (The labor of women in the evolution of the economy).

1926   *Autobiography.* Unpublished in Russian. English translation as *Autobiography of a Sexually Emancipated Woman*, London, 1972.

1927   *Bol'shaya lyubov'* (A great love). English translation, New York, 1929.

1972   *Izbrannye stat'i i rechi* (Selected articles and speeches), Moscow.

ARTICLES

(English translations only are given for titles of Russian articles)

1898   "Dobrolyubov's views on the fundamentals of education," in *Obrazovaniye*, nos. 9–11.

1900   "Die Arbeiterfrage in Finnland," in *Soziale Praxis, Zentralblatt für sozial Politik*, no. 9.

1901   "Industry and trade of the Grand Duchy of Finland," in *Nauchnoye obozreniye*, no. 7 (July).

1902   "The Land Question in Finland," in *Nauchnoye Obozreniye*, nos. 2–4. "The housing of the Finnish workers," in *Russkoye Bogatstvo*, no. 7, pp. 126–44. "Raftsmen in Finland," in *Russkoye Bogatstvo*, no. 9. "Socialism in Finland," in *Zarya*, no. 4.

1904   "Arbeiterbewegung in Finnland unter der russischen Regierung," in *Die neue Zeit*, no. 24. "Basic agrarian tendencies," in *Pravda*, no. 11.

1905   "The role of feminists and proletarian women in the women's emancipation movement," in *Severo-zapadnyi Golos*, no. 33 (22.i.1906). "The problem of morality from the positive point of view," in *Obrazovaniye*, nos. 10–11.

1906   "Ethics and social democracy," in *Obrazovaniye*, no. 2. "The results of the Mannheim congress," in *Sovremennyi Mir* (November). "Who are the social democrats and what do they want?" in *Rabochii yEzhegodnik* (St. Petersburg). "The workers' movement in Finland," in *Rabochii yEzhegodnik.*

1907   "Finland at the ballot box," in *Russkaya Zhizn'* (2 March). "The election campaign in Finland," in *Otgoloski*, no. 3, pp. 46–61. "The new Finnish parliament," in *Obrazovaniye*, nos. 4–7. "Two Tendencies," in *Obrazovaniye*, no. 10.

1908   "What is done in Russia to protect the labor of women textile workers?" in *Fabrichnyi Stanok*, nos. 1–2. "The woman worker in contemporary society," paper at the All-Russian Women's Congress, in *Trudy I vserossiiskogo zhenskogo s'ezda*, pp. 792–801.

1909   "About the organization of women workers in Russia," in *Golos sotsial demokrata,* nos. 10–11. "The woman worker at the first feminist congress in Russia," in *Golos Sotsial Demokrata,* no. 12 (under the name "A. Mikhailova").

1910   "Arbeiterbewegung in der Zeiten der Reaktion," in *Die neue Zeit,* no. 24. "Die ökonomische Lage der russischen Arbeiterinnen," in *Die Gleichheit,* nos. 24, 25, 26. "The results of the Second Women's Socialist Conference," in *Nasha zarya,* nos. 8–9. "The social movement in Finland," in *Obshchestvennoye dvizheniye v Rossii v nachale XX veka,* no. 4 (St. Petersburg). "The tasks of the congress on the struggle against prostitution," in *Vozrozhdeniye,* no. 5 (under the name "A. Mikhailova"). "Results of the congress on the struggle against prostitution," in *Sotsial-demokrat,* no. 14. "The Second International Women's Conference," in *Sotsial-demokrat,* no. 17. "The proletariat and the bourgeoisie in the struggle against prostitution," in *Pravda* (Vienna), no. 14. "The working women's movement in the West. The results of the Second International Socialist Women's Conference in Copenhagen," in *Zhizn',* no. 2. "The fate of humanity and the question of population," in *Zhizn'* (September).

1911   "Forms of organization of working women in the West," in *Delo Zhizni,* no. 1, pp. 79–88. "Women's day," in *Nasha Zarya,* no. 3, pp. 39–43. "The Equality of Women," in *Dresdner Volkszeitung,* 18.iii.1911. "On an old theme," in *Novaya zhizn',* pp. 174–95. Translated into English as "Love and the New Morality," Bristol, 1972. "Sexual morality and the social struggle," in *Novaya Zhizn',* no. 9, pp. 155–82. "The movement of housewives in France," in *Nasha Zarya,* nos. 9–10. "About our progress in Russia and the publication of the newspaper *Rabotnitsa,*" in *Die Gleichheit,* no. 19. "From the notes of an agitator abroad," in *Russkoye Bogatstvo,* no. 11 (signed "A.K.").

1912   "From the life of women textile workers in Belgium," in *Fabrichnaya Zhizn'* (February). "The international proletariat and war" (May Day speech in Stockholm), in *Socialdemokraten,* 2 May (also in *Izbrannye stat'i i rechi,* 1972). "The working women and the elections to the State Duma," in *Nevskii Golos,* 24 August. "A review of 'The work of the First All-Russian congress on the struggle with trade in women and its causes,'" in *Sovremennyi Mir* (July). "Two truths," in *Novaya Zhizn',* no. 8. "Women's right to the franchise in the Swedish parliament," in *Nasha Zarya,* no. 5. "Working women and the war," in *Luch,* 6 November. "New England. Correspondence from the West," in *Nasha Zarya,* nos. 11–12. "The union for the defense of maternity and the reform of sexual morality," in *Novaya Zhizn',* no. 11. "Women's day in Germany and Austria. A letter from Berlin," in *Delo Zhizni,* no. 4, pp. 239–54.

1913   "Women's day," in *Pravda,* 17 February. "A great fighter for truth and the freedom of women" (about August Bebel), in *Pravda,* 17 February (also in *Izbrannye stat'i i rechi,* 1972, pp. 113–24). "The women workers' movement," in *Nasha Zarya,* no. 2. "The new woman," in *Sovremennyi Mir,* no. 9 (English translation in *Autobiography of a Sexually Emancipated Woman,* London, 1972). "The defense of maternity," in *Nasha Zarya,* no. 9. "The work of women deputies in the Finnish parliament," in *Severnaya Rabochaya Gazeta,* no. 10. "The organization of working women and woman's right to freedom," in *Luch,* no. 127. "On the forthcoming conference of organized working women in Vienna," in *Novaya Rabochaya Gazeta,* 8 December.

1914   "Types and forms of maternity insurance," in *Novaya Zhizn',* no. 2. "Auch Russland wird einen Frauentag haben," in *Die Gleichheit,* no. 12. "Die Bedeutung des sozial-demokratischen Frauentags in Russland," in *Die Gleichheit,* no. 16.

"Tasks of the 'working woman's leaflet,' " in *Listok Rabotnitsy*, no. 1, 25 May. "The international women's conference," in *Nasha Rabochaya Gazeta*, 30 May. "The international tasks of Woman's Day," in *Severnaya Rabochaya Gazeta*. "The cross of motherhood," in *Sovremennyi Mir*, no. 11. "The war and our immediate tasks" (in Swedish), in *Forsvarsnihilisten*, no. 11. "The defense of the fatherland or international solidarity" (in Swedish), in *Stormklockan*, no. 51. "Staatliche Mutterschaftsversicherung," in *Die neue Zeit*, no. 33. "To all socialist women in all lands" (in Swedish), in *Stormklockan*, 15 November.

1915   "The Copenhagen conference," in *Nashe Slovo*, 29 January, 2 February. "What is to be done? A reply to socialists," in *Nashe Slovo*, 19 February. "The women's socialist international and the war," in *Nashe Slovo*, 7 March. "The international socialist women's conference in Berne," in *Nashe Slovo*, 7–8 April. "Bern and The Hague" (in Swedish), in *Socialdemokraten*, 29 May. "The Third International," in *American Socialist*, 23 October. "The consequences of the world war from the social, political, and economic point of view" (in Swedish), in *Klassenkampfen*, 19 November. "Why was the German proletariat silent during the July days?" in *Kommunist*, nos. 1–2 (September).

1916   "Do internationalists want a split?" in *International Socialist Review*, no. 7, January. "The attitude of the Russian socialists," in *New Review*, March.

1917   "At sea in the blockade zone" (in Swedish), in *Lordagskvelden*, nos. 9–11. "Who needs the Tsar and can we manage without him?" in *Letopis'*, January (also in *Izbrannye stat'i i rechi*, 1972). "The working women and the Constituent Assembly," in *Pravda*, 21 March. "Our tasks," in *Rabotnitsa*, nos. 1–2. "A serious gap," in *Pravda*, 5 May. "Where does revolutionary defensism lead?" in *Pravda*, no. 24, 5 April (also in *Izbrannye stat'i i rechi*, 1972, pp. 208–10). "Our memorial to the fighters for freedom," in *Pravda*, 6 March (also in *Izbrannye stat'i i rechi*, 1972, pp. 205–7). "In the front line of fire," in *Pravda*, 7 and 9 May. "Working women and the regional dumas," in *Pravda*, 26 March. "La vie politique et sociale: Amérique," in *Demain*, no. 13, Geneva, May, pp. 34–9. "La vie politique et sociale: Suede," in *Demain*, no. 13, May, pp. 46–8. "Speech at the First All-Russian Congress of Soviets of Workers' and Soldiers' Deputies on the Finnish question," in *Pervyi s'ezd rabochikh i soldatskikh deputatov*, vol. II, Moscow and Leningrad, 1931 (also in *Izbrannye stat'i i rechi*, 1972, pp. 217–22). "Speech at the Ninth Congress of the Finnish Social Democratic Party" (in Finnish), in *Suomen sosialdemokraattisen puolueen yhdeksännen puoluekokousen pöytäkirja* Helsinki 15–18 June, Turku, 1918; also in *Izbrannye stat'i i rechi*, 1972, pp. 214–16. "Women's battalions," in *Rabotnitsa*, no. 6. "Demonstration of soldiers' wives," in *Pravda*, 12 April. "Extraordinary congress of the Finnish Social Democratic Party," in *Pravda*, 13 June. "The first steps toward calling a conference of working women," in *Rabochii Put'*, 10 October. "The establishment of administrative tyranny," in *Rabochii Put'*, no. 4, 7 September. "When will the war end?" (written in September), in *Izbrannye stat'i i rechi*, 1972, pp. 225–7. "The bankruptcy of the slogan 'Civil Peace,' " in *Rabochii Put'*, no. 24, 30 September. "How should working women prepare for the Constituent Assembly?" in *Rabochii Put'*, 14 October. "The conference of working women and the party regions," in *Rabochii Put'*, 21 October. "The practical tasks of the conference of working women," in *Rabochii Put'*, 24 October. "Durch Bürgerkrieg zur Gleichberechtigung der Frauen," in *Jugend International*, no. 8. "The first conference of working women," in *Rabochii Put'*, 26 October. "The current tasks of the conference of working women," in *Pravda*, 24 October.

1918   "Why the Bolsheviks must win" (in Swedish), in *Stormklockan*, 1 May. "The cross of maternity and the Soviet republic," in *Pravda*, 1 October. "The town of the first rebels," in *Pravda*, 1 October. "The tasks and rights of working women in Soviet Russia," in *Izvestia*, 26 October. "Old age is not a cross but a deserved rest," in *Vechernye izvestiya*, 30 October (also in *Izbrannye stat'i i rechi*, 1972, pp. 243–5). "On the protection of maternity and childhood. Decision of the People's Commissariat of Social Welfare," in *Izvestia*, 19 November. "It is time to make an end of the 'black nests,' " in *Pravda*, 29 December (also in *Izbrannye stat'i i rechi*, 1972, pp. 248–9). "The priests are still at work," in *Pravda*, 29 December. "The first All-Russian Conference of Working Women," in *Pravda*, 5 October. "A letter to the working women of Red Petrograd" (written in November), in *Izbrannye stat'i i rechi*, 1972. "Working women on the labor front," in *Kommunar*, no. 19, 30 October. "Among the backward," in *Kommunar*, no. 21, 31 October.

1919 "Karl Liebknecht and Rosa Luxemburg—fighters, heroes, and martyrs," in *Rabochii Mir*, nos. 2–3. "Who have the working women lost?", in *Kommunar*, 21 March (also in *Izbrannye stat'i i rechi*, 1972, pp. 266–7). "Working women and soviets," in *Kommunar*, 2 April. "What are we fighting for?" in *Izvestiya Khar'kovskogo soveta i gubernskogo ispolnitel'nogo komiteta sovetov rabochikh, krest'yanskikh i krasnoarmeiskikh deputatov*, 7 May (also in *Izbrannye stat'i i rechi*, 1972, pp. 274–6). "The struggle with Tsar Hunger," in ibid., 13 May (also in *Izbrannye stat'i i rechi*, 1972, pp. 277–9). "Breakthrough in the countryside," in *Izvestia*, 23 May. "Whose will the golden harvest be?" in *Krasnyi Ofitser*, no. 3, Kiev, July (also in *Izbrannye stat'i i rechi*, 1972, pp. 280–2). "The activity of the Russian People's Commissariat of Social Welfare," in *Gosudarstvennoye obespecheniye*, no. 10, 1959. "Speech at the Second All-Russian Congress of RKSM," in *Izbrannye stat'i i rechi*, 1972, pp. 295–300.

1920 "The day of working women is a day of victory and struggle," in *Kommunar*, no. 50. "Our festival and our tasks," in *Pravda*, 8 March. "The working woman and the economic dislocation," in *Trudovaya Zhizn'*, 18 June. "The working woman and the Red Army," in *Ranenyi Krasnoarmeets*, no. 1, 5 July. "The First International Conference of Communist Women," in *Kommunistka*, nos. 1–2, June-July (also in *Izbrannye stat'i i rechi*, pp. 305–9). "Labor conscription and the protection of female labor," in *Kommunistka*, nos. 1–2. "Yet another victory for the communist women," in *Izvestiya*, 26 September. "Klara Zetkin," in *Pravda*, 26 September. "How we called the first All-Russian Congress of Working and Peasant Women," in *Kommunistka*, no. 2. "The family and communism," in *Kommunistka*, no. 2. Translated into English as "Communism and the Family," London, 1920 and 1971. "How and why the First All-Russian Congress of Working Women was called," in *Pervyi vserossiiskii s'ezd rabotnits 1918 i ego rezolyutsii*, Khar'kov. "Class war and the working women," in *Kommunistka*, no. 5, October. "The 'All-Russian Conference of Communist Women,' " in *Izvestiya*, 28 November. "The tasks of the departments for work among women," in *Kommunistka*, no. 5 (also in *Izbrannye stat'i i rechi*, 1972, pp. 310–15). "The labor republic and prostitution," in *Kommunistka*, no. 6.

1921 "The conference of communist women organizers of women of the East," in *Pravda*, 10 April. "International solidarity and the proletarian woman of today," in *The Workers' Dreadnought*, London, 30 April. "The last slave, woman," in *Kommunistka*, nos. 8–9. "The cross of maternity," in *Kommunistka*, nos. 8–9. "Report on the activity of SSRCP on work among women. For the All-Russian Congress of Women's Departments," in *Kommunistka*, nos. 8–9. "Trade unions and the working woman," in *Pravda*, 22 May. "Production and everyday life," in *Kommunistka*, nos. 10–11. "Autobiographical essay," in *Proletarskaya Revolyut-*

siya, no. 3. "Theses on communist morality in the sphere of marriage relations," in *Kommunistka*, nos. 12–13. "The fight against prostitution," in *The Workers' Dreadnought*, 27 August and 24 September. "Komintern and the second international conference of communist women," in *Pravda*, 13 November. "The third international and the working woman," in *Pravda*, 13 November.

1922 "The first letter. What a communist should be like," in *Molodaya Gvardiya*, nos. 1–2. "International day of working women," in *Kommunistka*, no. 2. "The creative in the work of K. N. Samoilova," in *Kommunistka*, nos. 3–5. "The second letter. Morality as a form of class rule and class struggle," in *Molodaya Gvardiya*, nos. 6–7. "The October revolution and the masses," in *Molodaya Gvardiya*, nos. 6–7.

1923 "The third letter. About the 'dragon' and the 'white bird', " in *Molodaya Gvardiya*, no. 2. "Make way for the Winged Eros," in *Molodaya Gvardiya*, no. 3. "Not 'principle', but 'method', " in *Pravda*, 20 March. "Norway and our trade balance," in *Izvestia*, 16 November. "The work of the women's departments in the new conditions," in *Pravda*, 13 April.

1926 "Marriage, women, and alimony," in *Ekran*, 6 November. "A common pot or individual alimony," in *Brak i sem'ya. Sbornik stat'ei i materialov po semeinomu pravu* (Moscow: Molodaya Gvardiya). "About the new law on the family and marriage," in *Natisk*, 8 March. "Marriage and everyday life," in *Rabochii Sud*, no. 5. "A mandate to the soviet from the joiners," in *Krasnyi Derevoobdelochnik*, no. 3. "In Kerensky's prison," in *Katorga i Ssylka*, no. 7 (36). "Decree on the wall," in *Krasnaya Panorama*, no. 45. "The first benefit from social welfare," in *Krasnaya Niva*, no. 45.

1927 "Revolutionary Mexico," in *Vechemaya Moskva*, 22 September, and *Izbrannye stat'i i rechi*, 1972, pp. 357–60. "What October gave the women of the West," in *Ogonëk*, no. 41, 9 October. "The opposition and the party rank and file," in *Pravda*, 30 October. "The great builder," in *Za Kul'turnuyu Revolyutsiya*, November. "Women fighters in the days of Great October," in *Zhenskii Zhurnal*, no. 11.

1930 "In memory of V. F. Komissarzhevskaya," in *Krasnaya Nov'*, no. 2.

1933 "Shock worker of the proletarian revolution" (about Krupskaya), in *Pravda*, 22–23 April.

1937 "Women in 1917," in *Rabotnitsa*, no. 31.

1945 "From my memories," in *Oktyabr'*, no. 9.

1946 "Lenin thought about the big things, but did not forget about the small," in *Vospominaniya o Vladimire Il'iche Lenine*, Moscow, 1969. "Lenin and working women in 1917," in *Rabotnitsa*, no. 1.

1947 "To the younger generation. Reminiscences," in *Rabotnitsa*, nos. 4–5.

1948 "Soviet woman—citizeness with equal rights," in *Sovetskaya zhenshchina*, no. 5, September. "The thirtieth anniversary of the All-Russian Congress of Working and Peasant Women," in *Rabotnitsa*, no. 12, December.

1949 "In memory of Nadezhda Konstantinovna Krupskaya" (written in February), in *Izbrannye stat'i i rechi*, 1972.

1962 "The American diaries 1915–1916," in *Istoricheskii arkhiv*, no. 1.

1970 "American diaries," in *Inostrannaya Literatura*, nos. 1–2.

SELECTED BIBLIOGRAPHY

BOOKS AND ARTICLES CONSULTED, IN ENGLISH

Evelyn Anderson, *Hammer or Anvil*, Gollancz, London 1945

Katharine Anthony, "Alexandra Kollontay," *North American Review*, September 1930

David E. Apter, *Ideology and Discontent*, Free Press, New York 1964

Dorothy Atkinson, Alexander Dallin and Gail Warshofsy Lapidus (eds), *Women in Russia*, Harvester Press, Brighton 1978

Paul M. Avrich, *Kronstadt 1921*, Princeton University Press, Princeton 1970

Angelica Balabanova, *Impressions of Lenin*, trans. Isotta Cesari, University of Michigan Press, Ann Arbor 1964

——, *My Life as a Rebel*, Harper, New York 1938

Alexander Barmin, *Memoirs of a Soviet Diplomat*, trans. Gerard Hopkins, Lovat Dickson, London 1938

Bessie Beatty, *The Red Heart of Russia*, Century Co., New York 1918

August Bebel, *Woman Under Socialism*, trans. Daniel de Leon, Schocken Books, New York 1975

Eduard Bernstein, *Evolutionary Socialism: A Criticism and an Affirmation*, Independent Labour Party Press, London 1909

Charles Bettelheim, *Class Struggles in the USSR: First Period, 1917–23*, trans. Brian Pearce, Monthly Review Press, New York 1976

Jerome Blum, *Lord and Peasant in Russia. The Ninth to the Nineteenth Century*, Princeton University Press, Princeton 1961

Anne Bobroff, "The Bolsheviks and Working Women 1905–20," *Soviet Studies*, October 1974

F. Borkenau, *European Communism*, Faber, London 1953

——, *The Communist International*, Faber, London 1938

Ekaterina Breshko-Breshkovskaya, *Little Grandmother of the Revolution*, ed. Alice Stone Blackwell, Little, Brown & Co., Boston 1930

——, *Hidden Springs of the Revolution*, Stanford University Press, London 1931

Maurice Brinton, *The Bolsheviks and Workers' Control 1917–1921. The State and Counter-Revolution*, Solidarity, London 1970

Robert Paul Browder and Alexander F. Kerensky (eds), *The Russian Provisional Government, 1917*, 3 vols, Stanford University Press, Stanford 1961

Louise Bryant, *Mirrors of Moscow*, Thomas Seltzer, New York 1923

——, *Six Red Months in Russia*, Doran, New York 1918

James Bunyan and H. H. Fisher (eds), *The Bolshevik Revolution, 1917–1918*, Stanford University Press, Stanford 1934

W. Carlgren, *Swedish Foreign Policy During the Second World War*, trans. A. Spencer, E. Benn, London 1977

Joel Carmichael, *Trotsky. An Appreciation of His Life,* Hodder & Stoughton, London 1975

E. H. Carr, *The Bolshevik Revolution 1917–23,* 3 vols, Pelican Books, London 1977
———, *The Interregnum 1923–4,* Pelican Books, London 1954
———, *Socialism in One Country, 1924–6,* 3 vols, Pelican Books, London 1958–64

William Henry Chamberlin, *The Russian Revolution 1917–21,* 2 vols, Macmillan, London 1935

Nikolai Chernyshevsky, *What Is To Be Done?,* Pathfinder Press, New York 1961

Barbara Clements, "Emancipation Through Communism: The Ideology of A. M. Kollontai," *Slavic Review,* June 1973

Stephen F. Cohen, *Bukharin and the Bolshevik Revolution,* Knopf, New York 1975

Robert Conquest, *The Great Terror,* Macmillan, New York 1968

Richard Crossman (ed), *The God That Failed,* Bantam Books, New York 1964

Robert V. Daniels, *The Conscience of the Revolution,* Harvard University Press, Cambridge, Mass., 1960
———, *A Documentary History of Communism,* Random House, New York 1960
———, *Red October,* Scribners, New York 1967
———, *The Stalin Revolution,* D. C. Heath & Co., Boston 1965

Isaac Deutscher, *The Prophet Armed: Trotsky, 1879–1921,* Vintage, New York 1954
———, *The Prophet Unarmed: Trotsky, 1921–9,* Vintage, New York 1959
———, *Soviet Trade Unions,* Royal Institute of International Affairs, London 1956
———, *Stalin. A Political Biography,* Oxford University Press, London 1949

Norton T. Dodge, *Women in the Soviet Economy,* Baltimore University Press, Baltimore 1966

Theodore Draper, *The Roots of American Communism,* Viking, New York 1957

Raya Dunaevskaya, *Marxism and Freedom,* Bookman Assocs, New York 1964

Walter Duranty, *I Write As I Please,* Simon and Schuster, New York 1935

Linda Edmondson, "Russian Feminists and the First All-Russian Congress of Women," *Russian History/Histoire Russe,* no. 3, part 2, University of Pittsburgh 1976

Ilya Ehrenburg, *People and Life,* 6 vols, McGibbon Kee, London 1961–6

Barbara Alpern Engel and Clifford N. Rosenthal (eds and trans), *Five Sisters, Women Against the Tsar,* Knopf, New York 1975

Friedrich Engels, *The Origin of the Family, Private Property and the State,* Pathfinder Press, New York 1972

Richard Evans, *The Feminists: Women's Emancipation Movements in Europe, America and Australasia 1840–1920,* Barnes and Noble, New York 1977

Merle Fainsod, *How Russia is Ruled,* 2nd edn, Harvard University Press, Cambridge, Mass. 1963
———, *International Socialism and the World War,* Octagon Books, New York 1973

Beatrice Farnsworth, "Bolshevism, the Woman Question, and Aleksandra Kollontai," *American Historical Review,* 81, no. 2, 1976

Marc Ferro, *The Russian Revolution of February 1917,* trans. J. L. Richards, Prentice Hall, Engelwood Cliffs 1972

Ruth Fischer, *Stalin and German Communism,* Harvard University Press, Cambridge, Mass. 1948

Sheila Fitzpatrick, *The Commissar of Enlightenment. Soviet Organisation of Education and the Arts under Lunacharsky,* Cambridge University Press, London 1970

Michael Futrell, *Northern Underground,* Faber, London 1963

Peter Gay, *The Dilemma of Democratic Socialism: Eduard Bernstein's Challenge to Marx,* Collier, New York 1962

Kent H. Geiger, *The Family in Soviet Russia,* Harvard University Press, Cambridge, Mass. 1968

Emma Goldman, *Living My Life,* 2 vols, Knopf, New York 1941

———, *My Further Disillusionment in Russia,* Doubleday, New York 1924

Gunnar Hagglof, *Diplomat,* Bodley Head, London 1971

Ruth Hall, *Marie Stopes, A Biography,* Virago, London 1978

Fanina Halle, *Women in Soviet Russia,* London 1934

———, *Women in the Soviet East,* New York 1938

Marguerite Harrison, *Marooned in Moscow,* Doran, New York 1921

Kaarè Hauge, "Alexandra Mikhailovna Kollontai: The Scandinavian Period 1922–45," Ph.D thesis, University of Minnesota 1971

George Haupt and Jean-Jacques Marie, *Makers of the Russian Revolution,* trans. D. M. Bellos, Gollancz, London 1974

Carol Eubanks Hayden, "The Zhenotdel and the Bolshevik Party," *Russian History/Histoire Russe,* no. 3, part 2, 1976

Alex Inkeles, *Social Change in Soviet Russia,* Harvard University Press, Cambridge, Mass. 1968

Max Jacobson, *The Diplomacy of the Winter War,* Harvard University Press, Cambridge, Mass. 1961

John L. H. Keep, *The Rise of Social Democracy in Russia,* Clarendon Press, Oxford 1963

Susan Kingsbury and Mildred Fairchild, *Factory, Family and Women in the Soviet Union,* New York 1935

Jeane J. Kirkpatrick, *Political Woman,* New York 1974

Alexandra Kollontai, *for her works in English see separate bibliography*

Nadezhda Krupskaya, *Memories of Lenin,* Panther Books, London 1970

Robert Lane, *Political Life,* The Free Press, University of Glencoe, Illinois 1959

Gail Warshofsky Lapidus, *Women in Soviet Society. Equality, Development and Social Change,* University of California Press, Berkeley 1978

V. I. Lenin, *The Emancipation of Women,* International Publishers, New York 1966

George Lichtheim, *Marxism: An Historical and Critical Study,* 2nd edn, Praeger, New York 1965

Marcel Liebman, *The Russian Revolution,* trans. Arnold J. Pomerans, Jonathan Cape, London 1970

Rosa Luxemburg, *Selected Political Writings,* ed. Dick Howard, Monthly Review Press, New York 1971

Angus McClaren, *Birth Control in Nineteenth-Century England,* Croom Helm, London 1978

Vera and David Mace, *The Soviet Family,* Garden City, New York 1964

Robert H. McNeal, *Bridge of the Revolution: Krupskaya and Lenin,* University of Michigan Press, Ann Arbor 1972

————, "Women in the Russian Radical Movement," *Journal of Social History,* University of California Press, Berkeley & Los Angeles, Winter 1971–2

Ivan Maisky, *Journey into the Past,* Hutchinson, London 1962

————, *Memoirs of a Soviet Ambassador,* Hutchinson, London 1967

Anton S. Makarenko, *The Collective Family: A Handbook for Russian Parents,* trans. Robert Daglish, New York 1967

William Mandel, *Soviet Women,* Pathfinder Press, New York 1975

Herbert Marcuse, *Eros and Civilisation,* Sphere Books, London 1969

————, *Soviet Marxism,* Routledge & Kegan Paul, London 1958

Gregory Massell, *The Surrogate Proletariat: Moslem Women and Revolutionary Strategies in Soviet Central Asia, 1919–29,* Princeton University Press, Princeton 1974

Mervyn Matthews, *Class and Society in Soviet Russia,* Allen Lane, London 1972

W. R. Mead, *Finland,* Faber, London 1968

Juliet Mitchell and Ann Oakley (eds) *The Rights and Wrongs of Women,* Penguin Books, London 1976

Barrington Moore, *Soviet Politics: The Dilemma of Power,* Harvard University Press, Cambridge, Mass. 1950

Peter Nettl, *Rosa Luxemburg,* 2nd edn, Oxford University Press, Oxford 1969

————, *The Soviet Achievement,* Thames and Hudson, London 1967

Alec Nove, *An Economic History of the USSR,* Penguin Books, London 1976

Richard O'Connor and Dale L. Walker, *The Lost Revolutionary: A Biography of John Reed,* Harcourt, Brace, New York 1967

Oyarzabal de Palencia, *Alexandra Kollontay,* Longmans, London 1947

Bernard Pares, *My Russian Memoirs,* Jonathan Cape, London 1931

Margaret Pertsoff, "Lady in Red: A Study of the Early Career of Alexandra Mikhailovna Kollontai," Ph.D thesis, University of Virginia, Charlottesville, Virginia 1968

Vladimir M. and Evodokia Petrov, *Empire of Fear,* Praeger, New York 1956

Morgan Phillips Price, *My Reminiscences of the Russian Revolution,* Allen and Unwin, London 1921

Arthur Ransome, *Russia in 1919,* Huebsch, New York 1919

John Reed, *Ten Days That Shook the World,* Random House, New York 1960

Wilhelm Reich, *The Sexual Revolution,* Vision Press, London 1969

Bernhard Reichenbach, "Moscow 1921," *Survey,* Paris October 1964

T. H. Rigby, *Communist Party Membership in the USSR, 1917–67,* Princeton University Press, Princeton 1968

Alfred Rosmer, *Lenin's Moscow,* trans. Ian Birchall, Pluto Press, London 1971

Sheila Rowbotham, "Alexandra Kollontai: Women's Liberation and Revolutionary Love," *The Spokesman,* London June and July 1970

————, *Hidden From History,* Pluto Press, London 1974

————, *Women, Resistance and Revolution,* Penguin Books, London 1974

Dora Russell, *The Tamarisk Tree: My Quest For Liberty and Love,* Virago, London 1977

Leonard Schapiro, *The Communist Party of the Soviet Union,* Eyre & Spottiswood, London 1960.

————, *The Origin of the Communist Autocracy,* LSE Publications, London 1955

Rudolph Schlesinger, *Changing Attitudes in Soviet Russia: The Family in the USSR*, London 1949

C. E. Schorske, *German Social Democracy 1905–1917*, University of California Press, Berkeley 1965

Solomon Schwartz, *The Russian Revolution of 1905*, University of Chicago Press, Chicago 1967

Nina Selivanova, *Russia's Women*, Dutton, New York 1923

Victor Serge, *Memoirs of a Revolutionary*, trans. Peter Sedgwick, Oxford University Press, Oxford 1963

——— and Natalia Sedova-Trotsky, *The Life and Death of Leon Trotsky*, trans. Arthur Pomerans, Basic Books, New York 1975

Jessica Smith, *Women in Soviet Russia*, Vanguard, New York 1928

Pitirim Sorokin, *Leaves From a Russian Diary*, Beacon Press, Boston 1950

Bette D. Stavrakis, "Women and the Communist Party in the Soviet Union, 1918–35," Ph.D thesis, Western Reserve University, Cleveland, Ohio 1961

Richard M. Stites, "M. L. Mikhailov and the Emergence of the Woman Question in Russia," *Canadian Slavic Studies*, Loyola College Montreal Summer 1969

———, "Women's Liberation Movements in Russia, 1900–1930," *Canadian-American Slavic Studies*, Boston, Mass. Winter 1973

———, *The Women's Liberation Movement in Russia: Feminism, Nihilism and Bolshevism 1860–1930*, Princeton University Press, Princeton 1977

N. N. Sukhanov, *The Russian Revolution of 1917* (abridged), ed. and trans. Joel Carmichael, Oxford University Press, Oxford 1955

Evelyne Sullerot, *Women, Society and Change*, London 1971

Werner Thönnessen, *The Emancipation of Women: The Rise and Decline of the Women's Movement in German Social Democracy, 1863–1933*, trans. Joris de Bres, Pluto Press, London 1973

Leon Trotsky, *The History of the Russian Revolution*, 3 vols, trans. Max Eastman, Simon & Schuster, New York 1932

———, *Problems of Life*, trans. Z. Vengerova, Methuen & Co., London 1924

———, *The Revolution Betrayed*, trans. Max Eastman, Doubleday, New York 1937

———, *Stalin: An Appraisal*, ed. and trans. Charles Malamuth, Harper, New York 1941

———, *Stalin's School of Falsification*, trans. J. Wright, Pioneer, London 1937

———, *Women and the Family*, Pathfinder, New York 1970

Robert Tucker, *Stalin as a Revolutionary, 1879–1929*, Pall Mall Press, London & Dunmow 1973

Ariadne Tyrkova-Williams, *From Liberty to Brest-Litovsk*, Macmillan, London 1919

Adam Ulam, *Lenin and the Bolsheviks*, Fontana Books, London 1977

S. V. Utechin, *Russian Political Thought: A Concise History*, Praeger, New York 1964

Albert Rhys Williams, *Journey Into Revolution, Petrograd 1917–1918*, Quadrangle Books, Chicago 1969

———, *Lenin, The Man and His Work*, Scott and Seltzer, New York 1919

———, *Through the Revolution*, Boni and Liveright, New York 1921

Bertram Wolfe, "Lenin and Inessa Armand," *Slavic Review*, New York, USA March 1963

———, *Three Who Made a Revolution*, Thames & Hudson, London 1956

Eli Zaretsky, *Capitalism, The Family and Personal Life,* Pluto Press, London 1976

Klara Zetkin, *Reminiscences of Lenin,* Modern Books, London 1929

BOOKS AND ARTICLES CONSULTED, IN RUSSIAN AND OTHER FOREIGN LANGUAGES

Akademia nauk SSSR, Institut istorii (Academy of Sciences of the USSR, Institute of History), "Khronika sobytii" ("Chronicle of Events"), in *Velikaya oktyabrskaya sotsialisticheskaya revolyutsia (The Great October Revolution),* 5 vols, Moscow 1957

———, *Revolyutsionnoe dvizhenie v Rossii v sentyabre 1917 g. (The Revolutionary Movement in Russia in September 1917),* Moscow 1961

A. A. Andreev, *Professional'nye soyuzy v Rossii v 1921–1922 godu (Trade Unions in Russia 1921–1922),* Petrograd 1922

Inessa Armand, *Ocherednie zadachi po rabote sredi zhenschin. Doklad na Vserossiiskom soveschanii organizatorov otdelov po rabote sredi zhenschin 28 marta 1920 g. v Moskve. (Current Tasks of Women's Work. Report at the All-Russian Conference of Women's Department Organizers, March 28, 1920, in Moscow),* Moscow 1920

———, *Rabotnitsy v Internatsionale (Women Workers in The International),* Moscow 1920

A. Artyukhina (ed.), *Vsegda s vami: Sbornik posvyaschenny 50-letiu "Rabotnitsy" (Always with You: An Anthology Dedicated to the Fiftieth Anniversary of "Rabotnitsa"),* Moscow 1964

Kendall E. Bailes, "Alexandra Kollontai et la nouvelle morale" ("Alexandra Kollontai and the New Morality"), *Cahiers du monde russe et sovietique,* Paris, October–December 1965

Bez nikh my ne pobedili by: Vospominaniya zhenschin-uchastnits Oktyabrskoi revolyutsii, grazhdanskoi voiny i sotsialisticheskogo stroitel'stva (Without Them We Would Not Have Been Victorious: Memoirs of Women Who Participated in the October Revolution, the Civil War and Socialist Construction), Moscow 1975

Vera Bilshai, *Reshenie zhenskogo voprosa v SSSR (The Resolution of the Woman Question in the USSR),* Moscow 1956

E. I. Bochkareva and S. Lyubimova, *Svetly put (A Bright Road),* Moscow 1967

Marcel Body, "Alexandra Kollontai," *Preuves,* Paris, April 1952

Bolshaya sovetskaya entsiklopedia (Great Soviet Encyclopaedia), 1st edn, Moscow 1928

Brak i byt: Sbornik materialov i statei (Marriage and Everyday Life: An Anthology of Documents and Articles), Molodaya Gvardia (Young Guard), Moscow 1926

Ya. Bronin, "K kharakteristike platformy rabochei oppozitsii" ("A characterization of the Workers' Opposition's Platform"), *Proletarskaya revolyutsia (Proletarian Revolution),* Leningrad, November 1929

P. Broué, *Le Parti bolchévique (The Bolshevik Party),* Paris 1963

Vadim Bystryanskii, *Kommunizm, brak i semya (Communism, Marriage and the Family),* Petrograd 1921

L. P. Chuiko, *Braki i razvody (Marriages and Divorces),* Moscow 1975

T. E. Chumakova, *Semya, moral', pravo (The Family, Morality and the Law),* Minsk 1974

Savva Dangulov, *Dvenadtsat' dorog na Egl (Twelve Roads to Egl),* Moscow 1970

E. Z. Danilova, *Sotsial'nye problemy truda zhenschiny-rabotnitsy (The Social Problems of the Woman Worker),* Moscow 1968

L. E. Darskii, *Formirovanie semi (The Formation of the Family)*, Moscow 1972

Deyateli SSSR i Oktyabrskoi revolyutsii: Entsiklopedicheskii slovar (Activists of the USSR and the October Revolution: An Encyclopaedic Dictionary), 3 parts, Granat, Moscow/Leningrad 1925–8. For biographies and autobiographies of many revolutionaries, including Alexandra Kollontai, Pavel Dybenko, Nadezhda Krupskaya, Konkordia Samoilova, Alexander Shlyapnikov.

Dokumenty vneshnei politiki SSSR (Documents on USSR Foreign Policy), 19 vols, Moscow 1960–74

A. Ermanskii, "Vserossisskii zhenskii sezd" ("All-Russian Women's Congress"), *Sovremenny Mir (Contemporary World)*, St. Petersburg, January 1909

E. Fortunato, "Nash drug Aleksandra Kollontai" ("Our Friend Alexandra Kollontai"), *Neva*, Leningrad 1959, no. 3

Jean Fréville, *Une Grande figure de la révolution russe: Inessa Armand (A Great Figure of the Russian Revolution: Inessa Armand)*, Paris 1957

A. Gilyarova (ed.), *Zhenschiny goroda Lenina (Women of Lenin's Town)*, Moscow 1963

Z. P. Igumnova, *Zhenschiny Moskvy v gody grazhdanskoi voiny (Women of Moscow During the Civil War)*, Moscow 1958

Anna Itkina, *Revolyutsioner, Tribun, Diplomat: Stranitsy zhizni Aleksandry Mikhailovnoi Kollontai (Revolutionary, Tribune, Diplomat: Pages From the Life of Alexandra Mikhailovna Kollontai)*, 2nd edn, Moscow 1970

N. F. Izmailov and A. G. Pukhov, *Tsentrobalt (Central Baltic Fleet Committee)*, Moscow 1963

Gustav Johansson, *Revolutionens ambassador: Alexandra Kollontays liv och gärning, åren 1872–1917 (Ambassador of the Revolution: Alexandra Kollontai's Life and Work Between 1872 and 1917)*, Stockholm 1945

S. M. Kalmanson (ed.), *Polovoi vopros (The Sexual Question)*, Moscow 1924

S. I. Kaplun, *Sovremennyi problemy zhenskogo truda i byta (Current Problems of Women's Work and Everyday Life)*, Moscow 1924

N. D. Karpetskaya, "Vovlechenie trudyaschikh zhenschin Petrograda v revolyutsionnoe dvizhenie, mart-yul' 1917 g." ("Involving Women of Petrograd in the Revolutionary Movement, March to July 1917"), *Vestnik Leningradskogo Universiteta (Leningrad University Chronicle)*, 1966, no. 8, pp. 45–53

V. Kayurov, "Na zare revolyutsii" ("At the Dawn of the Revolution"), *Proletarskaya revolyutsia (Proletarian Revolution)*, Moscow 1923, no. 1

A. G. Kharchev, *Brak i semya v SSSR (Marriage and the Family in the USSR)*, Moscow 1964

A. V. Krasnikova, *Na zare sovetskoi vlasti (At the Dawn of Soviet Power)*, Leningrad 1963

L. Kritzman, *Geroicheskii period velikoi russkoi revolyutsii (The Heroic Period of the Great Russian Revolution)*, Moscow, n.d.

Nadezhda Krupskaya, "Inessa Armand", *Kommunistka*, Moscow, October 1920

———, *O rabote sredi zhenschin (Concerning Work with Women)*, Moscow 1926

———, *Pamyati Inessy Armanda (Memories of Inessa Armand)*, Moscow 1926

———, *Sobranie sochinenii (Collected Works)*, Moscow/Leningrad, n.d.

Praskovia Kudelli (ed.), *Rabotnitsa v 1905 g. v S. Peterburge (The Working Woman in 1905 in St. Petersburg)*, Leningrad 1926

V. V. Kuzin, *Borba kommunisticheskoi partii s anarkho-sindi-kalisticheskim uklonom v*

1920–1922 gg. (The Communist Party's Struggle with the Anarcho-Syndicalist Tendency of 1920–1922), Moscow 1958

R. Labry, *Une Législation communiste: recueil des lois, decrets, arrêtés principaux du gouvernement bolchéviste (Communist Legislation: A Review of the Principal Laws, Decrees and Arrests of the Bolshevik Government)*, Paris 1920

E. Lavrov, "Polovoi vopros i molodezh" ("The Sexual Question and Young People"), *Molodaya Gvardia (Young Guard)*, Moscow 1926, no. 2

Claude Lefort, *Éléments d'une critique de la bureaucratie (A Partial Criticism of the Bureaucracy)*, Geneva 1971

Henryk Lenczyc, "Alexandra Kollontai," *Cahiers du monde russe et sovietique*, Paris 1973, no. 14

Lenin, *Polnoe sobranie sochinenii (Full Collected Works)*, 5th edn, 56 vols, Moscow 1958–66

Leninskii sbornik (Selected Works of Lenin), 3rd edn, 35 vols, Moscow/Leningrad 1925

E. G. Lorentsson, "A. M. Kollontai v Shvetsii" ("A. M. Kollontai in Sweden"), *Novaya i noveishaya istoria (Recent and Most Recent History)*, Moscow 1966, no. 1

A. Lozovskii, *Rabochaya kontrol (Workers' Control)*, Moscow 1918

Malaya sovetskaya entsiklopedia (Smaller Soviet Encyclopaedia), Moscow 1929

Emelyan Mindlin, *Ne dom, no mir (No Home But The World)*, Moscow 1967

Partiya v tsifrovom osveschenii (The Party Illuminated by Statistics), Moscow/Leningrad 1925

Perepiska sekreteriata Ts.K. RKP(b) s mestnymi partiinymi organisatsiyami, avgust-oktyabr 1918 (Correspondence of the Secretariat of the Bolshevik Party Central Committee With Local Party Organizations, August to October 1918), 6 vols, Moscow 1969

Pervyi vserossisskii sezd rabotnits 16–21 noyabrya 1918 g. i ego rezolyutsii (The First All-Russian Congress of Working Women, 16–21 November, and its Resolutions), Kharkov 1921

G. D. Petrov, "Aleksandra Kollontai nakanune i v gody pervoi mirovoi voiny" ("Alexandra Kollontai Before and During the First World War"), *Novaya i noveishaya istoria*, 1969, no. 1

———, "A. M. Kollontai v gody pervoi mirovoi voiny" ("A. M. Kollontai During The Years of the First World War"), *Istoria SSSR (History of the USSR)*, Moscow/-Leningrad 1968, no. 3

———, "Meridiany druzhby" ("Meridian Lines of Friendship"), *Moskva (Moscow)*, 1967, no. 1

———, "O broshiure A. M. Kollontai, *Komu nuzhna voina*" ("Concerning A. M. Kollontai's pamphlet, *Who Needs War?*"), *Sovetskie arkhivy (Soviet Archives)*, Moscow/Leningrad 1968, no. 5

Pis'ma P. B. Akselroda i Yu. O. Martova (The Letters of P. B. Axelrod and Yu. O. Martov), Russian Reprint Series, ed. Alexandre Solovev and Alan Kimball, The Hague 1967

G. V. Plekhanov and P. B. Akselrod. *Perepiska (Correspondence)*, Moscow 1925

R. Podlyaschuk, *Tovarisch Inessa: Dokumental'naya povest' (Comrade Inessa: A Documentary Narrative)*, 2nd edn, Moscow 1965

K. Ryabinskii, *Revolyutsia 1917 goda (The Revolution of 1917)*, 6 vols, Moscow 1926

Ryadom s Leninym: Vospominania o N. K. Krupskoi (Alongside Lenin: Memories of N. K. Krupskaya), Moscow 1969

A. Ryazanova, *Zhenskii trud (Women's Labor)*, Moscow 1924

Jacques Sadoul, *Notes sur la révolution bolchévique (Notes on the Bolshevik Revolution)*, Paris 1971

Konkordia Samoilova, "Konferentsiya rabotnits i organizatsionnaya rabota" ("The Conference of Working Women and the Work of Organizing It"), *Pravda*, 9 December 1917

———, *Organizatsionnye zadachi otdelov rabotnits (Organizational Tasks of the Working Women's Departments)*, Moscow 1920

Galina Serebryakova, *O drugikh i o sebe (About Other People and About Myself)*, Moscow 1968

Aleksander Shlyapnikov, "Fevralskaya revolyutsiya i evropeiskie sotsialisty" ("The February Revolution and European Socialists"), *Krasnyi Arkhiv (Red Archive)*, Moscow 1926, no. 2

———, "K oktyabru" ("Just Before October"), *Proletarskaya revolyutsiya (Proletarian Revolution)*, Moscow 1922, no. 10

———, *Nakanune 1917 goda (On the Eve of 1917)*, 2 vols, Moscow 1920

———, *Semnadtsatyi god (The Year 1917)*, 3 vols, Moscow 1923–7

L. S. Sosnovskii, *Bol'nye voprosy: zhenschina, semya i deti (Some Painful Questions: Woman, Family and Children)*, Leningrad 1926

Lyudmilla Stal, "Rabotnitsa v Oktyabre" ("The Working Woman in October"), *Proletarskaya Revolyutsia*, Moscow 1922, no. 10

E. Stasova, *Stranitsy zhizni i borby (Pages of My Life and Struggle)*, Moscow 1960

———, *Vospominania (Memories)*, ed. V. N. Stepanov, Moscow 1969

Polina Vinogradskaya, *Pamyatnye vstrechi (Memorable Meetings)*, 2nd edn, Moscow 1972

———, "Voprosy byta" ("Questions of Everyday Life"), *Pravda*, 26 July 1923

———, "Voprosy morali, pola, byta i tovarishch Kollontai" ("Questions of Morality, Sex, Everyday Life, and Comrade Kollontai"), *Krasnaya Nov (Red Virgin Soil)*, November 1923

Vera Vladimirova, *Revolyutsia 1917 goda (The 1917 Revolution)*, 4 vols, Leningrad 1924

A. P. Yakushina, "Iz Istorii antivoennoi deyatel'nosti bol'shevikov pod rukovodstvom V. I. Lenina" ("The History of the Bolsheviks' Antiwar Activities Under V. I. Lenin's Leadership"), *Voprosy istorii KPSS (Questions of the History of the CPSU)*, Moscow 1962, no. 2

Ivan Yanzhul, *Ocherki i issledovania (Sketches and Investigations)*, Moscow 1884

Emelian Yaroslavskii, "Moral i byt proletariata v perekhodnyi period" ("Morality and Everyday Life of the Proletariat in the Transitional Period"), *Molodaya Gvardia*, 1926, no. 3

Zhenschiny russkoi revolyutsii (The Women of the Russian Revolution), Moscow 1968

Zhenschiny v russkoi revolyutsii (Women in The Russian Revolution), Moscow 1959

Grigorii Zinoviev, *Rabotnitsa, krest'yanka i Sovetskaya vlast (Working and Peasant Woman and the Soviet Power)*, Petrograd 1919

Mark S. Zorkii, *Rabochaya oppozitsia (Workers' Opposition)*, Moscow 1926

BOLSHEVIK PARTY DOCUMENTS
Reports of Party Congresses

Sixth (1917) *Shestoi sezd RSDRP(b): protokoly (Sixth Congress of the Russian Social Democratic Party [Bolsheviks]: Minutes)*, Moscow 1958

532 | ALEXANDRA KOLLONTAI

Seventh (1918) *Sedmoi ekstrennyi sezd RKP(b), mart 1918 goda: stenograficheskii otchet (Seventh Extraordinary Congress of the Russian Communist Party [Bolsheviks], March 1918: Stenographic Record)*, Moscow 1920

Eighth (1919) *Vosmoi sezd RKP(b), mart 1919 goda: protokoly (Eighth Congress of the Russian Communist Party [Bolsheviks], March 1919: Minutes)*, Moscow 1959

Ninth (1920) *Devyatyi sezd RKP(b), mart-aprel 1920: Protokoly (Ninth Congress of the Russian Communist Party [Bolsheviks], March 1919: Minutes)*, Moscow 1921

Tenth (1921) *Desyatyi sezd RKP(b): stenograficheskii otchet, 8–16 marta 1921 goda (Tenth Congress of the Russian Communist Party [Bolsheviks]: Stenographic Record, 8–16 March 1921)*, Moscow 1921

Eleventh (1922) *Odinadtsatyi sezd RKP(b), mart-aprel 1922 goda: stenograficheskii otchet (Eleventh Congress of the Russian Communist Party [Bolsheviks], March to April 1922: Stenographic Record)*, Moscow 1961

Twelfth (1923) *Dvenadtsaty sezd RKP(b): stenograficheskii otchet, 17–25 aprelya 1923 goda (Twelfth Congress of the Russian Communist Party [Bolsheviks]: Stenographic Record, 17–25 April 1923)*, Moscow 1923

Reports of Party Conferences

Seventh (April 1917) *Sed'maya (Aprel'skaya) vserossiiskaya i Petrogradskaya obschegorodskaya konferentsiya RSDRP(b), aprel 1917 goda: protokoly (The Seventh [April] All-Russian and Petrograd City Conference of the Russian Social Democratic Labor Party [Bolsheviks], April 1917: Minutes)*, Moscow 1958

Eighth (December 1919) *Vos'maya konferentsiya RKP(b), dekabr' 1919 goda: protokoly (Eighth Conference of the Russian Communist Party [Bolsheviks], December 1919: Minutes)*, Moscow 1961

Resolutions and Decisions

Kommunisticheskaya partiya i organizatsia rabotnits (The Communist Party and the Organization of Women Workers), Moscow/Petrograd 1919

KPSS v rezolyutsiakh i resheniakh sezdov, konferentsii i plenumov Ts. K. (The Communist Party of the Soviet Union in the Resolutions and Decisions of its Congresses, Conferences, and the Plenary Sessions of its Central Committee), 8th edn, vol. 2, 1917–24, Moscow 1970

Materialy po voprosu o gruppe Rabochei Oppozitsii na XI sezde RKP: Otchet komissii i rezolyutsiya XI sezda RKP o nekotorykh chlenakh "Rabochei Oppozitsii" (Documents on The Question of the Workers' Opposition Group at the 11th Congress of the RCP: Report of the Commission and Resolutions of the 11th Congress concerning certain members of the "Workers' Opposition"), Moscow 1922

Otchet otdela Ts.K. RKP po rabote sredi zhenschin za god raboty (Russian Communist Party Central Committee Report on Work Among Women For the Past Year), Moscow 1921

Tsentral'nyi komitet. Otdel po rabote sredi zhenschin (Central Committee. Department For Work Among Women), Sbornik instruktsii Otdela Ts.K. RKP po rabote sredi zhenschin (Instruction Manual Issued by the Central Committee of the Russian Communist Party Concerning Work Among Women), Moscow 1920

SOVIET CONGRESSES AND RESOLUTIONS

First (1917) *Pervyi vserossiiskii sezd sovetov: Stenograficheskii otchet (First All-Russian Congress of Soviets: Stenographic Record),* Moscow 1931

Second (October 1917) *Vserossiiskii sezd sovetov: Stenograficheskii otchet (All-Russian Congress of Soviets: Stenographic Record),* Moscow 1918

Sovet rabochikh i krasno-armeiskikh deputatov. Protokoly zasedanii (The Soviet of Workers' and Red-Army Soldiers' Deputies. Minutes of Sessions), Moscow 1925

INTERNATIONAL CONGRESSES AND CONFERENCES

Compte rendu analytique publié par le secrétariat du Bureau socialiste internationale (Analytical Account published by the Secretariat of the International Socialist Bureau, of the Seventh International Congress in 1907 at Stuttgart, and the First International Conference of Socialist Women), Brussels 1908

Compte rendu analytique . . . (of the Eighth International Congress in Copenhagen in 1910, and the Second International Conference of Socialist Women), Copenhagen 1911

Otchet o pervoi mezhdunarodnoi konferentsii kommunistok (Account of the First International Conference of Communist Women, in 1920), Moscow 1921

ORGANIZATIONS AND RUSSIAN TERMS

AGITPROP (Agitation and Propaganda)   A department of the Bolshevik central committee.

BUND (General Union of Lithuanian, Polish, and Russian Jewish Workers)   Founded in 1897. Joined the Russian Social Democratic Party at its first congress in Minsk in 1898. Left after the second, and rejoined it after the Fourth Congress in 1906.

COMINTERN (Third International, or Communist International)   First Congress, 2–7 March 1919.

DUMA (House of Representatives)   Set up in tsarist Russia after the 1905 revolution. First Duma, April to July 1906; Second Duma, February to July 1907; Third Duma, 1907 to 1912; Fourth Duma, 1912–1917.

GPU (Government Political Administration)   Political police force set up in 1922 to replace the *Vecheka* (q.v.). Itself replaced by the OGPU, 1922–34. Then came under NKVD (Ministry of the Interior). Now the KGB.

KADETS (Members of the liberal Constitutional Democratic Party)   Founded by businessmen, Masons, and landowners, in October 1905.

MEZHRAYONKA ("Interdistrict" group, i.e. Social Democrats unaffiliated to either Bolsheviks or Mensheviks)   Created in St. Petersburg in 1913. Several thousand strong when at the Sixth Bolshevik Party Congress in August 1917, led by Trotsky and Lunacharsky, they joined the Bolsheviks en masse.

NEP (New Economic Policy)   Inaugurated in 1921, it introduced a grain tax on peasants, thereby encouraging a certain amount of private trade.

NEPMEN   The new managers, directors and "Red merchants," who prospered under this new economy; *"Nepwomen"* were the wives of these men, or the women who kept them company.

NKVD   People's Commissariat for the Interior.

ORGBURO (Organizational Bureau)   Five-member central-committee body set up at the Eighth Party Congress in 1919 to supervise staffing of local party organizations and decide the priorities of their work.

OSVOBOZHDENIE (Liberation)   Liberal group, with paper of the same name published between 1902 and 1905 under the direction of P. Struve. The group later became the nucleus of the *Kadets* (q.v.).

OSVOBOZHDENIE TRUDA (Liberation of Labor)   The first Russian Marxist group, founded by Plekhanov in Geneva 1883.

RADA   Pre-soviet Ukrainian councils.

RSDRP (Russian Social Democratic Workers' Party)   Founded in 1898 at Minsk Congress, split at Second Congress in 1903 into Bolshevik and Menshevik factions. Many party organizations in exile abroad continued to be run under joint leadership.

SOVIETS   Emerged in the 1905 revolution as councils elected by strike committees to

535

coordinate and supervise their demands. The first and most important soviet was the St. Petersburg soviet, led by Trotsky, then close to the Mensheviks; but soviets rapidly spread to other towns throughout Russia. By February 1917, when soviets were resurrected after the bourgeois revolution, they were known as "soviets of soldiers' and workers' deputies"; the Petrograd Soviet shared power with the Provisional Government, undermining the latter's authority, until October 1917, when the Bolsheviks came to power with the slogan "All Power to the Soviets."

UNION OF STRUGGLE FOR THE EMANCIPATION OF THE WORKING CLASS Marxist intellectual circles in St. Petersburg were united by Lenin in 1895. Similar union in Kiev two years later, and elsewhere in Russia.

USSR Union of Soviet Socialist Republics.

VECHEKA, or CHEKA (Extraordinary Commission for the Struggle Against Sabotage and Counter-Revolution) Instituted on September 7, 1917. Replaced in 1922 by the GPU (q.v.).

ZEMSTVO Local administrative authority instituted three years after the emancipation of the serfs, in 1864, with control over local administrative matters but subordinated to provincial governors and the Ministry of the Interior. Without any executive powers, it came under much police pressure at the end of the nineteenth century, as liberal *zemstvo* landowners adopted increasingly radical positions. By 1905 it was officially representative of conservative public opinion.

ZHENOTDEL Women's Department of the Party, formed September 1919 and closed 1930.

INDEX

women, 127, 267, 389–90; St. Petersburg Textile Union, 138–39, 145, 147, 173–74, 195; 1st Congress of Trade Unions, 267; 4th Congress, 389

Trade Union International, 423

Trepov, General, 16

Trotsky, Lev Davydovich, and First St. Petersburg Soviet, 104, 109; and "permanent revolution," 103–104, 457; and Bologna Bolsheviks' school, 177–78; in New York, 227, 237; and February 1917 Revolution, 238; during "July Days," 269; during October 1917 Revolution, 277–81; and Red Army, 315, 349, 375; and transport crisis, 367–68; and Workers' Opposition, 368ff; and Tenth Party Congress, 380ff; and 3rd Comintern Congress, 394; and Eleventh Party Congress, 402; opposition to Stalin, 415, 432–39, 447, 451; expelled from Party, 459; assassination, 479; and Kollontai, 109, 227–28, 237, 279, 439

Trotskyists, 451

Trubnikova, Maria, 3

Trudovik Party, see "Laborites"

"Tsektran," 367–68, see also Trotsky and transport crisis

Tsvetkov, Alexei, 287–88, 297, 300–301

TUC, 194

Tugan-Baranovsky, 75

Turgenev, Ivan, 10, 26, 30, 48

Tukhachevsky, Marshal, 471

Tyrkova, Ariadna, 98–99, 112, 120, 247, 289

Ukraine, Kollontai's family connections with, 7; and Bolsheviks' peace negotiations with Germany, 303, 304, 307–12; Dybenko's activities in,

332–41; Kollontai visits, 1919, 338–44; 1920, 352

"ultimatists," 138, 146, 151

Union of Charity Organizations, 57

Union of Russian Factory Hands, 93; women's section of, 93

Union of the Russian People, 47

Union of Struggle for the Emancipation of the Working Class, 44–45, 50, 52, 53–57, 60, 75–76, 79, 108, 124; women in, 55, 78–79

Union of Unions, 101

Union of Women's Equality, see Russian Union of Women's Equality

United Opposition, 450, 457

unmarried mothers, 161, 181, 219–20, 324–27, 443

Uritsky, Mikhail, 200, 210, 303, 309

USA, Kollontai visits, 225–34; 1916, 236–38

Vandervelde, Emil, 182, 183, 190

Vasilev, Dr., 123, 145

venereal disease, 327, 345, 414

Verdi, Giuseppe, 18, 25

Versailles Peace Treaty, 349, 423

"Vertrauensmann," 69

Vinogradskaya, Paulina, 428–31

Vitkovskaya, Lyolya, 28

Voitinsky, B. S., 110

Volfson, S., 413

Volkenstein, Olga, 98, 147

Volkova, 151, 164, 176

Volodarsky, V. V., 225, 227, 233, 257, 268

Volsky, Stanislas, 178

Vorovsky, V., 268–70

Vorwärts, 201, 206, 207, 208

Wagner, Richard, 25

waifs, 284, 304, 414, 429

War Communism, 313, 336, 350, 358

War Theses, 211–12, 216